INTRODUCTORY ANIMAL HUSBANDRY

THE MACMILLAN COMPANY
NEW YORK · CHICAGO
DALLAS · ATLANTA · SAN FRANCISCO
LONDON · MANILA

BRETT-MACMILLAN LTD.
TORONTO

INTRODUCTORY ANIMAL HUSBANDRY

THIRD EDITION

ARTHUR L. ANDERSON

PROFESSOR OF ANIMAL HUSBANDRY
IOWA STATE COLLEGE

New York

THE MACMILLAN COMPANY

Library of Congress catalog card number: 58–5502

PREFACE

The purpose of this book is to acquaint the student with the fundamental problems and essential general concepts of livestock production in the United States. The content is somewhat comprehensive, yet it is arranged and presented to meet the needs of beginning students at the collegiate level. It has been the intention to make available to the reader much factual information from various sources. An attempt was made to draw together many of the basic facts on livestock production known by producers and scientists. The book is designed primarily for use as a text for college students, yet the subject matter is presented so as to be useful in teaching vocational agriculture, particularly as a reference text.

Although it has been the intention to make this presentation up to date, it should be pointed out that the subject matter is not static. In the livestock field, as in others, readjustment must constantly be made to meet changing conditions. Our agriculture, and consequently animal husbandry, has been changed by group action and other forces. The added use of science, greater specialization, readjustment to foreign relationships, and our changing diet have very directly affected livestock raising.

Perhaps more evident is the effect of farm mechanization upon agriculture in general and livestock in particular. Equally striking have been the changes in our marketing of livestock and the merchandising of meat, milk, wool, and other animal products. Currently available data such as outlook reports, market reports, and reviews may be used to provide an interest approach to many of the sections.

The material included is that which has been quite definitely accepted. This is mainly a survey of animal husbandry and marketing. Some controversial issues are discussed; it was the intention to present the available facts on such subjects. Theories which still are unproved are generally omitted.

Each part is devoted to one kind of livestock and includes chapters or parts of chapters dealing with types, markets, market classifications, prices, feeding, management, and breeding. Rather specialized chapters in each part cover the processing and distribution of the animal products or other special considerations, such as wool of sheep, milk secretion of dairy cows, etc.

The order of presentation is based upon several years of teaching experience in this field. Yet the various parts are so written and cross-referenced that the order can be changed to suit the convenience of the instructor. It seemed logical to start each kind of livestock with its place in farming and ranching and then to follow with market requirements, marketing methods, processing, and merchandising, closing with feeding, management, and breeding. The subject of breeds has been added to this revision in response to suggestions from many sources. The material on feeding and breeding is quite general. References on these and other subjects are suggested at appropriate places; a list of reference books is included at the end of the book.

The published material on animal husbandry was drawn upon freely in compiling and writing the text. Much material was drawn from various sources at the Iowa State College. Stenographic help was generously provided by this institution. The United States Department of Agriculture and various agricultural colleges and experiment stations supplied subject matter and illustrative material requested. For all of this and for the many pictures loaned for use as cuts the writer is deeply indebted. Credit is given for the material as it appears.

Through long association with his co-workers at Iowa State College, the writer has acquired many ideas and judgments included in this book. Many have helped in securing data and illustrations and in preparing the manuscript; many have been generous with suggestions to the author. To all of these persons grateful appreciation is expressed.

To the publishers the author is especially indebted for their survey indicating the type of book wanted and for their provision for careful review of the manuscript prior to publication.

CONTENTS

CONTENTS

Part I–CATTLE

Chapter 1

LIVESTOCK IN AGRICULTURE

The raising of animals is as old as civilization itself, for our common farm animals were domesticated before the beginning of written history. Paleolithic man hunted animals for food and raiment; his successor, the Neolithic man, tamed and confined them. It was in this Neolithic or New Stone Age that men first practiced agriculture, which included the raising of domestic animals.

DOMESTICATION OF ANIMALS

Animal domestication no doubt began as a means of safeguarding the food supply for times when hunting was poor. It is believed that the first animal to be domesticated was the dog. Animals were early used as beasts of burden, both for draft and pack; the horse was among the first subjugated by man.

The domestication of animals was one of the essentials in the development of civilization, according to Shoosmith.[1] "The domestication of animals led to the increase of population and the strengthening of tribal habits and directly gave rise to that division of a labour apart from which civilized life is impossible." The opinion is often expressed that man might never have risen above barbarism if it had not been for the servitude of animals.

Certain characteristics distinguish domesticated animals from wild animals. Those animals which have been domesticated are naturally tamer. They thrive under artificial conditions and reproduce regularly in confinement. Some animals are not subject to domestication. The zebra and the American bison are in that class. Even though very young individuals of

[1] F. H. Shoosmith, *Life in the Animal World*, p. 253. Robert M. McBride & Company, New York, N.Y., 1937.

either of these are captured and trained, they fail to reach a state of domesticity, and their response is often unpredictable.

Domestic animals were spread in various directions from the place or places of origin to sections that afforded a favorable environment. In the spread throughout the world animals were modified in physical characteristics to conform with environmental conditions. Man was responsible for distribution of the domestic forms; in fact, colonists included such animals as were available in their native land among their possessions in migrations. Colonists, travelers, armies, and missionaries extended the frontiers of livestock raising to the new lands. Colonization brought domestic animals to this continent. We have not contributed any new species to the group, although several new breeds have been created in the United States.

ANIMAL HUSBANDRY

Animal husbandry deals with the production of domestic animals, or livestock, and embraces all phases of breeding, feeding, and management. Through the fund of knowledge gathered by experiment and experience, the usefulness of domestic animals to mankind has been greatly expanded. The livestock raiser has a profound interest in the marketing, processing, and distribution of animal products because his success is in a large degree dependent upon consumers' acceptance of the animal products. The consumer is often quite far removed from the producer. The pork chop, for example, may move great distances and pass through several hands from the producer to the processor and finally to the consumer. A consumer wants a high-quality product at a cost comparable with that of other goods. Both quality and cost can be markedly affected in the progress from producer to consumer. The efficient and economical marketing, processing, handling, distribution, and merchandising of animal products is therefore a matter of concern to producers and consumers alike.

It has been stated that much animal husbandry is still in the realm of opinion. Our knowledge has come in part from experience. Much that was formerly accepted as fact has been subjected to careful investigation. Cattle raising on the range, for example, was at one time based entirely upon past experience handed on by word of mouth. Today practices in the enterprise have been tested experimentally, and the modern western cattleman has the benefit of scientific research in addition to the colorful experience of his predecessor. The scientific method has brought among other things, methods of production and of disease and parasite control which have enabled the livestock raiser to produce more and better animal products at lower cost. Livestock production has shifted from an art to a science.

Food and clothing are primary needs of mankind, and agriculture since it supplies these needs, is fundamental. Less than 22 million people who reside on farms make available our domestic supply of food and clothing materials and the many other essentials of farm origin. With the increase in efficiency in farming fewer people are needed as workers on our farms. The average size of farms has been increasing in spite of the fact that there has been a significant increase in farms with less than 10 acres. The ratio of farm population to total population is less than one to eight. The number of people included in the farm population who work at non-agricultural jobs has increased. This serves to bring out the dependence of the entire population upon farmers. Farmers in turn are dependent upon industry for many goods and services.

FUNCTIONS OF THE LIVESTOCK ENTERPRISE

The functions of livestock as a part of good farming or ranching may be stated as follows:

1. To supply a market for pasturage and other unmarketable roughage.
2. To furnish a home market for marketable grain and roughage.
3. To provide manure for the maintenance of the fertility of the soil and also to control soil erosion.
4. To provide a profitable use for labor and managerial ability.

In short, livestock provide a means for disposal of farm-raised or ranch-raised feeds, including pasture, and permit the marketing of a concentrated product which removes but little of the soil's fertility. This in turn gives a use for farm labor and management ability which can be dovetailed with crop production. Livestock production results in wider distribution and diversification of farm income. When home-raised animal products are available, the diet may be improved.

In recent years, with the advent of extensive mechanization in agriculture, many production schemes have been developed. In most instances these are specialized feeding plants based on bulk handling of purchased feeds. This concentrate part of the ration is made of a mixture of many feeds and may include as well minerals, vitamins, drugs, antibiotics. This applies especially to the feeding of feeder beef cattle, sheep, and pigs. Specialized feeder pig raising units are a recent development.

SOIL CONSERVATION AND LIVESTOCK PRODUCTION

As we are confronted with a national problem of conserving our soil to prevent agricultural decline, the use of livestock in maintaining soil fertility takes on great significance. We have but little virgin land to exploit or develop. Therefore, we must conserve for ourselves and posterity the productive capacity of our soils. Soil composition and treatment affect the nutritive value of forage and, to some extent of grains.

In programs for soil conservation the tendency has been toward more hay and pasture crops as against those which involve more intensive tilling of the land. With more land for grazing, our livestock population must be shifted to utilize more pasture crops. With proper management of pasture lands the land and the crops derived from it may be improved.

A permanent agriculture should be based upon land utilization rather than the shaping of the crop program to comply with a proposed livestock program. If that which is grown is adaptable to the soil and climate and due consideration is given to soil improvement, then livestock that will make economical use of the feed will give a balanced farm program. Livestock farming is effective in crop utilization and, if manure is conserved, much of the native soil fertility can be retained. Integration of crop and livestock enterprises, making use of modern methods of soil retention and adding nutrients that may have been depleted, will give permanence to the land's productivity. Only by such means can the productive capacity of our farms be maintained.

THE MANAGEMENT OF LIVESTOCK

The maintenance and management of a livestock enterprise should be directed toward the fulfillment of certain objectives. If livestock are to contribute to profitable farming, a well-thought-out plan of production and system of management and marketing are essential. It is obvious that the place occupied by livestock raising is quite largely dependent upon the agricultural characteristics of the region. When a ranch or farm produces a usable supply of feed (pasture, roughage, or grain) the operator may well consider the marketing of it through livestock. On land that is uncertain in grain crop production, a shift to feed crops or grass may be advisable for steadiness of income.

In many systems of farming, livestock constitute a major enterprise. On general farms where sufficient livestock are kept to utilize the pasture and to consume a good part of the hay and the feed grain grown, farm incomes are usually higher than on farms that sell grain.

The relative position of livestock and other produce of farms is variable, some farms having no livestock, others making it their major product. The importance of livestock is evident since it is the source of more than one half of our agricultural income. Livestock and livestock products constitute one of our largest industries in volume of business. However, crop production is not to be minimized, for livestock convert crops into salable materials or cash income. Such farm products as feed grains, hay, fodder, and silage have farm value but are marketed mainly through livestock. The efficient manager attempts to maintain a proper balance among the capital, land, and labor involved.

KIND OF LIVESTOCK TO KEEP

There are many factors to consider in choosing a livestock enterprise for a ranch or farm. For the general farm, livestock combinations give the greatest possibility of uniform financial returns. Some of the more important factors that determine the most useful kind of livestock to produce are:

1. Size of farm, productive capacity of the land, amount of home-grown feed that can be raised, and amount of usable pasture land
2. Amount and kind of building equipment
3. Financial resources available
4. Ability, skill, and likes of the operator
5. Amount of labor available for use on livestock
6. Location of the farm with respect to markets (expenses of marketing vary with the distance of shipment; producers near centers of consumption may have low marketing costs, but other costs are usually higher).
7. Costs of all the items that enter into production. Without a margin of profit there is no incentive for production.

LEGISLATION AND AGRICULTURAL PRODUCTION

Farm legislation has been a factor in the shifts in agricultural production. The economic control it imposes has been mainly on the crops grown, but this in turn affects livestock production. The production, marketing, and storage of crops have been affected by laws which have for their general objectives the improvement of the economic and social condition of the farmer. To accomplish this end, many adjustments in the use of our agricultural land have been imperative. Our federal legislation has involved, among others, the principles of price maintenance, ever-normal granary storage, soil conservation, crop insurance, production allotment, farm security, surplus commodities purchase, and commodity credit.

Federal legislation that has been helpful to farmers has also been of value to city dwellers. Through the national marketing of surpluses, food has been available to distressed urban populations, consequently improving the national diet.

LAND USE IN THE UNITED STATES

The land area of the United States is approximately 1,904 million acres. Of this total area, 1,158 million acres or about 60 per cent is classified as land in farms. This is actually all land in farms and includes areas of land not under cultivation and land not being used for pasture or grazing. It includes the land under control of farm operators. It does not include non-agricultural land or land grazed or pastured neither owned nor leased by the operator. Much land not in farms is used for grazing. This land is classified, according to major use, as grazing land, public and private, and forest land grazed, public and private. Nearly one-fourth of our total land area is such grazing land, which yields pasturage for cattle, sheep, and other livestock.

Land use is not constant. There is continual shifting of crop production based on the demand for agricultural products and the productive capacity of the land. Less than one half of the land in farms is cropland, and some of this is idle. Nearly one half of our farm land is in pasture. The balance is woodlot, wasteland, roads, and farmsteads.

The farm cropland produces a large amount of feed crops fed to domestic animals on the farms. With crops like corn, for example, the farm value of the crop may be six times the cash income from it. A crop like tobacco presents the other extreme, since the farm value and cash income are about the same. It is mainly a cash crop. The corn crop is chiefly a feed crop and is marketed largely as livestock products.

Considering the grazing land, the farm pastures, and the feed crops grown, the production of nearly 70 per cent of our land has its production marketed as livestock or livestock products.

CLASSIFICATION OF FARMS ON MAJOR INCOME

The farms of our country are classified in census reports into various types on the basis of major income. The leading classes of commercial farms and the percentage in each group are as follows, according to the agricultural census report: [2]

COMMERCIAL FARMS CLASSIFIED AS TO SOURCE OF MAJOR INCOME

MAJOR INCOME	PERCENTAGE OF ALL CLASSIFIED FARMS
Miscellaneous and unclassified	31.2
Field crops	29.9
Livestock	14.5
Dairy	11.5
General	7.3
Poultry	3.2
Fruit and Nut	1.7
Vegetable	0.7

[2] U.S. *Census of Agriculture,* 1954, Preliminary. Bureau of Census, Department of Commerce, 1955.

The above table includes only the commercial farms or those from which the value of the products sold was $1,200 or more. Some other farms are listed as commercial if the income was less than given above and if the operator worked off the farm less than a certain number of days or if the value of products sold exceeded the non-farm income. Slightly more than two-thirds of all farms were classified as commercial. For a farm to be placed in a given class, the given product or group of products, for example Dairy, must amount to 50 per cent or more of the value of all farm products sold.

On nearly 30 per cent of our farms livestock, dairy products, or poultry are the main source of income.

The distribution of the value of agricultural products sold from our farms is somewhat different from that given above, since it includes the income from all farms regardless of the amount sold. The following breakdown of farm products sold, taken from the census report, considers the value of all farm products sold within a given year regardless of who shared in the receipts.[2]

PERCENTAGE OF INCOME FROM VARIOUS FARM PRODUCTS SOLD

SOURCE OF INCOME	PERCENTAGE DISTRIBUTION OF VALUE OF PRODUCT SOLD
Field crops	40.3
Livestock and livestock products	28.6
Dairy products	13.5
Poultry and poultry products	7.8
Fruits and nuts	4.9
Vegetables	2.6
Horticultural specialties	1.8
Forest products	0.5

The farm income from livestock, dairy products, and poultry is about one-half of the total income. This proportion is changeable, depending upon the relative value of the various farm products and the amount produced. This figure applies to farm products sold and does not give credit for farm products consumed on the home farm. As well as providing income, the supply of livestock and poultry products greatly improves the diet of the farm population.

AGRICULTURAL REGIONS

Within our country we recognize several distinctive areas on the basis of the predominant kind of agriculture. These distinctive types of agriculture result from different physical conditions determining what crops can be successfully grown. Such conditions as soil composition and moisture, topography, and temperature affect the vegetation and crops grown. These in turn are related to livestock production. In Figure 1 the extent of the different regions is shown. Agriculturally, the eastern part of the United States is quite different from the western. The dividing line approximates the 103-degree parallel of longitude except that it veers to the northwest in Montana and to the southeast in Texas. (See Figure 6 for range boundaries.) To the east of this division a humid climate prevails; to the west an arid climate prevails, except along the west coast and the north border.

The thirteen following crop belts or areas are recognized:

1. Grazing and irrigated crops region
2. Cotton belt
3. Corn belt
4. Hay and dairy region
5. Corn and winter-wheat belt
6. Spring-wheat region
7. Hard-wheat region
8. Forest and hay region
9. Humid subtropical crop belt
10. Columbia plateau wheat region
11. North Pacific forest, hay, and pasture region
12. Pacific subtropical crop region
13. The middle Atlantic truck crop belt

There is a strong tendency toward regional specialization of different kinds of farming in the United States.[3] These regions are somewhat like the crop belts or areas. Three major types of farming are given which are based mainly on livestock. They are: range livestock, feed grains and livestock (corn belt), and dairy. Other types are: wheat and small grains, fruit, truck and mixed farming, cotton, tobacco, special crops and a large catagory of general farming.

GEOGRAPHICAL DIVISIONS OF THE UNITED STATES

The agricultural regions of our country do not coincide with commonly used geographical divisions. The latter are convenient divisions of the census reports, but within a division there is a great difference in the major agricultural production of crops. The agricultural census is taken with the census of population in each decennial enumeration. Of late we have taken also a mid-decennial agricultural census. The census geographical divisions

---

[3] "Generalized Types of Farming in the United States," *Agri. Inf. Bull. 39,* Bureau of Agricultural Economics, U.S.D.A., 1950.

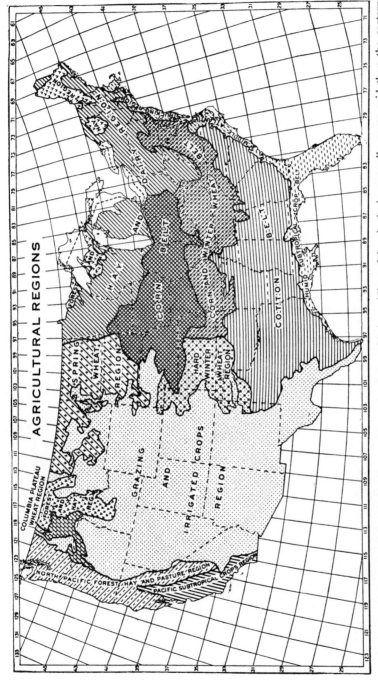

Fig. 1. The agricultural regions. The section west of the 103rd meridian of longitude is generally more arid than the eastern part, except in the northwest. The crops and livestock raised are influenced by the soil, topography, temperature, and crops grown. (U.S.D.A.)

11

are shown in Figure 2. These sections are New England, middle Atlantic, east north central, west north central, south Atlantic, east south central, west south central, and mountain. Such subdivision of the country facilitates a discussion of our agriculture and therefore of our animal husbandary. It is somewhat confusing, since these geographical divisions do not correspond to the principal crop belts. The corn belt, for example, is mainly but not wholly in the north central region. The crop belts are distinctive, but their margins are not sharply defined.

Fig. 2. Map of the United States, showing the geographical divisions. (U.S. Census.)

Chapter 2

CATTLE

Cattle were used by man before the keeping of records. Prior to their domestication, cattle were hunted for food and other usable materials. Just when man confined cattle so that a steadier supply of cattle products would be available is not definitely known.

ORIGINS

TIME OF DOMESTICATION

This change, domestication, was probably contemporary with man's transition from savagery to *the first primitive civilization,* early in the Neolithic Age. Herding of cattle was one of the first indications of the superiority of one tribe over another. In South Africa, for example, the keeping of cattle marked the Hottentot as superior to the nomadic Bushman who lived by the hunt. Cattle have served through the ages as objects of worship and mythology, sacrificial offerings, sources of meat, milk, and hides, beasts of burden and a means of power. Early drawings, carvings, and writings of ancient Mesopotamia, Egypt and India indicate man's use of cattle in those countries as early as 4000 to 5000 B.C. The word "cattle" supposedly is another form of the words "chattel" and "capital," meaning goods or property. Cattle among many primitive peoples have been the most valuable goods and not infrequently a measure of value of other property.

From the early centers of culture domestic cattle spread to all parts of the world with colonization and the development of civilization.

ZOOLOGICAL CLASSIFICATION

Domesticated cattle are classed in the family *Bovidae,* ruminants which have hollow horns and hoofs with an even number of toes. Fossil remains of this family have been ascribed to the Miocene Age. Domestic cattle are descended from wild cattle of the genus *Bos.* Besides cattle this genus includes the following living forms: banteng, bison, gaur, gayal, musk ox, true buffalo, yak, and zebu.

Groups of genus bos

Five groups or subgenera are noted in the genus *Bos.* Following are the various groups and the species which are found in each:

1. Taurine. Included here are common and humped cattle. Further discussion of this group follows in a subsequent paragraph.

2. Bibovine. This group embraces the banteng, gaur, and gayal, which are closely related and cross readily. These are humped forms native to southern India. A few of the gaur have been domesticated; the gayal has long been more or less domesticated. The banteng is widely domesticated.

3. Leptobovine. This group is now extinct. Fossil remains of this subgenus have been found in France, Italy, and India.

4. Bisontine. Embraced in this group are the yak and the bison, which have voices resembling those of swine. The yak is indigenous to the mountainous areas in central Asia, and wild herds still exist in that section. The domesticated form of the yak is regarded as being a cross between the wild yak and some of the taurine group. To this group belongs the American bison, incorrectly called buffalo, which resisted domestication except for the "cattalo," the cross with cattle.

5. Bubaline. This group is that of the true buffalo of Asia and southeastern Europe. They are widely used for draft, for beef, and for milk production.

In usefulness to man the taurine group leads; however, the Asiatic buffalo, banteng, gayal, and yak have been successfully domesticated.

TAURINE GROUP

Commonly, cattle are grouped under one species, *Bos taurus;* however a separate species name *(Bos indicus)* is given to the zebu group, those of the division bearing a hump. A wide variety of the zebu group exists in Asia and Africa. They have been used to improve the cattle of the coastal region of the Gulf of Mexico as well as in other places in the tropical region suited for cattle raising. The hump over the shoulders, large drooping ears, and different call distinguish the zebu from domestic cattle. No wild forms of the zebu have been found, and its domestication was as early as 4000 B.C. It is quite probable that the zebu was derived from Indo-Malay cattle or the banteng. In this country the zebu is commonly known as the Brahman.

EUROPEAN CATTLE

Our domestic cattle descended mainly from European cattle. Often mentioned in writings on European prehistoric cattle are those of the lake dwellers of Switzerland, which are referred to as "little marsh cows." Many wild species of cattle are mentioned in the early history of European cattle. Perhaps these might be more correctly termed geographical varieties. These are of interest because our present cattle probably descended from these varieties. Four wild forms were the foundation for our common breeds. Morse [1] considered these so closely related that some, perhaps all, might be regarded as varieties of the *Bos primigenius.*

Early species of European cattle

The division into species is based largely upon skull characteristics, but differences of opinion exist as to the grouping.

Following is a discussion of the early species of European cattle and also the probable breed descendants from each species.

1. Bos taurus primigenius. This is the urus, aurochs, or giant ox that existed in the early Neolithic Age. They were very large cattle, being six or seven feet high at the withers. The following breeds supposedly descended from the species. Holstein-Friesian, Shorthorn, Aberdeen Angus, Polled Shorthorn, Red Polled, Dutch Belted, Galloway, West Highland, and Normandy. The Ayrshire also probably descended from the *primigenius* crossed with the *longifrons,* although at least one authority would classify this breed as well as the West Highland and Galloway to the *longifrons* species.

2. Bos taurus longifrons. This species, often referred to as the "Celtic ox," was much smaller in size than the *primigenius* and also existed in the Neolithic Age. Its smaller size is regarded by some authorities as being due to unfavorable environment. Among the breeds existent today, the Brown Swiss and Jersey probably descended from this species. Guernseys probably came from this same foundation stock crossed with *primigenius.*

3. Bos taurus brachycephalus. These are the short-headed cattle of our present breeds. Kerry, French Canadian, Brittany, Sussex, Devon, and probably the Hereford came from this foundation. However, some authori-

---

[1] F. W. Morse, "The Ancestry of Domesticated Cattle," 27th *Annual Report* B.A.I., U.S.D.A., 1910, p. 187.

ties claim that Herefords should be credited to the *primigenius* species and the Kerry and Brittany to the *longifrons*.

4. Bos taurus frontosus. This species has been found in fossil remains in Sweden. The breeds of Sweden, the Simmenthal, and other spotted breeds now in Switzerland and South Germany are of this type.

Domestic cattle are largely from the *primigenius* and the *longifrons,* as will be noted by the breed classification. The wild white cattle, because of their nearness to prehistoric forms, are of interest to students of domestic genealogy and are discussed in the following paragraph.

Wild white (or Park) cattle [2]

This breed is the nearest in existence to the prehistoric forms. There is disagreement about the ancestral form of this breed—*Bos primigenius, Bos longifrons,* or both. These wild white cattle persisted as late as the seventeenth century in certain parks and forest areas in England and southern Scotland. The color is white, but the tips of the horns, the muzzle, the circle around the eyes, and the hoofs are black. The ears are black or brownish-red inside and about the same color on the outside. In form, Park cattle are of the beef type, but the quarters are rather thin and muscular. A Park Cattle Society in England promotes the interests of this breed and maintains its purity.

INTRODUCTION OF CATTLE TO NORTH AMERICA

The first cattle to reach the western hemisphere were brought over by the Norsemen who landed in "Vinland" (Massachusetts) in 1000. Cattle were brought to North America by Christopher Columbus on his second voyage in 1493, and in 1525 cattle of the Spanish type were taken from the West Indies islands to Vera Cruz, Mexico. Portuguese traders brought cattle and hogs to Newfoundland and Nova Scotia in 1553. The first cattle importation credited to the country which is now United States was made in 1535 to Virginia, but they perished or were slaughtered. The first sizable importation reached Jamestown in 1611. Cattle production increased rapidly in New England, and cattle owned by individuals were grazed in herds. With the growth of the population and subsequent increase of cattle, the common pasture (or commons) for the villages became inadequate for the herds. Therefore, many new towns were settled. About two centuries later there was another movement of cattle into the United States from Mexico. These were of the Spanish type or "longhorn cattle," which were first brought to Mexico in 1521.

[2] Alvin H. Saunders, "The Taurine World," *National Geographic Magazine,* Vol. 48, No. 6, 1925, p. 645.

GROWTH OF THE CATTLE INDUSTRY IN THE UNITED STATES

In historical sequence, cattle raising followed hunting in the frontier and was in turn succeeded by pioneer farming. The cattleman followed the hunter and trapper in the settlement of our country and was supplanted by the permanent settler, who also raised cattle. Cattle raising had crossed the Alleghenies and penetrated Ohio and Kentucky by 1800, and by 1860 was quite well established in Illinois and Missouri.

Fig. 3. A Longhorn steer. At one time these were quite common on the Texas range. Now they are comparatively rare. Compared with present-day cattle they are leggy, rangy, thin fleshed, and slow maturing.

By 1870 cattle were quite generally distributed throughout the entire country. The Great Plains were established as a cow country soon after 1880. The "longhorn" cattle came in from the south and the descendants of the British breeds from the east. The longhorn cattle were frequently driven in large herds over trails many of which became very famous. As early as 1850 and until the late '80's millions of cattle traveled the cattle trails from Texas to cattle ranges in the northern Great Plains and to slaughter centers. In the early days trailing was a necessity because there were no railroads or meat-packing plants in the West. The hide and the tallow were the main products of cattle slaughter when it was difficult to market the carcass or meat.[3]

Later, the cattle industry became centralized in the western range because of the available pasture, and in the north central section because of the abundance of concentrated feeds and pasturage. Cattle numbers have increased since 1870 and have shown cyclical movements. In proportion to the total number of cattle in the United States the numbers of cattle in the north and south Atlantic sections have decreased, while those in the south central have changed but slightly. The north central and the western sections alone have been responsible for our expanded cattle production. Our country has been settled by migratory waves which have moved from east to west. Industrial production has predominated toward the eastern seaboard and for the most part has been widely separated from our most fertile farm land. Cattle, especially of the beef type, has moved toward and centered around feed-producing areas. It has been estimated that the average pound of meat travels 1,000 miles from the place of production to the point of consumption. Dairy cattle, on the other hand, tend to cluster near centers of human population because of the problem of transporting the milk and milk products. With the exception of the roughage, feeds for dairy cattle near large industrial centers are shipped in from grain-growing areas.

CATTLE NUMBERS AND NUMBER OF PEOPLE IN UNITED STATES

From 1860 to 1890 human and cattle population moved forward together in the United States, with approximately the same number of each. With industrialization cattle population leveled off and human population continued to increase. Up to 1890 the majority of people lived on farms. That time marked the beginning of the steady increase in growth of the urban population, while the rural population tended to remain stationary. The rapid growth of the large cities was coincident with the change in the rates of increase of the two populations. The increased efficiency in cattle production for both milk and meat made up in part at least for the difference in rate of increase. This is true of other kinds of livestock. We have more productive livestock in terms of products; and we get more from each unit of breeding livestock. Improvement has been made in our methods of feeding. Improvement of livestock has been made through selective breeding. We now have fewer than 60 cattle and calves, of which about one fourth are milk cows, per 100 persons in the United States.

---

[3] The longhorn cattle was virtually extinct in this country by 1920. There are two chief herds of longhorns remaining in the United States, one at the Wichita Mountains Refuge near Cache, Oklahoma, and the other in the Niobrara National Wildlife Refuge near Valentine, Nebraska.

WORLD CATTLE POPULATION AND DISTRIBUTION BY CONTINENT

Cattle numbers are never static. An enumeration at any one time merely serves to indicate the extent of production in various continents or countries. Also, the population does not indicate the commercial production of either beef or milk. Cattle in India, for example, are not used for beef extensively as they are in South America. One other discrepancy should also be pointed out. Few countries use methods comparable to ours in estimating cattle population. The following estimates are averaged where yearly estimates are available and are not comparable in time of year when the estimate is made or method of determination. In many instances they are probably but rough approximations.

CATTLE—NUMBER ON VARIOUS CONTINENTS

1946–1950 Average [4]

CONTINENTS	THOUSANDS
Asia	293,600
South America	126,500
North America	112,700
Europe	95,800
Africa	86,500
Oceania	19,100
U.S.S.R.	50,800
Total for world including U.S.S.R.	785,000

The U.S.S.R. is not included in the separate continents for it is in two continents. Asia is first in total number of cattle (which includes buffaloes). Recently cattle numbers have increased.

CATTLE POPULATION IN LEADING CATTLE COUNTRIES

The United States is exceeded in aggregate cattle numbers only by India (which includes buffaloes). We have a relatively small proportion of world cattle numbers, yet the United States is the largest producer of beef in the world. The South American countries, because of the excess production over their domestic needs, are large factors in the world trade in beef. Some countries with fairly large cattle numbers contribute but little to world trade. In many countries cattle and buffaloes are used extensively for draft purposes and provide but little milk or meat.

The following tabulation of cattle numbers in various countries is based

[4] *Foreign Agriculture Circular,* U.S.D.A., 1956.

on a 5-year average where this was available. In some cases only one estimate was available for the period.

CATTLE—NUMBER IN LEADING CATTLE COUNTRIES

1952–1956 Average [5]

COUNTRY	THOUSANDS
India	200,320 *
United States	94,410
U.S.S.R.	60,825
Brazil	58,483
Argentina	41,980
France	16,840
Australia	15,553
Mexico	15,360
Colombia	13,913
Union of South Africa	11,691
Germany, Western	11,546
Canada	9,069
Tanganyika	6,392
Federation Nyasaland & Rhodesias	4,230
Estimated World Total	890,960 *

* Includes buffaloes.

ORIGIN OF BREEDS

Our cattle breeds are mainly of European origin. The breeds are comparable to geographical varieties, and many are named for their native homes. Certain characteristics became manifest in cattle of the different areas and tended to distinguish them from other cattle. A desired type with desired features of form, color, horns, etc., was used for a pattern, and cattle of a common ancestry were selected and bred to meet the requirements. When a useful type was developed in a locality, outside blood was no longer introduced and more intensive breeding was practiced. As the number increased and more herds were established, the next step was to form a record association. The foundation stock would be registered, and purebreds regarded as only those descended from the foundation individuals. Breeders usually formed organizations to conduct the record or herdbook and to advertise and promote the breed. Some records have been private enterprises. A list of the record associations is given in the appendix.

The distinctive external characteristics of a breed which are rather uniformly transmitted constitute what is known as "breed type." It comprises the particular features that distinguish one breed from another. These features are not of great economic value in market stock production. Such

[5] *Foreign Agriculture Circular,* U.S.D.A., 1956. Average of 5-year period if available, otherwise for any year or years within the period.

things as shape of head, horns, carriage of ears, and color are examples. Breed type has a commercial value to the purebred breeder. In a way these features (such as the white face of Hereford cattle) serve as a trade-mark, or distinguishing characteristic, which to some extent indicates pure breeding. Emphasis on features of breed type that are of little or no consequence may be harmful in selection when it diverts emphasis from more important characteristics.

CLASSIFICATION OF BREEDS

CLASSIFICATION OF BREEDS ACCORDING TO TYPE

"Type," as rather widely used with reference to livestock, means the principal use for which the kind has been developed. In cattle, for example, meat and milk have been the main objectives. Each of these aims has been related to the form of cattle. The relation of type to production varies in different animals. Standards of perfection setting forth physical character, temperament, and other features affecting the efficiency for the principal objective or type are available. For each type these are made up in score-card form. In addition to beef and dairy cattle, one group of cattle raisers has a twofold ideal which is called "dual-purpose type."

The beef type and dairy type of cows are quite similar in internal anatomy and skeletal structure. The type difference is primarily the amount of fleshing and in the females the amount of secretory tissue in the mammary system.

Cattle are also used for draft purposes. For moving heavy loads on soft ground or on unprepared roads, oxen are quite suitable. Under such conditions they also have a small usage as riding and pack animals. Although oxen are patient, steady, and strong, they have yielded to horses and mules as draft animals on improved roadways.

The common cattle breeds in the United States, classed according to type or purpose for which they have been primarily produced, are as follows:

BEEF BREEDS	DAIRY BREEDS	DUAL-PURPOSE BREEDS
Aberdeen Angus	Ayrshire	Devon
Beefmasters	Brown Swiss	Milking Shorthorn
Brahman (zebu)	Dutch Belted	Red Poll
Brangus	French-Canadian	
Charbray	Guernsey	
Charolaise	Holstein-Friesian	
Galloway	Jersey	
Hereford	Kerry	
Polled Hereford		
Polled Shorthorn		
Santa Gertrudis		
Shorthorn		
West Highland		

Fig. 4. The present day beef type. A Hereford heifer, H. D. Miss Zato Onward A 31. Owned by the Hull Dobbs Ranch, Ft. Worth, Texas.

Fig. 5. The present-day dairy type. Holstein-Friesian cow, Montvic Rag-Apple Colanta Abberkerk, a notable producer and a cow of desirable conformation. Owned by Mt. Victoria Farms, Hudson Heights, P.2, Canada.

RELATIVE NUMBERS OF DIFFERENT BREEDS [6]

The registered purebred cattle have not been enumerated separately since the fifteenth census. The breeds listed previously have changed in order of numbers from time to time. Breeds numerous today may not hold that position. For many reasons the numbers change at variable rates; consequently, a count at any time is like a picture taken at the finish of a race, and may not indicate standing before or after. In the fifteenth census the more numerous breeds ranked in number of registered purebreds as follows: Holstein-Friesian, Hereford, Jersey, Shorthorn, Guernsey, Ayrshire, Aberdeen Angus, and Brown Swiss.

The U.S. Department of Agriculture obtains the new registration of purebreds annually from the cattle registry associations. For a 10-year period the breeds reported ranked as follows in the annual number of purebred registered.

PUREBRED CATTLE—AVERAGE YEARLY REGISTRATIONS FOR A RECENT TEN YEAR PERIOD. AS REPORTED BY BREED ASSOCIATIONS AND OTHER SOURCES. UNITED STATES [7]

BREED	NUMBER
Hereford	497,237
Holstein-Friesian	165,983
Aberdeen Angus	102,439
Guernsey	90,107
Shorthorn *	74,812
Jersey	65,860
Polled Hereford	43,861
Ayrshire	24,419
Brown Swiss	21,497
Brahman	15,760
Red Poll	4,478
Devon	481

* Includes beef, milking, and Polled Shorthorns.

PROPORTION OF THE CATTLE WHICH ARE PUREBREDS

The registered purebred cattle represented 3.0 per cent of all the cattle in the country. Of the farms reporting cattle in the fifteenth census (which was

[6] The last report on registered purebred number is given in the Fifteenth *Census of the United States*, 1930, Vol. IV, p. 67. The U.S.D.A. reports annually in *Agricultural Statistics* the number of purebred cattle registered by the various record associations.

[7] *Agricultural Statistics*, U.S.D.A., 1954. *Farmers Bulletin* 1443, U.S.D.A., 1954. Breed Association reports.

about 3 out of 4) only 1 in 12 reported registered purebreds. There were purebred cattle that had been recorded with the various breed associations on about 394,000 farms.

With the growth of the cattle industry there was a great expansion in the production of purebreds. In production capacity there is little difference between high grades and purebreds. The successive use of purebred sires on a herd results in seven-eighths pure breeding in the third generation. The use of purebred sires increases rapidly the pure breeding in a herd, which is what happened during the period of expansion of purebreds. The emphasis has more recently shifted to improving the breeds rather than expansion of numbers, for there is a limit to the purebreds that can be sold to commercial producers at a profitable price. The commercial grower is now more interested in what improvement might be made with a new sire than in the mere statement of pure breeding. In buying a bull for a high-grade herd the producer of commercial cattle wants a herd sire that will improve his herd.

Chapter 3

BEEF CATTLE—GENERAL VIEW

Coincident with colonization, cattle of various types were introduced. With the extension of agriculture, cattle became distributed throughout this country wherever feed supplies were available. Because of the nature of feeds, markets, or other factors, in some areas cattle of the dairy type became most numerous and in other sections beef cattle.

AREAS OF BEEF CATTLE RAISING

Beef cattle production of course varies for the different areas. The raising of feeders is common in some sections, the feeding of baby beeves in others. This differentiation is based upon the relative production economy of the different classes of feeds. In areas where pasturage and roughage are relatively cheap, cattle are mainly grown; in sections with ample supplies of concentrated feeds, more fattening is practiced. The last agricultural census indicated that cattle were kept upon 76.3 per cent of all farms and that the average-sized herd was 26 head. Less than 14 per cent of the farms in the west north central states have no cattle. Iowa has the largest proportion of farms having cattle. The Pacific states have the greatest number of farms or ranches without cattle.

The various geographical areas in which different kinds of beef cattle raising or production are practiced are shown in Figure 6. The two distinctive areas are the western range, which is known as the great breeding ground, and the corn belt, in which native and western cattle are finished for market. Within each section variations of the common practice are noted. For example, heavy feeding is not wholly uncommon in the western range region, and there is some pasturing and forage feeding on farms in the corn belt. Within each large division several areas of specialized feeding exist, and there is continual changing and shifting of the cattle population

25

in accordance with the feed situation. Droughts, for example, reduce cattle on the ranges.

The western range

The Great Plains, the Rocky Mountains, the Intermountain, and the Pacific coast regions comprise the western range country. In the 17 western states are found approximately 46 per cent of the total cattle population and more than 60 per cent of all beef cattle. Of our national forests about two thirds are important for grazing. It has been estimated that 10 million domestic animals, including the natural increase, graze for some period on national-forest ranges. The total land in grazing districts,[1] within the United States is about 266 million acres which includes both federal land and non-federal land, administered by the Bureau of Land Management and others. Grazing is barred in most national parks and in considerable areas of forest-service and other public lands. Where permitted, grazing on public land is on a controlled basis, and permits are issued.

Texas, Nebraska, Kansas, South Dakota, and Oklahoma are the states of heaviest beef cattle production; the states in the intermountain area, Nevada, Utah, Idaho, and Arizona, have fewer beef cattle.

In this vast western area, with much range in vegetation because of varying climate, rainfall, and altitude, there is not even cattle distribution. Also, cattle of various ages, finishes, and breeding are sent to the markets from the different areas.[2] The growing out of cattle on grass is the major line in the cattle enterprise, and as a consequence young cattle, mainly calves and yearlings, comprise the largest portion of their marketable receipts. In the range country cattle production is mainly a cow-and-calf type of enterprise, with relatively large units. Some of the steers, especially those with some age, may have sufficient finish to go direct to slaughter from the ranges, but the younger steers are most often fed before they are finally slaughtered. Feeding areas of a specialized nature are also prevalent in the western range country; for example, there are beet pulp feeding sections and a Texas cotton cake feeding section centered around the utilization of these by-products.

These feeding areas are concentrated in regions of available supplies of feeds because it is usually more economical to move the cattle to the feed than the feed to the cattle. It has been estimated that the cropland and irrigated pastures in the range country provide 35 per cent of the feed consumed by range livestock. In irrigated areas a farming type of cattle production prevails.

[1] General Services Administration data for June 30, 1955, *Senate Document 100*, 84th Congress, 2d Session.

[2] These specialized areas in the western range, indicating the producing and grazing sections and feeding areas, and approximate production of each, are shown in L. B. Mann, "Western Cattle and Sheep Areas," *Circ. C–103*, Cooperative Division, Farm Credit Administration, 1936.

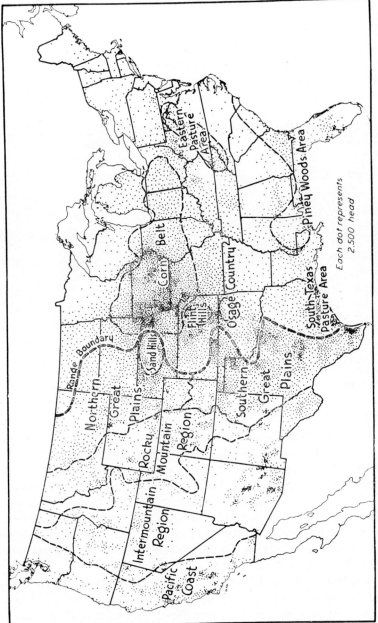

Each dot represents
2,500 head

Fig. 6. The distribution of cattle in the United States and the area of cattle production. (*Cattle Handbook,* National Livestock Marketing Association.)

27

About one half of the cattle from the western ranges are sold for slaughter, the remainder are purchased for further feeding or grazing. In the early fall the unfinished cattle predominate in the western range receipts, and many of these are fed further before they are slaughtered for beef. Most of them go to feed lots for finishing on concentrates; others go to the farms for roughage and pasture feeding. The Flint Hills of Kansas, the Osage Pastures of Oklahoma, the Mineral Point region of Wisconsin, and the Appalachian or eastern grazing region are the better known of the grass-fattening areas.

Fig. 7. Beef steers raised on the western range and finished in the corn belt. Grand Champion load of steers at the 1956 International Livestock Exposition. Bred by Kreycik Bros., Wood Lake, Neb. Fed and exhibited by John F. Mommsen & Sons, Andover, Iowa.

The corn belt

In the corn-belt area a different type of cattle raising prevails. Dairy cattle occupy a more prominent place, and in beef production more intensive methods are followed. With a fertile soil and ample rainfall for the growth of corn and other grains, general farming is practiced, and cattle raising is adapted to the type of agriculture. Smaller farms with higher priced land preclude the raising and grazing style of cattle production practiced on the western range. Cattle production is more intensive; pastures are used, but to a lesser degree than in the range country; and much more fattening or finishing of cattle is practiced.

Beef breeding herds maintained in the corn belt produce finished young cattle for the market (baby beeves) or purebred breeding stock. The corn belt is unique in location, being between the range country and the centers of dense population which are beef-deficient sections. The natural marketing movement of cattle and beef is, in the main, from west to east. In the western regions there is a natural movement in the opposite direction. Many cattle in the eastward movement pass through the corn belt and are fed out on corn-belt farms. In addition, many cattle are raised and finished on these farms. Range cattle sold as feeders go mainly to the corn belt for further feeding. Some are further fed on roughage feed or pasture, others fed on concentrates for a short time, or warmed up, while still others are fully finished before returning as beef. The range country absorbs some of the purebred breeding stock (mostly bulls) from the corn-belt section. These corn-belt farms have productive pastures; in fact, the farmers who grow more than the average amount of grass have more livestock of all kinds than those below the average in grass production. An increase in the growing of pasture and roughage on cash grain farms is usually accompanied by increased numbers of livestock.

Fig. 8. A beef breeding herd on pasture in the Pacific Coast region. Kennybrook Ranch, Kenwood, Calif.

Appalachian and Great Lakes regions

Beef cattle represent but a small portion of the total cattle in the north Atlantic region, as dairy cattle predominate. There is some grazing of cattle on the bluegrass pastures in the Appalachian or eastern pasture region. In this area, which includes part of Kentucky, Tennessee, Virginia, West Virginia, and North Carolina, cattle are fattened on pasturage principally, plus a relatively small amount of concentrates. There is a tendency to feed older cattle and some stocker cattle in this area, usually cattle from this section are not the best in quality. The greater portion of these cattle are from the beef breeding herds within the territory. Some are sold as feeders, while others are sold fattened principally on grass on the farm where they were reared. The area around Lancaster, Pa., is of note as a cattle-finishing section.

Cotton belt—southern states

Until recently the cotton belt has not been an extensive cattle raising section, with the exception of Texas and Oklahoma. Lately cattle numbers have expanded at a more rapid rate in the south than in other sections. There has been a big improvement in the breeding of southern cattle. Also, diseases and parasites once quite common are now being successfully controlled. Rations have been improved and, with specialization in cattle production, crops adapted to such production, including pasturage, have been expanded. Year-around grazing is one of the natural advantages of the south.

LEADING STATES IN BEEF PRODUCTION

Texas is the leading state in cattle numbers. The states have changed from time to time in their rank in cattle population. In reports it is common to list the cattle as to total or all cattle, and as to milk cows and heifers. If the milk cows and heifers are subtracted from the total cattle population, the remainder would be mostly beef cattle. A ranking of the states on such a basis follows.

CATTLE—TOTAL NUMBERS MINUS MILK COWS AND HEIFERS
IN LEADING STATES, AVERAGE OF 5 YEARS [3]

STATE	THOUSAND HEAD
Texas	7,294
Iowa	4,301
Nebraska	4,158
Kansas	3,513
South Dakota	2,608
Missouri	2,512
Oklahoma	2,491
Illinois	2,386
California	2,168
Montana	2,117
Colorado	1,822
Minnesota	1,440
Florida	1,396
Louisiana	1,307
North Dakota	1,249
Wyoming	1,070
Oregon	1,040
Total United States	60,099

[3] *Livestock Market News, Statistics and Related Data*, 1955, U.S.D.A., 1956.

BEEF AND VEAL FROM DIFFERENT TYPES

It is estimated that about 55 per cent of our beef and veal supply comes from beef cattle, while dairy cattle, or herds kept for milk, furnish about 35 per cent of the entire volume. Dual-purpose cattle, or those kept for milk as well as beef production, contribute 10 per cent of the total supply. It should be pointed out that dairy cattle furnish most of our veal.

The proportion of beef derived from cows has been increasing because of the younger age and lighter weight at which other cattle, especially steers, are slaughtered. About 40 per cent of our total supply of meat from cattle, that is both veal and beef, comes from cows.

Grain fattening is more general with beef cattle than with dairy cattle, as would be expected. High finish on dairy cattle brings much less return than on cattle of beef breeding. It has been estimated that not more than 25 per cent of the number of cattle slaughtered, exclusive of veal calves, are grain fattened. Probably under 40 per cent of beef bred cattle are grain finished, although a much larger proportion has had some grain.

CHANGES IN NUMBERS OF CATTLE

Peaks in the cattle population occurred in 1891, 1905, 1918, 1934, 1945 and 1956; lows appeared in 1896, 1912, 1928, 1938, and 1948. The average interval between peaks and also between lows is about 14 years in the "production cycles." When cattle prices are relatively high, normal marketing of the production is restricted; more are held for breeding stock on the farms and ranches. With low prices for cattle, there is liquidation of the breeding herds, and marketings are comparatively heavy. The supply of feed is also a factor. Numbers vary because of these conditions, and a cyclical movement in cattle numbers exists. The purchasing power of products from dairy cattle has tended upward, while that for beef cattle has remained about the same for the last half century.

CHANGES IN NUMBERS OF CATTLE OF DIFFERENT TYPES

Cattle in the census report are listed as milk cows and all cattle. The latter group includes, in addition to the milk cows, all other dairy- and beef-type cattle. Yearly estimates of these numbers are made by Agricultural Marketing Service, Crop Reporting Board of the U.S. Department of Agriculture on January 1. From 1890 the number of milk cows increased until 1935. Even in years of recession of all cattle numbers, the milk cows showed increases. There was a decline in milk-cow numbers following 1935. A peak in numbers occurred in 1945, which was followed by a reduction. The dairy cattle population appears to be more stable than formerly having been in the 23 millions for the past eight years.

The change in numbers of all cattle on farms is due mainly to changes in the numbers of beef cattle. From 1949 to 1956 there was a 62 per cent increase in beef cows. Half of our cows are now beef cows, whereas in 1924 only one fourth were so classified. This fact is shown in Figure 9, which also indicates the cyclical movement of the cattle population. The increase in dairy cows has been quite regular, with few slight deviations, while other cattle have varied markedly in numbers and have largely accounted for the cyclical movement in all-cattle numbers.

CATTLE ON FARMS JAN. I

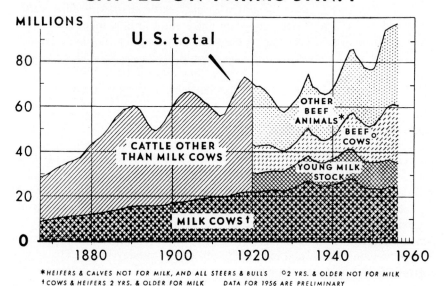

Fig. 9. Cattle numbers have been increasing. Milk cows on farms have not shown much change in late years. Cattle other than milk cows fluctuate more than milk cows. (U.S.D.A., Agricultural Marketing Service.)

In comparing the human population with that of the cattle population we note a greater increase of the former. In other words, we have fewer cattle per capita than formerly. Although dairy cows have approximately maintained their numbers, other cattle, which are principally beef cattle, have increased. The use of dairy products in our diet has expanded with this change. Per capita beef consumption has not changed materially, as the change in the cattle population has been largely offset by increases in the productive rate of our cattle.

SHOW-RING CLASSIFICATION OF BEEF CATTLE

In the show ring beef cattle are classed into breeding and market or fat cattle. At some shows classes are also provided for feeder cattle. Breeding classes are for purebreds, while market or fat and feeder classes are for purebreds, grades, and crossbreeds. In each division considerable disparity exists in the classifications at the different shows. Most of the livestock shows are held in the last half of the year, as the state fairs are generally held in the fall. However, there are some prominent livestock shows in the winter and early spring. Consequently, classes and base dates are not uniform. With beef breeding cattle the common base dates are January 1, May 1, and September 1. To make allowances for size differences, a show-yard classification is made. In market or fat cattle this is based on weight and age; in breeding classes age is used. The tendency has been toward the elimination from the classification of older and heavier classes.

At the 1957 International Livestock Exposition the three age classes for individuals (steer, spayed, or martin heifer) [4] purebred, grade, or crossbred in the fat-cattle division, ranged in age from senior calves to junior yearlings. The limitation on age was that no animal calved prior to January 1, 1956 could compete. The competing individuals, therefore, were under 2 years of age. No steer could be shown that had more than one pair of its milk teeth replaced by permanent teeth. (See page 48.) Group classes for fat cattle including carloads (15 head) and groups of three, were also included, as were champions and grand champions. At some shows carload classes are available for breeding bulls and also heifers.

Beef breeding individuals at the 1957 International Livestock Exposition were divided into six classes for bulls and six classes for heifers in the Aberdeen Angus, Hereford, and Shorthorn breeds. Group classes, as well as champion and grand champion classes, were included.

At livestock shows the common individual classes for beef breeding cattle are two-year-old, senior yearling, junior yearling, summer yearling, senior calf, and junior calf. Group classes include two bulls, three bulls, get of sire, two females, pair of yearlings, pair of calves, and graded herd.

State fairs, livestock shows and expositions, district and county fairs publish premium lists or a preliminary classification in which are listed the various livestock classes. They also include the rules and regulations. A prospective exhibitor ought to know and understand the show classification and rules.

[4] Definitions of steer, bull, cow, and heifer appear on pages 77 and 78, martin heifer on page 198.

Chapter 4

BEEF TYPE

Type with reference to livestock denotes a kind of form, shape, conformation, or general appearance related to utility. A typical form (such as is evident in beef type) common to a number of individuals of a kind or species is referred to as "type." In general, there is a relationship between form and performance. To the extent that this relation exists, the form can be used as a measure of value. In slaughter animals there is a fairly high correlation between form and carcass value. The value of a beef carcass, for example, depends upon quality, conformation, and finish, which can be determined from the appearance of the animal on foot with a fair degree of accuracy. It is obvious that a thick, meaty beef carcass can not be secured from a slaughter animal that is lean and angular. The ideal of beef type implies not only high utility value of the carcass but also high acceptability of the steer from the producer standpoint. The ideal beef steer, then, is one that has made rapid and economical gains, and, as well, is high in grade or market value for a slaughter animal. The qualities which indicate rapidity and economy of gains other than weight for age are rather intangible.

The judging, selecting, or evaluating of beef steers is based on the individuality of the steer. Desirable individuality is a composite of the demands of beef consumers and the requirements of cattle producers or a sum of the characteristics of an ideal animal. The ideal or standard of perfection sets forth the external features which affect the animal's commercial value. A steer making the maximum gain on the minimum of feed is desired by the producers; the consumer wants good-quality beef at reasonable cost.

DETAILED DESCRIPTION OF THE IDEAL BEEF TYPE

The beef steer score card

The score card is valuable for teaching the beginner the various parts of the beef steer, their comparative value, and also the terms used to describe the qualities of any part or parts. The finished beef steer is taken as the ideal, since it is in greater demand than bulls, heifers, or cows on the finished-cattle market, and consequently sells for higher prices. Steers commonly yield carcasses superior to those of cows and heifers. The score card for breeding animals is based on the beef steer standard of perfection: the model beef breeding bull or cow is one capable of producing a calf which, when finished, will be an ideal steer. The essentials of type are the same for steers, heifers, cows, and bulls.

The score card is a description of the external features of a model, or perfect animal. Pictures, outlines, figures, and true-type figures are likewise highly useful in depicting the ideal to the student, so that perfection or the lack of it may be appreciated in the live animal. The parts of the steers are shown in Figure 10.

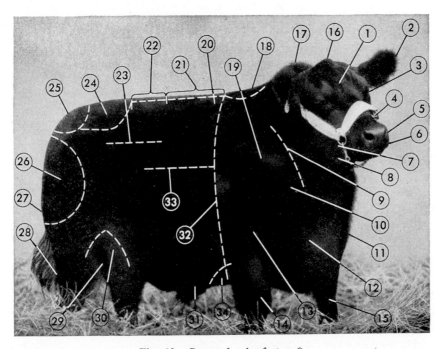

Fig. 10. Parts of a beef steer.*

1–Forehead	10–Shoulder Point	19–Shoulder	28–Hock
2–Ear	11–Dewlap	20–Crops	29–Cod
3–Eye	12–Brisket	21–Back	30–Hind Flank
4–Face	13–Forearm	22–Loin	31–Sheath
5–Nostril	14–Knee	23–Loin Edge	32–Chest or Heart
6–Muzzle	15–Shank	24–Rump	Girth
7–Jaw	16–Poll	25–Tail Head	33–Ribs
8–Throat	17–Neck	26–Round or Thigh	34–Fore Flank
9–Shoulder Vein	18–Top of shoulder	27–Twist	

* The feet and dewclaws are not shown.

Suggested student score card for a market steer

Following is a score card suitable for a market steer in prime condition.

· FINISHED MARKET STEER

Scale of Points

GENERAL APPEARANCE—49 points:

1. WEIGHT—score according to age, estimate weight

6 months	450 pounds
12 months	850 pounds
18 months	1,100 pounds
24 months	1,300 pounds

2. FORM—broad, deep, low set, symmetrical, stylish, straight top line and under line, not paunchy
3. QUALITY—hair soft and mossy, hide pliable, bone, head, and horns fine, body and fleshing smooth and even, neither rolly nor patchy
4. CONDITION—degree of fatness, indicated by spinal covering, rib covering, fullness of purse and flank, proper texture and finish indicated by a mellow yet firm and springy touch
5. DRESSING PERCENTAGE—high condition, trim middle, thin hide, good quality

HEAD AND NECK—5 points:

6. MUZZLE—broad, nostrils large
7. EYES—large, clear, quiet expression
8. FACE—short, clean cut
9. FOREHEAD—broad
10. EARS—medium size, fine texture
11. HORNS—fine texture, medium size, well shaped
12. NECK—short, thick, throat clean

FOREQUARTERS—9 points:

13. SHOULDER VEIN—full, plump
14. SHOULDER—well covered with flesh, wide and smooth on top
15. BRISKET—neat and trim
16. LEGS—medium length, straight, wide apart, short, arm full, shank fine

BODY—23 points:

17. CHEST—deep, wide, crops full
18. RIBS—long, well arched, broad across top, covered with thick, smooth, firm flesh
19. LOIN—broad, covered with thick, smooth flesh
20. FLANK—full, even with under line

HINDQUARTERS—14 points:

21. HOOKS—well laid in and smoothly covered
22. RUMP—long, wide, level, smooth at tailhead
23. THIGHS—plump, deep, wide, and thick
24. TWIST—deep, plump
25. LEGS—straight, short, shank fine

Scoring of market steers is not common except in instruction. For classroom instruction, students may score by listing the difference between the perfect score on each item and that allotted the individual being appraised, or by listing the amount allotted each part. The total score may be used in comparing different individuals. Ranking on each score-card point is another method of score-card use. By this method a final rating can be made which corresponds to place in the class. Score-card judging is not applicable to comparative or show-ring judging because much time is involved and because a proper balance of point emphasis cannot be obtained. Recently, the tendency has been to simplify the score card in appraising farm animals.

Score-card parts

The points of the score card will be discussed separately.

1. General appearance. The general appearance may be divided into weight, form, quality, finish, and dressing percentage. About one half of the value of the steer is included under general appearance, which deals with the outline of the steer.

A. WEIGHT. The capacity for weight increase is determined by heredity; feeding and management determine the extent to which that capacity is fulfilled. Heredity, then, sets the pattern, and the environment governs the extent of completion. Of all the items considered in evaluating market steers, weight for age is the most important from the producer's standpoint, because rapid gains are usually economical gains. Large size is desired to get fast gains, but there is a limit. If there is too much size the carcass will lack the fat and lean required at a given age and weight. As cattle are sold by weight, the buyer is not concerned with weight as it is related to age unless this influences the grade of the carcass. Slow-gaining, late-maturing beef cattle are lacking in beef quality. To the meat packer weight of a slaughter animal on foot is an important factor, because it places the carcass in a weight class that yields retail cuts of particular weights and finish. Though some heavy carcasses are in demand, the demand has been consistently shifting toward finished cattle of lighter weights.

Sex, like age, is linked with weight, since the males are heavier at all ages. Breed differences in weight are also present. Following is a table of suggested ages and weights which may be regarded as a good standard for well-fed steers of different ages.

AGE, MONTHS	WEIGHT, POUNDS
Birth	80
6	450
12	850
18	1,100
24	1,300

B. FORM OR CONFORMATION. When finished, the beef steer is broad, deep, and low set. A poor steer in form is narrow, shallow, rangy, and leggy. A top-grade beef carcass in form is yielded only by steers that are wide, deep, muscular, and fairly short legged. Straightness of the top line, under line, and side lines is highly desirable. The top line is perhaps of importance only as it is related to appearance, but the side lines and bottom lines are of greater economic importance because they have to do with trimness of middle and balance of parts. A good beef steer must be balanced or symmetrical; that is, all parts must be uniformly well developed. In general a steer should be of the conventional form rather than comprest or compact, for it will then be heavier when in comparable condition or finish.

C. QUALITY. The grader of beef carcasses attaches more importance to the item of quality than to any other single point. We want, then, in the beef steer, to give attention to those features of quality which carry over into the carcass. Smoothness of form and fleshing are highly desirable. A soft mossy coat of hair and pliable not heavy hide are indicators of quality. Refinement of head, horns, and bone also denotes quality. Refinement in this regard can be carried too far, because sufficient strength and ruggedness are prerequisites to profitable performance in the feed lot.

A steer with a clean-cut head, not too heavy bone, fine hair coat, pliable hide free from roughness in fleshing, and smooth throughout is one with quality. Such steers yield high-quality carcasses. A course, rough steer will not produce a high-quality, attractive carcass which in the retailer's display case will have appeal to the buyer.

D. FINISH OR CONDITION AND FLESHING. Top-selling beef carcasses must carry a sufficient amount of fat. Consequently, the market steer must be finished or high in condition. Lack of finish is a common fault in market steers; yet overfinishing is not uncommon in heavy, older cattle. There is a demand for heavy, highly finished cattle, but it is rather limited. Finish beyond that desired by consumers is uneconomical because it is costly to produce and much fat must be trimmed off by the retailer before selling.

The finish of a steer may be appraised fairly accurately at some distance. However, close differences can be ascertained only by handling. The cover-

Fig. 11. Champion Hereford Steer, 1955 International Livestock Exposition, exhibited by Lyle Lewter, Lubbock, Texas.

Fig. 12. An ideal Aberdeen Angus Steer, "Shorty," Grand Champion of the International Livestock Exposition in 1954. Shown by Janice Hillinger, Manly, Iowa.

ing of spine, rib, and point of the shoulder indicates the fatness, and so does the fullness of the flank and purse (scrotum after castration). The handling of the fleshing should be mellow, yet firm and springy. The covering of flesh may be too soft or too hard as well as insufficient.

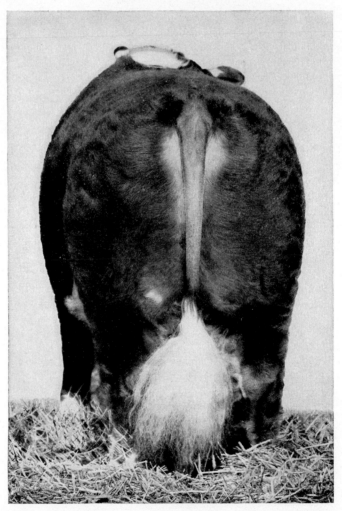

Fig. 13. Rear view of International Livestock Exposition grand champion steer, Judge Roy Bean.

Fleshing that is fat and lean is to the consumer the major economic feature of beef. Muscling with sufficient fat surrounding it and intermixed between the muscle fibers and that is tender and tasty is the demand of the beef consumer. Lean meat of muscling is commonly referred to as "natural fleshing" by the cattle raiser. (See Figure 17.) Uniform, heavy fleshing which is mellow to the touch, thick over the back, ribs, and loin, and heavy in the rounds in the steer on foot give the fleshing required in a top carcass.

Fig. 14. Shorthorn steer, Penn. State Bandolier, Grand Champion Steer at the 1956 International Livestock Exposition.

E. DRESSING PERCENTAGE OR YIELD. This is the ratio of carcass weight to live weight. To determine dressing per cent or yield, the weight of the chilled carcass is divided by the live weight and multiplied by 100. If, for example, a 1200-pound steer would yield a 720-pound carcass the dressing per cent would be 60. Cattle that are highly finished, trim middled, and light in the hide, shanks, and head will yield a relatively high proportion of carcass when slaughtered. As the carcass is worth more per pound than the by-products, a high carcass yield adds to market value. Although light-middled, fine-boned steers may dress high, it is obvious that these qualities can be carried too far, economical production considered. There is a medium ground; we want evidence of high dressing, yet it must be compatible with productive characters such as ruggedness, and capacity to consume feed. (See page 131.)

2. Head and neck. Of all the main divisions of the score card the head and neck are allotted the fewest number of points and are of minor consequence in the meat value of a slaughter beef animal.

F. HEAD. A medium-sized head is suggested under quality. In shape a rather short, wide head with a broad muzzle is desired. By the appearance of the head the temperament and disposition may be estimated. A lymphatic temperament and quiet disposition are the attributes of a good feeding steer.

Fig. 15. Determining the finish or condition on a market steer. The spinal and rib covering, appraised by handling, indicates the fleshing of a steer.

G. NECK. A short, thick, muscular neck, clean at the throat, is required in a good steer. Such a neck is compatible with the general requirement in form. A long-legged, rangy steer would have a long, thin neck.

3. Forequarters. The forequarters on the live steer on the score card are not comparable with the forequarters on the beef carcass, mainly because a section between the fore- and hindquarters is designated as "body." The forequarter is a section of lesser value than all other portions except the head and neck.

H. SHOULDER VEIN. The junction between the neck and the shoulder is blended together at the shoulder vein. This part is full and plump in a good steer so that no marked division can be noted.

I. SHOULDER. Briefly, the shoulder, as it is the source of a wholesale cut of wide demand, should be well covered with flesh, wide and smooth on top. A smooth blending of this part with the others is desired. Heavy, rough shoulders, opened too wide on top, are not uncommon.

J. BRISKET. A minimum of brisket is wanted in a slaughter steer because this is one of the lowest priced cuts. Consequently, a neat, trim brisket is suggested for the ideal.

K. LEGS. Actually, the legs are of little consequence when the steer is finished, provided they are ample to carry him, on marketing, across the scale. However, usefulness in the feed lot is based on adequate legs, and style is influenced by the legs. Straight, fairly short legs set wide apart are desirable, and a well-developed muscular arm is preferred.

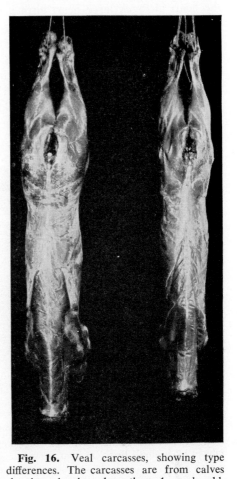

Fig. 16. Veal carcasses, showing type differences. The carcasses are from calves slaughtered when less than 1 week old. Heavy muscling, shown in the carcass on the left, is typical of the beef type. Calves of dairy breeding have carcasses like the one on the right.

4. Body. The body embraces some of the important high-priced cuts and is as a consequence a division which receives nearly one fourth of the points on the score card. In general, great width should typify the ideal steer. Extremes are to be avoided. The very compact animal is undesirable and the tall rangy one is inefficient in the use of feed. Slaughter cattle with thick meaty bodies will yield carcasses which have the desired form.

L. CHEST. The chest is that portion between the shoulders and immediately behind them and includes the part called the "crops." Great width and depth with well-filled crops are required. In fact, a steer cannot be too wide or deep in the chest. The girth of a steer just back of the fore leg is the heart girth. A large heart girth indicates constitutional vigor.

M. RIBS. As commonly used, the ribs include the back. On the carcass this portion is the wholesale cut of beef known as the "ribs." A straight, wide back is desired, and in usage this term is restricted to the top part of the ribs from the shoulders to the beginning of the loin at the last rib. As this portion yields one of the higher priced beef cuts, it should be heavily, smoothly, and firmly fleshed. The thickness of the flesh is determined by a touch with the palm and fingers.

Fig. 17. A grand champion carload of finished steers. Grand champion load of steers, 1949 International Livestock Exposition. Aberdeen Angus steers fed and exhibited by Schmidt Bros., Delmar, Iowa.

N. LOIN. The loin extends along the top line from the ribs back to the hip or hook. The beef cut loin extends somewhat farther back on the carcass than on the live steer, as indicated in Figures 10 and 45. The specifications used for the ribs or back hold for the loin. When broad, heavily fleshed, and smooth, it complies with the requirements. Of the wholesale cuts the loin is in the greatest demand and sells for the highest price per pound. Along the top line, especially on the rear part of the back or the forward part of the loin, there may be adhesions of the hide to the vertebrae, and a depression in the fleshing develops as the animal is fattened. Such a depression is called a "tie."

O. FLANK. A flank that is full and even with the under line is desired in the fattened steer.

5. Hindquarters. The hindquarter on the score card is not comparable with that on the carcass, as the latter includes all portions back of the wholesale cut known as the rib. On the score card the hindquarter includes all parts posterior to the loin. This division is mainly the beef round on the carcass.

P. HOOKS. The prominence of the hips is known as the "hooks" in cattle. A finished steer should not have a visible prominence of the hooks. An inconspicuous, smoothly covered hook is desirable.

Q. RUMP. The part of the steer along the top from the hook to the tailhead is known as the rump. A part of this is included in the wholesale beef cut, the loin, and the remainder is made up of the rump. A long, wide, level rump which is smoothly fleshed is desired. Often finished cattle are rough and patchy at the rump and tailhead.

R. THIGHS. The outer part of the round which is below the rump is termed the thigh. It should be plump, deep, wide, and thick. Too often beef cattle are light in the hindquarters or not uniform in width. When narrow behind or high in the thighs, a light round in the carcass results. Plumpness is desired, as a short shank of round gives a larger proportion of round that can be merchandized as round steak.[1]

S. TWIST. The inner thigh is termed the "twist" and is a contributing portion to the beef round. It should be deep from the tailhead and also plump.

T. LEGS. The hind legs, like the forelegs, should be ample to carry the weight of the finished steer. In the good steer they must be short, straight, and not too heavy in the shank. As in the front legs, ample bone is needed, but it can be excessive.

PROCEDURE IN JUDGING BEEF CATTLE

The ability to evaluate livestock is essential for success in livestock production. Evaluation may be of a single animal, such as the selection of a herd sire, or it may be in ranking the individuals in a group, such as culling in a herd of breeding cows or class of beef steers. Practice to develop the ability to evaluate livestock is obtained in livestock judging or in placing of classes. As will be pointed out later, all of the available facts must be considered in making a selection. Production records and other information are to be scrutinized in making breeding herd choices.

[1] An abnormality termed "double muscled" appears occasionally in cattle. It is identified by the thickness and fullness of the thighs, with deep grooves between the muscles. It appears to be inherited, as an incomplete recessive with variable expressivity. The heterozygote may be favored in selection, but the homozygote is an undesirable animal commercially.

The essential steps in judging livestock or placing a class are as follows:

1. Knowledge of the ideal.
2. Observation and examination of the individuals.
3. Comparison of the individuals in the class.
4. Ranking, conclusion, or judgment.
5. Explanation for placing, or reasons.

Fig. 18. Front view of a champion Shorthorn Steer at the International Livestock Exposition.

In proceeding with the placing of a class of slaughter cattle, it is suggested that first a survey be made of the entire group by walking around and observing from some distance. General features, such as weight, form, quality, and condition, are appraised in a general way. Then follows a more detailed study or inspection of each individual in the class at closer range from the side, rear, and front. Finally, by handling, the fleshing is appraised, as are some features of quality. The amount and smoothness of the flesh are determined by touch or handling of the rib, back, loin, shoulder, and spinal covering.

Weight estimates from measurements

Many studies have been made on the relation of weights to various measurements of beef cattle. Of the usual measurements it appears that the heart girth is the most closely correlated with weight.

A method devised by Johnson [2] makes possible the estimate of weight from body measurements. The accuracy has been tested on the common breeds of cattle including fat or finished cattle and feeder cattle. The greatest error with any group was 5 per cent, and for 431 head the error was 3.6 per cent.

Two measurements are used. They are (1) the heart girth taken directly behind the shoulders, and (2) the length taken from the pinbone to the prominence on the shoulder, which is located in mature cattle 1 inch back of the point of the shoulder. The latter measurement is taken with the animal standing squarely on its feet with its head straight forward. The heart girth measurement is not influenced materially by the position of the animal.

The formula follows:

$$\frac{(\text{Heart girth, inches})^2 \times \text{length, inches}}{300} = \text{weight in pounds}$$

For example, if the specimen of cattle taken had a heart girth of 80 inches and a length from shoulder prominence to the pinbone of 60 inches, it would have an approximate weight of 1,280 pounds.

Age of cattle as determined by the teeth [3]

Cattle when mature have eight incisor teeth on the lower jaw. On the upper jaw a dental pad occupies the place of the incisors. Age may be estimated from the appearance and wear of the permanent or second incisor teeth. A calf at birth has two or more of the temporary incisors, and in a month's time all of the temporary incisors have made their appearance. The center pair of temporary incisors will be replaced by a pair of permanents at 15 to 18 months, and these are up in wear at 2 years. The intermediate or second pair of permanent incisors appear at 2½ years and are fully developed and in wear at 3 years. At 3½ years the second intermedi-

[2] D. W. Johnson, "Livestock Weights from Measurements," *Extension Folder 70*, Minn. Agr. Ext. Div., May, 1939.

[3] George W. Pope, *Farmer's Bull. 1066*, U.S.D.A., August, 1919.

ates or laterals appear, which are mature at 4 years. At 4½ to 5 years the corner incisors are replaced, and a full set of permanent incisors in wear is typical at 5 years of age. Beyond this age the incisors show signs of wear, and the shape of the wearing surface is changed, being more triangular as the teeth are worn down and are distinctly separated. Also there is less arch or curvature of the teeth forward as age advances. (See Fig. 19.)

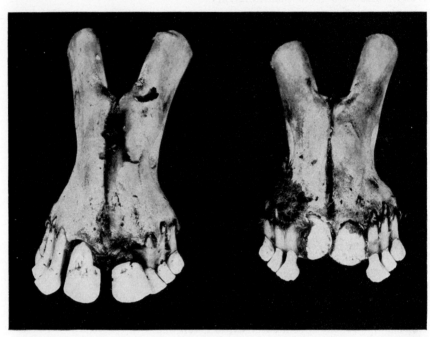

Fig. 19. Lower jaws of cattle showing the incisor teeth. The specimens were prepared by removing most of the tissue except the teeth and bone. Lower jaw on the right shows a typical mouth 15 to 18 months of age; the center pair of permanent incisors is about to erupt at the gum line. The jaw on the left is typical of 24 months of age; the center pair of permanent incisors is up in wear and there are 3 pairs of temporary incisors showing.

Slaughter steer grades determined from weights and measurements

A method for determining the slaughter grades of steers from weights and measurements has been devised by Knapp.[4] The use of these methods permits the inexperienced grader to estimate quite accurately the market grade of slaughter steers by weights and measurements. For example, a steer measuring 44 inches high at the withers with a weight between 716 and 828 pounds would class as good. With greater weight the grade would

[4] Bradford Knapp, "Determination of Slaughter-Steer Grades from Weights and Measurements," *Cir. 524,* U.S.D.A., May, 1939.

be choice or prime, and for a lesser weight the grade would be medium or plain. As the height of the steer at the withers is increased the weight is increased, as would be expected. Better grades outweigh the poorer grades. However, beyond a certain height additional height is accompanied with a lowered market grade; so a tall steer would grade low even though he was finished.

Fig. 20. The rear view of a champion steer herd. Aberdeen Angus steers shown by the Iowa State College, Ames, Iowa.

Two measurements, height of withers and heart girth, are also related to market grade. A steer 44 inches tall at the withers and with a heart girth of 63¾ to 68 inches, for example, would grade good, where as steers of larger girths would grade higher and those with smaller girths would grade lower. Further relationships between market and weight, weight and heart girth are given in the circular. These are based on a study of 167 steers of Hereford, Shorthorn, Aberdeen Angus, and dairy breeding.

Chapter 5

CATTLE MARKETS

Different agencies are involved in the movement from the livestock producer to the meat consumer. In some instances these number only a few—for example, the cattle raiser may slaughter and sell or barter carcasses direct to consumers. However, this is a rather simple case. Most beef must move some distance to the consumer because the surplus beef-producing areas are in the middle western section of our country and the consuming population is in the east; there is also some movement to the deficit areas on the west coast. Cattle marketed for beef may pass through a central market or direct to the meat packer. After processing, the meat moves through various channels to the consumer.

The marketing system is not static. Changes are continually being made. The avenues through which beef or other meat moves are constantly shifting in response not only to new surplus and deficit areas but also to changes in marketing methods. Up until the time of World War I the tendency was toward centralization of marketing and slaughter. Since then there has been a marked tendency toward decentralization.

METHODS OF DISPOSING OF LIVESTOCK

The producer of livestock is confronted with a perplexing problem of where to market his livestock, for he usually has a choice of many outlets. In order to select intelligently the best market, the seller must have considerable information at his disposal. He must know the relative costs of marketing for the different available markets, so that comparisons can be made on the basis of net returns. He must know market classes and grades, so that he can evaluate his cattle.

Following are the common methods of disposition of livestock:

1. They may be sold to the local livestock buyer.

2. The owners in certain localities pool their livestock and ship it co-operatively. These are known as "livestock shipping associations."

3. Livestock may be sold through livestock auction-sale barns. Use of this outlet has increased greatly in certain sections, and there are seasonal auction sales, especially where feeder cattle are sold. (See page 62.)

4. A sale may be made direct to meat packers either at the plant, at their concentration yards, or to their buyers in the field. Direct marketing is defined for slaughter animals as sale to slaughterers at places other than the central livestock market, where the services of a commission company are employed by the seller.

5. Livestock may be shipped to a central market, consigned to a commission company, which acts as the owner's agent and makes the sale.

6. Livestock are at times consigned to slaughterers, and settlement is made on the basis of yield and grade of the carcass.

7. Local butchers or feeders may purchase the livestock direct from the owners.

8. Home slaughter is practiced, and there is some sale or barter of meat not used for home consumption.

EARLY CATTLE MARKETS

As cities developed in this country, a market for beef was created. Prominent early cattle markets were at Philadelphia, Baltimore, Boston, New York, and Albany. It was not until the beginning of the eighteenth century that cattle were taken from grazing areas to urban centers for slaughter. The cattle were driven from the cattle-growing sections to the large cities on the eastern seaboard. These cattle were sold at markets already established for eastern cattle near large cities. George Renick in 1805 drove 50 head of large heavy steers from the Sciota Valley in Ohio to Baltimore, where they were disposed of through the city butchers. Following this original trailing of cattle droves, numerous others followed, and it was not until the advent of rail transportation that trailing ceased. Rail shipment began soon after 1850 but was supplemented with trailing to points of shipment, and until the year 1880 extensive trailing of cattle was practiced in southwestern United States.

The drovers of cattle passed on information to one another about the cattle markets. Those returning from the market would advise those with incoming droves on the source of the strongest bids and the general condition of the market. From this developed the plan of one drover staying on the market and charging a fee for bringing sellers and buyers together. The next step was the development of the livestock commission companies.

CATTLE TRAILING

As cattle raising moved westward, the distance from the large eastern markets was increased. As the frontier was pushed west and agriculture went west with the settler, greater distance separated the livestock grazing and feeding areas from the meat-deficient area on the eastern seaboard. Often trailing was interrupted for cattle from the midwest areas like Illinois with a feeding period in the grain crop producing area of Ohio. Fat cattle shrink heavily in trailing and, with the settlement of the country, the practice became inconvenient and uneconomical. The development of railroad transportation afforded the cattle grower greater accessibility to markets for fattened cattle. The drover continued to operate beyond the transportation lines and brought in livestock to the market on the railroad.

RAILROAD TRANSPORTATION OF CATTLE

The first experimental attempt to ship live cattle by rail was in 1852, but it was not until 1860 that much livestock was transported to markets by railroads. Many railroad centers then became the seats of central or terminal markets. The extension of the railways into the grazing areas extended the raising of livestock and caused a gradual increase in livestock numbers.

Although motor trucks have reduced the number of livestock shipped by rail, in 1953 over 21,000 carloads of livestock were received at the Union Stockyards, Chicago.

WATER TRANSPORTATION AND CATTLE MARKETING

When livestock production moved over the Allegheny Mountains, most of the animals were marketed by trailing until railways were developed. Water transportation also entered into the early market picture; shipping by boat down the Mississippi and the Ohio and up the Atlantic coast provided an outlet for live animals and cured meat.

With the growth of water transportation on the Great Lakes and numerous canals, some meat was shipped by boat to the East, especially through the Erie Canal. The Civil War closed off the Mississippi route, and soon thereafter the railroads opened up shipping facilities for the midwest.

DEVELOPMENT OF CENTRALIZED MARKETING

Following the Civil War there developed the central marketing system. Livestock was consigned to large terminal markets located at Chicago,

Fig. 21. The Sioux City stockyards and "Packingtown." The hog barns are in the center foreground. Beyond are the cattle pens, adjoining the hog barns on the north. The large building partially surrounded by the cattle pens is the Livestock Exchange Building. To the left, on the banks of the Missouri River, is the sheep barn. To the right are the packing plants of Armour, Cudahy, and Swift. The Sioux City yards cover 80 acres of ground and have a capacity of 25,000 cattle, 40,000 hogs, 25,000 sheep, and 1,000 horses and mules. (Sioux City Stockyard Co.)

53

Kansas City, and elsewhere. On these markets commission merchants representing the owners sold the livestock to large packing plants near or at the central market or to small plants there and elsewhere. The smaller plants, especially those at or near the eastern markets, were represented on western markets by order buyers. Many central markets developed in the midwest. Slaughter cattle converged toward these markets in the eastward movement and then fanned out toward the east. The majority were slaughtered at or near the terminal market.

Fig. 22. Cattle Buyer looks over lot of finished cattle in the Chicago Union Stock Yards with commission man. (Swift & Company.)

A public livestock market or central market is one which complies with certain federal government regulations. On such livestock trading centers facilities are provided for receiving, caring for, and handling livestock; the privileges of buying and selling livestock are available to all. There are about 100 markets in this category, and over 60 are regularly included in the U.S. Department of Agriculture reports.

WHERE SLAUGHTER CATTLE ARE RAISED

The various areas of cattle production have been discussed previously. The surplus areas in beef production are in the west central and eastern mountain states. Iowa, Nebraska, Kansas, and Texas have a large surplus of beef. The population of the Pacific states and Texas has grown more rapidly than the rest of the country. This has caused rapid growth of the packing industry in the West and moved the lines of east-west movement of livestock eastward, as shown in Figure 23.

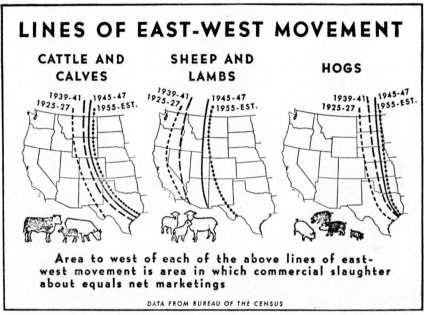

Fig. 23. The lines of the east-west movement of livestock have moved eastward. This is due to the rapid increase of the population in the Pacific states and Texas. (U.S.D.A., Bur. of Agri. Economics.)

Cattle are raised in areas where production is low in cost and efficient. This involves greater costs in getting the beef to the consumer, for these areas are far from the centers of consumption. Since this drawback is overshadowed by lower production cost, the total cost to the consumer is less.

LARGE CATTLE MARKETS

The central markets vary from year to year in their total receipts. The total receipts are made up largely of livestock sold at the yards and designated as "salable" receipts. When cattle numbers are lessened in an area served by a central market, the receipts are, of course, reduced. This is usually preceded by heavy receipts because of liquidation. Chicago, because of its location, has long been a large cattle market. Although there are many officially recognized public markets widely distributed in the

United States, the principal markets are within or adjoining the corn belt. Following is a list of the larger central markets and their cattle receipts (excluding calves) for a 5-year period.

CATTLE, YEARLY TOTAL AND SALABLE RECEIPTS AT PUBLIC MARKETS

Average of 5 Years—1951 to 1955 [1]

MARKET	TOTAL AVERAGE	SALABLE AVERAGE
1. Chicago, Ill.	2,072,317	2,036,170
2. Omaha, Neb.	2,045,710	1,980,489
3. Kansas City, Mo.	1,503,883	1,189,343
4. Sioux City, Iowa	1,306,104	1,251,135
5. S. St. Paul, Minn.	1,080,423	1,042,405
6. St. Louis NSY, Ill.	1,049,193	842,631
7. Denver, Colo.	998,331	817,675
8. Fort Worth, Tex.	798,262	620,008
9. Oklahoma City, Okla.	737,644	685,523
10. St. Joseph, Mo.	706,316	677,130
11. Los Angeles, Calif.	449,224	440,327
12. Pittsburgh, Pa.	409,039	41,041
13. Indianapolis, Ind.	405,015	393,027
14. Wichita, Kans.	369,696	322,160
15. Sioux Falls, S. D.	364,836	359,834
Total	20,806,806	17,511,014

LARGE CALF MARKETS

Calves on the central markets are listed separately from cattle. Such calves are usually under 500 pounds in weight. This includes veal calves and also other calves under 1 year in age and weighing less than 500 pounds. Below is a list of large central calf markets and their receipts for a 5-year period.

CALVES, YEARLY TOTAL AND SALABLE RECEIPTS AT PUBLIC MARKETS

Average of 5 Years—1951–1955 [2]

MARKET	TOTAL AVERAGE	SALABLE AVERAGE
1. Milwaukee, Wis.	482,697	373,604
2. S. St. Paul, Minn.	470,958	456,978

[1] From reports of Livestock Division, Agricultural Marketing Service, U.S.D.A., based on reports submitted by stockyards companies.
[2] From reports of Livestock Division, Agricultural Marketing Service, U.S.D.A., based on reports submitted by stockyards companies.

MARKET	TOTAL AVERAGE	SALABLE AVERAGE
3. St. Louis NSY, Ill.	377,484	285,988
4. Kansas City, Mo.	285,836	178,573
5. Fort Worth, Tex.	283,763	219,101
6. San Antonio, Tex.	239,256	178,480
7. Houston, Tex.	237,004	199,799
8. Springfield, Mo.	175,669	175,699
9. Omaha, Neb.	143,189	126,758
10. Oklahoma City, Okla.	132,129	112,257
11. Louisville, Ky.	128,781	124,567
12. Denver, Colo.	123,403	91,069
13. Sioux City, Iowa	117,331	102,713
14. Chicago, Ill.	115,365	106,372
15. Detroit, Mich.	109,423	43,566

HOLDOVER CATTLE

Livestock unsold when trading stops, usually at 3 P.M., are held over and sold at the next marketing period. These holdovers are believed by some to have a depressing effect upon the market price the following day. Investigations have failed to reveal any significant relation between holdovers and price movements.

THE CHICAGO LIVESTOCK MARKET

A stockyards near Myrick's Tavern 3 miles south of Chicago was started in 1837. A cattle market in Chicago known as the "Bull's Head Yards" was opened in 1848. The present Union Stockyards began in 1865 and supplanted the seven scattered markets then in existence in Chicago. John B. Sherman organized the Union Stockyard and Transit Company in that year, and 320 acres of land were purchased at 39th and Halsted Streets. Gradually the market facilities were expanded. The stockyards now has an area over 500 acres.

In 1865, the first year of operation, the cattle receipts of the Union Stockyards at Chicago numbered 613 head. The growth in receipts was rapid, and by 1876 the yearly receipts numbered over 1 million head. The 2-million mark was reached in 1887 and 3 million in 1889. The largest yearly receipts were in 1918, when 3,789,922 cattle, exclusive of calves, were received at the yards. Calves had their year of heaviest receipts in 1925 when 847,762 passed through the yards.

Receipts of cattle and calves at the Chicago market have lessened. From 1940 to 1949 the yearly receipts of cattle have been in the 2 millions all years except four, when they were just under the 2-million mark. The state origin of cattle receipts on the Chicago Market is shown in Figure 24.

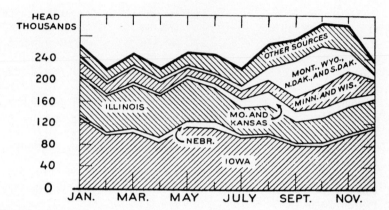

Fig. 24. State origin of cattle receipts at Chicago Union Stockyards Market. Receipts from the western states are high in the fall. (U.S.D.A., Bur. of Agri. Economics.)

The average yearly receipts and shipments from the Chicago market for a recent period were as follows: [3]

LIVESTOCK	RECEIPTS	SHIPMENTS
Cattle	2,072,317	928,900
Calves	115,336	16,519
Hogs	3,446,678	579,372
Sheep	672,277	195,054
All Kinds	6,306,638	1,719,846

Chicago market—grand totals of livestock handled

The size of the Chicago market can be appreciated from the magnitude of the receipts and shipment during the 90 years of its existence.

GRAND TOTAL—90 YEARS LIVESTOCK RECEIPTS AND SHIPMENT, UNION STOCKYARDS, CHICAGO, ILL.

Ninetieth Annual Report, 1955

LIVESTOCK	RECEIPTS	SHIPMENTS
Cattle	203,542,825	76,566,722
Calves	25,771,157	2,225,235
Hogs	543,467,886	122,790,958
Sheep	232,194,589	56,718,862
Horses	4,014,546	3,610,403
Total	1,008,991,003	261,402,136

[3] *Drovers Journal Yearbook of Figures of the Livestock Trade,* Chicago Daily Drover Journal, 55th ed., 1956.

CENTRAL MARKETS AND HOW THEY FUNCTION

At the central or terminal markets the facilities for buying and selling are available for all. There are several organizations which operate on the usual central market. The stockyard company, transportation company, commission agencies, and buyers combine in making a central or terminal livestock market. Following is a discussion of these organizations as well as their functions.

Stockyard company

The land, yards, and equipment for unloading and handling the livestock are owned by the stockyard company. Employees of this company unload, count, yard, feed, and water the livestock, and the company also provides weighing facilities. The stockyard company derives its income from a yardage fee, and the sale of feed and other service charges. Yardage is higher for truck shipments than rail shipments because of the smaller droves. At the Union Stockyards in Chicago the yardage is $1.00 per head for cattle and $0.55 per head for calves from rail receipts, with certain maximums for loads. Feed prices charged are changed from time to time depending upon feed costs.

Stockyard transportation company

This company provides the equipment for moving the cars of livestock from the tracks of different railroads to the unloading docks in the stockyards. It handles the outgoing as well as the incoming shipments. The charges are made on the car basis.

Commission companies or organizations

On the central market the services of commission companies are usually utilized by the owners of the livestock. Since they charge a fee for their services in proportion to the number sold, they are called "commission companies." There are also farmers' cooperative commission organizations that function in the same capacity. Salesmen from these concerns represent the owners of the livestock, as they are familiar with market trading and market conditions. They also represent the livestock feeders in making purchases of feeder cattle. The stockyard company allots blocks of pens to each commission house in which livestock consigned to them are penned by the stockyard company employees. A charge is made by the commission company for the selling and buying service. The amount of the charge is dependent upon the kind and weight of the livestock, the number in the consignment, and many other factors.

Fig. 25. Slaughter cattle in the Union Stock Yards, Chicago, Ill. Crossbreeds, straightbreeds and grades of various breeds are among the receipts.

Buyers

Many kinds of buyers are on the central stockyards markets. Following are the common groups.[4]

1. Packer buyers. These representatives of the meat-packing plants purchase livestock for slaughtering plants, of which several are near the markets.

2. Order buyers. The order buyer represents packing plants or others at some distance from the yards and executes their buying orders.

3. Yard traders. Individual buyers who buy for resale at the yards are known as yard traders. They buy principally livestock suitable for further feeding and sort it into groups for resale.

4. Miscellaneous buyers. As the trading facilities are open to all, there are other buyers on the market who are not included in the above groups.

The livestock exchange

This is an organization of the commission houses doing business on the market. Its functions are to fix the schedule of charges for the selling and buying of livestock, to establish and enforce the rules pertaining to trading, and to handle the shippers' claims for livestock injuries and losses. There is also a National Livestock Exchange made up of membership from the local units.

[4] In June, 1940, W. S. Clithero of Armour and Co. stated that on the Chicago market there were 39 cattle buyers for the 3 large packers, 32 men buying for the 12 local small packers, 44 order buyers for packers all over the country, 23 to 32 buyers on the market 2 or 3 days of the week buying for small packers outside Chicago, 98 to 115 traders and speculators, and 12 to 20 stocker and feeder buyers.

Traders' livestock exchange

Commission companies act as buying and selling agencies and do not buy livestock on their own account. Those who buy and resell at the market on their own account are yard traders. These traders have their local and national organizations.

Other organizations on the central market

1. Banks. The transactions on the central markets are for cash or are transfers of credits. Banking facilities are essential for the conduct of the business of the terminal livestock market.

2. Market publications. On large central markets there are publications which disseminate to their readers the news of the market.

3. Governmental organizations. On a large market there are government employees for the market news service, veterinary inspection, and other services.

CORN-BELT FARM DAILIES

The *Chicago Daily Drovers Journal,* which is the largest of the livestock publishing institutions, was founded in 1873. It, with the following, comprise the membership of the Corn Belt Dailies, the publications of the midwestern livestock industry: *Omaha Daily Journal-Stockman, Kansas City Daily Drovers Telegram,* and the *St. Louis Daily Livestock Reporter.*

The *Chicago Daily Drovers Journal* publishes annually a *Drovers Journal Yearbook of Figures of the Livestock Trade,* the fifty-seventh issue of which was for 1957. This publication gives data on the marketing of farm products.

LIVESTOCK AT THE CENTRAL MARKETS

At the receiving or chute office the bills of lading for rail shipments are posted for the information of the commission men. The cars of livestock arriving by train are switched to the unloading docks by the stockyards transportation company. Employees of the stockyards receive the waybills, unload the livestock, and deliver it to the pens of the commission company to which it is consigned. In the pens the livestock are fed and watered. The commission man orders the feed, which is handled by the stockyard company. A salesman from the commission house offers the livestock to the various buyers. When a sale is made, it is on the basis of the price per 100 pounds live weight.

After the sale the stock is driven to the scale, which is operated by the stockyard company. A ticket is made out at the scale house, which indicates the buyer, seller, and sale price. The weight is stamped on the sale ticket. As the livestock leaves the scale, it becomes the property of the buyer, and it is penned in his pens until it is removed for slaughter or reshipment.

The buyer of the livestock makes payment for it to the commission company, which in term remits to the shipper. The cost of shipping and selling is deducted, and the net returns are delivered to the shipper. The deductions from the total returns include the charges for transportation, yardage, feed, insurance, commission, and other items.

LIVESTOCK AUCTION SALES

During the 1930's there was a great increase in the livestock auction markets or "sale barns" in the United States. With the growth and development of the terminal public stockyard markets in the latter part of the nineteenth century livestock auction markets practically disappeared. Beginning in the twenties some such markets were again started in the middle west. By 1952 there were over 2,500 different yards holding livestock auction sales; since then there has been some decrease in the number. Such markets are now widely distributed throughout our land but are concentrated particularly in areas of heavy livestock production. A study [5] was made by the agricultural marketing service of the U.S.D.A. of the livestock auction markets for one year. In comparing the receipts of the 2,322 auctions with that of the 64 terminal markets for that year, it was found that the number of cattle sold through each type of outlet was about equal; however, four times as many calves were sold at the auctions as at the terminal markets. The number of hogs sold at the auctions was about two-thirds the number sold at the terminal markets; the number of sheep and lambs sold at the auctions was about four-fifths the number sold at the terminal markets.

For each species of livestock sold through the markets about one-half was purchased for slaughter by or for packers. Of the nonslaughter animals livestock producers and feeders were the most important buyers; dealers and order buyers bought about two-thirds as many animals as the producers and the feeders.

Of the livestock sold on the markets three-fourths were consigned and delivered by the farmers, ranchers, and feeders, and dealers brought in most of the balance. That the markets were rather local in scope is indicated by the fact that more than half of all kinds of livestock came from within a radius of 25 miles of the market.

[5] Gerald Engelman, "The American Livestock Auction Market," U.S.D.A., June, 1956.

COOPERATIVE CATTLE MARKETING

COOPERATIVE SHIPPING ASSOCIATIONS

The local cooperative shipping associations pool together shipments of livestock for their members and ship them to the livestock market. Very few shipping associations are located in the territory surrounding public stockyard markets or interior packing plants. The local manager weighs the livestock as it is assembled. In mixed shipment, marking for identification is a necessary service which the manager performs in addition to handling the details of shipping. The livestock may be sold through any of the usual channels. These associations perform the same functions as do the local buyers. The increased use of trucks has caused less need for pooling of livestock in car lots. Consequently, cooperative shipping associations have decreased in number. Also, with the greater dissemination of market news by radio and press, and the improvement of market classing and grading, livestock owners are in closer touch with the market. With greater flexibility in shipping, owing to the use of trucks and the development of more market outlets, producers have become less dependent upon the shipping associations.

COOPERATIVE COMMISSION ASSOCIATIONS

A committee of the American Farm Bureau made a study of livestock marketing, and their report with a plan of action was given in November, 1921. Twenty-one terminal cooperative livestock sales agencies were formed in the next 4 years. The cooperative livestock sales agencies function in the same way as livestock commission companies. These organizations endeavor to return to the members a patronage dividend. They are not usually members of the local livestock exchange, but they have a central organization.

SHRINK AND FILL IN MARKET CATTLE

The loss in weight from the feed lot to the market is known as "shrink." At the yards livestock are fed and watered, which constitutes "fill." The loss in weight or shrinkage is largely from the passing of feces and urine and the moisture in the expired air, or "excretory shrink." Some loss from the body tissues, or tissue shrink, results from metabolic changes. These no doubt begin very soon after the food in the digestive tract ceases to supply nutrient material. It has been estimated that, considering the limit on the time en route, this loss is seldom greater than 10 pounds per steer.

In shipment the animal is virtually fasting. Energy is needed for the vital processes of the body, and to supply this need there is an actual breakdown of body tissue.

The shrink or loss in weight is expressed as a percentage of the feed-lot or home weight. A 1,200-pound steer at the point of shipping that has a final sale weight of 1,170 pounds has a weight loss of 30 pounds, or a shrink of 2.5 per cent. As previously mentioned, cattle are usually fed and watered before they are sold. The sale weight then does not reflect the maximum loss in weight in shipping, for some has been regained by fill.

FACTORS IN CATTLE SHRINKAGE

The factors related to shrink in shipment have been studied. Following are the conditions related to shrink:

Hours in transit and distance traveled

The limit of the length of shipment of cattle is 28 hours, when they must be fed, watered, and rested. It is common, when a long ship is anticipated, for the shipper to sign a release which accompanies the waybill and permits the transportation company to extend the limit to 36 hours.

The longer cattle are en route and the greater the distance traveled, the greater the shrinkage. However, the rate of shrink diminishes with the distance.

Conditions during the shipping period

Extremes in weather influence the amount of shrinkage. Handling in loading, comfort in the car, and handling en route also affect shrink. Cattle loaded roughly in crowded, uncomfortable cars and given a rough ride with frequent stops and rough starts, will shrink heavily.

Condition of the cattle when loaded

In general, there should be no great deviation from normal in feeding or handling of cattle before shipment. Changes in amount or kind of feed, shrinking or filling before shipment are to be avoided in order to hold shrinkage to a minimum.

The nature of the ration fed

On some rations cattle will shrink more in shipping than on others. Rations mostly of roughage usually cause cattle to shrink more than do concentrated rations.

The weight regained at the market

If conditions are favorable and if livestock are given sufficient time in the yards before they are moved to the scales, the weight recovery will be greater and the net shrinkage relatively low. The fill will vary with the amount of weight loss incurred before the cattle are unloaded, rested, fed, and watered. With a heavier loss there is usually a greater recovery. It is estimated that it would take at least 48 hours on feed and water for cattle to recover their initial weight.

SHRINKAGE IN SHIPMENT

Average estimates of a number of market buyers and salesmen have been summarized by Armour Livestock Bureau. Shrinkage varies with weight of the cattle, degree of finish, distance of shipment, and other factors. Following is a tabulation of the usual range of shrinkage.

SHRINKAGE OF CATTLE IN SHIPMENT [6]

Per cent of live weight

	TRUCK		RAILROAD		
	50 Miles	100 Miles	400 Miles	1,000 Miles	2,000 Miles
Steers					
1,200 pound grain fed	3–5%	3½–5½%	4–6%	5– 7%	6– 9%
baby beeves					
600–1,000 pounds	3–5%	3½–5½%	4–6%	5– 7%	6– 9%
750 pound feeders	4–6%	3½–5 %	5–7%	6– 9%	8–10%
1,200 pound grass fed	4–6%	5 –7 %	7–9%	8–10%	10–12%
She stock					
1,000 pound cows	4–7%	5 –8 %	6–9%	7–10%	8–11%
800 pound heifers	3–5%	4 –6 %	5–7%	6– 9%	7–10%

It will be noted that the largest amount of shrinkage, relatively, occurs on short hauls. Roughage- and grass-fed cattle shrink more heavily than grain-fed cattle. The actual weight loss increases with the length of the shipment. Severe weather conditions or long periods off feed will cause low blood sugar and result in low muscle glycogen which is a cause of dark-cutting beef carcasses.

CATTLE BUYING AND FILLS

The gains in weight made by filling, other than water, are largely feed that is in the digestive tract. This is of no particular value to the meat packer on slaughtering; in fact it may be a disadvantage. Since buyers attempt to estimate dressing percentage in purchasing cattle, the tendency is for them to discount for fills in making bids. Heavily filled cattle tend to borrow a value from other cattle, inasmuch as cattle buyers check the yields of cattle purchased and slaughtered. Consequently, if serious errors of estimate are made, the tendency is to lower estimates subsequently. Feeding and watering of cattle to the extent that it arrests restlessness and has a quieting effect may be justified, but beyond that it seems an economic waste.

[6] Information from Edward N. Wentworth, Armour and Co., August, 1950.

GOVERNMENT REGULATIONS OF CATTLE MARKETING

In 1921 by an Act of Congress the Packers and Stockyards Administration [7] was set up to ensure and enforce fair-trade practices and free competition in livestock trading or terminal markets. This jurisdiction applies to stockyards with an area of 20,000 square feet exclusive of alleyways. In application it affects packers, stockyard companies, and all marketing agencies. The Packers and Stockyard Act applies to more than 60 terminal markets, 500 livestock auction markets, 2,300 commission firms, 28,000 dealers, and 1,900 meat packers. Discriminative practices, such as apportionment of supply so as to create a monopoly, manipulation or controlling of prices, and combination or agreement for any kind of apportionment by meat packers, are violations. Stockyard companies and agencies such as commission companies are required to furnish reasonable services without discrimination at a posted schedule of rates and charges.

The Secretary of Agriculture is given the power under the act to conduct hearings on violations of the act and to prescribe reasonable charges, rules, etc., when necessary. The Secretary may inflict fines for violations of the rules and regulations. However, the offending organization may have recourse to the courts.

GOVERNMENT REPORTS FROM CATTLE AND OTHER LIVESTOCK MARKETS

The market news is gathered and disseminated by a bureau of the United States Department of Agriculture. The news reaches interested persons by letter, press, wire, and radio, and covers a wide number of commodities. Livestock offices are located in several midwestern terminal markets, and there are also regional offices for pooling the statistics. This is now included in the Livestock Branch of the Production and Marketing Administration.

Livestock branch, production and marketing administration

Included in this branch are divisions listed as Market News, Packers and Stockyards, Procurement, Programs Analysis, Standardization and Grading, Wool, and others. The activities of these various divisions fall within the broad fields of (1) the collection and dissemination of crop and livestock production and other agricultural statistics; (2) the gathering and reporting of current market information from terminal markets, shipping points, and producing sections; (3) standardization and inspection to provide a uniform system for measuring gradations in quality of farm and food products, and a common language in merchandizing these products; (4)

[7] Packers and Stockyards Act, 1921. General Rules and Regulations of the Secretary of Agriculture, U.S.D.A., B.A.I. Order 323, 1930.

research and demonstration in a standardization, grading, preparation for market, handling, and other related phases of marketing; and (5) the administration of "rules of fair play" in the merchandising of farm commodities.

Many reports are issued by the Agricultural Marketing Service dealing with market news on livestock, meats, and wool, and with livestock numbers and production estimates. These reports may be procured without charge by addressing this organization, United States Department of Agriculture, Washington, D.C.

Terms used in market reports

The Livestock Market News Division of the Production Marketing Administration has standardized the definitions for rather commonly employed livestock market terms. These terms are in the categories of supply, demand, activity, price trends, quotations and clearance of market livestock; and they frequently occur in market reports. Briefly, these terms are described below and have the following meanings.

1. Supply. This is the number of head on a given market for a day and is given in actual figures. In the absence of actual figures, relative statements, *larger* or *smaller*, are given relative to the receipts of the preceding marketing day.

2. Demand. The eagerness on the part of the buyer to purchase livestock is referred to as demand. The demand may be *good* or *poor* as compared to the day before.

3. Activity. This refers to rapidity of sales. To describe the situation, the terms *active, moderate*, and *slow* are used.

4. Price trends. Reference to price movements is given in the price trends. The following terms are employed for trends:

    a. Higher. Sales are mostly at higher prices.

    b. Strong. Some sales are at higher prices.

    c. Steady. No material change in prices from the preceding day.

    d. Weak. Some sales at lower prices but mostly steady or about the same.

    e. Lower. The bulk of sales are made at lower prices.

    f. Uneven. Many sales out of range of the general trend.

5. Quotations. In this category are given the actual prices paid by grades and weights for the livestock sold.

6. Clearance. This refers to the number received that are sold at the end of the market day. The terms *complete* and *incomplete* are employed to describe the clearance. Livestock unsold are "holdovers."

TRANSPORTATION OF CATTLE

In market receipts a distinction is made between rail and nonrail shipments. The latter group were formerly referred to as the "drive-in" receipts because they were driven into the yards. Now these are almost entirely truck shipments. During the 1953–1955 period at the 62 principal markets 83 per cent of the calves and 81 per cent of the cattle were classified as "drive-in"; these were all the animals except those received by rail and were mostly "truck-ins." Nearly 23 million head of cattle and calves were trucked to market in 1955. More hogs were trucked in than cattle and calves, while fewer sheep and lambs reached the markets by truck.

The markets vary in the proportion that is shipped by means other than rail. Comparatively, the Denver market has a small proportion of truck receipts, and Sioux Falls has a large proportion. Some rather large livestock markets, such as Springfield, Ill., Joplin, Mo., and Fort Wayne, Ind., receive all of their livestock shipments by truck. Rail shipments predominate for long shipments, whereas truck shipment is favored for short hauls.

SHIPMENT BY TRUCK

Truck shipments have increased greatly in recent years. The first shipment of livestock by motor truck to a public market was made in 1911, and by 1935 the truck was used for more than half of the livestock delivered at the livestock markets. Improved roads have given the shipper access to a greater diversity of markets and also have made convenient the shipping of smaller droves. The motor truck moves livestock from the farm to the slaughtering plant or stockyard conveniently and quickly, and as a consequence with but little weight loss or shrink. Motor transportation rates have declined in the past decade, while railroad rates have remained practically the same. The number of cattle per truck for safe loading is given below. (See pages 281 and 282 for maximum loading of calves, which is the same for hogs and calves.)

CATTLE PER TRUCK

FLOOR LENGTH, FEET	AVERAGE WEIGHT, POUNDS					
	450	*600*	*800*	*1,000*	*1,200*	*1,400*
8	8	7	5	4	4	3
10	10	8	7	6	5	4
12	13	10	8	7	6	5
15	16	13	10	9	8	7
18	20	16	13	11	9	8
20	22	18	14	12	10	9
24	27	22	17	15	13	11
28	31	25	20	17	15	13
30	34	27	22	19	16	14
32	36	29	23	20	17	15
36	41	33	26	22	19	17
42	48	39	31	28	22	20

NUMBER OF CATTLE IN A RAILROAD CAR

Railroad cars in which livestock are shipped to market are usually either 36 or 40 feet in length. The size of the car and the size of cattle determine the number which can be loaded in a car. For comfort in shipping the car should be loaded heavily enough so that the animals stand fairly close together; however, crowding is to be avoided. Tabulated below is the average number of head of different weights which can be loaded in a car.

CATTLE PER RAILROAD CAR [8]

CAR SIZE, FEET	AVERAGE LIVE WEIGHT, POUNDS											
	300	400	500	600	700	800	900	1,000	1,100	1,200	1,300	1,400
36	60	50	42	37	33	30	27	25	23	22	21	19
40	67	56	46	40	37	33	30	27	25	23	22	21

MARKETING EXPENSES

Transportation is usually the largest item in market expense. A study in 1947 indicated that the expenses in marketing cattle, calves, hogs, sheep, and lambs from producers to slaughter plants or feed lots averaged 72 cents per 100 pounds. Of the total expense, transportation by both rail and truck accounted for more than 60 per cent of average expenses; the services of marketing agencies and feed used account for the balance. The average expense given above does not include the services of farmers handling and selling their own livestock or losses in animals in transit or at the market.

With feeder cattle it is possible to get a feeding-in-transit privilege from 1 day to 12 months, which may reduce the over-all shipping cost.

As market costs vary less than livestock prices, the marketing costs are higher proportionately when livestock prices are low than when they are high. For example, in 1947 marketing expense averaged 3.5 per cent of the average price for 100 pounds received by farmers; in 1943, when prices were very low, it was 13.5 per cent.

INJURY AND DEATH LOSSES IN MARKETING CATTLE

Damage so severe that bruise marks are noted on the carcass is not at all uncommon. A recent slaughter test with cattle showed that nearly 7 per cent were bruised. This survey also showed a small percentage crippled and dead. The loss through damage of livestock being marketed or "han-

[8] *Bull. 20,* Swift & Company, May, 1941.

dling loss" has been estimated at over 50 million dollars a year in the United States. The bruise marks on the carcass cannot be determined with accuracy at the time of sale. The processor, therefore, discounts all purchases enough to make allowance for a certain loss from bruises. Badly bruised cattle have cuts and bumps upon them, but the extent of the damage can be determined only by examination of the carcass. Consequently, greater damage is anticipated where there is evidence of bruising. Horned cattle sell at a discount because of damage which the horns invariably produce on the carcasses of other cattle in the lot. Nearly all cattle marketed now are without horns. Crippled animals are purchased at lower prices than animals that are sound. Dead animals are sold on the basis of tankage prices.

The livestock producer is the heaviest loser from damage to livestock being marketed. Even though the individual shipper is indemnified for the loss in the form of a claim payment from the shipping railroad or truck company, the services of these shipping agencies are set sufficiently high to cover losses.

Factors that influence shipping losses

The conditions that have been found to affect shipping losses in livestock may be listed as follows:

1. The type of transportation used
2. The species or kind of livestock shipped
3. The class within a kind or species
4. The distance the livestock is transported
5. The season of the year
6. The carefulness of the trucker

These factors have been investigated by the Minnesota Agricultural Experiment Station.[9]

There are, no doubt, many other factors responsible for damage in shipping. Livestock fed on adequate rations and normally developed are better able to withstand shipping damage and losses than poorly fed, underdeveloped stock. Injuries during loading and unloading are also a factor.

In one survey [10] in which horn damage was not severe, the distribution of causes of bruises was as follows:

1. Crowding, bumping, and rushing—66 per cent
2. Trampling—14 per cent
3. Cane, whip, and club—10 per cent
4. Horns and other causes—10 per cent

[9] A. A. Dowell and R. J. Eggert, "Death and Crippling in Livestock Marketing," *Bull. 342,* Minn. Agr. Exp. Sta., May, 1939.
[10] "Livestock Conservation Handbook," Livestock Conservation, Inc., 1955.

The type of transportation (rail and truck) and the kind of livestock and their relationship to losses are discussed further in the following paragraphs.

Extent of crippling and death loss in market cattle

The extent of crippling and death losses at some of the principal midwest livestock markets has been surveyed by the National Livestock Loss Prevention Board. This survey includes losses appraised at the time of unloading and does not include damage done in the stockyard.

The survey covers livestock dead and crippled on arrival by railroad and truck at Kansas City, St. Joseph, Omaha, Sioux City, and St. Paul. Following is a 2-year summary of their findings:

PERCENTAGE OF DEAD AND CRIPPLED CATTLE AND CALVES ON
ARRIVAL BY RAILROAD AND TRUCK AT FIVE
MIDDLE WESTERN CENTRAL MARKETS [11]

LIVESTOCK	PER CENT DEAD		PER CENT CRIPPLED	
	Rail	*Truck*	*Rail*	*Truck*
Cattle	0.018	0.026	0.030	0.068
Calves	0.085	0.190	0.126	0.288

It will be noted that calves are more subject to shipping losses than are cattle. With cattle and calves the death and crippling losses in truck shipment are greater than in rail shipment.

Among kinds of livestock, the death loss is the greatest in sheep and the least in cattle. In amount of crippling, swine rank highest, with calves, sheep, and cattle following in the order named.

Livestock Conservation, Inc.

This organization came from the consolidation of the National Livestock Loss Prevention Board and the Livestock Sanitary Committee in 1951. The organization is working toward the reduction of animal diseases and losses in marketing livestock. Its object is to initiate and encourage education and research, to correlate and coordinate present activities and information, to secure new data, to disseminate correct information, and to promote practical and proper methods of reducing and eliminating preventable livestock losses during the marketing process. Apparently, this campaign has been successful, for there seems to be an irregular trend downward in shipping losses. That there is great need for further loss-prevention work is indicated by the recent estimate of the organization.

[11] H. R. Smith, "Losses in Marketing Livestock," *National Livestock Loss Prevention Board Report,* 1948.

Precautions for preventing losses in marketing livestock

By careful attention to the following details, losses in marketing of livestock from deaths and crippling can be reduced. These precautions are suggested in the report [12] of the National Loss Prevention Board:

1. Dehorn cattle, preferably when young.
2. Remove projecting nails, splinters, and broken boards in feed racks and fences.
3. Keep out of feed lots old machinery, trash, and any obstacles that may bruise.
4. Do not feed grain heavily just prior to loading.
5. Use good loading chutes, not too steep.
6. Bed with sand, free from stones, to prevent slipping.
7. Cover sand with straw in cold weather, but no straw for hogs in hot weather.
8. Wet sand bedding in summer before loading hogs, and while en route. Drench when necessary.
9. Partition packing sows from lightweight butchers.
10. Provide covers for trucks to protect from sun in summer and cold in winter.
11. Always partition mixed loads to separate classes, and calves from cattle.
12. Have upper deck of truck high enough to prevent back bruises on calves below.
13. Remove protruding nails, bolts, or any sharp objects in truck or car.
14. Load slowly to prevent crowding against sharp corners and to avoid excitement. Do not overload.
15. Use canvas slappers instead of clubs or canes.
16. Tie all bulls in truck or car, and partition boars, stags, and cripples.
17. Set bull board in position and secure it before closing car door on loaded cattle.
18. Drive carefully. Slow down on sharp turns and avoid sudden stops.
19. Inspect load en route to prevent trampling of down cattle.
20. Back truck slowly and squarely against unloading dock.
21. Unload slowly. Don't drop animals from upper to lower deck; use cleated inclines.
22. Never lift sheep by the wool.

NATIONAL LIVESTOCK AND MEAT BOARD

The purpose of this organization is to increase the consumption of meat and meat products. Livestock sold for slaughter are assessed at the rate of

[12] Ibid.

25 cents per carload or, when in less than carload lots, at the rate of ⅓ cent for each calf or hog, ⅕ cent for each lamb, and 1 cent for each head of cattle until the contribution reaches 25 cents. This is deducted from the seller returns, but if he objects no charge is made on his consignment. The packing plants purchasing the livestock contribute a like amount.

Chapter 6

MARKET CLASSIFICATION
OF CATTLE AND CATTLE PRICES

MARKET CLASSES OF CATTLE

A trip to a livestock market on any marketing day will serve to emphasize the wide range of cattle offered for sale. The quoted prices paid for the various classes and grades of cattle may range many dollars per hundredweight from the lowest selling canner cow to the top-selling finished beef steer. The variation is due in the main to differences that would be manifest in the carcass, affecting its value and also its yield or dressing percentage.

Those engaged in producing, distributing, marketing, and processing livestock have need for a common classification system for market animals and, as a convenience, there has grown with the expansion of the livestock markets a system of classing and grading livestock. In 1902 Herbert W. Mumford prepared *Bulletin 78* of the University of Illinois on "Market Classes and Grades of Cattle with Suggestions for Interpreting Market Quotations." In this publication an attempt was made to standardize the existing market classes and grades. Market reporting service was started on the Chicago Livestock Market by the Bureau of Markets in 1918, and Mumford's suggestions were used as a tentative basis for formulating a classification of standard market classes and grades. From time to time this classification has been revised and altered to incorporate the suggestions of various agencies on the central markets. Classifications are not the same on all markets, and all agencies on any one market do not use the same terms for indicating various livestock market groups. Much progress has been made in standardization of terms and reports; livestock market reports, from the market news service of the federal government and from livestock papers, have greater meaning than they had in the past.

74

Principal uses for market cattle

There are three principal uses for market cattle. Most of the cattle received are slaughtered for beef, some are sold to go back into the country for further feeding (feeders and stockers), and a few are sold to go into dairy herds. On most markets the latter group is relatively insignificant. The central market has never developed into a sizable market for cattle of dairy breeding to be sold into dairy herds. Those sold on the central markets for dairy production are usually further divided into springers, milkers, and stockers. The cattle in the feeder and stocker division and their market classification will be discussed in Chapter 7. Included in this chapter will be the market classifying and grading of slaughter cattle of all ages and a discussion of prices of such cattle. Slaughter cattle are acceptable to the meat trade on foot and will yield meat that is wholesome and suitable for human food, barring condemnations. Cattle and slaughter calves produce beef, whereas young calves yield veal. There is no sharp dividing line between the two.

Standards of U.S.D.A. for livestock and meats [1]

Standardization in the field of livestock and meats consists mainly of three things: (1) developing units suitable for measuring these highly complicated products of nature; (2) devising methods and machinery for quickly and accurately applying those units of measurement; and (3) developing a set of unit or group names or labels having uniform and fixed meanings.

Uses of market grading systems to the producer

The livestock grower is confronted continually with problems of what to raise, where and when to sell. These problems cannot be neglected if livestock raising is to be successful. With market reports available which he can interpret, the livestock raiser can know what kind, class, grade, and weight is in greatest demand in proportion to its supply. He can likewise determine where his livestock should be sold to bring the greatest net returns. As seasonal market variations are available based upon the averages of previous years, the grower can plan his production and marketing accordingly. Outlook reports are more meaningful when the producer understands the commonly used terms of the market.

Purposes of classifying and grading livestock

Livestock are sorted into uniform lots to facilitate trading. Groups are made up that have about the same value. Extremes are eliminated so that

[1] C. E. Gibbons, "Advantages of Standards for Livestock and Meat," Misc. 266, 33, U.S.D.A., December, 1937.

the entire lot conforms to the specifications for the group. With the group uniform in characteristics it is then possible to determine market value and to report a market transaction in precise terms. A quotation such as "choice to prime yearling beef steers, 1,100 pounds, at a given price," is subject to rather accurate interpretation among all who handle market cattle.

Classifying and grading livestock

Market classes are the large divisions of livestock on the market after separation into use groups. The smaller or final division of market livestock is known as the "grade."

Classifying and grading are essentially for the same purpose. Successively, cattle are divided and redivided until finally lots of rather narrow variation in essential characters result. The final and most important division is into the market grade.

A *market grade* comprises a group of animals on the livestock market which have a narrow range of variation of essential characteristics and which usually sell within a comparatively narrow price range. When a lot or group is sold that is not within one grade, it may be designated by the two grade terms; for example, good to choice. When a wider range is included in one sale lot, it is designated as mixed grade.

Market class usually refers to groups differing from one another in sex or sex condition and in the development of the secondary sex characters. We have, therefore, these classes in cattle: steers, heifers, cows, bulls, and stags. Under calves, there are the two classes: vealers and calves.

Standard market classes and grades

Although the markets are not all the same in their classifications, the standard classification is becoming more widely used. Through the wider sale of graded beef by the meat retailers there has come a greater need for uniform classification of slaughter cattle. There still exists some disparity between markets, especially between corn-belt markets and those elsewhere. The characters related to value are reasonably stable and can be measured with a fair degree of accuracy.

Factors that determine market division of livestock

The attributes related to commercial value of market livestock are: sex condition, age, weight, form, quality, breeding, and finish or condition. In slaughter cattle attention is given to all these considerations. The class or large division depends upon sex, use, age, and weight; the grade depends upon form, finish, and quality. Within any group of beef carcasses the main features upon which merit is evaluated are conformation, finish, and quality.

Following is a tabulation of the market classes and grades which may be on the market, and this is followed by a brief description of each group.

MARKET CLASSES AND GRADES OF CATTLE

| | BASIS FOR GROUPING | | | | |
	Sex	Age	Use	Weight	Grade
Divisions within each group	Steers Heifers Cows Bulls Stags	Vealers Calves Yearlings Two-year-olds and older	Slaughter cattle Feeding cattle 1. Feeders 2. Stockers Dairy cattle 1. Springers 2. Milkers 3. Stockers	Heavy Medium Light Mixed	Prime or Fancy Selected Choice Good Standard Commercial Utility Cutter Canner

MARKET CLASSES

Sex classes of cattle

At present the sex classes are the market classes. This classification is also called "sex condition," for it involves groups that have been unsexed. Each of these groups has rather definite characteristics easily distinguishable and definitely related to the commercial value of the carcass. There are three sex conditions: male and female, and unsexed. The consumer of beef is not concerned with the sex condition of the live animal from which the beef has come. Little does he care whether the animal was male or female or unsexed or at what age the castration was performed. However, the consumer is definitely critical of the properties of meat which affect its eating qualities. Sex condition is highly related to palatability of meat, for it affects the quality, finish, and conformation of the carcass.

Cattle are therefore divided into five classes: steers, heifers, cows, bulls, and stags.

Steers. A steer is a male bovine that was castrated before his secondary sex characters had developed, that is, before the individual reached sexual maturity. Calves are castrated when a few weeks old or any time up to 4 and 5 months of age; 4 to 10 weeks is usually recommended. Castration causes a different development of the form, and beef from castrated animals is of higher quality, with superior texture, tenderness, color, and flavor. Steers are also more tractable in feed lots than bulls.

Heifers. A heifer is a young female bovine that has not had a calf and has not reached the stage of advanced pregnancy. Spayed or unsexed heifers are not greatly different from unaltered heifers; consequently they are classed in the same group.

Cows. A cow is a female bovine that has developed, through reproduction or with age, relatively prominent hips, a large middle, and other
physical characters typical of mature females.

Bulls. A bull is an uncastrated male bovine. On markets the term refers
to sexually mature individuals. In young calves no attention is paid to the
presence of the testicles, for they do not affect the carcass materially until
sexual maturity is approached.

Stag. A stag is a male that has been castrated after reaching sexual
maturity and in which the secondary sexual characters have developed.

Fig. 26. Cattle at the stock yards. Note the arrangement of the lots, alleys, gates
and runways. Saint Joseph, Mo., stock yards.

Age groups

Because of carcass differences related to age differences in slaughter
cattle, we have groups which include individuals of approximately the
same age. Calves, for example, yield meat of distinctive character and quality. Within this group there is a division into calves and veal calves. Under
3 months of age a calf will yield a carcass classed as veal. Calf carcasses
are from cattle younger than yearlings and older than veal calves. They
have passed the vealer stage, but they have not acquired sufficient maturity
to be classed as cattle. A vealer has been mainly milk fed; a calf has been
fed for a considerable time in part or entirely on feeds other than milk.

Cattle are divided into two groups by age. Yearlings, between 1 and 2 years of age, constitute the younger class. All older cattle, that is, those over 2 years of age, are commonly grouped together as 2 years old and over.

There are age limitations on certain grades of slaughter cattle. Since there is variation in the evidences of maturity, general age limitations are used in the descriptive standards for slaughter cattle. The approximate age limitations for specific grades of steers, heifers and cows are as follows: Prime—36 months; choice—42 months; good—48 months; and standard —48 months.

Age classification of slaughter cattle.   The total number of cattle slaughtered annually in the United States in recent years has been over 32 million head. In the breakup into calves and cattle older than calves about 36 per cent were in the former and 64 per cent in the latter group. The demarcation between the two groups is not uniform on the different markets. Usually calves are under 400 pounds in weight, but the cattle are not weighed as they arrive at the market and the classification is based upon the judgment of stockyard company employees when it is not indicated on the bill of lading. On some markets the weight is 500 pounds.

Use selection

Often the use to which cattle are put is designated as the market class. There are three main commercial uses: (1) slaughter, (2) feeding, (3) milking—heifers and cows. Any of the cattle or calves offered on the market can be in the slaughter class with the possible exception of those for dairy purposes. Cattle going immediately to meat processors are termed slaughter cattle; feeding cattle are those sold for further feeding. These, including beef stock females and feeding cattle, are discussed under Feeder and Stocker Cattle. The demand for feeding cattle influences the division made on a market between these two classes, for many cattle and calves on the market can go into either group. These are often referred to as "two-way" cattle.[2] The cattle and calves bring a higher price when sold as feeders than when disposed of as slaughter cattle.

Very few milking heifers and cows reach central markets. These may be springers, milkers, and stockers, and to qualify they must show dairy or milking qualities. A milker is a cow giving milk; a springer is a pregnant female due to calve shortly and possessing dairy characteristics. Heifers of dairy breeding sold for dairy production are called dairy stock heifers.

Weight divisions

In the breakup of market cattle and calves by weight groups it is common to have three classes: lightweight, medium weight, and heavyweight.

---

[2] "Two-way," with reference to market livestock, means two uses. Cattle suitable for slaughter or feeding are sold to the group that will pay more for them.

When lots of cattle of a kind are of several weight divisions, the lot is designated as "mixed weight." Market reports may have weight divisions for the higher grades of steers and heifers. All weights are used for the others except feeders.

Grades

The final step in the classifying process is grading. A grade includes all within a kind that sell for about the same price per pound. The grade is determined largely by quality, form, and finish. In cattle grading the terms, ranked in order of merit, are: prime, choice, good, standard, commercial, utility, cutter, and canner. However, all groups are not graded the same. For example, there are prime steers and heifers, but these grades are not used for cows and bulls. Commercial is the highest grade for beef from fully mature animals, and is the only grade not used for younger animals. In stocker and feeder classes the grade prime is not used because prime refers to high finish, which is not typical of feeder cattle. In lieu of prime, fancy or fancy selected is employed for feeders. As the variation within a market group of cattle is not the same, the number of grades for a class, subclass, age, or weight is variable.

SCHEDULE OF MARKET CLASSES AND GRADES FOR SLAUGHTER CATTLE

Following is an adaptation of the classification or schedules for slaughter cattle and calves from the publications of the United States Department of Agriculture on market classes and grades.[3]

SEX CLASSES	WEIGHT IN POUNDS	COMMONLY USED GRADES
Steers	700– 900 900–1,100 1,100–1,300 1,300–1,500	Prime, choice, good, standard, commercial, utility, cutter *
Heifers	600– 800 † 800–1,000 †	Prime, choice, good, standard, commercial, utility, cutter, canner
Cows	all weights	Choice, good, standard, commercial, utility, cutter, canner
Bulls	all weights	Choice, good, commercial, utility, cutter, canner
Stags	all weights	Choice, good, commercial, utility, cutter, canner

* See p. 79 for age limitations on grades.
† These weights for prime and choice; weights for good 100 pounds less.

[3] C. E. Gibbons, "Market Classes and Grades of Livestock," *Bull. 1360,* U.S.D.A., June, 1926; revised August, 1942; slightly revised December, 1948.

Don J. Slater, "Market Classes and Grades of Cattle," *Bull. 1464, U.S.D.A.,* August, 1940.

Don J. Slater and M. T. Foster, "Market Classes and Grades of Calves and Vealers," *Circ. 28,* U.S.D.A., November, 1936; slightly revised 1942.

This classification provides a group designation for nearly all kinds of slaughter cattle which come to the market. In actual practice not all of these divisions are found even in a large cattle market on a day of heavy receipts. Classifications may vary with changes in time, location, and other conditions. On the southern markets predominant weights and grades are slightly different than on other markets. Also this classification is not applied in the same way on all markets.

This schedule provides a place for every group into which buyers and sellers may wish to sort slaughter cattle. On smaller markets many of the divisions are lumped together. Not all of the grades are used in the various divisions. Those listed are the common ones which may possibly be used. However there is a canner grade in the lightweight groups of steers and heifers. The term "canner" indicates a low grade, but only a small amount of the meat from this kind is actually canned. In grade, canners are inferior to cutters, which are the source of some wholesale cuts of carcass beef. Boneless beef may come from cutters, canners or the higher grades.

CHARACTERISTICS OF IMPORTANT MARKET CLASSES AND GRADES OF CATTLE

For a detailed description of the typical individual in the various grades, reference should be made to United States Department of Agriculture publications listed on page 80.

Of the cattle slaughtered under federal inspection for a recent 10-year period, 49.1 per cent were steers, 35.9 per cent cows, 11.2 per cent heifers, and 3.8 per cent bulls and stags. A description of the various classes follows.

Beef steers

Beef steers are the top-selling slaughter cattle on the market, and the highest grade is prime. (See Figure 27.) Some grades may be joined when numbers in a grade are few.

Following is a tabulation of grade and slaughter weights of beef steers from the corn belt marketed at Chicago for a 5-year period.

BEEF STEERS FROM THE CORN BELT SOLD AT CHICAGO MARKET
PERCENTAGE OF TOTAL BY GRADES AND WEIGHTS BY GRADES

5 Years, 1951–1955

GRADES OF BEEF STEERS	PER CENT OF TOTAL RECEIPTS	AVERAGE WEIGHT, POUNDS
Prime	16.4	1,212
Choice	56.4	1,069
Good	30.3	1,006
* Commercial	5.7	941
Utility	1.2	877
All grades	100.0	1,096

* Subdivided into commercial and standard, June, 1956.

PRIME

CHOICE

GOOD

Fig. 27. U.S. grades of slaughter steers. The grades cutter and canner are not shown. The grade "Commercial" is now used for mature animals only and a new grade "Standard" applies to the younger animals formerly in this grade. (U.S.D.A., Production and Marketing Administration.)

82

STANDARD

COMMERCIAL

UTILITY

83

It will be noted that prime graded steers make up about one sixth of the steer receipts from the corn belt at the Chicago market. Steers graded choice make up over one half of the total, good steers more than one fourth. There is considerable year-to-year difference, depending mainly upon the availability and price of feed, and also upon the price of finished cattle. There has been a trend toward higher grades. However, the grades and specifications have been changed; so comparisons are difficult to make. It should be pointed out that the proportion of higher grade steers on the Chicago market is greater than in the United States as a whole.

Better grades have heavier weights, as would be expected, indicating greater finish. There is about a 60-pound spread between the utility, commercial, good, and choice grades; prime and choice outweigh good steers by more than 100 pounds.

In conformation, form, and quality prime steers meet approximately the requirements of an ideal steer. Lower grades lack these qualities and consequently yield carcasses which sell at lower prices. They also have lower yield or dressing percentage than prime steers. Prime steers are of first rank in form, quality, fleshing, and dressing percentage. Such steers are of beef breeding.

Baby beef

On the market baby beeves are in the yearling class. The carcasses to be designated as baby beef must be from good, choice, or prime animals of the beef breeds (steer or heifer) from 8 to 18 months of age and weighing 600 to 1,100 pounds on foot. Baby beef may be divided into: (1) fat calves—8 to 9 months old, weight 600 to 700 pounds; (2) regular or standard baby beeves—12 to 18 months old, weight 800 to 1,000 pounds; (3) heavier yearlings—18 to 24 months old, and over 1,000 pounds in weight. "Super baby beef" is sometimes used to refer to well-finished good-quality calves ready for market at 650 to 850 pounds.

Heifers

This group is nearly equal to beef steers in value when equal in conformation, finish, and quality. A few heifers will often pass in a load of steers with no discount in price. In heavier weights the disparity of the price widens because heavy heifers become more like cows in conformation and because older, heavy heifers are often with calf. Comparable grades of heifers sell for less than beef steers.

In appearance the best slaughter heifers approach the ideal beef type and are of beef breeding. (See Figure 28.) Lower grade heifers lack in form, quality, and finish, and the poor grades are of dairy breeding. Many comparisons have been made of steer and heifer beef, and these studies apparently warrant the following conclusions.

PRIME

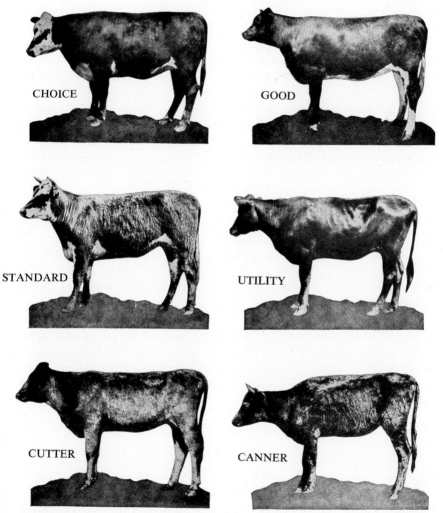

CHOICE

GOOD

STANDARD

UTILITY

CUTTER

CANNER

Fig. 28. United States grades of slaughter heifers. (U.S.D.A., Agricultural Marketing Service.)

Heifers finish at younger ages than do steers. The following characteristics are typical of heifers as compared to steers of comparable age, breeding, feeding, and management:

1. They are higher in finish, and the fat is more localized.
2. They are higher in dressing percentage if they are not with calf.
3. In market grade both on foot and in the carcass there is no consistent
difference from steers.
4. In the palatability of the beef there is no clear difference.

To produce beef comparable with steers, heifers must be of beef breeding, finished rapidly, and sold at light weights. Heavy heifers become
rough and patchy and are often in calf. Steer carcasses are heavier than
heifer carcasses in the rounds and in the ribs.

Pregnancy in heifers. In a study of the effect of pregnancy upon the
yearling heifers at the Illinois Agricultural Experiment Station [4] it was
found that pregnant heifers were less active, had more digestive activity.
Apparent slaughter merit, that is, on-foot appraisal of the slaughter value,
was lower for the pregnant heifers. The carcasses of the heifers pregnant
5 months were fatter and more desirable in finish. In composition the pregnant heifers had 5 per cent more fat, 3.5 per cent less lean, and 1.5 per
cent less bone in the carcass. No apparent change was made by pregnancy
in the weight of the wholesale cuts or the color and firmness of the fat.

Contrary to common opinion, in this one test the in-calf heifers yielded
as large a proportion of carcass as the open heifers. Although the pregnant uterus weighed on the average 30 pounds at the time of slaughtering,
this was overcome by the lighter hide and bone, the greater amount of fat
on the carcass, and a smaller fill. The pregnancy up to 5 months on the
yearling heifers appeared not to affect adversely productive capacity or
beef value.

The breeding of heifers 3 or 4 months prior to marketing may under
certain circumstances be advisable in the light of these findings, but marketing prior to marked change in appearance is desirable. Heifers heavy
in calf are heavy in the middle and usually patchy. Consequently they yield
lower and have rougher carcasses than open heifers.

Cows

Good grade cows are of beef breeding. Rather young cows which
approach heifers in form are termed "heiferettes" on some markets. (See
Figure 29.) Comparable grades of cows sell for much less per 100 pounds

[4] R. R. Snapp, *Beef Cattle*, 3d ed., Chap. 18, John Wiley & Sons, Inc., New York,
N.Y., 1939.

than heifers. Carcass differences account for most of this price difference, but heifers also yield higher than cows.

Bulls and stags

The better grades of bulls, choice and good, are often termed "beef" or "butcher" bulls to distinguish them from medium and common bulls, often called "bologna" bulls.

Butcher stock

On many markets this term is used to designate slaughter heifers, cows, bulls, and stags suitable to be sold in the carcass as block beef. Such beef is acceptable to the retailer in halves or quarters. This group excludes cutters, low cutters, or canners, which are not usable for block beef.

SEASONAL VARIATION IN SEXES MARKETED

Cows and heifers are lighter than steers when marketed. The seasonal variation in the market weights of cattle is therefore related to the proportion of cows and heifers in the cattle marketed. The spring months are the lowest in percentage of cows and heifers marketed and in the federal inspected slaughter. The greatest liquidation of the female stock occurs in the months of October, November, December, and January, which have the highest percentage of cows and heifers in the total receipts and supply of cattle slaughtered. Marketings are highly concentrated at the end of the grazing season for cattle and also for sheep. The movement to the feed lots of feeder cattle, which are mainly steers, accounts in part for the larger proportion of cows and heifers in the fall slaughter. The average percentage of cows and heifers in the slaughter ranges from less than 40 per cent in May to a high of nearly 60 per cent in November. (See pages 102, 128.)

YEARLY VARIATION IN SEXES MARKETED

Cow and heifer slaughter fluctuates more widely over a period of years than steer slaughter. If feed crops and pasture conditions are favorable, breeding herds are built up and the proportion of cows and heifers slaughtered is below average. Steer slaughter is reduced when feed supplies for cattle finishing are short.

SCHEDULE OF MARKET CLASSES AND GRADES FOR SLAUGHTER CALVES

Slaughter calves are usually between 3 and 8 months of age and weigh less than 500 pounds. They have been fed on feeds in addition to milk

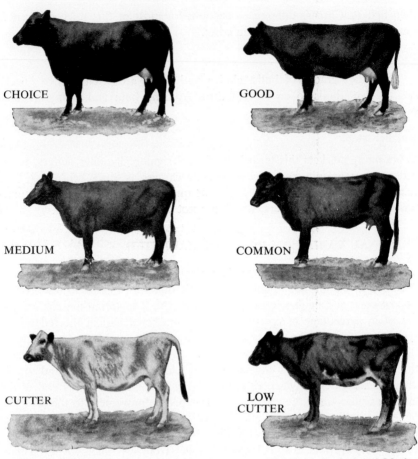

CHOICE

GOOD

MEDIUM

COMMON

CUTTER

LOW
CUTTER

Fig. 29. United States grades of slaughter cows. (U.S.D.A., Agricultural Marketing Service.)

and have passed the veal stage; many are sold as feeders, but a considerable number are sold for immediate slaughter. Calves of this kind are most numerous on markets nearest the range country, especially the southwestern part. The calf carcass is used as beef and produces a relatively large proportion of valuable by-products such as liver, tongue, heart, brains, sweetbreads, and fat, as well as hide.

Following is a schedule for slaughter calves.[5]

CLASSES	WEIGHT DIVISIONS	COMMONLY USED GRADES
Steers and heifers	Lightweight, 200 pounds down	Prime, choice, good,
Bulls	Medium weight, 200–300 pounds	standard, utility, cull
	Heavyweight, 300 pounds up	

[5] "Official United States Standards for Grades of Vealers and Slaughter Calves," *Service and Regulatory Announcement 113,* U.S.D.A., 1951.

In slaughter calves there are three classes based upon sex condition, for the sexual characters become manifest as the calf approaches the age limit. Similar weight divisions or grades are used for the different classes, that is, for steers, heifers, and bulls.

SCHEDULE OF MARKET CLASSES AND GRADES FOR VEALERS

Vealers are usually under 3 months of age and have subsisted largely on milk. The age range is from 3 weeks to 3 months, and the weight range is from 100 to 200 pounds. Relatively few are beyond these limits of age and weight. From two thirds to three fourths of the calves slaughtered are classified as vealers, and the balance are slaughter calves. The condemnation for immaturity is commonly under 1 per cent. It is required that calves should be at least 21 days of age for slaughter. Under-age veal calves are called "deacons" or "bob veal." Vealers are most numerous on markets near the dairying sections.

Following is the schedule for vealers.

CLASSES	WEIGHT DIVISIONS	COMMONLY USED GRADES
All classes	Lightweight, 110 pounds down	Prime, choice, good,
	Medium weight, 110–180 pounds	standard, utility, cull
	Heavyweight, 180 pounds up	

Little attention is paid to sex condition in veal calves because it is not very definitely related to quality, condition, or form of the carcass. Weight is the most important factor in determining the market price of veal calves. Finish, usually related to weight, is also an important grade factor. This group varies but little in weight and essential characteristics. Like slaughter calves, the by-products constitute an important item in returns to meat packers.

CATTLE PRICES

Cattle prices are variable because the volume of production is not adjusted to the demand for beef and other cattle products. High prices occur when the price level is high and beef production low. Meat is a perishable product, and the supply, which is not controllable, must be moved into consumption in a comparatively short period of time. Storage by refrigeration (freezing) may divert from immediate consumption some of the supply, also such processing as canning or curing. However, this must eventually be used for food, and storing adds to the cost.

The carcass is the most valuable product from cattle slaughter. Since our exports of beef are practically nil, our domestic market takes all the available supply. Some beef (especially canned from South America) is imported. The value of the carcass depends upon the demand and also the supply. With liberal supplies of meat or low consumer purchasing power, low cattle prices prevail.

CATTLE PRICES AND CATTLE NUMBERS

The prices of beef cattle tend to move in cycles which are related to cattle production and to such episodic influences as droughts. The cattle population moves in cycles which result from the cattle raiser's response to cattle prices. (See page 31.) Good prices cause expansion and poor prices liquidation. The numbers follow the price; so there is a lag of about 4 years, the length of time necessary for increased production to be reflected in marketing. The wavelike variations in numbers are about 15 years long, with the increasing period 7 years and the downswing 8. There appears to be some shortening of the cattle cycle. Cattle numbers have shown a constant expansion as well, coincident with the increase of our human population. Expansion in recent years has been largely in the numbers of beef cattle. As our population has slowed down in its rate of increase, the same will probably happen to cattle.

CATTLE PRICES BY MARKETS

Comparisons of market quotations from different stations indicate that cattle prices, even within a grade, are seldom the same. Markets near to one another show smaller price differentials than markets at some distance apart. In nearby markets adjustments in numbers marketed and prices paid can be more easily made than in markets some distance apart.

As would be expected, on a daily basis there may be considerable disparity between prices on cattle markets. On a longer period basis, market prices behave as though they were national in scope. In other words, prices of various classes and grades of market cattle tend to keep in line with one another.

CATTLE PRICES BY CLASSES AND GRADES

There is considerable spread in the cattle market from the lowest selling canner cow to the highest selling beef steer. As would be expected, this spread is greater when the top price is high. A market is found for all cattle offered for sale; the demand for beef is therefore a striated affair; all parts are not always in the same relationship. An oversupply of finished steers depresses the steer price, even though, for example, bologna bulls may be short in supply and relatively high in price. Similarly, within the class beef steers, the spread between grades is not constant but may be seasonal.

Following is a tabulation of slaughter cattle by grade based on a 3-year period and determined from yearly averages. This will serve to show the spread between usual class and grade price. As there is considerable year-to-year difference, the average may not be typical of a single year. (See Fig. 30.)

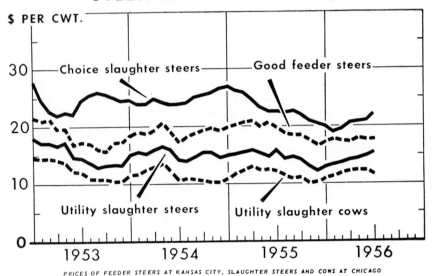

Fig. 30. Steer and cow prices. There is considerable year-to-year difference in prices for various grades and classes. (U.S.D.A., Agricultural Marketing Service.)

CATTLE PRICES BY GRADES, CHICAGO MARKET

3-year Average, 1951–1953 [6]

CLASS	GRADE	AVERAGE PRICE PER *100* POUNDS
Beef steers	Prime	$33.28
	Choice	30.76
	Good	28.34
	* Commercial	25.67
	Utility	22.26
	All grades	30.57
Veal calves	Prime and choice	32.22
Cows	Commercial	21.14

* Commercial grade was divided after this period, and the younger steers in this group are now designated as standard.

[6] *Agricultural Statistics,* U.S.D.A., 1954, p. 321.

Since steers and heifers are most in demand for beef, they are higher in price than cows. The lower grades of both steers and heifers are more nearly competitive with cows, but even the lower grades in these classes outsell cows.

RECEIPTS OF CATTLE AT PUBLIC MARKETS BY MONTHS

The shipment of cattle to markets is seasonal and as a consequence we have seasonal variations in cattle prices. Heavy receipts occur in the fall of the year, coincident with the close of the pasture season and the necessary limitation of the cattle on the range. Cattle, like sheep, are born in the spring and marketed in the fall. The monthly distribution of this movement of cattle and calves is shown by the table below.

The cattle and calf receipts on the public market are lowest in February. Several other months are about the same in cattle receipts. In the fall months cattle marketing is somewhat heavier. Reshipment of cattle to the country as feeders and stockers is also heavier in the fall of the year. There is less seasonality of cattle receipts than of hog receipts.

RECEIPTS OF SALABLE CATTLE AND CALVES BY MONTHS AT TWELVE PUBLIC STOCKYARDS

Per Cent, by Month, 10 Years [7]

MONTH	PER CENT OF CATTLE	PER CENT OF CALVES
January	8.2	7.4
February	7.0	5.9
March	7.5	6.3
April	7.2	6.1
May	7.0	6.3
June	7.4	6.9
July	8.2	7.7
August	9.1	8.7
September	9.7	10.2
October	11.2	14.6
November	9.5	12.1
December	8.0	8.0
	100.0	100.0

SEASONAL VARIATION IN BEEF STEER PRICES

To analyze the cattle market, the various classes rather than the composite of all cattle must be considered. There is seasonality in the receipts of cattle and calves and also in the slaughter. As previously pointed out,

[7] *Livestock Market News Statistics and Related Data,* 1954, U.S.D.A., 1955.

feeder and stocker cattle move to the market and to the feed lots mainly in the fall of the year. Thus cattle feeding softens the impact of the heavy fall run of cattle. Beef steers that have been fattened have a seasonality of marketing which is not the same for all grades. This is related to the prices for the different grades. The average beef steer prices by grades on the Chicago market are shown in Figure 31.

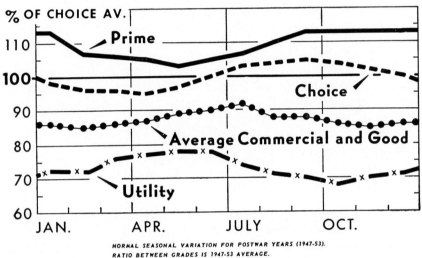

SEASONALITY IN STEER PRICES
Corn Belt Slaughter Steers at Chicago

NORMAL SEASONAL VARIATION FOR POSTWAR YEARS (1947-53).
RATIO BETWEEN GRADES IS 1947-53 AVERAGE.

Fig. 31. Beef steer prices by grades, Chicago Union Stockyards. The price range narrows in the late winter and spring and widens in the late summer and fall. There is more seasonal variation in the extreme than in the intermediate grades. (*Agriculture Handbook 83,* U.S.D.A., Agricultural Marketing Service.)

As the lower grades of beef steers compete more directly with cattle from the range or grass-finished cattle, the price of such grades is low during the heavy receipts in the fall. In fact, the prices of the lower grades show a tendency to move with feeder and stocker cattle prices. Higher grade cattle, that is, grain-fed steers, have a different seasonal pattern of prices than do cattle with less finish, which causes the seasonal widening of the price spread, as shown in Figure 31. The higher grades are also fed for longer periods and on rations higher in concentrates. Even within a narrow group, the years are quite different in average prices by months.

Following is a tabulation of the general average monthly prices at Chicago for native beef steers:

GENERAL AVERAGE MONTHLY PRICES AT CHICAGO FOR NATIVE BEEF STEER, 1945–1954 [8]

All weights 750 to 1800 pounds

MONTH	PRICE PER 100 LBS.	MONTH	PRICE PER 100 LBS.
January	$25.23	July	$27.45
February	24.32	August	27.75
March	24.56	September	27.93
April	25.07	October	28.20
May	25.62	November	28.06
June	26.37	December	27.19

10-Year Average—$26.39
Average of Years—$26.39
High Year—1951
Low Year—1945

These figures show the general tendency for the better grades of beef steers, since they predominate in the receipts. It will be noted that October is the high month and February is the low month, with a difference of $3.88 between the two monthly averages.

Feed conditions and cattle prices affect the market, causing deviations from the usual price pattern.

SEASONAL VARIATION IN HEIFER PRICES

As would be expected, slaughter heifers of the better grade tend to follow the prices for the higher grades of fed steers. Over a period of years the choice and good heifers under 850 pounds in weight are highest in price in the fall, usually September, and lowest in price in the spring, usually May.

SEASONAL VARIATION OF COW PRICES

The seasonal variation in slaughter cow prices is quite the reverse of the variation in steer prices, for peak prices occur in the spring and low prices prevail in the fall. This is due mainly to seasonal marketing: liquidation or culling of the cow herd occurs in the fall.

SEASONAL VARIATION OF VEAL CALF PRICES

Veal calves, which are mostly of dairy breeding, also show a price pattern by months on the Chicago market. Receipts are quite seasonal, for

[8] *Drovers Journal Yearbook of Figures* of the Livestock Trade, Chicago Daily Drovers Journal. 55th ed., 1955.

in dairy sections calves are dropped in the early spring and late winter and again in the fall. Veal calves are marketed when they are about 2 months of age; so peaks in marketing occur about 2 months after heavy calvings. Low prices attend heavier marketing; so low prices occur during the summer and again in the late fall. Highs in prices occur mostly in the early fall and winter.

Following is a tabulation of native veal prices at Chicago for a 10-year period based on yearly averages by months. The high and low years in the period are indicated.

AVERAGE MONTHLY PRICES AT CHICAGO FOR
NATIVE VEAL CALVES—1946–1955 [9]

MONTH	PRICE PER 100 LBS.	MONTH	PRICE PER 100 LBS.
January	$25.98	July	$23.20
February	25.54	August	25.58
March	24.34	September	23.84
April	24.49	October	23.93
May	25.33	November	23.36
June	24.33	December	24.01

High Year—1951
Low Year—1946

MARKETING MARGINS FOR BEEF

The difference between the price the consumer pays for beef and the price the farmer receives for an equivalent quantity of live cattle is termed the "marketing margin." It is a return to agencies handling the beef and it includes all charges for distributing and processing the product from the live animal on the farm to the meat in the consumer's hands.

The marketing margins for beef have fluctuated markedly in recent years. The U.S.D.A.[10] has made a study of marketing margins for U.S. Choice grade of beef. This grade accounts for about half of our supply of block beef. The margin on such beef gives a broadly representative picture of margins and costs of marketing for most grades of beef sold "fresh." Only about 25 per cent of all beef is sold as processed meat, that is, other than "fresh." The live and wholesale values and margins are shown in Fig. 32.

Following is a tabulation of the average marketing margin between the live weight price from several public livestock markets and the wholesale meat price at several large wholesale markets. This is based on a recent 7-year period.

9 "Drover Journal Yearbook of Figures," *Chicago Daily Drovers Journal*, 55th ed., 1955.
10 "Beef Marketing Margins and Costs," *Misc. Pub. 710*, U.S.D.A., Feb., 1956.

U.S. Choice Grade Beef

LIVE AND WHOLESALE VALUES AND MARKETING MARGIN

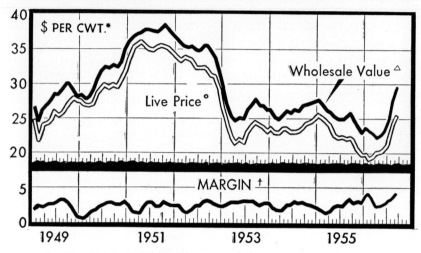

* Live weight basis   ○ 23 public stockyard markets
△ Value of 59 pounds of wholesale carcass beef (equivalent to 100 pounds of live weight) at five markets plus value of byproducts.
† Difference between the live price per 100 pounds of beef steer and wholesale value.

Fig. 32. Live and wholesale values and marketing margin for U.S. Choice Grade Beef. (U.S.D.A., Agricultural Marketing Service.)

LIVE-TO-WHOLESALE: MARKETING MARGIN PER 100 POUNDS LIVE WEIGHT, U.S. CHOICE GRADE CATTLE

From Yearly Averages, 1949–1955

LIVE WEIGHT	WHOLESALE				LIVE-TO-WHOLESALE MARGIN
	CARCASS	LIVE WEIGHT EQUIVALENT (59% YIELD)	BY-PRODUCT CREDIT	TOTAL VALUE	
$27.47	$46.23	$27.28	$2.71	$29.99	$2.52

It will be observed that the cattle cost $27.47 per 100 pounds and that comparable beef in the carcass sold at $46.23 per cwt. Considering the carcass yield, the 100 pounds live weight would return $27.28 for 59 pounds of carcass plus a by-product credit of $2.71, making a total value of $29.99. The difference or margin "live to wholesale" would therefore be $2.52.

The wholesale-to-retail margin, or the difference between the average composite retail price and the average wholesale price, at the same time was $13.64. In other words, the average pound of beef cost the consumer nearly 60 cents; this in turn had cost the retailer nearly 14 cents less. The retail-to-consumer margin includes the 20 per cent of the carcass representing suet, fat, bone, and trim which is sold at nominal price and which does not go to the retail trade. Therefore, the retailer must recover his initial cost and expenses and make his profit from the 80 per cent of the carcass weight that he can sell the consumer.

It takes over 2 pounds of choice grade live cattle to yield 1 pound of retail beef. In the study made it was found that the farm-to-retail or marketing margin was 23.3 cents per pound (bought by the consumer). The farmer's share of the retail price was 69 per cent.

CASH INCOME FROM MEAT ANIMALS

In agricultural income in the United States cattle and calves rank high; in fact, they return more cash income to the producer than all other slaughter animals together.

Following is the cash farm income from the different kinds of meat animals based on a 10-year period, 1946–1955, inclusive.[11]

AVERAGE YEARLY CASH INCOME

KIND OF MEAT ANIMALS	MILLION DOLLARS	PER CENT OF TOTAL
Cattle and calves	5,294	53.4
Hogs	3,397	37.5
Sheep and lambs	316	4.1
Total all meat animals	9,063	100.0

All that is included under cattle and calves is not from beef cattle, for it is the cash income from all cattle sold from farms for cash. Cattle and calves sales are responsible for more than one-half of our total national cash income from meat animals. In recent years they have been increasing their share of this total.

[11] "Livestock Market News Statistics," *Stat. Bull. 178.* Agricultural Marketing Service, U.S.D.A., 1956.

Chapter 7

FEEDER AND STOCKER CATTLE

CATTLE FOR FEEDING

Cattle feeding, or the finishing of range cattle, is quite widely distributed throughout the entire country but is primarily centered in the corn belt. In areas where feed grain is produced extensively the cattle feeder either raises cattle and feeds them until they are acceptable as slaughter cattle or purchases feeder and stocker cattle for feeding. The unfinished cattle move to regions of surplus feed for finishing. The general movement is from the range areas of the Great Plains and the Rocky Mountain states to the corn belt and other feeding regions for finishing. The finished beef is then moved eastward toward the large centers of human population.

There are some other special feeding areas. Notable among these are the cake feeding areas in Texas, the beet pulp feeding sections in Colorado, Nebraska, and Wyoming, and the Lancaster district in Pennsylvania. In some areas cattle are purchased for the utilization of concentrates mainly, with just sufficient roughage or pasturage to complete the ration. In other areas cattle are brought in to utilize pasture or roughage.

There has been an increase in the commercial type of cattle feeding and in the mechanization of handling the feed and the manure. There has been a tendency toward the feeding of specialized feeds such as urea, etc., and also toward use of more low grade roughages like corn cobs.

RANGE CATTLE

The cattle from the range country are largely of Hereford breeding. In feeder cattle, therefore, this breed predominates, although feeders of the other breeds are not uncommon. Cattle of nondescript and dairy breeding may be sold as feeders. In general, to classify as either a stocker or a
98

feeder, the individual must be produced primarily for beef and must be well past the veal-calf stage. It must show evidence of ability to take on additional weight and finish.

The essential feature in profitable livestock raising in the cattle ranching areas is low-cost feed. Successful management of the range depends upon the use of the proper number of grazing livestock of the kind suited for the range and the proper distribution of the livestock over the grazing area.

Growth of range cattle

As the feed supply is somewhat seasonal on the range, cattle have different kinds and rates of growth at different seasons. Under corn-belt conditions the rate of growth is not so directly related to the natural vegetation available, for grazing provides but a part of the feed supply. In the range country supplementary feeding is practiced. This consists mainly of feeding some protein supplement and hay. The extent varies in different areas and depends upon the grass available.

Lush et al.[1] studied the normal growth of range cattle at the Texas Ranch Experiment Station at Spur, Texas. They found in this investigation that the increase in weight of growing cattle on the range was usually very rapid from the middle of April until late summer and that in the fall months the rate slowed down. In the winter it was nearly at a standstill. Actually, losses in weight occurred in the late winter and early spring. The growth of the skeleton, especially the head and the length of the leg bones, was not affected by the paucity of feed in the winter period. However the growth of the pelvic bones and increase in body length and chest depth were somewhat lessened during the winter.

Young range cattle may not gain in weight during the winter if kept on the range, but they become older in appearance because of the growth of the head, legs, and hair.

MARKETING OF CATTLE FOR FEEDING

There are three main channels in the movement of cattle from raiser to feeder. The greater number pass through the public central market and are consigned to commission men who act as agents for the owners; buyers of feeders may make their own selection at the central market or make purchases through commission men. Many feeder cattle are consigned to auction markets. A large number of feeder cattle are purchased direct from the raiser, either by the feeder or by an agent.

[1] Lush, Jay L., et al., "Normal Growth of Range Cattle," Bull. 409, Tex. Agr. Exp. Sta., March, 1930.

Large feeder cattle markets

Most of the large central markets for feeder cattle lie between the range area and the corn belt where most of the cattle are fed out. The receipts on these markets are variable, and their rank in numbers of feeder cattle sold is changeable. When drought or other conditions cause liquidation in any area, the receipts on the markets serving that area are increased.

Following are receipts of several of the large markets for feeder and stocker cattle, based on reports for a recent 3-year period.

LARGE CENTRAL MARKETS FOR FEEDER CATTLE

Average Yearly Receipts for the 3-year Period, 1950–1953 [2]

MARKET	AVERAGE YEARLY RECEIPTS, THOUSAND HEAD
Kansas City, Kan.	554
Omaha, Neb.	449
Sioux City, Iowa	446
Denver, Colo.	398
San Antonio, Tex.	302
Oklahoma City, Okla.	274
Fort Worth, Tex.	240
Ogden, Utah	182
South St. Paul, Minn.	151
Wichita, Kan.	145
St. Louis *	137
All markets total	4,805

* Includes St. Louis National Stock Yards, Ill., and St. Louis, Mo.

The range cattle raiser may dispose of his cattle by sale as feeder calves, as yearlings, or as two-year-olds and older, or he may have them fed out on account or on contract, or he may have them pastured on contract. If sale is made they may be sold direct or through some agency or on a central market. In recent years there has been a decline in the movement of cattle from the public markets and an increase in the direct-to-feeder movement. Over 4 million head of feeder cattle pass through the central markets each year.

Direct marketing with feeders and stockers

There has been an increase in the proportion of feeder cattle that go direct to the feeder. It will be recalled that "directs" are those that are not consigned to commission companies on the public stockyard markets and

[2] *Agricultural Statistics,* U.S.D.A., 1954.

sold by them. In the case of directs the cattle may be purchased by the feeder from the raiser. In many cases they are handled by dealers and may be sold at auction barns.

The proportion of stocker and feeder cattle and calves coming from other states, classified as "directs" has ranged from 21 to 39 per cent. This covers shipments to the eight north central states and includes cattle that may have been stopped at a public stockyard for feed, water, and rest en route.

LARGE CATTLE-FEEDING AREAS AND STATES

In the estimate of livestock numbers made by the U.S.D.A. January 1 each year, the cattle and calves on feed are listed separately. Other estimates of cattle on feed are made periodically. As would be expected, the areas having abundant supplies of feed rank high in the number of cattle on feed. (See Figure 33.) Following is a list of the states having large numbers of cattle and calves on feed.[3] It should be borne in mind that these estimates include cattle being fattened for market and that the amount of feeding will yield carcasses that grade good or better.

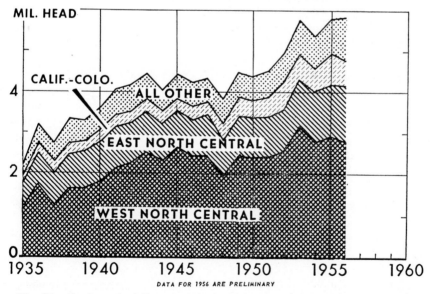

Fig. 33. Cattle on feed, January 1, in the United States. Note the large proportion in the north central states. There has been an increase in cattle feeding in the western states. (U.S.D.A., Agricultural Marketing Service.)

[3] *Agricultural Statistics*, U.S.D.A., 1955.

STATE	THOUSAND HEAD
1. Iowa	1,172
2. Nebraska	669
3. Illinois	575
4. Minnesota	363
5. Missouri	348
6. California	338
7. Colorado	270
8. Kansas	264
9. Indiana	230
10. South Dakota	215
11. Texas	161
12. Ohio	146

In the last few years California has shown a marked increase in cattle feeding.

The total number for the United States has been over 5 million head in recent years. Included in these estimates, listed by states, are only the cattle being fattened in a more or less distinct enterprise. Not included are the cattle of small operators, the cattle fed on distillery slop and "grass fat" cattle marketed in the fall.

Movement of feeder and stocker cattle

The peak in the movement of feeder and stocker cattle is in the fall. Over 50 per cent of the shipment of such cattle occurs during the months of September, October, and November. The end of the grazing period causes the cattle to move from the range country, and also at this time there is an abundant supply of feed in the feeding areas.

The ranchman sells his surplus stock in the fall unless supplemental feed is relatively cheap and the probable price in the spring appears favorable. Seldom is there much increase in cattle prices in the winter season; consequently, cattle on the range are reduced to a minimum in the fall. If prospective feeder cattle have been carried over the winter on the range, the summer range pasture available can in most instances carry them until fall. Nearly one fourth of all cattle received on the public markets during the fall are shipped out as feeders and stockers. Middlewestern farmers provide a demand for thin cattle to be used for fall grazing, roughage feeding, and grain feeding, particularly corn from the current crops.

With the demand for lighter beef, smaller cuts, and higher quality, there has come a great increase in the marketing of younger feeder cattle, mainly feeder calves. Cattle that mature more rapidly and finish at younger ages have been developed. There has been a decided increase in the marketing of calves and a decrease in the receipts of two-year-olds.

Seasonal variations in shipments of feeder and stocker cattle and calves to corn-belt farmers

As has been indicated previously, the fall is the heavy market period for feeder cattle. Cattle and calves are shipped to feeders in the corn belt every month of the year, and this represents a sizable portion of the market receipts. The monthly distribution of this movement is shown below.

FEEDER AND STOCKER CATTLE BOUGHT BY
CORN-BELT FARMERS BY MONTHS [4]

5 Years, 1951–1955

MONTH	PER CENT PER MONTH
January	4.95
February	3.56
March	4.09
April	8.70
May	4.09
June	3.58
July	4.48
August	7.18
September	12.67
October	22.77
November	16.23
December	7.40

Cattle and calves move together in rather close agreement. As would be expected, the movement of cattle and calves to the feed lots is more seasonal than the total market receipts and cattle slaughter. There is a seasonal variation in prices of feeders and stockers; low prices prevail in the fall and high prices in the spring.

REASONS FOR MARKET GROUPS

Trading in feeder cattle is facilitated by the use of market classes and grades. The standardization of terms, classes, and grades makes it possible to describe quite accurately the offerings of sellers and the requirements of buyers. From market reports given by the press, radio, mail, and wire, buyers can compare various markets where feeders are available. Livestock feeders place orders with buyers for feeder cattle on a specification basis which includes the grade.

The Agricultural Marketing Service of the U.S. Department of Agriculture collects and publishes reports on the feeder cattle markets and movement of feeder cattle, so that comparisons of various markets can be readily made.

[4] *Livestock Market News Statistics,* Agricultural Marketing Service, U.S.D.A., 1955.

GROUPS OF CATTLE THAT ARE SOLD FOR FEEDING

Cattle are sold either to slaughterers or to feeders. There is competition between the two groups for cattle that are carrying some finish—which are known on the market as "two-way cattle." In classifying and grading feeders and stockers, the class, age, weight, and grade are considered. The raiser, the feeder cattle dealer, or the yard trader arranges uniform lots of cattle acceptable to the feeder buyers. The outlook for cattle feeding influences the demand for cattle for feeding. When the ratio of feed costs to finished cattle is favorable, the number of cattle purchased for feeding is increased. This decreases the number of thinner cattle available for immediate slaughter, but as a consequence finished cattle will increase proportionally later. The corn-belt farmer or other feeder sells his feeds in the form of finished cattle. When the margin between the price of slaughter and feeder cattle is wide, more feeding results.

Following is a tabulation of the different market classes and grades which may be on the market, and a brief description of each group.[5]

MARKET CLASSES AND GRADES OF FEEDER AND STOCKER CATTLE

| | BASIS FOR GROUPING | | | | |
	Sex	Age	Use	Weight	Grades
Divisions in each group	Steers Heifers Cows Stags Bulls	Calves Yearlings Two-year-olds and older	Stockers Feeders	Heavy Medium Light Mixed	Fancy Choice Good Medium Common Inferior

Sex classes

In the usual classification sex classes are the market classes of feeder cattle. In some classifications the entire group of feeders is termed a market class, based on a commercial use. Since cattle in this group are sold for further feeding, they are designated as stockers and feeders to distinguish them from beef steers, butcher stock, cutters, canners, etc., and the sex classes are regarded as the classes.

The market classes of stockers and feeders based on sex or sex condition make up the main market classification. The terms descriptive of the sexes and sex condition have been previously described on pages 77–78.

Spaying or unsexing of heifers is not common; spayed heifers are quieter

[5] Adapted from "Market Classes and Grades of Feeder and Stocker Cattle," *Circ. 505*, U.S.D.A., October, 1938; slightly revised August, 1942.

in the feed lot than open heifers, but the operation is rather difficult and practically no premium is paid for spayed heifers when marketed. There is no advantage in buying spayed heifers in preference to open heifers for feeding. Feed consumption and costs of gains are not affected by spaying.

Steers predominate in the feeder and stocker receipts. Heifers and some cows are also included, and occasionally bulls and stags are sold as feeders. Unless otherwise qualified, however, a feeder or stocker is a steer.

Age groups

As range calves are dropped mostly in the spring of the year, it is common practice to group cattle sold for further feeding into age divisions. This grouping applies mainly to steers and heifers. Offerings consist mainly of calves, yearlings, and two-year-olds for both steers and heifers, but there are fewer of the older heifers sold. The age of cattle when put on feed is related to such factors as the length of the feeding period, rate of gain, and kind of feeds needed. Age, therefore, is an important problem confronting the prospective feeder. Young cattle will make growth while in the feed lot, whereas in older cattle there is less growth and more fattening. Young cattle, therefore, put on gains more cheaply than do older cattle, because their gains are higher in moisture and lower in fat.

Feeder and stocker cattle

Stocker cattle are usually younger and less mature than feeder cattle. Also, stockers are intended for the utilization of more grass and roughage than feeders, and as a consequence they are fed longer before they are returned as slaughter cattle. Stockers are not fattened immediately but are allowed to grow out on roughage before fattening. Feeder cattle on the market usually are higher in flesh and finish than stockers, but the distinction is arbitrary and based mainly upon the subsequent feeding and management.

With the increase of rapidly finishing young feeder cattle (calves and yearlings) the term "stocker cattle" has largely lost its significance, especially in the corn belt.

Weight groups

Cattle for feeding are sorted in weight groups to secure more uniform lots for feeding. Yard traders on central markets often perform this function. The subdivisions for weight are not widely standardized. The steers sold as feeders range from 500 to 1050 pounds with the break at 800 pounds. Heifers are from 500 to 750 pounds and calves are from 300 to 500 pounds. Often the terms "heavy," "medium," "light," and "mixed" are used to describe lots sorted for sale. The weight which is associated with age and fleshing is an important consideration in determining the feeding system to be used. The heavier cattle need a shorter feeding period and require a smaller necessary margin, because of the increase in value of a greater weight.

Grades

A grade includes animals that will sell for about the same price per pound. It is the last step in sorting or grouping for the marketing of a lot of cattle. We recognize six common grades—fancy, choice, good, medium, common, and inferior—although in some instances two of the grades may be joined together. For example, we may read of a quotation on heavy steer calves good to choice grade. In fact, it is common practice to combine the good and choice grades. (See Figure 34.)

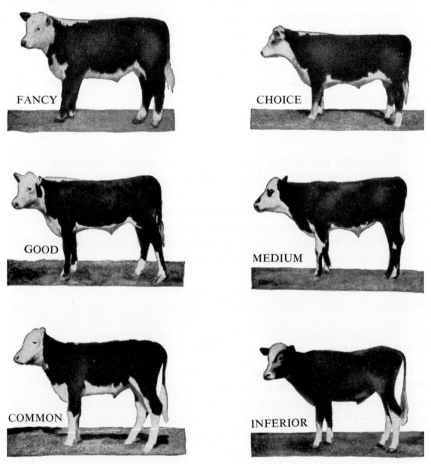

FANCY

CHOICE

GOOD

MEDIUM

COMMON

INFERIOR

Fig. 34. United States grades of feeder steers. (U.S.D.A., Production and Marketing Administration.)

GRADE FACTORS

The evaluation of feeder and stocker cattle is based upon certain requirements of: (1) conformation, (2) finish, and (3) quality. These terms have been previously defined in relation to finished cattle in Chapter 4. A discussion of their application to feeder and stocker cattle follows.

Conformation

"Conformation" means build, shape, outline, or general contour of the animal and refers to the degree of symmetry or relative proportion of its parts. The degree of conformation is determined by the proportionate relationships of width, depth, and length of body to one another. Animals of excellent conformation are very compact and symmetrical. The body is relatively wide and deep in proportion to its length. The head is relatively short and wide, the neck is short and thick, the crops are full, and the back, loin, and rump are relatively broad. The legs are relatively short and set wide apart, and the top line and under line are approximately straight and parallel. Animals of poor conformation are rangy, and the body is narrow

Fig. 35. Example of a poor feeder steer. Note the long legs, low back, rough and irregular fleshing, shallow body, and lack of blockiness desired in a beef steer.

and shallow in proportion to its length. The head is relatively long and narrow, the neck is long and thin, the crops are flat, and the back, loin, and rump are narrow in relation to the size of the body. The back may be high at the shoulders, low in the middle, and high at the tailhead. The legs are relatively long and set close together, and the under line is high in the chest and flank.

Finish

Finish is the quantity and distribution of fat. It is dependent upon inherited tendencies, age, and sex condition, as well as upon the quantity and kind of feed the animal has consumed. The degree of finish in feeder and stocker cattle is important because of its influence upon the length of time required for an animal to attain a given degree of finish as a slaughter animal. Finish in a feeder or stocker animal also indicates, to some extent, its general thrift and inherent ability to acquire additional finish. The degree of finish that may be possessed by feeder and stocker cattle of any grade varies within relatively wide limits. The higher grades of feeder and stocker cattle of all ages must have sufficient finish to show that the growth and development of the animal have not been retarded. Desirable finish may vary from the minimum amount which will show that the development of the animal has not been retarded to the maximum amount it may possess and still be considered a feeder or stocker animal.

Quality

Quality in an animal refers primarily to its breeding and refinement. Animals of excellent quality usually show the characteristics of high-grade or purebred beef breeds. These factors are evidenced by certain inherent characteristics of bone, hide, head, and smoothness in relation to both frame and fleshing. The animals possess thick muscling, medium-sized bone, a mellow hide, a clean-cut well-shaped head, and a high degree of symmetry and smoothness. They indicate in their general appearance that they will gain in weight and finish rapidly and will produce carcasses of exceptionally high grade if properly finished. Animals of low quality do not usually possess beef breed characteristics. They may possess either very heavy or very fine bone and tight hides. Their muscling is thin, and their bodies unsymmetrical and rangy. They indicate in their general appearance that they will not finish rapidly in relation to the quantity and kind of feed consumed, and will not produce carcasses of choice or prime grade even though they are extensively fed.

Fig. 36. Hereford steers raised in the range country. Many feeder cattle pass through public stockyards while en route from the range to the feed lots.

Other factors that may influence grade

Conformation, quality, and finish to a large extent determine the market grade of feeders. Yet other factors influence grade, some of which overlap these factors. The grade is affected by several other items related to the capacity to consume and convert feeds into economical gains.

Some other factors which may affect the feeding possibilities of feeders are:

1. Breeding. The differences in breeding are quite largely reflected in conformation, quality, and finish. In the selection of feeders enough emphasis is given this point to warrant separate consideration.

Purebred cattle or high grades will usually make more rapid gains in the feed lot than scrubs, and also their gains are made with less feed. The big difference between cattle of good and poor breeding, however, is that the well-bred steers will sell for much more when finished because of the higher acceptability of the finished carcass rather than because of the rapidity and economy of gains. Feeders of poor breeding or scrubby-like appearance are not finished so highly as are feeders of better grades. The carcasses of scrubs are of lower grades because of inferior quality and conformation, and it is not economical to fatten them heavily because that will not make up for the deficiency in form and quality.

Steers of good beef type will yield a relatively high percentage of carcass. Also carcasses from such steers will have a higher proportion of loins and ribs (higher priced cuts) and a lower proportion of cheaper cuts. The difference in the percentage of cuts is not great. Fat distribution on well-bred steers is more desirable, as is also the quality of the beef.

2. Horns. Most of the cattle sold for further feeding are hornless. They are either of hornless breeding or dehorned when young on the range or during the marketing process. Feeders that are horned are worth less per pound than those without horns because they require more room and may make less rapid gains. Young cattle that are not hornless should be dehorned if they are to be kept for a feeding period of the usual length. Older cattle are set back more by dehorning, and the loss from the setback may be more than the losses due to the horns.

Cattle with horns are less satisfactory in the feed lots and incur damage from horn bruises in loading and shipping. Horns are one of the major causes of bruising in cattle being marketed, and slaughter cattle with horns sell at a lower price because of damage to the hide and carcass.

3. Health and thriftiness. It is quite obvious that diseased or unthrifty cattle will not respond with good gains in the feed lot.

4. Temperament and Disposition. A nervous, irritable, high-strung feeder will not make fast, economical gains. Muscular activity increases energy production, and consequently less of the energy in the feed consumed by an active steer is available for body gains. It has been estimated that there is difference in metabolism from 20 to 30 per cent between standing steer and one that lies down.

5. Brands. Hide brands are used by ranchers for identification; when large or unsightly they detract from the value of the hide. In most western states it is required that the herd brand be recorded to avoid duplication. On some of the western markets brand inspectors are maintained in order to establish ownership of the cattle marketed. The brand establishes the herd source of the cattle, which may be helpful information to the person buying feeder cattle; but large brands detract from the animal's value. In some herds ear marks or wattles made by slitting the skin on the neck or dewlap serve to identify ownership or breeding.

Fancy-grade feeder and stocker steers closely approach the ideal in conformation, finish, and quality. They are relatively large for their age— breed and type considered—have the general appearance of exceptional thrift and vitality, and show ability to gain weight and finish rapidly. The body is very compact and symmetrical. It is very wide and deep in proportion to its length. The head is very short and wide, and the neck is very short. The legs are very short and set wide apart. The top line and the under line, as well as the lines of the sides, are approximately straight and parallel. The chest is very wide and deep, the crops are full, and the ribs are long and exceptionally well-sprung. The belly is very wide and deep but not paunchy. The back, loin, and rump are extremely full and wide in proportion to the size of the body, and the tailhead is even with the top line. The thighs are very wide, full, and deep in relation to the size of the animal, and the twist is thick and deep and exceptionally low in the seam.

Animals of this grade indicate in their general appearance a moderate degree of refinement. The head is exceptionally clean-cut in appearance, the bones of the legs are of medium size—type, weight, and age of animals considered—and the joints are smooth and free from coarseness. The hide is pliable and of moderate thickness. The flesh covering over the shoulders, crops, back, loin, and rump is very thick, firm, and of proportionately uniform thickness, giving the animal a plump and well-rounded appearance. The flesh covering over all parts of the body is mellow.

Calves from cows compared with calves from heifers

Calves from cows are usually heavier than those from heifers when they are sold from the range herd in the fall. Some evidence on the feeding outcome of calves under corn-belt conditions apparently indicates that the feed-lot performance of cows' calves is not sufficiently superior to the performance of heifers' calves to be an important factor in the purchase of feeder calves.

Best indexes of feeder grade [6]

What characteristics are indexes of the grade of a feeder? The following five characters judged by graders have been studied in relation to the grade of feeder cattle. Width of body, depth of body, thickness of finish, shape of head, and refinement (quality) were all found to be highly correlated with the grade of the feeder. Width was the best single index of the characters studied, while refinement ranked lowest.

It was found also that the physical characters judged or estimated were rather highly correlated with the final carcass grade of the cattle. These estimates made by grading experts showed close agreement between feeder characteristics and carcass value of the steers when finished.

Grades of feeder and slaughter steers

There is a rather high correlation between the grades of feeder steers and the grades of the resultant finished steers. The amount and quality of the ration and the length of the feeding period are the principal additional factors affecting the final grading of the slaughter steer. A choice feeder steer will, if properly handled, result in a choice finished steer. The grade may decline during feeding if the animal is not well fed. On the other hand it is possible to improve the grade with good feeding and handling. Better grades require heavier grain feeding and a longer feeding period than do

[6] O. G. Hankins and L. R. Burk, "Relationships among Production and Grade Factors of Beefs," *Tech. Bull. 665,* U.S.D.A., November, 1938.

the poor grades. With usual feeding conditions, the poorer grades tend to improve in grade and the better grades tend to decline.

Fig. 37.   Prime baby beeves from Texas ranches and feed lots.

ECONOMICS OF CATTLE FEEDING

Skillful buying and selling are essential for profitable cattle feeding. Economical feeding will not overcome poor judgment in buying feeders or selling the finished cattle.

In deciding upon a cattle feeding program and the probable profits from the enterprise there are two major considerations: (1) the cost of gains, (2) the probable difference between the buying and selling prices of the cattle. The price of cattle for feeding in the fall is dependent largely upon the general price level and the probable supply of feed—mainly the size of the corn crop. Feed costs and the efficiency of gains—that is, the feed required for a given gain—determine the major production costs. In addition there must be considered overhead or other costs involved.

As the cost of 100 pounds of gain may be more than the market price per 100 pounds of finished cattle, a margin is necessary for profit from cattle feeding.

MARGIN IN CATTLE FEEDING

The difference between the buying price per 100 pounds of a feeder or stocker and the selling price of the finished steer is termed "margin." (See

Figure 38.) If yearling feeder steers were purchased for $20.00 per 100 pounds in the fall and sold 5 months later for $23.50 per 100 pounds the margin would be $3.50. The difference needed to break even on the cattle-feeding enterprise is the "necessary margin." There are many variables which influence the necessary margin. The most important items to be covered are the cost and amount of the gains and the expense of transportation. Heavy cattle require less margin per head to break even than lighter cattle, because a greater initial weight is increased in value by feeding. Likewise, higher priced cattle require less margin because the original cost per pound is more nearly equal to the cost of the gain. Young cattle require less feed to make gains and cost more than older cattle; therefore, they have a lower necessary margin.

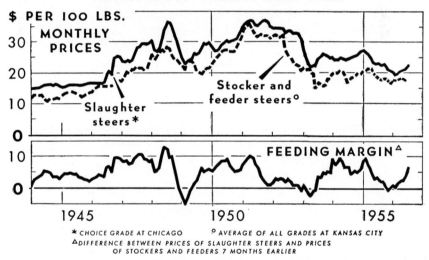

Fig. 38. Average prices of stocker and feeder steers and of good slaughter steers, 1944–1956, and margin between prices. It will be noted that prices for the two groups tend to move together. (U.S.D.A., Agricultural Marketing Service.)

GRADE OF CATTLE TO FEED FOR PROFIT

Supply in proportion to demand establishes the price of feeder cattle. Because of demand, higher grades, such as choice and good, sell for more than the lower grades like medium or common. The better grades usually make greater daily gains and require less feed for their gains. Likewise the higher grades require less margin for an equal-length feeding period, and also, when finished, they grade higher and sell for higher prices. The higher grades commonly use a larger proportion of concentrates and are fed for longer periods and to higher finish.

Lower grades of feeders may be as profitable as higher grades, for they cost less and use feeds of lower cost. The margin may be as wide or wider for low grades as high grades. The spread between grades does not remain constant, and the difference between various grades is not always the same for finished and for feeder cattle.

In Figure 38 the average price for stocker and feeder cattle and slaughter steers is given. It will be noted that prices of feeder and finished cattle tend to move together, also there is a seasonal fluctuation. Stockers and feeders are higher priced during the spring and early summer because of the demand for them for pasture feeding. Receipts of unfinished cattle are heavier when the pasture season closes, so lower prices prevail.

During the spring the spread in grades of slaughter cattle narrows, and in the fall the extreme in grades tends to diverge more from the average. This is due to the variable demand which exists and the supply available to meet that demand. Finished cattle of the higher grades are fewer and higher priced on the market in the fall. Poorer grades of finished cattle are relatively cheap in the fall because of the great number of partly finished cattle then on the market that are pasture fed.

The corn crop influences the number of cattle fed and also the probable margin. A larger than usual corn crop results in a heavy demand for feeders. This is followed by a larger than normal supply of fed cattle when the cattle are finished, and consequent narrow margins. A light movement of feeder and stocker cattle in the fall will usually result in a short supply of finished cattle and in wider margins.

Feeder cattle of the same market grade vary in their ability to make economical gains. Steers that make rapid gains and also sell high will bring a high net profit.

GAINS MADE BY FEEDER CATTLE

There is a positive correlation between the gains made in the feed lot and gain made on the range. Potential size, then, is a factor in selecting cattle for the feed lot. Smaller, lighter-weight feeder cattle will make slower feed-lot gains than larger, heavyweight feeders in a comparable environment. Feed consumption is an important factor in gains on the range, as well as on the feed lot, and larger cattle usually consume greater quantities of feed.

Previous treatment may have a marked effect upon feed-lot gains. If, for example, feeder cattle are light in weight because of a short feed supply on the range, they will make rapid gains in the feed lot during the recovery period. In U.S.D.A. trials, in which identical twin beef calves were the experimental animals, it was found that a low-energy intake for 3 to 6 months during the year caused no loss in growth potential, as long as health was maintained.

Within a group of cattle that have been exposed to similar feeding and management it is difficult to predict differences in feed-lot gains. In experimental trials it has been found that a physical score given at weaning time is not an index of subsequent feed-lot gains. Selection of feeder calves for rapid gain by visual appraisal may not be very effective.

AGE OF FEEDER CATTLE AND ECONOMY OF GAINS

The relationship of age to gains and economy of gains is shown by a summary made by Morrison.[7] The weight groups and their daily gains and nutrients needed for gains follow.

DAILY GAINS AND NUTRIENTS REQUIRED BY STEERS OF DIFFERENT WEIGHTS

WEIGHT GROUP, POUNDS	AVERAGE DAILY GAIN, POUNDS	TOTAL DIGESTIBLE NUTRIENTS FOR 100 POUNDS GAIN, POUNDS
100–200	0.93	225
200–300	1.33	319
300–400	1.44	376
400–500	1.51	429
500–600	1.85	426
600–700	1.71	529
700–800	1.79	553
800–900	1.53	708
900–1,000	1.62	731
1,000–1,100	1.53	808
1,100–1,200	1.48	885

It will be noted that the daily gain increases for a time with the increase in weight and then declines. The digestible nutrients increase quite regularly with weight and age because the older and heavier cattle require more feed just to maintain their weight, and the gains are composed of a larger proportion of fat which, because of its concentrate nature, requires more feed.

The feed requirements for fattening cattle from on-the-farm feeding records are given below. The requirements are given for several types of feeding programs and represent the average amount of certain feeds or their equivalent needed for the gains made.

[7] F. B. Morrison, *Feeds and Feeding,* 20th ed., The Morrison Publishing Company, Ithaca, N. Y., 1936, p. 643.

FEED REQUIREMENTS FOR FATTENING CATTLE [8]

Mostly Dry-lot Feedings

Grade, age and weight of the feeder cattle	Total gain	Daily gain	Months fed	Total feed consumed			
				Corn	Protein supplement	Hay	Pasture days
	(lbs.)	(lbs.)		(bu.)	(lbs.)	(lbs.)	
Good to choice, 2 yr., 880 lbs.	320	1.78	6	49	170	1,100	28
Common to medium, 2 yr., 860 lbs.	260	1.73	5	33	140	1,100	20
Good to choice, short-fed yearlings, 670 lbs.	370	1.76	7	50	200	1,200	30
Good to choice, long-fed yearlings, 600 lbs.	490	1.63	10	64	240	1,400	42
Common to medium, long-fed yearlings, 660 lbs.	300	1.54	6½	37	150	1,300	40
Good to choice, steer calves, 440 lbs.	560	1.70	11	63	260	1,400	36
Good to choice, heifers, 420 lbs.	390	1.44	9	44	200	1,200	16

Pasture Fed

Grade, age and weight of the feeder cattle	Total gain	Daily gain	Months fed	Corn	Protein supplement	Hay	Pasture days
Good to choice, yearlings, 650 lbs.	430	1.59	9	50	190	1,300	105
Medium, yearlings, 600 lbs.	300	1.54	6½	32	100	1,600	75
Good to choice, steer calves, 450 lbs.	550	1.67	11	52	190	1,800	130
Medium, steer calves, 420 lbs.	430	1.59	9	41	150	1,200	85

Lightweight, younger feeder cattle require a longer feeding period; older cattle may be fed out in a shorter period of time. Short-fed cattle are often termed "warm up." With the older cattle of comparable grades the grain-

[8] *The Midwest Farm Handbook* 4th ed., The Iowa State College Press, 1957.

to-roughage ratio on the dry-matter basis is narrower and the proportion of protein supplement is lower. When the protein supplement was fed in higher than average amount, faster gains and higher finish resulted.

CONTRACT FEEDING OF CATTLE

Contract pasturing of livestock is of long standing in this country, but it has been only in the 1930's that contract feeding has been practiced in any volume. In such an arrangement the grower supplies the cattle; the feeder furnishes the feed, equipment, and labor. The feeder receives his returns on the basis of the increase in the weight of the cattle. Such items as marketing expense, freight, etc., are included in the contract agreement. Under conditions of low prices for feeders and feeds and also curtailment of livestock credit, contract feeding increases. The feeder risks his feed and labor while the ranchman risks his cattle in the contract feeding, and in the cooperative venture a greater return is expected for both the cattle and feed than could be got by immediate sale.

Most of the complaints from the feeders of contract cattle have been on the weighing, sorting, and shrinkage of the cattle which commonly occurs at range loading points. With sufficient margin between the immediate sale price of feeders and the final sale price of finished cattle to pay for all costs involved, contract feeding will be successful, provided the contract is equitable to both the grower and the feeder. Much variation exists in the types of contracts for cattle feeding. They range all the way from "custom feeding" to arrangements for sharing profits and risks.

RETURNS IN CATTLE FEEDING

Cattle feeding is not always profitable. The finished steer when sold must return the initial cost of the steer, the feed cost, and the other costs if the enterprise is to break even. The manure is an indirect return from the feeding of cattle. It will be observed in Figure 39 that in the past there have been years in which cattle feeding was profitable and other years when the returns were less than the cost of the feeders and the feed.

CROPS RAISED AND CATTLE FEEDING

With the shift in the crop production on corn-belt farms to more land in grass and less in grain, the question arises as to the effect that this change may have upon livestock production. Farms in this region having more than the usual amount of land in grass also raise more than an average amount of all livestock. Increased production of soil-conserving crops will not reduce total feed production; as soil depletion is halted, crop yields are maintained or enhanced. Greater acreage in pasture or hay land is usually accompanied by increased livestock numbers to utilize the roughage produced. This will increase the feeding of home-grown concentrates

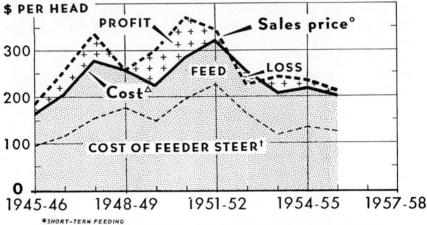

RETURNS IN STEER FEEDING
Costs and Sales Price for Yearling Steers, Corn Belt *

*SHORT-TERM FEEDING
º1,050-LB. CHOICE STEER, CHICAGO, APRIL-JULY, LESS TRANSPORTATION & MARKETING EXPENSE
△NO ALLOWANCE FOR MISC. COSTS OR CREDITS
†AV. FEEDER AND STOCKER STEERS, KANSAS CITY, AUG.-DEC., PLUS TRANSPORTATION

Fig. 39.   Returns in steer feeding. At times the sales price of the finished steer is less than the cost of the feeder and the feed. (U.S.D.A., Agricultural Marketing Service.)

and consequently decrease the cash grain sold. A comparison of grass and grain crop rotations on midwestern farms indicated that grass yielded a greater amount of feed units (corn or corn equivalent) with a lower production cost.

RAISING CALVES OR BUYING FEEDERS ON CORN-BELT FARMS

Investigations have indicated that under normal conditions the average farmer in the corn belt is able to raise calves for feeders about as cheaply as he can buy them and ship them in from adjacent markets. Raising the feeders and maintaining a beef breeding herd will, however:

1. Furnish a home market for a large amount of roughage for which there would be little other use; also for salable crops.

2. Make use of pasture land.

3. Provide employment for labor which at certain seasons of the year may be idle.

4. Provide a use for equipment such as barns and lots.

It is quite evident that the economics of raising feeders on an individual farm should be decided upon the basis of the resources for growing cattle on the farm. There may be years when feeders can be purchased more cheaply than they could be raised, but in those years the feeders are probably not profitable to the ranchman. In order to compete in the farming area, cheap pasture and roughage are needed.

Chapter 8

CATTLE SLAUGHTERING, PROCESSING, AND BY-PRODUCTS

CATTLE SLAUGHTER AND PROCESSING

Meat packing is a misnomer, as there is very little meat packed at the present time. This term derives from the "salting down" or "packing" of meats which dates back to colonial days. In the absence of refrigeration the colonist salted down or barreled meat for the winter season. In 1640 the Civil War in England brought a stop to the trade with the West Indies in which livestock, barreled pork, and beef were exchanged mainly for molasses. The New Englanders absorbed this trade with the West Indies, causing growth in America of cattle and hog production and meat packing for shipment.

The United States Census Bureau defines "Meat Packing Wholesale" as follows. This industry comprises establishments primarily engaged in the slaughter of cattle, hogs, sheep, lambs, calves, and other animals for meat to be sold fresh or to be used on the premises in canning and curing and in making sausage, lard and other products.

THE MEAT-PACKING INDUSTRY

Development of the meat-packing industry

Compared with the present meat-packing industry, pioneer livestock slaughter plants were crude and inefficient. When first established, meat packing was a seasonal industry, for slaughter was done mostly during the winter months. Cincinnati, shortly after 1830, became a leading meat-packing center. It was named "Porkopolis" because it had "perfected the system which packs 15 bushels of corn into a pig and packs that pig into a barrel and sends him over the mountains and over the ocean to feed mankind."

Later, packing plants were established in Chicago and Milwaukee. As the growing of livestock moved westward, the meat-packing industry followed in its wake. Cities on the Missouri and Mississippi Rivers developed into meat-packing centers. These are the river markets; they include South St. Paul, East St. Louis, Sioux City, Omaha, St. Joseph, and Kansas City. Later, other large slaughter points came into being in Denver, Fort Worth, and other cities west of the original river markets. Decentralization of meat packing, or the development of the interior markets, started in the early 1920's. Meat packing has always moved toward areas of livestock production, which tends to minimize livestock shipping losses and to lower costs.

The development of mechanical refrigeration permitted expansion of the industry. Up to the time of the Civil War, meat packing was principally of pork because much of it could be cured. Railroads were responsible for the location of large cattle markets, and refrigerator cars made it possible to move fresh beef some distance from the place of slaughter. The first practical refrigerator car used by western meat packers was designed by G. H. Hammond in 1875. A mechanical refrigeration plant in conjunction with a meat-packing house was used first in Chicago in 1880, and, beginning about 1890, mechanical refrigeration gradually replaced natural refrigeration.

Present status of the meat-packing industry

There are over 3200 livestock slaughtering plants in the United States that have an annual output of more than 300,000 pounds.[1] Livestock is slaughtered in 455 federally inspected plants, 952 non-federally inspected plants, and 1810 local plants. In addition there are numerous "butcher" slaughters that have a volume of less than 300,000 pounds. There are also many non-slaughtering meat-processing plants. In one year the federally inspected plants processed 78 per cent of the live weight of all commercial slaughter. For that year, the federally inspected plants accounted for the following per cent of the commercial slaughter on a live weight basis: 92 per cent for sheep and lambs, 85 per cent for hogs, 76 per cent for cattle, and 59 per cent for calves.

The chief manufacturing industries in the United States were ranked in the census of manufactures as follows, on the basis of the plant value of the products:

[1] *"The Livestock and Meat Situation,"* Agricultural Marketing Service, U.S.D.A., July, 1955.

1. Motor vehicle, bodies, parts, and accessories.
2. Steelworks and rolling-mill products.
3. Meat packing, wholesale.
4. Petroleum refining.
5. Bread and other bakery products.

The total sales of meat-packing companies was 9,439 million dollars in one year.

Modern meat-packing companies

The functions of the meat-packing company in which all of the phases of the business are carried on are as follows:

1. The primary task of transforming cattle, calves, hogs, and sheep into fresh beef, veal, pork, and lamb. This is the fresh-meat service of the packing industry.

2. The production of cured meats, particularly pork products such as ham, bacon, and shoulders. This also includes the production of corned beef and dried beef, as well as barreled pork and beef. This function permits a more uniform spread into consumption of uneven seasonal receipts of slaughter animals. Also, the availability of cured meat adds to the range of food selection for our diets.

Fig. 40. A Modern Meat Packing Plant. The Rath Packing Company, Waterloo, Iowa, an interior packer that slaughters over 3 million head of livestock annually and processes more than 1,000 meat items.

3. The production of manufactured food products. Some of the products from livestock slaughter are altered by a manufacturing process into acceptable food products. This includes such processing as the manufacture of (a) sausage from the blending of various meats with other ingredients; (b) margarine from beef fats blended with vegetable oils and milk; (c) meat products marketed as specialty products in a variety of forms, some of which are canned, such as meat loaf, headcheese, etc.; (d) vegetable products such as lard substitutes, vegetable margarine, salad oils, and cooking oils.

4. The processing of a large number of materials from the edible by-products. Such things as the hearts, livers, kidneys, sweetbreads, tongues, tripe, casings, oleo oil, lard, edible tallow, and gelatin are distributed as food products. A large number of biological materials obtained from livestock slaughter, such as rennin, pepsin, thyroid extract, insulin, and adrenalin are used for medicinal purposes.

5. The recovery and processing of inedible by-products. In this group of materials are the hides used for leather, wool, bones, blood, tankage, greases, soap, glue, and many other.

6. Miscellaneous products such as poultry, butter, eggs, and cheese are now sometimes handled by the large packing companies. These products are handled with meats because of their similarity in general distribution characteristics. Refrigeration and quick distribution are essential in the successful handling of dairy and poultry products as well as meat.

7. Research into new uses and markets for animal products.

8. Development of merchandizing methods and distribution systems for the disposal of the products of the packing plants.

American meat institute

An organization or association of meat packers was first established in 1906. It was later renamed the American Meat Institute and now has a membership of nearly 700 companies. The purpose is to coordinate the interests of those concerned with the American meat-packing industry. The major activities are in three fields;

1. Trade.   Improved business procedures are promoted.

2. Research.   By the application of scientific research in various fields there is continuous improvement in the quality of the industry's methods and products.

3. Education.   By various means the institute informs the public about the livestock and meat industry. The place of meat in the diet and the importance of the meat-producing industry are major considerations in this field.

Cattle slaughter and method of disposition

Retail and home slaughter are important outlets for market cattle and calves. The cattle and calves which are slaughtered by most fairly large packing plants are subjected to federal inspection. The total slaughter of cattle and calves by years is shown in Figure 41. The Meat Inspection Act, which became effective October 1, 1906, pertains to ante-mortem examination and inspection of all cattle and of the meat and meat food products which enter into interstate and foreign commerce. The meat-packing plants may be divided on the basis of their use of federal inspection and the nature of their business, that is, whether wholesale or retail. Following is a classification of cattle and calf slaughter for a recent 10-year period.

CATTLE SLAUGHTER CLASSIFIED
BY NATURE OF BUSINESS

	CATTLE (PER CENT)	CALVES (PER CENT)
Federally inspected, wholesale	69	55
All other wholesale and retail	27	40
Farm	4	5

Meat packing is essentially a wholesale business. More than three fourths of the total cattle slaughtered in the United States are slaughtered by packing plants conducting a wholesale business. Most of the beef and veal handled by such concerns is federally inspected. About 27 per cent of the cattle and 40 per cent of the calves slaughtered are handled by local packing plants which dispose of their products, wholesale and retail, within the state in which they are located. They are under the inspection of the state in which they operate. Also they may have federal inspection and have the diamond-shaped stamp on their meat which means that the meat has been inspected for wholesomeness. These plants account for a considerable portion of the retail slaughter as well. In such cases the meats are distributed through meat shops which are a part of the organization controlling the packing plant.

Farm slaughter is mainly for home consumption, though some meat so derived may enter the meat trade. About 5 per cent of calves and 4 per cent of cattle slaughtered are disposed of by this method.

Shifts have taken place in these various avenues of disposition. Home or farm slaughter is stimulated in times of low cattle prices, because the costs of meat distribution remain quite constant and make up a larger percentage of the cost of the meat to the consumer when slaughter cattle are low priced. There has been an increase in recent years in the slaughter of cattle and calves by wholesale establishments under federal inspection. Retail slaughter and also farm slaughter have declined.

Leading states in meat packing

Based on the plant value of packer products three states rank high. Illinois and Iowa rank first and second; Minnesota is third. This is on the basis of all meat products, not just beef and veal. The importance of the meat-packing business is indicated by the volume of meat production. In the past 10 years the total meat produced in the United States has ranged from 21 to over 25 billion pounds. Beef outranks pork in value of the product at the packing plants.

Centers of cattle and calf slaughter

At most large markets there is a heavy slaughter of cattle, but the markets do not rank the same on receipts and slaughter. The slaughter of cattle and calves at central cattle markets is listed below.

LARGE CENTER OF CATTLE AND CALF SLAUGHTER AT CENTRAL MARKETS

Average number slaughtered per year under federal inspection for the 10-year period 1944–1953 [2]

MARKET	AVERAGE YEARLY SLAUGHTER, THOUSAND HEAD		
	Cattle	Calves	Total
Chicago, Ill.	1,257	356	1,613
Omaha, Neb.	1,056	59	1,115
Kansas City, Mo.	821	260	1,081
South St. Paul, Minn.	741	428	1,169
St. Louis, Ill. and Mo.	667	523	1,190
New York, N. Y. and Jersey City, N. J.	452	489	941
Sioux City, Iowa	480	18	498
Denver, Colo.	347	33	380
All other stations	7,916	3,925	11,841
Total	13,742	5,713	19,455

National meat packers

There are some names which have been landmarks in the meat-packing industry. Philip D. Armour in 1863 started a meat-packing enterprise in partnership with Plankinton at Milwaukee, and established Armour and Co. at Chicago in 1867. Swift & Company had its origin at Barnstable, Mass., where G. F. Swift, Sr., built a slaughterhouse. Later (1875) Mr. Swift moved to Chicago and founded a meat-packing plant (1877), the beginning of Swift & Company.

[2] *Agricultural Statistics,* U.S.D.A., 1954.

CATTLE SLAUGHTER BY CLASSES

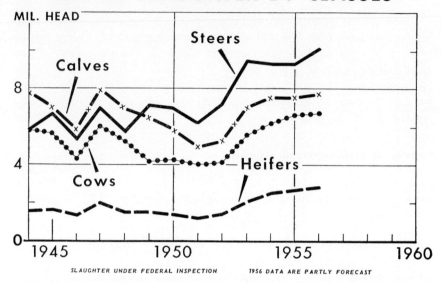

SLAUGHTER UNDER FEDERAL INSPECTION   1956 DATA ARE PARTLY FORECAST

Fig. 41. Cattle Slaughter by Classes. The trend in cattle slaughter has been upward. Steers are the largest and heifers the smallest of the four classes. (U.S.D.A., Agricultural Marketing Service.)

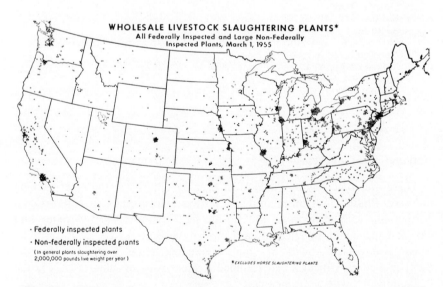

Fig. 42. Wholesale livestock slaughter plants. Slaughtering plants are widely distributed in the United States. (U.S.D.A., Agricultural Marketing Service.)

We have four national packers which are commonly referred to as the "Big Four." They are Swift & Company, Armour and Co., Wilson and Company, and the Cudahy Packing Company. Their combined slaughter comprised 47 per cent of the cattle, 46 per cent of the calves, 41 per cent of the hogs, and 68 per cent of sheep and lambs slaughtered in all wholesale slaughtering establishments in the United States. Three other companies are of considerable importance, particularly because of their pork operations. They are: John Morrell & Company, Geo. A. Hormel & Company, and the Rath Packing Company. Other large meat packers in this country include Oscar Mayer and Company, Cudahy Brothers Company, and Kingan and Company. Plants in which wholesale slaughtering is conducted include those operating under federal inspection and many that do not have such inspection. Most of the plants operated by the national packers are under federal inspection. See Figure 42 for locations of wholesale livestock slaughtering plants.

Central markets as a source of slaughter cattle and calves

Most of the cattle and calves slaughtered by packing plants that have federal inspection are purchased at the public stockyards. For a 10-year period, 61.1 per cent of the calves that were slaughtered under federal inspection came from the public stockyard markets, while 38.9 per cent were secured by the slaughterers from other sources. For cattle older and heavier than calves, the meat packers secured 76.2 per cent of those slaughtered under federal inspection from the central or public stockyard markets, while 23.8 per cent were purchased elsewhere.

The proportion of cattle moving from the farmer or local buyer direct to the meat packer using federal inspection has increased, but the growth of direct marketing has been much greater with hogs. Decentralization of meat packing has been greater in hog slaughter than in cattle slaughter, for the interior packers have made greater inroads into pork packing than into cattle slaughter. Terminal markets have maintained their sales volume of cattle much better than hogs. (See Figure 144.)

With the growth of slaughter by interior packing plants, the meat packers at the terminal markets established buying stations in the livestock-producing areas. These are referred to as "concentration yards."

Seasonal variation in slaughter of cattle

There is some seasonal variation in the slaughter of cattle by classes. (See Figure 43.) Cattle receipts are larger in the fall months, and the slaughter is slightly heavier at that time. However, the movement from the market as feeders and stockers takes the greater portion of the increased

receipts. Cattle slaughter is the lowest in February, March, and April; yet
the pooled cattle slaughter under federal inspection for a 10-year period
for these 3 months is 22.6 per cent of the yearly slaughter, with a fairly even

SEASONALITY IN CATTLE SLAUGHTER BY CLASSES

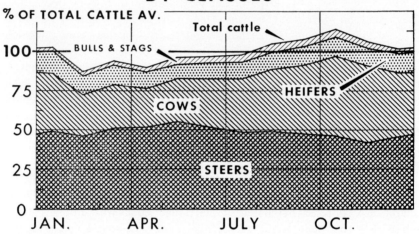

SLAUGHTER UNDER FEDERAL INSPECTION.   NORMAL SEASONAL VARIATION FOR POSTWAR YEARS (1947-53).
RELATIONSHIPS BETWEEN CLASSES ARE 1944-53 AVERAGE.

Fig. 43. Distribution of steers, cows, heifers, bulls and stags slaughtered by
months. Total cattle slaughter is normally greatest in October; the many cows slaughtered in that month are decisive. Steer slaughter is low in the fall because many are
sold as feeders. (U.S.D.A., Agricultural Marketing Service.)

distribution for each of the months. October, November, and December are
the heaviest 3 months in cattle slaughter, and for the 10-year period 27.7
per cent of the cattle were slaughtered in these months. About 46 per cent
were slaughtered the first half of the year and 54 per cent the last half.

Calf slaughter has been more variable than cattle slaughter in the last
few years.

THE SLAUGHTERING PROCESS [3]

In different plants the steps in cattle dressing vary, but in general the
process consists of the following: stunning, shackling, hoisting, sticking,
bleeding, then lowering to the floor for skinning, and completing the dressing while the carcass is being raised.

Prior to slaughter, cattle are handled in such a way as to reduce bruises

[3] *Readings in Packing House Practice*, Part II, *Beef, Mutton and Veal Operations*,
Institute of American Meat Packers, 1925.

to a minimum. Overfeeding and starving are to be avoided. Experience has indicated that normal treatment in all respects yields best results in cattle dressing. Excessive activity or excitement apparently hinder complete bleeding on sticking.

Steps in dressing cattle

Some plants are now using the endless-chain method of dressing. The steps in the conventional method of dressing are:

1. Cattle are driven into small pens for stunning. Electric prods are used at some plants. In any case heavy beating or prodding are reflected in the condition of the carcass. The stunning is done with a blow on the forehead from a light sledge hammer or captive bolt pistol which may have a penetrating bolt or instead a mushroom head which does not penetrate the skull. The side of the knocking pen lifts and the floor drops down so that the stunned animal is rolled out onto the killing floor.

2. The animal is shackled, hoisted, and then stuck and bled. While the animal is in this position the head is skinned and removed.

3. When the animal is lowered to the floor, the shanks are skinned and removed at the knees and the hocks. The hide is then ripped along the median line on the belly and removed from the sides and belly. The breastbone is split by sawing on the center line.

4. Beef hooks are inserted on the gam cord, and the animal is partially raised to a position known as "half hoist." In this position the hide is removed from the shanks, rounds, and rump. The "fell" or elastic tissue known as "facia" is just under the hide and attached to the flesh or meat. In the removal of the hide the fell is left on the carcass. Extreme care must be taken not to cut or score the hide, for this affects its market value. The hide is pulled and beaten off in parts to make the proper separation. In some cases this is done in part mechanically.

5. The carcass is hoisted to an overhead track, where the hide and viscera are removed. The viscera and the carcass are then examined by a United States government inspector, if the plant is under federal inspection.

6. The carcass is split and the tail is removed. The split vertebrae in the back and loin are cut with a scribe saw on the dorsal part and pounded back to give a thicker appearance.

7. The carcass is washed, then dried, and cloths are placed in the large blood vessels to prevent dripping.

8. It is common practice to shroud the better carcasses, that is, wrap them in a sheetlike cloth after washing so they will have a smoother appearance when unshrouded after chilling. Trimming is also an important step which affects the appearance of the carcass.

Slaughter of veal calves

Veal carcasses are usually sold as entire carcasses to meat dealers, and often they are sold with the hide on. In some plants the calves are skinned during the dressing process, and at some plants skinned carcasses are covered with a protective material such as knitted bags.

The advantage of leaving the hide on in the dressing and chilling is that it reduces water loss by evaporation, protects the carcass, and has a bleaching effect. Veal is higher in moisture than other meats.

The endless-chain method of dressing, much like that used in dressing sheep, is used with veal calves. A wheel hoist is used to hoist the shackled calves to the rail. Sticking and bleeding follow, after which the next operation is washing. This process must be complete when the hide is not removed. Following this operation, the dressing proceeds in much the same way as that of cattle.

Kosher slaughter

This method of slaughter differs from the usual procedure in that the cattle or calves are not stunned. The throat is cut with a special type of knife, and the killing is done by a trained man known as the "Shochet." The slaughtering is under the supervision of a Rabbi or a representative of the Rabbinical Board. Two objectives are in mind in this slaughtering method. They are: instant death and rapid, free flow of blood from the animal. There is also kosher inspection of the lungs while dressing, and finally the carcass is marked on the brisket with a cross inside a circle, date of slaughter, and the name of the inspector. The carcass is cut in the evening of the day the animal is slaughtered, and early the next day the wholesale cuts are in the retail shops. Usually beef is cut 36 to 48 hours after slaughter, but kosher beef is broken up into wholesale cuts within 12 hours after slaughter. Rapid chilling for kosher beef is therefore imperative. Calves, sheep and lambs are also kosher slaughtered. (See pages 165 and 166.)

WHOLESALE BEEF AND VEAL

Average live weight and dressing percentage of cattle and calves

In a monthly survey of wholesale slaughters by the U.S.D.A., information is obtainable on the average weight and dressing yield of livestock slaughtered under federal inspection in the United States. For the 8-year period 1947–1955 the range in weight (yearly averages) of cattle slaughtered was from 945 to 992 pounds, and the mean of the yearly averages was 974 pounds. The average dressing yield was 54.6 per cent. Feed conditions as well as the market situation influence the weight to which cattle are fed before they are marketed. When the ratio of feed prices to cattle prices is wide, that is, when feed prices are relatively low and cattle prices high, cattle are fed out to heavier weights.

For the same 8-year period veal calves slaughtered in the United States weighed 215 pounds, with the yearly averages ranging from 206 to 226 pounds. Apparently, heavier calves are now being marketed, since for the preceding decade the average weight was 208 pounds. The average dressing yield for the 8-year period was 55.6 per cent on the basis of dressed with the hide on.

Dressing percentage or carcass yield

Steers that are fat, trim middled, refined in the head, hide, and bone, and of the beef type will dress high. A high yield of carcass is desirable, for carcass usually sells on the wholesale market for twice as much as the purchase price per pound. The weight lost in dressing, which is the source of the by-products, is worth much less per pound than the carcass; some of it is valueless, and it also has a water loss upon processing. In cattle usually 85 to 88 per cent of the income to the meat packer is from the carcass.

The better grades of beef steers have the highest carcass yield, while thin canner cows have low dressing yields. Shrink and fill prior to slaughter, of course, influence yields.

Following are the usually expected average dressing per cents or yields and the usual range for various classes.[4]

ESTIMATED RANGE IN CARCASS YIELD OF CATTLE
AND CALVES BY GRADES

GRADE	ESTIMATED YIELD, PER CENT OF LIVE WEIGHT	GRADE	ESTIMATED YIELD, PER CENT OF LIVE WEIGHT
Steers		Canner Cows	
Prime	61–65	Heavy	42–44
Choice	59–63	Light	40–42
Good	57–60	Common	38–40
Commercial	53–57	Butcher Bulls	
Utility	50–54	Commercial	54–60
Heifers		Utility	51–53
Choice	59–62	Bologna Bulls	
Good	56–58	700 lbs., up	54–56
Commercial	52–55	500–699 lbs.	51–53
Utility	48–52	499 lbs., down	48–60
Butcher Cows		Calves and Vealers *	
Good	57–59	Prime	60–65
Commercial	52–54	Choice	56–62
Utility	47–49	Good	54–58
Cutter Cows		Commercial	50–55
Heavy	44–48	Utility	46–52
Light	43–45	Cull	40–46

* Hides off.

4 From Department of Marketing, American Meat Institute, Sept., 1952.

Of the champions in the carcass competition for steers and heifers at the International Livestock Exposition [5] the highest dressing percentage was made by Bamboo H., an Aberdeen Angus senior yearling steer shown by the Iowa State College that weighed on foot 1,270 pounds and dressed 70 per cent. At a late International the highest dressing carload was a group of 1,139-pound Aberdeen Angus steers shown by J. F. Mommsen & Sons, Miles, Iowa, that dressed 66.6 per cent.

Federal meat inspection [6]

The work [7] of the meat inspection service has been summarized as:

1. Supervision of the sanitation of plants.
2. Inspection of animals before slaughter to eliminate those unfit for food.
3. Careful examination of the head, glands, internal organs, and carcass of each animal immediately after slaughter.
4. Inspection of processing, such as curing, canning, and freezing of meat, and making sausages and similar products.
5. Disposal of condemned material.
6. Supervision of marking and labeling of meat and meat food products.
7. Maintaining laboratories to obtain chemical, bacteriological, pathological, and zoological information needed by inspectors.

Most of the meat entering into interstate and foreign shipment is slaughtered under federal inspection. A round purple stamp on the carcass indicates it has been inspected and passed as wholesome food. (See Figure 44.) The inspectors are trained personnel employed and paid by the federal government. The inspection is maintained at establishments where cattle, sheep, swine, or goats are slaughtered or meat is processed for food purposes if the carcasses or meat products enter in whole or part into interstate or foreign trade. The federal meat inspection laws do not apply to farm slaughter and slaughter by retail butchers and dealers. Retail butchers and dealers are required to obtain certificates of exemption from inspection in order to ship meat and meat food products in interstate or foreign commerce. Also such meat may

Fig. 44. The round stamp is the U.S. Inspection Stamp. The number indicates the establishment. (U.S.D.A., Agricultural Marketing Service.)

[5] Data from *Review and Album,* International Livestock Exposition, Chicago, Ill., 1948.

[6] John R. Mohler, "The Inspection Stamp as a Guide to Wholesome Meat," *Agricultural Information Bulletin No. 92,* U.S.D.A., April, 1949.

[7] *Agricultural Research No. 12,* vol. 4, U.S.D.A., June, 1956.

have an official federal diamond-shaped stamp, which applies to meat of local slaughterers that has been inspected for wholesomeness.

Recently inspection of livestock and meat products was conducted at about 1,200 establishments located in nearly 500 cities and towns.

The inspection prior to slaughter, or ante-mortem, results in three divisions: *condemned,* which are not passed for food; *passed,* which merely means passed on the one examination; and *suspected,* which is used for animals suspected of being affected with disease or conditions that may cause condemnation in whole or part on special post-mortem examination. Of the livestock passed in the ante-mortem examination the majority are passed for food when inspected during slaughter. Some carcasses or parts of carcasses are condemned or considered not fit for human consumption. The main category condemned on foot is "moribund," which includes animals found dead in the pen at the time of inspection. Some calves are condemned for immaturity.

Following are listed, in order of rank, the common causes of condemnation of carcasses in cattle and calves.

1. Septicemia and abscess or pyemia.
2. Pneumonia, pleurisy, enteristis, peritonitis, etc.
3. Immaturity (in calves).
4. Emaciation.
5. Tumors, carcinoma, sarcoma, etc.
6. Tuberculosis.
7. Injuries.

In condemnation of parts, actinomycosis, tumors and abscesses, tuberculosis, and injuries are the common causes.

Meat defined

Flesh used as food is usually referred to as "meat." It is the clean, sound, edible portion of striated muscle of an animal. The official definition of meat of the U.S. Department of Agriculture is as follows:

Meat is the properly dressed flesh derived from cattle, from swine, from sheep, or from goats sufficiently mature and in good health at the time of slaughter, but is restricted to that part of the striated muscle which is skeletal or that which is found in the tongue, in the diaphragm, in the heart, or in the esophagus and does not include that found in the lips, in the snout or in the ears; with or without the accompanying and overlying fat and the portions of the bone, skin, sinew, nerve, and blood vessels which normally accompany the flesh and which may not have been separated from it in the process of dressing it for sale.

It will be noted that this definition restricts the use of the word "meat" to that from cattle, swine, sheep, and goats. When used with reference to other animals it is to be prefixed by kind of animal. For example, we may have horse meat, buffalo meat, etc.

When the designation red is used in connection with meat, it refers to beef, veal, pork, lamb, and mutton, in contrast with poultry meat, chicken, and turkey.

Meat by-products are any clean, sound and properly dressed edible parts other than meat, which have been derived from one or more carcasses of cattle, swine, sheep, or of goats sufficiently mature and in good health at the time of slaughter. Meat by-products from animals other than cattle, swine, sheep, and goats must be designated by the proper prefix.

Disposition of carcass beef

Beef carcasses may be divided into two groups:

1. Beef suitable for "block beef" or to be sold by the retailer "over the block." Such beef is purchased by the retailer in sides, quarters, or the wholesale cuts.

2. Beef unsuited for the retail trade as wholesale cuts and which is handled by the beef-cutting department of the meat-packing plant. This lean beef is boned, and the beef is retailed as boneless cuts, canned, made into sausage, cured, or dried and smoked. There has been an increase in sausage production, which has caused increased demand for boneless cuts. About one fifth of the cattle slaughtered are used for boneless beef and beef trimmings.

Wholesale cuts of beef

Block beef is broken up into cuts desired by the meat retailers. Considerable beef is shipped and delivered to retail shops as sides and quarters. The wholesale or primal beef cuts are available to meat dealers, which permits greater flexibility of distribution. The hindquarter is commonly separated from the front quarter between the twelfth and thirteenth ribs. One rib is left on the hindquarter. About 48 per cent of the carcass weight is in the hindquarter and 52 per cent in the front.

The wholesale cuts of beef are not the same on all markets. In the Chicago style of cutting, for example, the wholesale cut known as the rib has the seven last ribs on the front quarter, and the chuck five, while the New York style of standard wholesale cut of rib includes eight ribs, and the short chuck has but four. On the New York market a wholesale cut known as the "New York full chuck" may have seven, eight, or nine ribs. The beef

BEEF CHART

Wholesale and Retail Cuts

Numerals in circles ◯ refer to wholesale cuts and major subdivisions of such cuts. Letters refer to retail cuts.

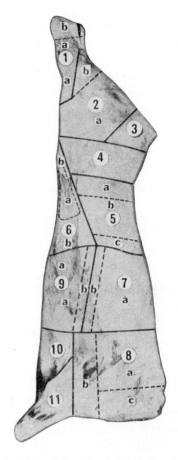

① HIND SHANK
  a. Soup bones
  b. Hock

② ROUND
  a. Round steaks or roasts
  b. Pot roast

③ RUMP
  Roasts or steaks

④ LOIN END
  Sirloin steaks or roasts

⑤ SHORT LOIN
  a. Porterhouse steaks
  b. T-bone steaks
  c. Club or Delmonico steaks

⑥ FLANK
  a. Flank steak
  b. Stew or ground beef

⑦ RIB
  a. Rib roasts or steaks
  b. Short ribs

⑧ CHUCK
  a. Chuck rib roasts or rib steaks
  b. Arm pot roasts or steaks
  c. Stew or ground beef

⑨ PLATE
  a. Stew, ground beef, or boned and rolled pot roasts
  b. Short ribs

⑩ BRISKET
  Stew or boned and rolled pot roasts

⑪ FORE SHANK
  Soup bones or ground beef

YIELDS OF WHOLESALE CUTS AND SUBDIVISIONS
Percentage of Carcass Weight

① to ⑥	HINDQUARTER	48.0%		Kidney knob	3.5%
① to ③	Round and Rump	24.0%		⑥ Flank	3.5%
	① Hind shank	4.0%	⑦ to ⑪	FOREQUARTER	52.0%
	② Buttock	15.5%		⑦ Rib	9.5%
	③ Rump	4.5%		⑧ Chuck	24.5%
④ and ⑤	Full loin inc. suet	20.0%		⑨ Plate	8.0%
	④ Loin end	8.0%		⑩ Brisket	6.0%
	⑤ Short loin	9.0%		⑪ Foreshank	4.0%

Fig. 45. Beef carcass, indicating the wholesale and retail cuts. (U.S.D.A., Agricultural Marketing Service, Livestock Division.)

cuts such as round and rump, loin, rib, and chuck are common on the markets for wholesale beef cuts, but these cuts differ on the various markets in size and shape.

The Chicago style of standard wholesale cuts is more completely discussed in this text. In Figure 45 is a diagram of the regular wholesale cuts of beef, also the retail cuts common for those parts.

Wholesale cuts of veal

The wholesale cuts of veal are usually fewer than for beef carcasses. Also, whole carcasses are used more in the trade than are sides, quarters, or other wholesale cuts. Heavier veal carcasses are divided up more generally than the lighter weight carcasses. Splitting is not so common, and when the two quarters are sold unsplit they are called a "saddle"; for example, there is a hindsaddle and foresaddle.

The common wholesale cuts of the veal carcass are shown in Figure 46.

BY-PRODUCTS FROM CATTLE AND CALF SLAUGHTER

The carcass is referred to as the "primary product," and the other materials yielded from cattle and calf slaughter are known as the "by-products." A packing-house by-product is anything of value, other than dressed meat, produced in the slaughter of animals.

Packing-house by-products include a host of materials. Some plants merely sell their raw slaughter by-products from the killing floor to other companies for manufacture into finished products. Other meat-packing companies process the slaughter by-products rather completely and sell such finished products as soap, glue, etc. Some also manufacture products similar to packing-house by-products, like lard substitutes that are not derived from livestock slaughter.

RETURNS FROM SLAUGHTER BY-PRODUCTS

The returns from the sale of by-products from livestock slaughter are minor compared with the returns from the sale of the carcass. The probable return to the packers from the meat and by-products is as shown below.

Sheep rank first and hogs last in percentage of return from the slaughter by-products. Expressed another way and considering the hide value, sheep, cattle, and calves bring in considerably more return from slaughter by-products than do hogs.

Although it may appear that the by-product income is a minor item when the volume of slaughter is considered, the aggregate return is sizable. The complete recovery and utilization of the packing-house by-products

VEAL CHART

Numerals in circles ○ refer to wholesale cuts. Letters refer to retail cuts.

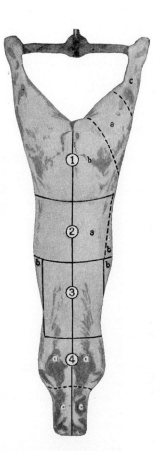

WHOLESALE CUTS

  ① and ② HIND SADDLE
    ① Leg
    ② Loin
  ③ and ④ FORE SADDLE
    ③ Hotel rack
    ④ Shoulder

RETAIL CUTS

  ① LEG
    a. Cutlets
    b. Roast
    c. Stew

  ② LOIN
    a. Loin and kidney chops
    b. Stew

  ③ HOTEL RACK
    Rib chops

  ④ SHOULDER
    (shank and breast not shown)
    a. Roasts
    b. and c. Stew

YIELDS OF WHOLESALE CUTS AND SUBDIVISIONS

Percentage of Carcass Weight

① and ② Hind saddle	49.0%	③ and ④ Fore saddle	51.0%
① Legs	40.0%	③ Hotel rack	8.0%
② Loin	9.0%	④ Shoulder	43.0%

Fig. 46. Veal carcass, indicating the wholesale and retail cuts. (U.S.D.A., Agricultural Marketing Service, Livestock Branch.)

has long been one of the distinctive features of the packing industry, yet with sheep this is less than 20 per cent and with hogs less than 5 per cent of the slaughter income.

PROPORTION OF SLAUGHTER INCOME FROM MEAT,
BY-PRODUCTS, AND HIDE OR PELT [8]

All Figures in Per Cents

	CARCASS MEAT	EDIBLE BY-PRODUCTS	INEDIBLE BY-PRODUCTS	HIDE OR PELT	TOTAL
Cattle	85.2	5.3	1.7	7.8	100
Lambs	74.6	3.0	3.8	18.6	100
Calves	75.6	7.5	1.5	15.4	100
Hogs	96.3 *	2.2	1.5		100

* Includes lard.

Fig. 47. Final inspection of dressed beef by U.S. government inspectors. (Swift & Company.)

BY-PRODUCTS FROM CATTLE SLAUGHTER

Groups of by-products

The by-products are usually divided on the basis of edibility. Some of the edible by-products are meats and often are confused with the principal

[8] *Agri. Res. Bull. 10,* Swift & Company.

product. Included in the edible offal are the heart, liver, and tongue, which are referred to in the trade as "meat specialties," or "fancy meats." The products not used for food are termed "inedible offal." When designated as "edible" all of the ingredients are clean, wholesome, and edible. If federally inspected, the meat and meat products are from animals that have been inspected and passed as fit for food. Edible materials are suitable for human food, the quality of the ingredients is acceptable, and so is the manufacturing and handling.

There is also the group of primary by-products, such as blood, hides, and glands, which may be sold as such, and secondary or manufactured by-products such as glue, gelatin and casings.

The following will be recognized as the primary by-products from livestock slaughter, or materials commonly processed further into manufactured by-products:

Blood	Fats	Stomachs
Hides	Intestines	Bladders
Skins	Glands	Eyes
Hoofs	Livers	Embryos
Horns	Spinal cords	Lungs
Dewclaws	Bile	Gullets
Hair	Gallstones	Heart arteries
Wool	Sinews	Gall bags
Bones	Genitals	Spleens
		Inedible trimmings

Slaughter by-products combined for utilization

Of the above primary by-products there is a wide range of manufactured products as indicated below. These are common to all slaughter animals.[9]

Blood
    Whole blood (Leather
      finishing & protective colloids) $\longrightarrow$ Dried blood $\begin{cases} \text{Plywood adhesive} \\ \text{Livestock feeds} \\ \text{Protective colloids} \end{cases}$
    Hemoglobin
    Plasma $\longrightarrow$ Blood albumen (Thermosetting adhesives)
               (Textile printing & dyeing)

Bones
    Marrow (Pharmaceuticals)
    Dried bones (Novelties)
    Bonemeals $\longrightarrow$
    Protein (Ossein)
      Ossein gelatin
        (See pork skins)

      Bone meal feeds (Livestock & poultry feeds)
      Bone meal fertilizers
      Special bone meals
           Calcium phosphates
           Bone for water treatment
           Copper moulds

[9] H. H. Young, "By-Products of the Meat-Packing Industry," *Chemical and Engineering News,* American Chemical Society, vol. 20, p. 1660, Dec., 1942.

Bone glue
(Dry, liquid & flexible glues)
Neatsfoot oil (from shins & knuckles) ⟶ Leather dressing
Tallow
↕
Fats
Tallows (Beef, lamb & veal) ⟶ Sulfated tallows (Textile & leather
finishing)
Greases (Pork) ⇄ Stearine ⟶ Soap   Insecticides, weed
Lard (Edible) ⟶ Grease oil (Textile lubrica-   killers
tion)   Lubricants, candles
(Metal cutting)   Cutting oils, oil for
Fatty alcohols (Lubricants)   (Burning oil)   Metal working &
(Detergents)   polishes
—————————————⟶ Soap ⟶ Fatty acids ⟨ Detergents, wetting
Fats   agents
Cosmetics   Fine chemicals
Pharmaceuticals   Amides, alcohols
Anti-freeze   Amines, esters
Glycerine —————⟶ ⟨ Nitroglycerine   Acid chlorides
↓   (Powder & explosives)   Nitrites
Trimethylene glycol   Plastics (Glyptal resins)
↓   Plasticizers
(Hectographs, printer rollers, cellophane)

Cyclopropane
Monoglycerides
(Emulsifying agents)
Gallstones (of value to Orientals—reasons unknown)
Bile ⟶ Bile acid pharmaceuticals (Glycocholic, taurocholic, dehycrecholic &
desoxycholic acids)

Wash waters (Effluent) ⎫
Cook waters (Stick)   ⎬ ⟶ Fat and protein concentrates (Poultry & live-
⎭   stock feeds)
Paunch manure ⟶ Waste

BY-PRODUCTS FROM CATTLE AND CALVES

Blood   (See composite page 139)
Hides
Trimmings ⟶ Glue stock ⟶ Hide glue
Cowhides ⎫
Bullhides ⎬ ⟶ Leather
Kipskins ⎭

Hoofs, horns, ⎫   ⎧ Protective colloids
dewclaws   ⎬ ⟶ Keratin meals ⟶ ⎨ Plaster retarder
⎭   ⎩ Fertilizer

Hair   (Felting)
      Earhair ⟶ "Camels" hair brushes
      Tail switches ⟶ Curled hair
Bones   (See composite page 139)
Fat

   Caul
   Ruffle   } Edible
   Brisket   tallow | Oleo oil →   { Candy / Margarine / Baking
   Kidney
   Trimmings } Oleo
   Skimmings } Stock → | Oleo
                         Stearine   Margarine
                         ⟶ Compound shortenings

Weasands
Middles
Rounds   } Sausage casings
Bungs
Bladders
Glands
   Pancreas
   Pituitary
   Thyroid
   Parathyroid
   Suprarenal
   Pineal   Pharmaceutical
   Ovaries   preparations
   Testes
Liver
Spinal cords
          Cholesterol
          Sphingomyelin
Gall bag
      Gallstones   (See composite page 140)
      Bile
Sinews } ⟶ Hide glue   Technical gelatin
Pizzles }   stock ⟶ High test glue
Grout   Tallow ⟶ (See composite page 140)
Rennet   Stick
Liver   Tankage
Eyes
Lungs
Gullet
Heart artery
Gall bag
Spleen   Poultry   }
Peck   ⟶ Livestock } Feeds
Genitals   Special   }
Paunch
Inedible trimmings

Calves yield the above by-products plus fine leathers and gelatin from calf-skins and rennet for cheese manufacture.

Yield of various products

The main by-products from cattle slaughter yield approximately as indicated below for an average steer.

WEIGHT (BY PER CENT) OF VARIOUS STEER PRODUCTS [10]

	OF GREEN PRODUCT	OF FINISHED PRODUCT TO LIVE STEER
Beef	55.6	54.3
By-products		
Hides	7.2	5.9
Fats	5.0	3.3
Head	3.4	2.2
Feet	1.5	1.1
Blood	3.8	0.7
Casings	1.2	0.8
Miscellaneous	5.4	3.2
Valueless materials	10.1	10.1
Shrinkage	6.8	6.8
Additional shrinkage through processing		11.6
	100.0	100.6

It will be noted that there is further shrinkage of the by-products in processing, so that of the 45 pounds of by-product yielded from 100 pounds of live animal 18.4 pounds is shrinkage or weight loss. Likewise 10.1 pounds of valueless material is yielded. The salable by-products from 100 pounds of slaughter animal weigh 17.2 pounds. Thus a 1,000-pound steer would yield 172 pounds of by-products.

Value of by-products equal to processing cost

In a comparison of the prices of live cattle and beef carcasses of comparable grade, it will be noted that the wholesale value of the carcass is about equal to the cost of the animal on foot. The returns to the packer from the sale of the by-products will cover the operating market expense and the profit. The beef steer, then, will bring on the market about what the carcass will return to the slaughterer. A direct relationship exists between wholesale prices of meats and cattle prices.

By-products vary markedly in price. At times they may be worth more than the cost of slaughtering and dressing the beef animal. Then the meat packer can sell the carcass for the cost of the animal, and make a profit.

[10] Rudolf A. Clemen, *By-Products in the Packing Industry,* p. 9. University of Chicago Press, Chicago, Ill., 1927.

In recent years the by-product credit [11] has been $2.52 for 100 pounds live weight of U.S. grade Choice cattle that cost the packer $27.47 per 100 pounds. During this same period the carcass wholesale value per 100

Fig. 48.   Converting sides of beef into the wholesale cuts desired by the retail dealers. (Swift & Company.)

pounds was $46.47. If the carcass yield was 59 per cent then the return from the sale of the carcass would bring in less than the cost of the steer.

Two factors affect the relation between livestock prices and meat prices: the cost of processing and the value of the by-products. The cost of meat to the consumer also includes all costs involved after the meat leaves the packing plant. (See page 173.) A lowered return for by-products may be an important factor in decreasing livestock prices.[12]

Two of the by-products from cattle, hides and fats, merit further discussion because of their value.

[11] "Beef Marketing Margins and Costs." *Misc. Pub. No. 710,* U.S.D.A., Feb., 1956.
[12] "The Current By-Product Situation," *Monthly Letter to Animal Husbandmen,* Armour Livestock Bur., Vol. 12, No. 12, March, 1932.

Fig. 49. Meat products in the refrigerated room being prepared for shipment. (Swift & Company.)

Cattle and calf hides

Hides are the most valuable of the cattle by-products. In heavy steers of high quality the hide is usually 9 per cent of the total value of the live steer. The hides of low-grade cows, which have a lower carcass yield and a carcass of lower value, may be worth 15 per cent of the total value. As calf skins are of high value because they are used for the highest quality leather, they comprise 20 per cent of the value of the calf on foot.[13]

In recent years hides have declined in relation to the price of cattle and for the past decade they have been worth approximately the same per pound as steers on foot.

Some of the factors related to the price of hides are the place of removal (packer or country), age, sex, and weight of the cattle from which they are derived, the presence of brands, and the method of cure. Hides are sold by weight, usually, and the heavier hides are more desirable. Packer hides, because they are uniformly removed, properly handled and graded, and available in larger lots, bring higher prices than country hides.

Hides from cattle infested with ox warbles may be of lower value be-

---

[13] "Hides and Leather as Cattle By-Products," *Monthly Letter to Animal Husbandmen,* Armour Livestock Bur., Vol. 15, No. 4, January–March, 1937.

cause of grub holes. These are more prevalent in the spring of the year. If five or more grub holes are found in a hide, the hides are discounted 1 per cent per pound. This grubbing privilege of the buyer lasts from November 1 to May 31. Hides soiled with manure or other dirt are also reduced in price, as are hides from kosher-killed cattle (because of the large throat cut). Cut, scored, or damaged hides are likewise sold at lower prices.

Some of the important classes of cattle hides were of the following average price at Chicago for the period 1951 to 1955, inclusive.[14]

PACKER HIDES	AVERAGE PRICE, ϕ/LB., CHICAGO
Steers	
Heavy Natives	16.89
Heavy Texas	14.90
Butt Branded	14.85
Colorados	14.14
Cows	
Heavy Natives	17.71
Light Native	19.59
Branded	16.43
Bull	
Native	12.65
Branded	11.65

Hide price history and seasonal variation [15]

The trend of hide prices was moderately upward from the beginning of this century to the outbreak of World War I. Inflation and deflation following the war caused violent fluctuations in hide prices. Seasonal variation occurs mainly because of seasonal variation in quality. From December to April hide prices decline, for winter-yielded hides are of lower quality because of long hair, dirt, and grub holes. From April to November hide prices move upward, in spite of greater supplies, because of improved quality.

Hides and skins are of three kinds: (1) hides from mature animals, (2) kips, skins from immature or undersized animals, which range from 15 to 25 pounds cured weight, (3) calf skins, from young calves, which weigh 15 pounds. Differences in price for the various grades are due to quantities of each grade available and the requirements of consumers.

Beef fats

The various fat products which arise from the processing of beef fats have been indicated previously. This processing involves refining, bleach-

---

[14] *Livestock Market News Statistics,* Agricultural Marketing Service, U.S.D.A., 1956.

[15] "Hide Prices, the Tariff and Marketing Methods," *Monthly Letter to Animal Husbandmen,* Armour and Co., Vol. 7, No. 5, August, 1926.

ing, and deodorizing. A finished product results that may be either edible or nonedible. The oleo oil and stearine are prominent fat by-products from cattle.

PROFITS TO MEAT PACKERS

The net return to packing plants conducting slaughtering operations is relatively low. Meat packing is a highly competitive business. There is competition, first, in the buying of livestock, and second, in the sale of meats and meat products. More than a thousand meat packers in the United States compete with one another, as well as with local butchers, custom slaughtering, and home butchering, in providing consumers with meat. The extent of this competition is indicated by the distribution of slaughter. (See page 125.) Most of the packing operations are comparatively simple, and restrictive patents do not curtail competition in meat processing. Consequently, new packers can easily enter the field. It is also imperative that the successful packer handle a large volume of product at a low cost per unit. That such is the case is indicated by a survey of data from the United States Department of Agriculture by the Institute of Meat Packers.[16] The net worth, sales, and profits of companies conducting slaughtering operations for the period 1945–1954 inclusive were averaged. The number of plants from which information was obtained was variable from year to year. It was found that the net earnings for the period were:

1. $.009 for each dollar of total sales.
2. $.25 for each 100 pounds of livestock.
3. $.40 for each 100 pounds of dressed meat.
4. 8.5 per cent of the net worth.

The slaughtering of farm animals in modern meat-packing plants under the factory system is highly efficient and therefore economical. Each worker has but one specialized step to perform in the process of dressing, and skill in performance of that duty is soon acquired. For the most part, the carcasses are moved to the workers by conveyers, and the various steps are standardized so that the entire process is swift, efficient, and economical.

There is much cyclical fluctuation in the production of livestock, but, since the cycles are not of the same duration, it is seldom that low production in two kinds of livestock occurs at the same time. The volume of meat packing is relatively stable. Even though production of meat animals remains fairly uniform, profits to meat packers fluctuate rather violently. Profits are high when prices are high or rising and low when prices are falling.

[16] *Financial Results of the Meat Packing Industry,* American Meat Institute, Chicago, Ill., 1955.

Chapter 9

MARKET CLASSIFICATION
OF DRESSED BEEF AND VEAL

CLASSIFICATION OF BEEF AND VEAL

To facilitate trade in dressed beef, the carcasses or wholesale cuts are divided into groups with similar characteristics. Within each group or lot there is uniformity in the various features related to the market value of the beef. As no two carcasses are identical, the limits of each group are arbitrary; hence differences in grading occur. The classes are the larger divisions, and these are subdivided into grades which include units which sell at about the same price per pound. In some classes there are subclasses, which are the weight divisions. Although the carcasses or wholesale cuts are classed and graded, the entire process is commonly referred to as "grading."

By the use of classes and grades, beef is divided into lots for trade which includes carcasses, or wholesale cuts, of similar value. The class and grade convey to the prospective buyer rather definite qualifications. A market quotation of beef given for a specific class and grade has a definite meaning to one familiar with the terms of the trade. It can be readily seen that a buyer can purchase beef by class and grade, without inspection, and know approximately what he will receive.

FRESH BEEF

The fresh beef entering into regular channels of trade is either "fresh chilled" or "fresh frozen." These terms refer to the general method of handling rather than to actual differences in the beef. About ¾ of our beef is sold fresh; the balance is sold as processed meat. Fresh chilled beef is held at temperatures ranging from 34° to 38°F for from 24 to 36 hours. Usually, soon after it is chilled it is moved into the retail trade. Under ordinary refrigeration it may be "aged" from 2 to 6 weeks or longer. Changes take place in the meat when so held which increase the palatability. A recent development is aging at higher temperatures with control of bacterial growth; this hastens the process.[1] Only the better grades are aged, because finish is necessary to retain soundness during aging and because consumers of the better grades are willing to pay for the increased palatability gained by aging.

Fresh frozen beef has been subjected to a temperature of —10° to —20°F, frozen solid, and stored at O°F. Such meat can be held for indefinite periods if kept frozen. Beef stored in frozen condition for 15 months showed slight but definite deterioration in quality. The bulk of export beef is handled in this fashion. Consumers of beef in the United States prefer "fresh chilled" beef, and it has been estimated that 97 per cent of the fresh beef sold is so handled.

BASIS FOR GROUPING CARCASSES

The main features which form the basis for grouping of market beef are quality, conformation, and finish. Only sound and wholesome beef is subject to grading. Diseased, bruised, or partially decomposed meat is "off grade." Definitions and brief descriptions of each of these terms, adapted from U.S. Department of Agriculture publications, follow.

Quality. Quality is a characteristic of the flesh and the fat included therein. It pertains primarily to the thickness, firmness, and strength of both the muscle fiber and the connective tissue. It also involves the amount, consistency, and character of the juice or extractives which surround and permeate the muscle fiber and connective tissue. It is strongly influenced by marbling. Color does not determine quality; however, like finish it serves as an excellent index to quality.

The best quality in beef implies full, well-developed, firm muscular tissue or flesh, with a minimum of strength in fiber and connective tissue. The best beef possesses a high proportion of juice to dry fiber, but this moisture is of such consistency that the flesh when chilled remains firm and resilient. There are also liberal deposits of fat between the muscle fibers, giving the cut surface a streaked or marbled appearance. This fat, together

---

[1] The "Tenderay Process," developed by M. D. Coulter at the Mellon Institute of Industrial Research, is used to age beef in 2 or 3 days. The beef is held at a temperature of 60°F and humidity of 90 per cent in the presence of sterilamps, which inhibit mold and bacterial growth. *Annual Meat Packers Guide, 1940,* Davis Publications, Chicago, Ill.

with the juice or extractives, gives the meat juiciness and flavor. The cut surface of excellent beef has fine grain and is smooth and velvety to sight and touch. The color is a light or cherry red.[2] The cut surface also presents a sheen or reflection not apparent in beef of lower quality. This is due to the fine grain of the meat, the consistency of the juice, and the oil of the fat which gives a smooth surface that reflects light much better than the relatively dry, or watery, coarse fiber of poorer quality beef.

Low quality in beef involves the opposite of most of the good characteristics. Poor beef is usually of dark red color, because the muscle has been subjected to prolonged, vigorous exercise and has therefore had a relatively large blood supply. For the same reasons the muscles are made up of strong, tough fibers, and the connective tissues are comparatively thick and tendinous. The amount of juice is small or it is thin and watery. There is no marbling. As a result the meat is stringy, tough, and inferior in flavor. The ratio of muscle to connective tissue is relatively low, as is also the ratio of flesh to bone. The grain is coarse, and the general appearance is watery or fibrous.

The quality of beef depends on a number of factors, of which breeding and feed are among the most important. Sex and age likewise have an important bearing on the quality of beef.

Quality determines the palatability of the meat and the ease with which it can be prepared for human consumption. Quality is the most important factor in determining grade of beef.

Determination of quality in beef.   Quality is rather difficult to determine, for it pertains chiefly to the inner or concealed parts of the carcass, examination of which requires more than superficial inspection.

To determine quality with exactness it is necessary to have a cut surface, or cross section, exposed to view. There is such close relationship between conformation, finish, and quality that the beef grader can nearly always depend on a high degree of quality where the degree of the other two factors is high.

Quality is indicated to the beef grader by the color, texture, grain, and degree of marbling of the beef and also by the color and character of the chine and breastbone as well as by the age and origin of the cattle considered.

[2] The problem of dark-cutting beef has been studied by the National Livestock and Meat Board. In 4 years 1,742 club calf carcasses were studied. The dark cutters were successively less each year. About 4.4 per cent of the calves in the junior livestock feeding show of the International were dark cutters, and in addition 8.5 per cent were classed as shady cutters for the 4-year period, 1938 to 1941. Low muscle sugar, lower glycogen, and high pH (low acid) was characteristic of the dark cutter. Observation indicates that inadequate feeding and exposure to cold weather or "chilling" were contributing factors to dark-cutting beef. Calves cutting lightest in color had received a higher ratio of grain to protein supplement than those which were "off color." *Twenty-sixth Annual Report,* National Livestock and Meat Board, 1948–1949.

Conformation

The term "conformation" covers the general build, form, shape, contour, or outline of carcass, side, or cut.

The best conformation involves short shanks and necks, deep plump rounds, thick full loins, well-fleshed ribs, and a thickness of flank commensurate with the depth of barrel and chest cavity. Carcasses with poor conformation are typified by angularity in general outline, prominent hip- and shoulder bones, long thin necks, shanks, and rounds, shallow loins, and a decided lack of symmetry in the carcass or side.

The conformation or form is dependent on the skeleton, the depth of flesh, and the thickness and distribution of external fat. Conformation is largely a matter of breeding, although feed and care have an important influence. Conformation has much to do with determining the relative attractiveness of the carcass or side. Its chief significance lies in the fact that it indicates the ratio between meat and bone and also the ratio between the more desirable and higher priced cuts, such as rounds and loins, and the so-called "coarser" or low-priced cuts, such as chucks and plates.

Finish

The term "finish" refers to the amount, color, character, and distribution of exterior, interior, intermuscular, and intramuscular fat.

The best finish involves a smooth, even covering of brittle, flaky, white fat over most of the exterior surface of the carcass, averaging not more than ¾ inch thick over the top of the loin and ribs, and an even, though much thinner, covering of flaky white fat on the interior surface of the ribs; also heavy, but not excessively "bunchy" or wasty deposits of white fat over the kidneys, in the crotch, and in the chest cavity. It also involves relatively heavy deposits of fat between the larger muscles and a liberal distribution of fat along the connective tissues and between the muscle fibers. This latter characteristic gives the cut surface a streaked appearance and is known as "marbling." In a highly finished carcass there is a projection of fat out between the split chine bones, a liberal "overflow" of fat over the middle of the ribs, and a marked intermingling of fat with the lean (feathering) between the ribs. The rounds, shanks, neck, and belly are the last portions of the anatomy to be covered with fat; hence, generally speaking and with due regard for the maximum depth over the hips, loins, and rumps, the more extensive the distribution of fat over these surfaces the higher the finish.

Other factors

Many other factors are involved in grading beef, and consequently many other terms are used in describing and differentiating the various grades. These are all merely subdivisions of the three factors already named and described.

Age, for example, frequently has much to do with indicating the grade of a carcass, but age in itself has no bearing on grade, except as it affects conformation, finish, and quality. Similarly, fat is always considered in grading meat, but fat is one of the elements which go to make up quality and finish, and naturally contributes to conformation. The same is true of such secondary factors as color, grain, marbling, and thickness of flesh. All either are included as factors under one or another of the three main characteristics or serve merely as indexes of conformation, quality, or finish.

MALE AND FEMALE BEEF CARCASSES COMPARED

Male carcasses may be distinguished from female carcasses by the following characteristics:

1. Larger size.
2. Presence of cod fat in steers and stags, and also the absence of an udder.
3. Plump, heavy rounds and loins.
4. Heavier, more muscular shoulders.
5. Shorter, thicker necks.
6. Larger, heavier bones and knee joints.
7. Larger proportion of lean meat to total weight.
8. Less fat, especially in the kidney knob and on the rump.
9. Tendinous ring near the posterior point of the aitch- or pelvic bone.
10. Less distance between the aitchbone and the tail root and less distance between the posterior tips of the aitchbone. In other words, the pelvic opening is smaller in male carcasses.

In carcasses from very young cattle there is little or no difference between the sexes; in fact, it is not until the approach of maturity that sex distinction becomes manifest in the various features of the carcass.

AGE GROUPS OF BEEF CARCASSES

There are four groups of beef carcasses based upon age. These are:

1. Mature beef.
2. Yearling beef.

3. Calf beef.
4. Veal.

There is no sharp line of distinction between the groups; in fact, the first two are commonly not separated. The groups have fairly clear characteristics in the middle of each range, but borderline cases exist and the dividing lines between veal and calf, calf and yearling, and yearling and mature beef are not too clearly defined.

Determination of age in the carcass

The age of the animal yielding the carcass may be approximated from the color and flintiness of the bones. Bones of younger cattle are softer, more porous, and more red in color, whereas bones of older cattle are flinty and white. In younger cattle there is more cartilage and less bone. On the carcasses of young beeves, small buttonlike cartilages on the dorsal part of the vertebrae are evident when the carcass is split.

MARKET CLASSES AND GRADES OF DRESSED
BEEF AND VEAL

A discussion of the market classes and grades of each group follows, along with a somewhat detailed description of some of the groups.

SEX GROUPS OF BEEF CARCASSES AND CUTS

The sex groups of beef are steer, heifer, cow, bull, and stag. Actually, the sex distinction formerly made in beef grading is no longer made except that carcasses from bulls and stags are placed in separate classes. Steer carcasses, because of their superior properties, are placed in higher grades and cow carcasses go in lower grades.

The sex groups of beef described

Steer beef. In conjunction with the characteristics typical of the male, the cod fat identifies the steer carcass. Carcasses of steers are of higher quality than those of stags and bulls and are superior in conformation and finish.

Heifer beef. Heifer beef ranks next to steer beef in quality, conformation, and finish. To qualify for this class the individual must be beyond the veal or calf stages and must neither be far advanced in pregnancy nor have produced a calf. The compact form, less prominent hips, less spread in the ribs and loin, and greater curvature of the aitchbone and pelvic arch distinguish the heifer from the cow carcass. Also, the udder is removed from the cow carcass. In fatness there may be some difference, for there is usually less on a heifer carcass and it is more uniformly distributed.

Cow beef.   In quality and finish cow beef ranks below steer or heifer beef but above bull or stag beef. In conformation, however, cow carcasses are inferior to all other market classes. Females that have produced one or more calves or are heavy with calf at the time of slaughter are classed as cows. Angular conformation, flat loins, light rounds, prominent hips, arched ribs, and thin flesh typify the cow carcass. When the carcass is fat, as it usually is, the fat is uneven in distribution, of yellow tinge, and oily in appearance.

Bull and stag beef.   A male bovine that has reached sexual maturity is the source of bull beef. Bull carcasses are of large size, heavily muscled, dark in color, and usually quite devoid of fat. Heavy front quarters and a short, thick, crested neck are typical of the bull carcass. The male carcass features are manifest, but there is no cod fat as in the steers, and the color is very dark red and may have a bluish cast. Most of this beef does not enter the fresh-beef trade but is disposed of for sausage and dried beef.

Males castrated after reaching sexual maturity are termed "stags" and yield stag carcasses. There is within this class great variation, related to age of castration. If the animal was castrated when young, the carcass approximates steer or heifer carcasses in conformation, quality, and finish. However, if castration was postponed until the secondary characteristics were well developed, the carcass is quite similar to that of a bull.

GRADING BEEF

It is obvious that all beef within a class is not the same in value. Further separation of the carcass classes is accomplished by using grades. There are eight standard grades of beef: prime, choice, good, standard, commercial, utility, cutter, and canner. All of the grades are used for steers and heifers; the lower grades exclusive of standard are used for cows, bulls, and stags.

Beef grades defined

Steer, heifer, and cow carcasses are graded together on the market, that is, without respect to sex or sex condition and wholly upon their characteristics as beef. Bull and stag beef carcasses are placed in separate classes for grading. When beef of these classes is identified as to grade, the class, either bull or stag, is also designated. Thus we have three class groups of beef carcasses: (1) steer, heifer, and cow; (2) bull; and (3) stag. Grades in the various classes are not comparable in quality. In other words, the grade "good" is not the same quality in all classes.

The official United States standards for grades of carcass beef and the specifications for each grade are changed from time to time as experience gained in their use indicates that modification is desirable. A recent change was the dividing of the commercial grade. The younger cattle carcasses formerly in that grade are now known as standard. The commercial grade now is for carcasses of cattle over 48 months old.

It is obvious that carcasses may vary considerably in the general grade factors—conformation, finish and quality—carcasses in a given grade will show a range in the grade factors. For interpretation of standards the U.S.D.A. Agricultural Marketing Service uses color photographs illustrating combinations of characteristics which qualify carcasses for the lower limits of each grade.

Beef grading, like the grading of any meat or meat product, is far from being exact. There are no natural divisions which specifically distinguish one grade from another; rather there is a continuous range from the top to the bottom. Also, since various characteristics are considered in grading numerous combinations are possible. Further, these characteristics are now estimated subjectively, and some are incapable of being measured objectively. Consequently efforts are being made to improve our methods for measuring the quality characteristics of meat.

Shown below is a tabulation of the dressed beef market classes and grades.

STANDARD MARKET CLASSES AND GRADES FOR DRESSED BEEF

CLASS	GRADE	GRADE
Steer, heifer	Prime	Choice
and cow *	Choice	Good
Bull	Good	Commercial
Stag	Standard	Utility
	Commercial	Cutter
	Utility	Canner
	Cutter	
	Canner	

* Beef from mature animals is not eligible for the top 4 grades.

The specifications for the official United States standards for grades of carcass beef describe the characters generally representative of the midpoint of each grade.

A description of the beef included in two grades—prime and cutter adapted from the "Official United States Standards for Grades of Carcass Beef" [3] follows.

[3] "Official United States Standards for Grades of Carcass Beef," *Service and Regulatory Announcement No. 99*, U.S.D.A., June, 1926. Amendment No. 1, July, 1939. Amended December, 1947. Amended June, 1956.

Prime.   Prime grade beef carcasses and wholesale cuts are blocky and compact and very thickly fleshed throughout. Loins and ribs are thick and full. The rounds are plump and the plumpness extends well down toward the hocks. The chucks are thick and the necks and shanks short. The fat covering is fairly smooth and uniformly distributed over the exterior surface of the carcass. The interior fat is abundant in the pelvic cavity and over the kidney. The protrusion of fat between the chine bones is liberal and the overflow of fat over the inside of the ribs is abundant and fairly evenly distributed. The intermingling of fat with the lean in evidence between the ribs, called "feathering," is extensive. Both the interior and exterior fats are firm, brittle, and somewhat waxy, but the interior fat may be slightly wavy or rough. The cut surface of the rib eye muscle is firm and has a smooth, velvety appearance. It has abundant marbling and the marbling is extensive, especially in the heavier carcasses. The color may range from a pale red to a deep blood red but shall be uniform and bright. The chine bones are usually soft and red, terminating in soft, pearly white cartilages.

Carcasses showing evidence of maximum maturity permitted in the Prime grade have chine bones tinged with white and cartilages on the end of the chine bones are slightly ossified. Carcasses must also be symmetrical and uniform in contour, and the rib eye muscle must be fine in texture.

Regardless of the extent to which other grade factors may exceed the minimum requirements for the grade, a carcass must have certain evidences of quality to be eligible for the Prime grade. The cut surface of the muscle must be firm, fine in texture, and bright in color. Slightly abundant marbling must be evident in the rib eye muscle of carcasses, with soft, red chine bones terminating in soft pearly white cartilages. Progressively more marbling is required in carcasses with evidences of more advanced maturity. Carcasses which are only moderately compact and blocky with only moderately plump rounds and moderately thick fleshing may meet the minimum requirements for the Prime grade provided they have finish and evidences of quality equivalent to the midpoint of the Prime grade. (See Figures 50 and 51.)

Only beef produced from steers or heifers will qualify for the Prime grade.

Descriptions of the grades choice, good, standard, commercial, and utility are omitted here. See the Official Standards.

Cutter.   Cutter grade beef carcasses and wholesale cuts may be very rangy, angular, and irregular in conformation and very thinly fleshed throughout. The loins and ribs are very flat, thin, and shallow. The rounds are very long, flat, and tapering. The chucks are very flat, thin, and shallow.

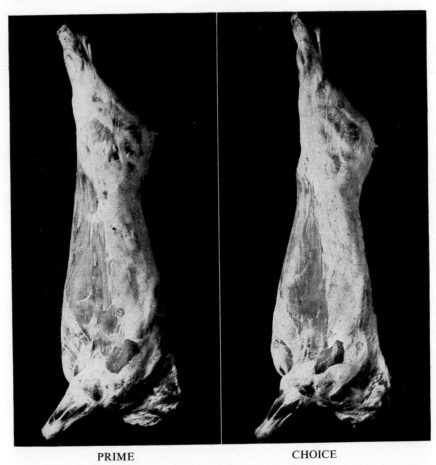

PRIME   CHOICE

Fig. 50. Sides of beef representive of the grades Prime and Choice. A ribbon grade stamp is placed by a government grader on all the principal wholesale cuts. (U.S.D.A., Agricultural Marketing Service.)

The neck and shanks are very long and tapering. The hip and shoulder joints are very prominent. The degree of exterior fat covering may vary from a very thin covering that is confined almost entirely to the ribs and loins in the beef produced from younger cattle to a thin, more extensive covering in the beef produced from mature cattle. The interior fat is confined largely to the pelvic cavity and the kidney and may vary from a very small quantity, if any, in these parts in beef produced from younger cattle to a limited quantity in that produced from mature cattle. The cut surface of the lean muscle shows no marbling, is coarse, and is usually soft and watery. The color may be two-toned or shady and usually ranges from a slightly dark red to a very dark red. The bone is usually hard and white.

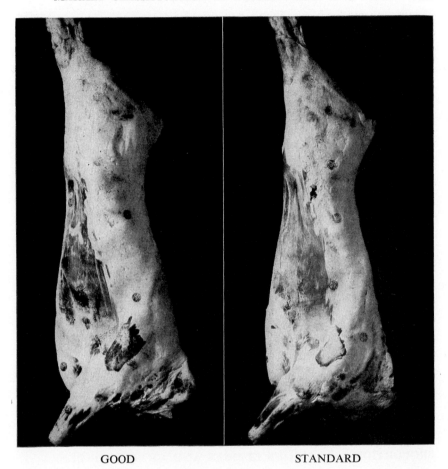

GOOD   STANDARD

Fig. 51. Sides of beef representive of the grades Good and Standard. A ribbon grade stamp is placed by a government grader on all the principal wholesale cuts. (U.S.D.A., Agricultural Marketing Service.)

The Cutter grade of beef may be produced from steers, heifers, and cows. That produced from cows constitutes a relatively large percentage of the beef eligible for this grade. A lower grade, Canner, is described in the Official Standards.

Objective grade specifications

Grades based upon objective measurements rather than upon descriptions in subjective terms would lead to greater accuracy in evaluating grade differences. Studies have been made to develop measurements that could be applied to beef carcass grading. In correlating various measurements with grade, it was found that the measurement most highly correlated to grade was thickness of fat over the longissimus dorsi (eye) muscle between the 12th and 13th ribs exposed when the carcass was ribbed down.[4] Carcass length and carcass weight in that order were related to grade but less closely.

CARCASS GRADES AND FATNESS

The higher grades of carcasses are fatter than those of lower grades. The relationship of finish to grade is illustrated from the following data on the average physical composition of various grades of steer carcasses. This study, made by the U.S. Department of Agriculture, covered data from 71 cattle of the final feed-lot weight of 557 to 941 pounds.[5]

AVERAGE PHYSICAL COMPOSITION OF BEEF STEER CARCASSES

	CHOICE	GOOD	COMMERCIAL	UTILITY
Average final feed lot weight	879	880	903	793
Average chilled carcass weight	523	512	520	436
Percentage of carcass in				
Separable fat	31	24	20	15
Separable lean	53	57	59	64
Edible portion	84	82	80	79
Bone, ligament, and tendon	16	18	20	21

The separable fat is that which can be dissected out, and this is determined by physical separation rather than chemical analysis. It will be noted that as the grade is decreased, the fat is lessened, the lean increased, the edible portion decreased, and the bone, ligament, and tendon increased.

PROPORTION IN VARIOUS CLASSES AND GRADES OF BEEF

The proportion of slaughter cattle in the various classes is influenced by the current cattle situation and the feed supply. When cattle numbers on farms and ranches are increasing, female stock makes up a smaller proportion of the total receipts of market cattle. Likewise, when numbers are decreasing, there is liquidation of breeding stock resulting in a large proportion of female stock in the total receipts.

As previously noted, beef steers on foot over a period of years are graded about 73 per cent prime and choice, 30 per cent good, 6 per cent commercial, and 1 per cent utility on the Chicago market. Carcass grades

[4] E. S. Clifton and Geoffrey Shepard, "Objective Grade Specification for Slaughter Steer Carcasses," *Research Bulletin 402,* Iowa Agricultural Experiment Station, November, 1953.

[5] O. G. Hankins and M. T. Foster, "Approximate Physical Composition of the Primary Cuts from Steer Carcasses of Different Market Grades," U.S.D.A., *Pamphlet,* April, 1940.

are much the same in distribution. The average grade for steers is higher on the Chicago market than on most markets. Steers make up about 47 per cent of the slaughter cattle federally inspected, heifers and cows about 49 per cent. Bulls and stags make up but a very small proportion of the slaughter cattle.

STANDARD CLASSES AND GRADES OF WHOLESALE CUTS OF BEEF

As considerable beef is wholesaled in the form of cuts such as loins, ribs, rounds, chucks, plates, flanks, and shanks, rather than as sides or quarters, classes and grades are also used for these cuts.

Standard grades have been set up by the U.S. Department of Agriculture. They are similar to the carcass grades and use the same terms: prime, choice, good, standard, commercial, and utility, for the different cuts. It is possible to grade the wholesale cuts more accurately than the entire carcass because the cutting exposes a fairly large surface. The grade is determined by an evaluation of the degree of conformation, finish, and quality of the wholesale cut irrespective of the grade of the original carcass. Low cutters are not broken up into wholesale cuts, and the low grades of bull and stag beef are not usually sold over the butcher block.

BONELESS OR BONED BEEF

The practice of boning beef at packing plants and distributing it boned to the trade, either chilled or frozen, increased greatly during the period of World War II. Frozen boneless beef developed in response to a need for a compact product to feed the armed services. Beef, when boned, is easier to preserve, transport, and prepare. The saving in storage space is quite striking, since for 100 pounds there are required in storage 3 cubic feet for boneless beef, 4.56 cubic feet for frozen carcass beef, and 6 cubic feet for chilled carcass beef. A beef carcass yields 70 per cent of boneless cuts of which 40 per cent is roasting or frying meat, 30 per cent is boiling or stewing meat, and 30 per cent is chopped meat for patties or loaves.

CLASSES OF VEAL AND BABY BEEF

YEARLING BEEF CARCASSES AND CUTS

The carcasses of steers or heifers may be subclassed as yearling beef or "baby beef" [6] when lacking the maturity of mature beef and when more

---

[6] Some confusion exists concerning the use of the term "baby beef." In the meat trade it is often used for lightweight beef, whereas the producers and feeders com-

mature than calf beef or veal. Yearling beef is of lower finish or fatness, less marbled, less firm, lighter red, and also softer and smoother in texture than mature beef. Also, in form, the yearling carcass is less thick, and the bones are less flinty. Yearling beef carcasses are not so heavy as mature beef carcasses.

There is a variation in the age of yearling beef, but it usually comes from cattle ranging between 8 and 18 months of age. In growth, the beef animal passes through the different stages in which, if slaughtered, it would yield veal, calf beef, yearling beef, and mature beef. The changes are not the same in all individuals. However, usually an animal up to 3 months of age will yield a veal carcass, and an animal from 3 to 6 months, a calf carcass.

GROUPS OF CALF CARCASSES AND CUTS [7]

Calf carcasses are from individuals older than veal calves (3 months) and younger than yearling beef (8 to 10 months). They come chiefly from the western range and are sometimes called "grass veal." The calf carcass is larger than that of the vealer. It is also coarser in texture and the flesh is distinctly reddish in color. The fat is greater in amount, white in color, and firmer. The fat color is partially dependent upon the ration.

CALF CARCASSES

The receipts of calves are confined principally to the fall of the year, but range from June to November. The source is mainly from the beef producing areas of the western range, but a few are marketed from the corn belt.

The veal characteristics of the flesh begin to disappear at 12 to 14 weeks of age, and gradually as age advances the carcass assumes properties typical of beef. Compared to veal, the calf carcass is larger; the usual range in weight with the skin off is from 150 to 350 pounds, with by far the greatest number occurring in the last 150 pounds of the range.

A complete outline of the commonly used classes and grades of calf carcasses follows.

---

monly refer to well-bred, fairly matured, well-fattened cattle between 8 and 18 months of age as "baby beef."

[7] W. E. Davis and C. M. Harris, "Market Classes and Grades of Dressed Veal and Calf Carcasses," *Circ. 103,* U.S.D.A., 1930; slightly revised August, 1942.

CLASSES AND GRADES OF CALF CARCASSES

CLASSES	WEIGHT *	GRADES
Steers	Medium	1. Prime
Heifers	Light	2. Choice
Bulls	Heavy	3. Good
	150–350 lbs.	4. Standard
		5. Utility
		6. Cull

* These weights are with skin off and should be increased by 10 per cent to include the skin, in which condition most young calves are sold. Older calves and heavier calves are sold with the skin off.

The grading is based upon evaluation of quality, conformation, and finish.

WHOLESALE CUTS OF CALF CARCASSES

The wholesale cuts of the calf carcasses are similar to those of veal, and five grades—prime, choice, good, medium, and common—may be applied to the cuts.

GROUPS OF DRESSED VEAL CARCASSES [8]

Veal carcasses

"Veal" is the term applied to carcasses from cattle slaughtered under about 3 months of age. The largest numbers (about 90 per cent) are between 3 and 6 weeks old when killed. In size the carcasses usually range from 50 to 100 pounds when skinned. The receipts of vealers are quite seasonal and come mainly from the dairying areas, as more than three quarters of the calves are marketed in the first 5 months of the year. Veal calves are more numerous on cattle markets which are near large dairy districts. Below are the market classes and grades of veal carcasses.

CLASSES AND GRADES OF VEAL CARCASSES

CLASSES	WEIGHT *	GRADES
Steers	Light	1. Prime
Heifers	Medium	2. Choice
Bulls	Heavy	3. Good
	50–100 lbs.	4. Standard
		5. Utility
		6. Cull

* These weights are with the skin off and should be increased by 10 per cent to include skin on. Most veal carcasses are sold with the skin on or are covered with some protective material.

[8] W. E. Davis and C. M. Harris, "Market Classes and Grades of Dressed Veal and Calf Carcasses," *Circ. 103,* U.S.D.A., 1930; slightly revised August, 1942.

Quality is the main item in determining the grade, being more important than conformation and finish. Sex has no influence on the quality of veal.

Wholesale cuts of veal

The method of cutting up the veal carcass differs on the different markets. The two main wholesale cuts are the hindsaddle and the foresaddle. These are further divided, the hindsaddle into: (1) leg, (2) loin, and the foresaddle into: (1) rack, (2) chuck. The latter cut includes the neck, shoulder, breast, and shank. These cuts are grouped into grades similar to those used for carcasses.

STAMPED OR BRANDED BEEF

FEDERAL GRADED AND STAMPED BEEF [9]

Standards developed by the U.S. Department of Agriculture for meat grading were first used in New York in 1924, mainly for the contract sale of meat. These classes and grades made possible the sale of meats for future delivery, based upon standard specifications. After a period of experimental demonstrations, grading and stamping was established in 1928 as a regular service, on a fee basis, under the provisions of the Federal Food Products Inspection Act. Grading offices are located in many meat-packing and wholesaling centers. A ribbon grade stamp is used for this purpose (see Figure 52), whereas the round and diamond-shaped stamps indicate wholesomeness.

The packer, wholesaler, or retailer for whom the grading is done pays for the services of the official grader, who is a federal employee, on an hourly basis. A roller stamp and a vegetable-compound stamping fluid are used. The carcass is stamped the entire length; also, the label appears on the principal retail cuts. During the war period, with compulsory grading, considerable quantities of all meats were graded or certified as complying with specifications by the U.S. Department of Agriculture. Following the war, grading was restored to a voluntary basis.

In a recent year 46 per cent of all beef commercially slaughtered was officially graded; 21 per cent of veal and calf; 33 per cent of lamb and mutton. The grand total of meat officially graded has been 6 billion pounds for the past five years.

Many packing plants have their own stamping and grading systems, used in lieu of, or supplementing, the government service.

[9] "U. S. Graded and Stamped Beef," *Leaflet 122* (revised), U.S.D.A.; "Beef Grading and Stamping Service," *Leaflet 67,* U.S.D.A.; "Facts on Meat Grading," *Consumer's Guide,* Vol. 5, No. 7, August, 1938; "Federal Beef Grading," *Misc. Pub. 391,* A.M.S., U.S.D.A.; "U. S. Grades For Beef," *Leaflet 310,* U.S.D.A., June, 1951.

Fig. 52. Ribbon grade stamps for federally graded beef. (U.S.D.A., Agricultural Marketing Service.)

Carcass market classes and grades used for stamping

The classes and grades as previously described are fixed by stated requirements; so there is no variation, seasonally or geographically. In July, 1939, a revision was made in federal beef grading to simplify the grades and to make it easier to buy on the basis of quality or grade. A single standard system was inaugurated under which the name of each class (such as steer, heifer, or cow) was eliminated from the stamp and the graded carcass beef and wholesale cuts were divided first into 5 later into the 6 classes: (1) prime, (2) choice, (3) good, (4) standard, (5) commercial, and (6) utility. For a period of time the differentials between the grades of dressed steer beef have been $3.46 between prime and choice, $3.00 between choice and good, and $2.75 between good and standard. As a consequence, the buyers of beef are assured definite qualities in branded beef, which remain quite constant. The purchaser need not inspect each carcass or wholesale cut to secure a definite quality. It is claimed that this system of grading protects the consumer against misrepresentation of quality and enables him to make intelligent price comparisons and to purchase the quality that suits his purpose. This service is used in the retail trade and also by federal, state, and city institutions, hotels, restaurants, steamship lines, and railway dining cars.

PACKER GRADED AND BRANDED BEEF

Packers often use grades of beef carcasses different from the federal grades, and stamp or brand certain of the better grades. Grading is done during the processing in the packing plant. In the Armour and Co.[10] plants it is done at three different times. First, when the carcass has been split and washed, it is graded by experienced graders. This is known as "hot grading." The following day the carcasses are "cold graded" in the coolers, and the last grading is done when the carcasses are "ribbed down," usually on the loading rack, prior to shipping out. In "ribbing" the beef carcasses, the hindquarter is separated from the front quarter, exposing the large muscle which lies on either side of the backbone. The color of the muscle, the marbling, and the texture which can be determined in this separation may affect the grade. There is quite close agreement among the grades determined at different times.

Systems of grade identification are not the same for all packers [11] Armour and Co. use 36 standard grades—9 each for steers, heifers, cows, and the group: bulls and stags are designated as 30's, 40's, 50's, and 60's, respectively. The groups and the commercial quality is indicated by the last figure of the number as follows:

0—Prime	5—Fair
1—Choice	6—Plain
2—Good	7—Common
3—Good medium	8—Very common
4—Medium	

According to this system, a prime steer carcass would be indicated as 30. A carcass marked 30 must be blocky, or short coupled, with thick full ribs and loins, and plump rounds. The covering must be of thick, smooth white fat, neither "gobby" nor wasty. The meat must be firm, with bright red color, of fine grain, and well marbled. The vertebra where split must be red except in very heavy older steers, in which it is a pinkish white. A 38 steer carcass would be thin, with but little fat, which would be yellow. The meat would be dark red and soft. It will be noted that, in this system, a good heifer would be 42; a medium cow 54; and plain bull or stag 66.

---

[10] "Beef Grading," *Armour Magazine,* Vol. 4, No. 4, June, 1938, p. 9.

[11] These are based upon what is known as the "institute system" which was developed by the Institute of American Meat Packers for the standardization of beef grading.

These grades are for the wholesale trade and are not consumer grades. Consumers consider principally tenderness and flavor, whereas the retailer, in buying a carcass, is influenced by many factors such as necessary trimming for resale.

Armour and Co. have their brands which are stamped on beef. Their brand names are Star, Quality, Banquet, and Armour. Wilson and Company, Inc., apply their brands to beef, using Certified, Special, Ideal, Leader, and Wilsco. Other companies also follow this plan. (See Figure 53.)

RETAILER'S RESPONSE TO GRADING AND STAMPING BEEF

According to reports made by Ashby et al.[12] a significant number of Illinois meat retailers are handling graded or branded beef or both. In the opinions of the retailers surveyed, government grade-stamped beef was more consistent in its grade than packer brand-stamped beef. It was pointed out that, with a wide use of standard grades, retailers would be able to make more accurate comparisons

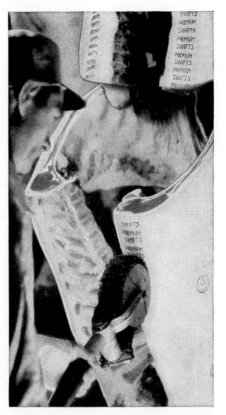

Fig. 53. Branding a quality product with a company brand name. (Swift & Company.)

of wholesale beef quotations. This survey indicated that a number of consumers are interested in buying beef on the basis of actual grade, and that even consumers with lower incomes will buy quality beef when it is available.

KOSHER BEEF [13]

Beef from cattle slaughtered and dressed in accordance with certain

[12] R. C. Ashby et al., "Graded and Branded Beef," Bull. 479, University of Illinois, August, 1941.

[13] "What 'Kosher' Means to the Meat Industry," Monthly Letter to Animal Husbandmen, Armour Livestock Bur., Vol. 10, No. 3, June, 1929.

Jewish rites is termed "kosher beef," which means wholesome according to religious rules and regulations of the Jewish faith.

"Kosher" [14] meat, such as beef front quarters or chucks, is declared unfit for consumption 72 hours after it is slaughtered unless it is washed. Two additional washings are permitted if the 72-hour extensions are expiring. Meat not acceptable for the Jewish trade is referred to as "tref." The time limit does not apply to Kosher sausage or prepared meats. It has been estimated that of the approximately 6 million Jews in the United States less than 20 per cent conform strictly to the laws governing kosher food.

As most of the Jews in the United States live in the eastern states, large numbers of live cattle are shipped from the large midwestern livestock markets to be slaughtered in or near the eastern consuming areas. This procedure makes the beef available sooner after slaughter. Jewish holidays and festivals influence the meat trade, because the buyers of kosher beef are absent from the market on holidays, kosher livestock are seldom slaughtered on Jewish holidays, and there is no kosher slaughtering on Saturday.[15]

The requirement of the religious law is that veins must be removed before the meat is delivered to the consumer. In this country only the forequarters are used by the kosher butchers, and often the rib cut is removed. The kosher square-cut chuck which makes up about 33 per cent of the weight of a beef side consists of the ordinary chuck, plate, brisket, and shin, and includes four or five ribs of the forequarter. Other cuts also used are marked with Hebrew markings. (See Figure 54.) As the less tender cuts—mostly chucks and plates—from the carcass are used, the kosher trade requires high-grade slaughter animals. Usually the best heavy cattle and choice young cattle, mostly steers and some fat cows and heifers, are used for kosher beef. There is also koshered veal, which ranks second only to beef in the kosher trade. (See page 130.)

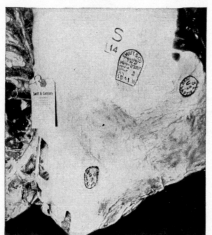

Fig. 54. Kosher beef with the kosher stamp of approval. (Swift & Company.)

[14] "Kosher" means ritually prepared, or fit to eat, while "tref" is derived from "terefah," which means "torn by wild beasts," hence ritually unfit.

[15] The Jewish holidays are given in "The Significance of Jewish Holidays to the Livestock Producer," *Agr. Res. Bull. 9,* Swift & Company, July, 1937.

Chapter 10

BEEF AND VEAL DISTRIBUTION AND CONSUMPTION

TRANSPORTATION

Meat is usually delivered to the retailer by truck. Some meat-packing plants maintain wholesale markets at which meat retailers can purchase their supplies. Meat salesmen, representatives of the packing plant, travel a regular truck route and deliver meat as well as take orders. At points some distance from the plants, salesmen are used to gather the orders, and deliveries are made by rail or truck. There has been a rapid increase in the movement of freshly killed beef by refrigerated motortruck; chilling of the beef takes place en route.

BRANCH HOUSES AND CAR ROUTES

Large packing plants develop two avenues of distribution: the branch house and the refrigerator car route. The branch houses operated in large cities receive a supply from the packing plant of their company by refrigerator car or truck and serve as distribution points for retailers. The car route system was first developed to serve retail meat dealers in towns and villages along a railroad line. A drayman meets the train on its arrival in a route town, and the goods for that town are unloaded and delivered to the dealer in that locality. With the development of better roads, refrigerated trucks have partially replaced the railroad service.

167

MEAT REFRIGERATION

As meat is a perishable product, it must be refrigerated to maintain its freshness. Refrigeration must be maintained at a rather narrow range in temperature; there must be proper humidity to keep the meat in the most desirable condition. Ventilation is also a factor in successful refrigeration, and meat cuts must hang separately when they are refrigerated.

Refrigeration controls deterioration, and its use has made a supply of acceptable meat widely available. Chilled beef may be held for a period of 2 to 6 weeks. Freezing, which will preserve beef for months without unfavorable effects, is used under many circumstances. The quick-freeze method is the most satisfactory for maintaining the original properties of the meat. In this method the temperature is lowered rapidly to about $-10°F$ or lower.

CONSUMPTION

QUALITIES IN MEAT DESIRED BY THE CONSUMER

The consumer wants palatable meat agreeable to the taste. The palatability of the meat is influenced by the tenderness, juiciness, and flavor of the fat and the lean. Meat has savory and satiety value as well as high food value. Attractiveness in appearance is a large factor in selling meat to the housewife. The proportion of lean and fat, and the color of both, affect the appeal of the meat to the buyer. Buyers prefer marbling in their beef; most of them show a preference for light or medium lean and white fat. Some consumers show a preference for yellow fat, although in beef grading white fat is decidedly preferred. Lower income groups discriminate more against the fat in beef, which is preferred by higher income groups.

To the buyer price is often the dominant factor in meat selection. The purchaser wants palatable meat at a reasonable cost. In fact, if the cost seems too high, meat substitutes are used or less meat is purchased. Meat constitutes a major expenditure and is the main item in the usual meal; consequently, the housewife selects meats with care.

A survey among American housewives indicated that 44.2 per cent preferred the quality of meat supplied by their present retailers, while 25.5 per cent used retailers convenient in location.[1] Economical prices were mentioned only in the case of the poorer classes. Where there was dissatisfaction with the meat dealer, more than one half of it was due to poor quality of meat.

[1] Robert B. Hinman and Robert B. Harris, *The Story of Meat*, p. 235, Swift & Company, 1939.

NECESSARY FOODS

Food is looked upon as a necessity rather than as a luxury. The expenditure for food is quite constant in the family budget. Consumers normally spend about 5.7 per cent of their disposable income for meat, excluding lard and poultry meat. Information on how people spend their money, obtained from the National Resources Committee, has been the basis for the determination of a "luxury index." [2] With an average annual outlay per consumer unit of $1,502, about $428 was spent for food. Of the various items, food with a luxury index of 54 appeared to benefit from increased spending power of consumers about one half as much as all items combined. With higher incomes increased expenditures for food are for better quality and more services rather than greater total volume of food.

Meat had a luxury index of 44 as compared with wheat products 1, vegetables 36, dairy products 67, and fruit 79. In other words, meat to the consumer is in a higher luxury class than wheat products and vegetables but lower than dairy products and fruit.

Of the individual meats the luxury indexes are as follows: pork 18, beef 54, veal 58, poultry 80, lamb 100. Lamb, therefore, is the most luxurious of the meats, while pork is the lowest. Pork has, then, a low elasticity of demand, since consumers tend to use the same quantity irrespective of price.

PER CAPITA MEAT CONSUMPTION IN VARIOUS COUNTRIES

Consumption of meat is greater in the new countries of the world than in the older countries. Food habits and religious restrictions, as well as the available supply, affect the amount of meat consumed. People in the temperate regions consume more meat than those in the tropics.

The meat-consumption estimates of some countries have been summarized by the Department of Marketing, American Meat Institutes, from U.S. Department of Agriculture and United Nations reports.[3] Although the estimates are incomplete, they indicate that at least 4 countries, New Zealand, Australia, Uruguay, and Argentina, have higher meat consumption per person than the United States. The per capita consumption of meat, poultry and fish for several countries is tabulated on the next page.

---

[2] *Farm Economics,* No. 123, February, 1941, New York State College of Agriculture, Cornell University, Ithaca, N.Y. The luxury index is based on comparisons of expenditures by people of different income levels and is weighted by the amount of total outlay for each group.

[3] Data from J. Russell Ives, American Meat Institute, Chicago, Illinois, Jan., 1957.

PER CAPITA CONSUMPTION OF MEAT, POULTRY, AND FISH IN SPECIFIED COUNTRIES

(Listed in Order of Total Per Capita Consumption of Meat, Poultry & Fish)

COUNTRY	MEAT, LBS./CAPITA	POULTRY, LBS./CAPITA	FISH, LBS./CAPITA	TOTAL, LBS./CAPITA
New Zealand	216	6	16	238
Australia	211	10	10	231
Uruguay	199	8	4*	211
Argentina	187	5	8	200
UNITED STATES	161	26	10	197
Canada	146	30	15*	191
Denmark	124	6	51	181
Norway	76	3	99	178
Sweden	107	4	51	162
France	125	13	20	158
United Kingdom	128	5	21	154
Belgium	98	6	31	135
Western Germany	104	4	26	134
Ireland	97	10	13	120
Netherlands	87	3	26	116
Portugal	42	5	64	111
Cuba	83	4	24*	111
Austria	100	1	7	108
Spain	51	2	51	104
Switzerland	95	4	4	103
Chile	51	11	23	85
Italy	39	5	20	64
Greece	31	4	26	61
Yugoslavia	49	6	2*	57
Mexico	38	8	6	52

Meat figures include beef, veal, lamb, mutton, goatmeat, horsemeat, and pork, carcass weight basis. They exclude variety meats and game, and are for 1955.
Poultry figures are on a ready-to-eat basis, generally for 1954–55.
Fish figures are for the most part on a fresh, landed-weight basis for 1954–55, but figures with * are for various years between 1946 and 1950.

PER CAPITA MEAT CONSUMPTION IN THE UNITED STATES

Well-defined cycles in meat consumption occur, moving with the volume of production of meats since most of our meats are domestically produced. Meat usually provides 25 per cent of the total protein and 15 per cent of the energy of our national diet, but we have marked fluctuations in consumption. We consume most of the meat we produce, and if our livestock population is high meat consumption is high until livestock numbers are reduced. In times of liberal supplies meat moves into storage; the reverse takes place when production is low. When good crops are produced, livestock are marketed at heavier weights, using up feed surpluses. When crop production is below average, livestock are sold at lighter weight but herd numbers are reduced. Liquidation when feed supplies are short tends to keep the supply of meat fairly stable.

In the past 10 years the average meat consumption per person has been 148.17 pounds. For the year 1932 consumption was at a low ebb—the per capita consumption was but 116.7 pounds. In 1947 consumption was high —155 pounds per person.

From 1946 to 1951 the average per capita consumption of beef was 67.1 pounds and of veal 8.91 pounds. (See Figure 55.) In the past 30 years, yearly consumption of beef per person has ranged from 46.4 pounds in 1932 to 81.2 pounds in 1955. Veal consumption has ranged from a low of 6.3 pounds per person in 1929 to 12.4 pounds in 1944.

In recent years there was a definite downward trend in beef consumption and a slightly upward trend in veal consumption. Since about 1925 our exports of beef have disappeared, and we have imported some beef.

RED MEAT CONSUMPTION PER PERSON

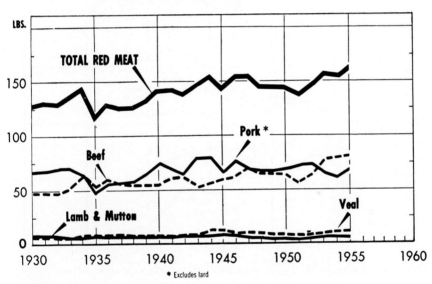

Fig. 55. Meat consumed per person in the United States. (U.S.D.A., Bur. of Agri. Economics.)

PER CAPITA CONSUMPTION OF PRINCIPAL AGRICULTURAL PRODUCTS

The per capita consumption of all farm products has remained quite stable since 1920. During the prosperity period it was but 2 per cent above the average, and in the depression it was only a fraction of a per cent below. The consumption of agricultural products is shown in the following tabulation.

Agricultural nonfood products such as cotton, wool, flaxseed, and tobacco vary more in consumption than do the food products. Also, they are affected more by changes in general business activity.

Changes in the pattern of food consumption have been very marked. We are consuming more meat, including poultry meat, dairy products, eggs, fruit, and vegetables than formerly. Accordingly we consume less grain and cereal products, potatoes, sweet potatoes, sugars, and sirup. The change in per capita consumption or the trends in our eating habits is shown in Figure 56. In recent years there has been a big increase in the consumption of frozen vegetables and fruit juice. Change in our eating habits, together with enrichment or fortification of cereal products, has brought significant increases in our daily intake of minerals and vitamins.

TRENDS IN OUR EATING HABITS*

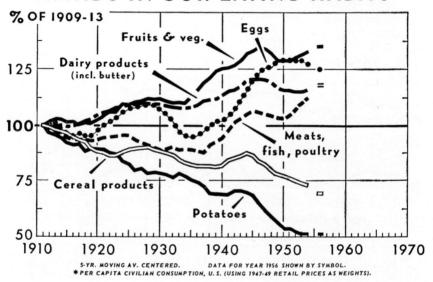

5-YR. MOVING AV. CENTERED.   DATA FOR YEAR 1956 SHOWN BY SYMBOL.
*PER CAPITA CIVILIAN CONSUMPTION, U. S. (USING 1947-49 RETAIL PRICES AS WEIGHTS).

Fig. 56. Changes in the per capita consumption of food, expressed as a per cent of 1909–13 consumption. We now consume more dairy products, fruits, and vegetables but we consume less of the grain products and potatoes. (U.S.D.A., Agricultural Marketing Service.)

Two factors guide food selection: (1) taste preference and (2) relative prices. Different foods compete with one another for a place in the consumer's diet. In prosperous times the demand for higher quality meats and the spread between meat grades in retail prices increases. Further, changes in food production, processing, and marketing affect the pattern of food consumption.

PRICES

RETAIL MEAT PRICES

Since the demand is not the same for all retail cuts, prices asked for the different cuts are different, so that all the cuts will move into the trade. Shifts in consumer preference frequently occur, but definite cuts are in demand and consequently high priced; others are in less demand and priced lower so they will sell.

For an 8-year period [4] the retail price per pound of round steak for the United States has been 95.3 cents; during the same period rib roast averaged 74.7 cents, and chuck roast was 60.4 cents.

RELATIONSHIP BETWEEN CATTLE PRICES AND BEEF PRICES

The spread between the prices paid for cattle and the prices at which beef is sold is often questioned, both by producers and by consumers. It should be pointed out that all of a beef steer is not carcass and that the different retail cuts of beef are not all equally in demand among consumers. Higher priced beef cuts are those in greatest demand.

U.S. Choice Grade Beef

WHOLESALE AND RETAIL VALUES AND MARKETING MARGIN

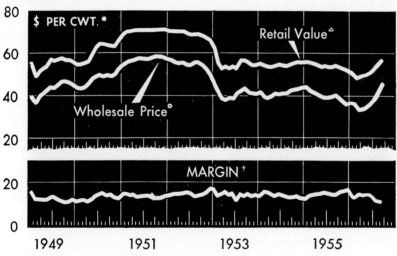

Fig. 57. Wholesale and retail values and marketing margin, for U.S. Choice beef. (U.S.D.A., Agricultural Marketing Service.)

[4] _Livestock Market News Statistics,_ Agricultural Marketing Service, U.S.D.A., 1956.

An explanation of the spread between live cattle and beef prices is given on page 96. This is also shown in chart form. (See Figures 32 and 57.)

The retailer of meats must make his profit, expenses, and initial cost from about 80 pounds out of 100 pounds of carcass beef he buys. The other 20 pounds are fat, suet, bone, and trim which do not go into the retail trade and which bring but a nominal price. Further, as indicated above, the various retail cuts must be priced so that the entire carcass will move into the trade. For example, in a recent price analysis it was found that the gross return to the retailer was about the same from the round and from the chuck from a Choice-grade beef carcass. The chuck represented about 19 per cent of the carcass weight and the round about 10 per cent. Therefore the round, which is mainly steak, had to sell for nearly twice as much per pound as the chuck, which is mainly used for roasts.

Increased margin, or difference between wholesale and retail price, may be caused by an increase in consumer services in processing and merchandizing or by a rise in the cost of such services.

MEAT PRESERVATION [5]

There are four general methods of meat preservation: drying, smoking, salting, and freezing. According to Wentworth, meat drying originated in the arid countries, probably in northern Asia, and the practice was brought to the American continent by immigrants who crossed the Bering Strait. Smoking no doubt came into use through the drying method. Meat drying was hastened by the heat from fires, and a smoke flavor was developed which would overcome objectionable odors of decomposition which arise on slow drying.

Salting has long been a method of meat preservation, and saltpeter has long been used as a preservative of natural color. The dryness and hardness resulting from drying, smoking, and dry salting were overcome by the wet pickle method. "Wet-pickled" beef is known as "corned beef."

Freezing was a natural development in the temperate and arctic regions. Meat storage by refrigeration developed with the growth of artificial refrigeration. Most beef is sold fresh and is refrigerated (not frozen) until it is retailed.

In the quick-freeze process, the objectionable changes in meat subjected to ordinary freezing are eliminated.

[5] "Meat Preservation," *Monthly Letter to Animal Husbandmen*, Armour and Co., Vol. 14, No. 5, January–March, 1939.

Fig. 58. Loading beef carcasses into a railroad refrigeration car. (Armour & Company.)

SAUSAGE [6]

In the meat trade the word "sausage" is applied to many meat products other than fresh, cured or frozen beef, pork, veal, and lamb. This term covers an extensive group of prepared meat products and is not restricted to ground pork alone. Beef is used extensively in various kinds of sausage. Large meat packers manufacture more than 150 different items in their sausage departments. Sausage is a highly concentrated meat product of rather uniform quality with but little waste. The development of its manufacture has enabled packers to utilize completely all meat products. Furthermore, it affords a means of softening the effects of market gluts of livestock because it is not a perishable product.

Sausage consists mainly of trimmings from the cutting rooms and cer-

[6] "Growing Outlets for Beef," *Monthly Letter to Animal Husbandmen,* Armour and Co., Vol. 16, No. 1, April–June, 1937.

"Importance of the Sausage Trade to the Meat Industry," *Monthly Letter to Animal Husbandmen,* Armour and Co., Vol. 7, No. 7, October, 1926.

tain special parts of cattle and hogs which are separated from carcasses on
the killing floor. Beef from bull carcasses, because of its leanness, is especially desirable for sausage. Other materials such as spices and cereals are

Fig. 59. A retailer selecting beef at a meat packer's branch house. (Swift &
Company.)

blended with the meat to secure the desired flavor and consistency and to
lower the cost. The commonly used cereals are rice, flour, corn flour, and
potato flour. In plants under government inspection the cereals in most
manufactured meat food products must not exceed 3½ per cent of the
weight of the finished product. Sausages with more than 3½ per cent cereal
must be labeled imitations.

Sausage has increased in popularity and is widely used in the United
States among all kinds of consumers—not only the lower income groups, as
in times past. It is a convenient product for the consumer because of its
keeping qualities and because it requires no preparation. In recent years
consumption of meat in the sausage category has expanded very rapidly.
The total amount of such products consumed is now nearly 1½ billion
pounds.

Sausages are divided into three main groups.

1. Domestic sausage. This includes such items as fresh pork sausage, frankfurts, and bologna. Frankfurts (wieners) are approximately half beef and half pork, plus some less costly materials such as cereals and dried milk. After the mixture is put into casings the sausages are cooked and smoked.

2. Dry sausage. This is often called "summer sausage." It is firm to the touch, low in moisture content, and is eaten without cooking. Dry sausage is popular with persons of foreign birth.

3. Sausage specialties. Specialty products made in the sausage department include such materials as meat loaf, minced ham, jellied meat, corned beef, chile con carne, headcheese, and luncheon meats.

Fig. 60. Buying meat at a modern retail market. The trend is toward more self-service meat cases in the modern food store. (Swift & Company.)

COLD STORAGE OR FREEZER LOCKER PLANTS

Beginning about 1935, cold-storage locker plants with individual lockers for storing foods increased materially in use. One of the first locker plants was at Chico, California, where cold storage was available to farmers as early as 1908.[7] The first such plant in the midwest was started in 1910 at Crete, Nebraska, and in the early 1920's lockers came into wide use in the Pacific northwest. A survey [8] in Minnesota indicated that of the 179 locker plants in the state, 57 were cooperatively owner. The detailed information secured in this survey showed that 17 per cent of the patrons resided in town and that of the meat handled 47.1 per cent was beef, 48.0 per cent pork, 2.3 per cent veal, 0.6 per cent poultry, 0.4 per cent mutton and lamb, and 1.6 per cent other meats.

Many of the locker plants maintain facilities for processing meat. The plants provide for slaughtering meat animals, processing, cutting, wrapping, and freezing meat; they also grind, cure, and smoke meat, and render lard, as required by their patrons. Farmers use the facilities of the locker plants because through them they can secure fresh meat (frozen) throughout the year, either from their farm slaughter or from livestock processed at the plant. The possibility of securing higher quality meats at some saving in cost, as compared with purchasing from the local retail meat dealer, attracts some patrons. On the basis of 500 pounds of meat per locker, the cost to the urban locker renter per pound of meat stored will range from 4¾ to 7 cents per pound.[9] This includes brokerage for buying the meat, processing charge, locker rental, shrinkage, curing and smoking of hams and bacon, and grinding hamburger and sausage. Time of purchase, volume used, and cost of service will affect the savings made.

Food storage by freezing in lockers makes possible improved diets for farm families. About 2,800 frozen-food locker plants were operating in 44 states in 1940. In 1955 there were over 10,000 plants in the United States with more than 8 million individual lockers.[10] Also, there has been a big increase in home freezer units. Their advantages for the storage of meats are:

1. Meats preserved by freezing resemble fresh meat in flavor more than do canned meats.

2. Home slaughter for freezing can be less seasonal, and can be carried out throughout the year.

3. Less labor, materials, and equipment are needed than in preservation by canning.

4. Waste due to improper canning and refrigeration is eliminated.

5. Through efficient use of cold storage lockers better meats are available for farm families more uniformly throughout the year, at lower cost.

[7] L. B. Mann, "Refrigerated Food Lockers," *Circ. C–107,* Farm Credit Administration, 1938.

[8] A. A. Dowell *et al.,* "Cold Storage Locker Plants," *Bull. 345,* University of Minnesota, 1940.

[9] Marvin A. Schaars, *Cold Storage Locker Plants* (mimeographed), University of Wisconsin, 1938.

[10] *Agricultural Marketing,* U.S.D.A., July, 1956.

Rural electrification has been one cause of the increase in cold storage lockers. Cold storage plants use electric power, and the electric refrigerator in the home makes it possible to hold frozen food for a time before consumption. Some of the drawbacks to food lockers are that it is not always convenient to get the materials from the lockers when they are needed and that food lockers may be more costly than storage by canning and curing.

PREPACKAGED FROZEN MEAT

The increase in the number of frozen-food locker plants and home freezers has been accompanied by a rapid rise in the sales of prepackaged frozen meats. There are many firms spread throughout the United States, usually in or near large cities, operating plants producing frozen specialties such as chip steaks, cutlets, chopettes, and various ground meat products. These specialty meat items are made from the lower grades of meat by means of slicing machines and hydraulic presses. Cuts uniform in size and weight are produced. By means of central prepackaging and freezing it is possible to increase the efficiency of labor in the handling of meats. Furthermore, with freezing, shrinkage and spoilage losses can be reduced. Since the meat is trimmed and the bone and excess fat removed at the central packaging point, savings can be effected in distribution costs. Prepackaging and freezing can therefore reduce overhead cost in the retailing of meats.

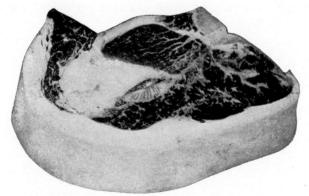

Fig. 61. A porterhouse steak. This cut is usually the highest priced of the common meat cuts. (National Livestock and Meat Board.)

MEAT EXPORTS AND IMPORTS

Usually, our exports of beef and pork exceed our imports, but this is not always the case. Following drought years, with decreased livestock numbers and resultant decreases in domestic supplies, imports of both beef and pork are attracted.

Normally we import considerable quantities of canned beef from South America, mainly from Argentina and Uruguay. Of this, 80 to 85 per cent is canned corn beef. Because of quarantine regulations to prevent the introduction of foot-and-mouth disease, fresh beef is not imported to the United States from South America. Some livestock is imported, most of it for slaughter. The bulk of this trade is of slaughter cattle from Canada. Since but a small amount of beef is imported or exported, the foreign trade has practically no effect upon prices in this country.

Meat is an important factor in world trade. Argentina is the world's largest exporter of meat, followed by New Zealand, Denmark, and Australia, in the order listed. These four countries account for about two-thirds of the movement into international trade.

IMPORT DUTIES

Beef and veal, fresh, chilled, or frozen, are subject to a duty of 3 cents per pound under the tariff of 1930 (modified). Prepared or preserved beef is subject to an import duty of the same rate but not less than 20 per cent ad valorem. Fresh, chilled, or frozen pork is subject to a duty of 1¼ cents per pound; hams, shoulders, bacon, and other prepared and preserved pork are subject to a tariff of from 1⅝ to 2⅗ cents per pound.

The duty on cattle imported is 1½ cents per pound, and there is a quota on such imports. The duty on swine is 1 cent per pound; for sheep and lambs it is $1.50 per head.

Chapter 11

BEEF CATTLE FEEDING
AND MANAGEMENT

FEEDING OF BEEF CATTLE

The development of a beef calf is dependent largely upon the individual's inheritance and the nutrition that it receives. Quantity and quality of feed to a large degree determine actual growth and development, the capacity for which is inherited. Gains in weight may be affected by enzymes, hormones, or similar materials. Other factors which may alter growth are water supply, temperature, light, and other environmental conditions. Development may also be affected by toxic substances in the ration, for example, the presence of selenium in forage. In the United States feeding practices with beef cattle differ widely from one section to another, depending upon feed supply and climatic conditions.

This textbook does not intend to cover all the details of feeding. Rather it gives, a survey of nutritional requirements and of beef cattle feeding and management practices. Several references on livestock feeding are listed at the end of the book. Following is a discussion of feeding problems in beef cattle raising.

NUTRITIONAL REQUIREMENTS OF BEEF CATTLE

Use of nutrient material

The nutrients in feeds are used mainly by young cattle for maintenance, growth, and fattening. Protein, carbohydrates, fats, minerals, vitamins, and water are consumed so that they may yield their sustenance to the animal, and this is reflected mostly in growth and fattening after maintenance requirements have been met. Food is digested and its nutrients become available for absorption; then it enters the circulation and is carried to the place where it is used. Finally, when nutrient material is broken down to the metabolic end products, these are excreted.

The uses of food by cattle may be listed as follows:

1. For growth and development of body tissues. Growth is the coordinated increase in the structural and other portions of the body which takes place until the individual becomes mature or adult. This includes the formation and enlargement of such tissues as bone, muscle, skin, and horn.

2. To repair and replenish worn-out tissue.

3. For the formation of body fat.

4. To provide energy for heat or to perform work.

5. In the productive female, for fetal development and for milk production.

Food may be regarded as serving two purposes: maintenance and production. The first includes maintaining the body, upkeep of body tissues and body temperature, and the energy for the vital processes such as the beating of the heart. Production includes accumulations arising from growth, fattening, and fetal development, as well as milk and work production.

Essential nutrients

Certain food constituents are essential to the normal growth and development of an individual. The term "nutrient" refers to any food constituent or group of food constituents of similar composition which aid in the support of animal life. When first used it applied to protein, carbohydrates, and fats. Now we regard the following as essentials in the diet or ration.

1. Proteins.
2. Fats.
3. Carbohydrates.
    a. Crude fiber.
    b. Nitrogen-free extract.
4. Minerals.
5. Vitamins and similar materials.
6. Water.
7. Unknown factors.

Cattle, being ruminants, can utilize some simple nitrogenous compounds such as urea, which are converted into protein by microorganisms. However, urea must be used in very small amounts and fed under proper conditions.

Requirements of beef cattle

Feeding standards, which are tables of feed composition and animal requirements, are generally based upon groups of nutrients, protein energy-producing nutrients, minerals, and vitamins.

The protein requirement is generally given as digestible protein, which is the part of the total that is removed in passing through the digestive tract. The energy-producing nutrients are expressed in various standards as digestible carbohydrate equivalent, total digestible nutrients, or net energy. In feeding standards the dry matter is also listed, because if this requirement is not met the individual is not satisfied.

By means of feeding standards we can ascertain the average nutrient needs for a common farm animal and then combine feeds in the correct proportion to approximate the needs.

A 1,000-pound beef cow that is pregnant and being wintered should have daily, according to the Morrison Feeding Standard,[1]

DRY MATTER, POUNDS	DIGESTIBLE PROTEIN, POUNDS	TOTAL DIGESTIBLE NUTRIENTS, POUNDS	CALCIUM, POUNDS	PHOS-PHORUS, POUNDS	CAROTENE, MILLI-GRAMS	NET ENERGY THERMS
14.2–20.0	0.7–0.8	7.5–10.5	0.044	0.037	55	5.6–7.9

With the composition of the available feeds known, it can be readily seen how a balanced ration may be determined. The requirements given above would be met by a ration consisting of 25 pounds of corn or sorghum silage, 10 pounds of straw or stover, and 1.5 pounds of cottonseed meal.

It will be readily recognized that the balanced ration, if based upon total protein and energy nutrients needed, may not fulfill the needs for the quality of the nutrients or the minerals or vitamins.

Relation of weight to maintenance. Many conditions affect the requirement for maintenance. Such things as size, age, weight, and sex influence the amount of food needed daily for maintaining the tissues of an animal. Submaintenance feeding results in the breakdown of tissue and loss of weight. Maintenance needs vary with the weight of the animal, but the proportion is not direct. For example, a 1,000-pound steer does not require twice as much feed for maintenance as a 500-pound steer. The active tissues of the body do not increase in direct proportion to gains in weight, and, further, heat losses are more in proportion to body surface than to weight. Consequently, maintenance feeding standards are proportional to some power (0.73 for energy, 0.72 for protein) of the live weight.

[1] F. B. Morrison, *Feeds and Feeding,* 22nd ed., The Morrison Publishing Co., Ithaca, N.Y., 1956.

Growing and fattening requirements. In common feeding practices growth and fattening go on simultaneously in beef cattle from birth to maturity. With steers being finished for market the fat percentage increases materially on heavy feeding. During that period the water and protein percentage decreases, while the mineral matter or ash decreases gradually.

The feed requirement for steers that are being fed out for market must be sufficient to take care of maintenance and to provide a surplus to make possible weight increases. The amount of the latter is dependent upon the amount and quality of the feed consumed.

A comparison of nutritive needs can be made from data in Morrison Feeding Standard for 900-pound steers of the different classes.

DAILY REQUIREMENTS PER 900-POUND HEAD [2]

	DRY MATTER, POUNDS	DIGESTIBLE PROTEIN, POUNDS	TOTAL DIGESTIBLE NUTRIENTS, POUNDS	CAL-CIUM, POUNDS	PHOS-PHORUS, POUNDS	CARO-TENE, MILLI-GRAMS	NET ENERGY, THERMS
Growing beef cattle fed for rapid growth	17.3–19.7	0.93–1.03	10.1–11.5	0.035	0.033	50	8.7– 9.9
Calves being fattened for baby beef	17.7–20.3	1.64–1.82	13.5–15.5	0.044	0.040	50	12.7–14.6
Fattening year-ling cattle	18.9–21.7	1.64–1.82	15.4–17.2	0.044	0.044	50	14.2–15.8
Fattening 2-year-old cattle	20.7–23.5	1.53–1.78	14.6–17.4	0.044	0.044	50	13.3–15.8

The protein requirement is higher for the calves and yearlings than for 2-year-old cattle of comparable weight because of the greater need for growth. The 2-year-old steers, on the other hand, have a larger capacity for feed. The total digestible nutrients required are also higher.

Reproduction and lactation requirements. A newborn calf is more than two-thirds water. There is also accumulation of protein, fat, and minerals in the growing fetus which calls for increase in intake of nutrients in the pregnant cow. In normal reproduction there is also an increase in the weight of the cow other than the fetal growth. Inadequate nutrition will hinder normal lactation and reproduction.

Since milk production is a secondary consideration with beef cows, the nutrition needs for this are not great.

PRACTICES IN THE FEEDING OF BEEF CATTLE

A division of feeding practices might be made upon the basis of the

[2] *Ibid.*

age of the cattle being fed and the principal purpose for which they are fed. Problems in feeding and management pertain to the breeding herd, the calf crop, and to fattening cattle for market. Season may be used as a further division of feeding practices. The year's plan and program may be divided by the season, for feeding and management are not the same in all seasons.

The breeding herd in summer

The herd of beef cattle is turned on the pasture or the range for the pasture season. Feed other than pasture, with the exception of salt or mineral, is not usually allowed. The breeding herd is limited in most instances to the amount of grazing land available. On good pasture or range when the herd is not crowded, nutritional conditions are at their best, and sanitary conditions are unsurpassed. As pasture is a comparatively low-cost feed in most cases, it is desirable to use pasture as completely as possible for the breeding herd.

Fig. 62. A beef breeding herd of Shorthorn cows and their calves on pasture. Good pasture is essential for the economical maintenance of the breeding herd. Roy D. Arnold, Sterling, Ill.

There are two kinds of pasture: the native grass on permanent pastures such as bluegrass, buffalo grass, etc., and the crop pastures such as the clovers. In farming areas the latter are used somewhat for breeding herds for herds may be a part of crop rotation. The crop pastures usually give greater yields, and the excess can be used for hay. The best pasture in the corn belt will carry one cow per acre. In most cases it will take more than 1 acre per cow. With permanent pasture more area is needed. In the western range country 20 to 40 acres of pasture per cow per year are often used. Supplementary feeding is practiced when forage is short.

Overgrazing may cause damage to pastures and ranges and is inadvisable. Moderately heavy grazing will give greater gains per acre than light grazing, and with good management heavy grazing can be successfully practiced. Provision should be made, if the pasture is heavily stocked, to supplement the pasture in case of drought. If cattle fail to make fair gains during the pasture season, the stocking is too heavy.

The breeding herd in winter

The crucial period in the feeding and management of the breeding herd is during the winter season. Ample supplies of feed and adequate housing are prerequisite to success in winter handling. As economy is a foremost consideration in feeding the herd, roughage under most situations comprises the major portion of the ration. Concentrates are used only when the supply or quality of the roughage is inadequate. In farming areas the crop fields are commonly gleaned by cattle, and in the winter-wheat area this crop may be pastured during the winter without adversely affecting the grain yield. Hays and silages are used to supplement the graze from crops. As cows are on pasture at least one half of the year, they can withstand a good deal of winter underfeeding. In sections where winter shelter is needed for reasonable comfort, sheds or barns open to the south will suffice in most situations. Economy is to be used in providing shelter; elaborate buildings are not necessary.

Feeding of concentrates usually increases the cost of the ration. The need for such feeding is dependent upon the condition of the cattle as well as on the quality and quantity of the remainder of the ration. The condition or fleshing of the cow herd will indicate the sufficiency of the ration. When the cows fail to gain in weight and lose flesh, a protein supplement is needed if the ration is carbonaceous. If the protein intake is ample, concentrated feeds like grain are needed. Cows heavy in calf or suckling calves may need special feeding. On the range, when the winter pasture is insufficient, cattlemen often resort to the feeding of cottonseed, soybean, or linseed cake, from 1 to 2 pounds per cow per day, or an equivalent amount of other feed such as grain or hay. There has been increased use of feeds in pellet or cube form for range feeding, and these include energy-rich feed with protein supplement. When the vegetation is snow-covered and the temperature is low, supplemental feeding is indicated.

In practice a ration such as given on page 183 would be quite satisfactory if good quality feeds were included in the ration, and if salt and other minerals were fed. Other rations for wintering or dry-lot feeding of mature beef breeding cows follow:

		Pounds Per Day
1.	Nonlegume hay	20–30
	Protein Supplement	½– 1
2.	Legume hay	5–10
	Nonlegume hay	16–20
3.	Corn Silage	50–60
	Protein Supplement	½
4.	Corn Silage	25
	Oat Straw	10
	Soybean Oil Meal	1½

The above are suggested rations to be varied in poundage according to the size of the cow. The condition of the cows, the quality of the roughage, and the pasturage available are further factors to consider in formulating the ration and in determining the daily allowances. Maximum use of pasturage and roughage is essential for low-cost maintaining of the breeding herd. Grain or other concentrates are needed under adverse circumstances and if calves are being suckled. An average gain of ½ pound per day during the last 5 months of pregnancy is required for fetal development.

The calf crop in summer

Most beef calves are dropped on pasture. On corn-belt farms spring calves are heavier at weaning time, and the crop is larger than with fall calves. The cost of keeping the cow herd on farms is lower when spring calves are produced.

1. Under farm conditions.   If pasture conditions are good, the calves are allowed to graze with the cows except on some farms where the calves are kept in a barn or lot near the barn while the cows are pastured some distance from the farmstead. In the latter case the cows are brought twice daily to the calves for suckling. The use of a creep permits the feeding of grain or other concentrates to the calves without interference from the cow herd. Farm-grown calves may, if expedient be raised on skim milk like dairy calves.

2. On the range.   Calves receive no special care unless it is necessary. The cows drop the calves on the range, and the calves continue on the range with the cows. The attendant is on hand to give such service as may be necessary. Dehorning, castration, marking, branding, and vaccination for blackleg are completed at the time of the roundup. When calves are 6 to 8 months old they are weaned by separation from their dams. Bull calves are castrated when they are 3 to 4 weeks old.

The calf crop in winter

The spring calves are weaned at the end of the pasture season in the fall. Fall-born calves are more difficult to raise than those dropped in the spring, for they are smaller and less able to withstand adverse weather. Winter rations often are inadequate or incomplete as compared with a ration that includes pasture. Fall-dropped calves require heavier winter feeding and more shelter than do spring-dropped calves. Spring calves and yearlings do require some special attention during the winter season, because that time may be crucial in their development.

The fattening of cattle in summer

In some areas of the United States fairly well-finished beef is produced on pasture alone. In general, summer feeding is feeding on pasture and winter feeding is dry-lot feeding, although this is not always so. Even during the pasture season, many cattle being fed are kept in dry lots. The fattening period may extend through the winter and the summer, especially with young cattle. It has been found to be a poor practice to put fattening cattle on grass if they have been on heavy-concentrate feeding in dry lot. Cattle fed only roughage in the winter may well be finished on grass.

Fig. 63. Cattle being fed on pasture. Hereford steers from the T.O. Ranch being fed out at the Southside Stock Farm, Rockbridge, Ill.

For sufficient finish on the cattle to sell well it is generally necessary to feed concentrates plus pasture. The combination feeding plan, that is, combination of grass and concentrates, is followed mostly in areas where forage is to be used and where grains are grown. Under this system the concentrates needed are about half the amount used in dry-lot feeding. In practice the level of grain or concentrate feeding ranges all the way from none to full feeding. When feeder cattle are purchased for this method, older cattle are preferred to calves.

The fattening of cattle in winter

The feeder and stocker cattle raised in the western range area on the native short grasses moved for finishing into regions where concentrated feeds are grown. More than half the cattle are finished in the corn belt. Corn is the most used of our basal concentrates for cattle fattening, although barley, rye, grain sorghums, oats, wheat, and molasses are also used. Cottonseed meal and similar protein concentrates are used to build up the protein content of such rations. Silage, especially corn, is used in great quantities, as are also alfalfa, clover, and other hays.

There are a great number of feed combinations that have given satisfactory results in dry-lot cattle feeding. Also there are many conditions which alter the quantities of various feeds to be allowed for best results.

The following suggested rations are for a 600-pound steer and represent about what would be fed at the midpoint of the usual winter feeding period.

1. Shelled corn—16 pounds
   Legume hay—7 pounds
2. Shelled corn—14 pounds
   Non-legume hay—6 pounds
   Protein supplement—1½ pounds
3. Shelled corn—12 pounds
   Mixed hay—4 pounds
   Corn silage—10 pounds
   Protein supplement—2 pounds
4. Shelled corn—10 pounds
   Legume hay—6 pounds
   Corn silage—20 pounds
   Protein supplement—1 pound

Steer and heifers on feed with the above ration should also have free access to salt and a mineral mixture.

Fig. 64. Fat cattle in the feed lot. Hereford steers being fed out at Sugar Grove Farm, Aurora, Ill. Note the hogs following the cattle.

STOCK OF FEEDS AND LIVESTOCK FEEDING

In years when feed production is at a high level, feeding is stimulated and livestock numbers increase. Slaughter animals are fed to heavier weights. Storage stocks of meats increase, and supplies of feed are accumulated on ranches and farms. When short crops are raised the reverse takes place, and feeding is restricted, numbers of livestock decrease, and slaughter animals are marketed at light weights. Storage stocks of meat are lessened, and surplus feed supplies disappear. Livestock absorb part of the impact of extremes in feed and production, because there is liquidation of livestock with short feed supplies and expansion when feed supplies are generous.

MANAGEMENT OF THE BEEF CATTLE ENTERPRISE

The role of the manager is to see to it that the livestock on the farm or ranch do well the things for which they are kept. The efficient manager directs the economical conversion of the home-grown feeds into livestock products. A plan of management suitable to the situation is the first essential in successful production, and this is followed as a guide to the objectives.

A PLAN OF MANAGEMENT

Whether the final objective is the production of commercial beef cattle, feeder cattle, or breeding cattle, there are certain circumstances which the operator should consider in formulating a plan. A discussion of these major considerations which may affect such a plan follows.

The usable feed supply

As cattle are kept primarily to use feed, a careful estimate of the probable supply and the amount needed is imperative for careful planning. Rations carefully planned to use efficiently all home-grown feed plus purchased supplements are essential for economical production. A margin of safety is also essential as insurance against a forced liquidation when natural supplies fall short, such as in droughts or crop failures. A balance between usable feeds and animal needs is desired.

The equipment required

The equipment and buildings needed for the cattle enterprise need not be extensive or expensive. Most general farms are sufficiently equipped for handling a lot of feeding cattle or a cow and calf enterprise. A herd of 20 breeding cows or an equal number of fattening cattle should be the approximate minimum for a small farm.

The labor involved

A plan of cattle raising should consider the labor available and also the competing labor demands. Cattle feeding may dovetail very well with general farming in labor demands. A use for labor is provided in cattle feeding which will give a return when other uses are very small. A study [3] on cornbelt farms indicated that 6½ hours of labor per year were required to care for a stock cow on the average farm, while milk cows on these same farms required an average of 99 hours.

The market outlook

The immediate, as well as the long-term, outlook is pertinent to profit in cattle raising. In planning a system of cattle raising, attention should be given to the factors that affect prices. Outlook reports are available. The usual seasonal variations in the different classes and grade have been discussed. With commercial cattle, the manager should endeavor to have the kind that are in demand ready for market when the prevailing market price is relatively high. This involves knowledge of what is wanted and of times

[3] J. A. Hopkins, W. D. Goodsell, and R. K. Buck, "An Economic Study of the Baby Beef Enterprise in Southern Iowa," *Res. Bull. 272,* Iowa Agr. Exp. Sta., April, 1940.

when supply is low in comparison with demand. A good manager will avoid mistakes in when and where to market, and also will know when and where to buy feeders or other replacement stock. To top the market with beef steers is the fond hope of many cattle producers; this means to have the best selling load or group of steers on a market on one marketing day. It is not always related to the most profit from the feeding enterprise.

The cycle of cattle numbers previously described is related to cattle prices and probable profits. The skilled operator takes advantage of these changes in profitability by altering his plans.

Keeping records

A livestock enterprise involves many phases and many transactions. Detailed written records are helpful to the operator in directing his business. With complete information at his disposal the manager may know what phases or parts of the enterprise are profitable. Management plans should be altered when a project is unprofitable, and the elements entering into production costs, such as feed, labor, and equipment use, should be changed so that profits may be made. The most desirable records depend upon the nature of the enterprise. For cattle feeding few records are needed; with a cow and calf business more records are desirable; with a purebred herd still more records are needed. A financial record is advantageous with a cattle-feeding project. With breeding herds, breeding, production, identification, and marketing records are helpful. Records permit intelligent selection of individuals for the breeding herd. With a purebred herd such records are indispensable. A program of breeding and a schedule of matings are essential adjuncts in selection (see production testing, page 220).

The exact plan will vary with the nature of the enterprise, as well as with the various features of the individual farm or ranch. A suitable plan will provide for the efficient use of all the facilities of the plant for the specific kind of production. Extra supplies of feed may be consumed by expansion; short crops will naturally cause a restriction.

Specific problems of management

Feeding and management overlap in any livestock enterprises. Many tasks which require the attention of the operator, usually at a specific time, may be regarded as managerial. Commercial feeding or cattle finishing presents the fewest problems of management of any of the beef cattle enterprises. A cow and calf herd involves a breeding program and a continuous selection plan. Furthermore, care of the calves entails such items as starting on grain, dehorning, castration, blackleg vaccination, and weaning. Under range conditions the handling of cattle requires special equipment, such as corrals and dehorning and branding chutes.

Chapter 12

BEEF CATTLE BREEDS
AND BREEDING

Robert Bakewell, an English farmer who lived from 1725 to 1795, is credited with being the founder of the study of animal breeding, which, briefly stated, is the reproduction of animals and their improvement. His activities in the breeding of Longhorn cattle, Leicester sheep, and Shire horses became noteworthy about 1760. His success is attested by the demand for his rams, which were auctioned at annual ram-lettings. As much as 1,200 guineas was received for the yearly rental of a ram. Many breeders of livestock studied and followed his methods. Bakewell established such principles as "like produces like," "breed the best to the best," and "inbreeding produces prepotency and refinement." His program was to improve his livestock in (1) utility of form, (2) quality of flesh, and (3) efficiency in the feed lot. Bakewell kept records, and his success in livestock production marked the beginning of livestock improvement.

The Shorthorn herdbook, started in 1822 in England by George Coates, was the first cattle herdbook to be established. A studbook to record the pedigrees of horses winning important races was started in 1791.

In order to understand how inheritance may be affected, we should consider the reproductive process, the breeds, breeding systems, and breeding stock selection, which are briefly discussed in the following paragraphs.

Livestock producers, by various mating systems and by selection, can to some extent control the heredity of their animal productions. As chance is involved in the segregation and recombination of the characters, perfect control is by no means possible. All progeny of a mating are not the same except in the case of identical twins, because each individual develops from a separate ovum and sperm and each receives a sample of inheritance from

193

the sire and the dam. There can be a measure of control of the animals producing and the matings permitted.

THE REPRODUCTION PROCESS

REPRODUCTION

Heifers arrive at sexual maturity soon after they have reached 1 year of age. Ample nutrition speeds up the advent of puberty; a low level of nutrition arrests sexual development. The "in-heat" period is a part of the estrus cycle. This cycle is a series of changes in the reproductive tract and related organs which is completed usually in about 3 weeks. Toward the end of the estrus, one or more ova are shed from as many Graafian follicles on the ovary and pass through the oviduct to the uterus. Mating at this time, if conditions are favorable, will result in fertilization, or a union of the ovum and the spermatozoon, and pregnancy.

The heat periods, or times of sexual receptivity, are from 12 to 24 hours in length, and are usually 21 days apart. Insemination in the middle of the in-heat period results in the highest conception rate. Heat periods are quite uniform throughout the year in cattle, but there is some tendency to intensification in the late spring and early summer. The cycle of estrus begins again about 6 weeks after calving. Upon conception, a pregnancy period of 282.1 days occurs under normal conditions, although the period may range from 270 to 290 days. As the standard deviation is about 5 days, about two-thirds of the pregnancies would terminate within the range of 282.1 ± 5 days. There appears to be significant differences in the length of the gestation period among the beef breeds. The Hereford has the longest period and the heaviest calves at birth; the Aberdeen Angus has the shortest gestation and the lightest calves; the Shorthorn was intermediate in both respects. The average birth weight is 85 pounds with a range from 40 to 140 pounds. It is usually recommended that heifers should not be bred until they are 18 to 20 months of age, for calving at a young age may affect the ultimate size of the cow and the growth of the calf until weaning time. It has been found advantageous to breed wellgrown good yearling heifers, to calve at 2 years of age.

A yearling beef bull may be used for service, but should not run with the cow herd. A yearling may be used for 12 cows during a breeding season and a two-year-old for 25 to 30 cows. A mature bull can be used to breed 40 to 50 cows in a season. With pasture breeding the number is reduced about 50 per cent. In the western range country one active mature bull is kept for each 20 to 30 cows.

Breeding efficiency has a marked effect upon the profitability of the cattle enterprise. In well-managed herds, animals that are sterile or irregular in breeding are quickly identified and removed. In some herds bulls are care-fully examined for breeding fitness and are regularly tested for quality of semen; those found unsatisfactory for breeding are not used. Poor quality semen is indicated by dead or abnormal spermatozoa.

Fig. 65. A model Hereford bull, T.R. Zato Heir. Owned by the Turner Ranch, Sulphur, Okla.

BASIS OF INHERITANCE

The gametes or male and female sex cells result from a process whereby the chromosomes are reduced to one half of the number in the body cells. In cattle it is believed that there are 24 pairs of chromosomes which carry the hereditary factors. The units of heredity are the genes, which are ar-ranged on the chromosomes. In the development of the sex cells (oögenesis and spermatogenesis) and the loss of one half of the chromosomes, the chances are even as to which of a pair is retained and which is lost. In fer-tilization the resultant zygote has the sum of the chromosomes of the two gametes, the same as the number characteristic of the species.

Prepotency

Certain individuals have the property of being able to transmit their characters to their offspring to a higher degree than others. This ability, known as "prepotency," is based upon dominance, which is the overshadowing by one character of the other member of an allelomorphic pair. For example, in cattle the polled character is dominant and its allelomorph,

Fig. 66. Model Hereford breeding cow. Donlette Jordan, grand champion female at the American Royal and International Livestock Exposition. Owned by Black and Largent, Granbury, Tex. (American Hereford Association.)

horned, is recessive. A polled bull mated to a horned cow will produce calves that are nearly all hornless, for the polled character is nearly complete in its dominance. Occasionally scurs occur, especially in the second and third generations of crossbreds; therefore this character is not a simple dominant-recessive in its behavior.

Dwarfs

Beyond the ordinary variations in size, there occur very small or dwarf individuals. There are several kinds of dwarfs, but the one of most concern is the "snorter" dwarf, which is due, apparently, to a simple autosomal recessive gene. The short-legged type—comprests and compacts—which might be termed "small type" is due to a dominant or semidominant gene. This type had a period of popularity.

The rate of occurrence of snorter dwarfs has increased; we are now developing means to identify the carriers and to eliminate them from breeding herds. The snorter dwarf is a very small, thick, short-legged individual having a peculiar head with a bulging forehead, prominent eyes, overshot protruding lower jaw, and protruding tongue. Such dwarfs breathe very heavily, have chronic bloat, and seldom live to maturity.

Apparently, in beef cattle selection, preference has been given to the "carrier" or heterozygote. With dwarf-gene carrier parents one-fourth of the calves would be dwarfs; one-fourth dwarf-gene free; and one-half normal-appearing carriers. All producers of snorter dwarfs should be discarded, for they are carriers. It is obvious that if only one parent is a dwarf-gene carrier, no dwarfs are produced. Many methods are being investigated for discovering the dwarf-carriers at a young age.

Fig. 67. Model Aberdeen Angus bull, Black Bardolier of White Gate. Owned by White Gate Farms, Flanders, N. J. (American Aberdeen Angus Breeders' Assotion.)

MULTIPLE BIRTHS

Twins occur occasionally; triplets and quadruplets are comparatively rare. In beef cattle there is about one twin in every 200 births. The rate is higher in dairy cattle, which have one in less than 100 births. The rate is not uniformly distributed in the cow population. Multiple births are more frequent in some breeds than in others, the Holstein having one of the highest rates. Twins become more likely as the age of the cow increases, up to 8 or 9 years. Spring and early fall matings have a higher rate of twinning. Twins are 10 per cent lighter in birth weight than single calves; also, they have a shorter gestation period.

In cattle very few identical twin calves occur; these come about from the division of a single fertilized ovum. All twins that appear alike are not identical. Only about 6 per cent of cattle twins are identical—paternal or monozygotic. Identical twins are useful in research projects, for, because of their identical inheritance, they can be used to measure with accuracy the effect of various environmental treatments.

The balance of cattle twins, about 94 per cent, are from two fertilized ova. Such fraternal twins are no more alike than full sibs, and it is possible that they may be half sibs; that is, they may be by different sires.

Fig. 68. A model Aberdeen Angus breeding female, Pauline of Great Oaks. Owned by the Great Oaks Stock Farm, Rochester, Mich.

Freemartin

About 94 per cent of heifer calves twinborn with bulls are sterile; these are called "freemartins." Such individuals are female in appearance, but may develop malelike characteristics. The external genitalia are smaller than normal and the vagina is short and underdeveloped.

The explanation for this occurrence is that, with vascular anastomosis, or the intermingling of the blood supply of both fetuses in the uterus, male hormones, which develop before those of the female, arrest the development of the reproductive organs of the female twin. Experimental proof is lacking for this explanation. In other mammals vascular anastomosis does occur, but it is thought that the freemartin rarely occurs. It may be explained on the basis of the high sensitiveness of the cattle gonads to hormones.

CALF CROP

About 87 calves are dropped each year per 100 cows and heifers 2 years old and older. The calving rate is the highest in the West Northcentral states and the lowest in the South Atlantic states.

Time of calving

By far the greatest percentage of calves are born in the spring. About 50 per cent of the calf crop is dropped in March, April, and May. There is also an increase in calving in September and October. There are advantages in favor of either spring or fall calves, but on the range spring calving is the most advantageous. Spring-dropped calves get more milk from their dams, are better able to withstand winter weather than are fall calves, and can be sold at weaning time in the fall. Fall calving is more commonly practiced under farming conditions than on the range.

ARTIFICIAL INSEMINATION

Artificial insemination is the deposition of spermatozoa into the female reproductive system by other than natural service. It is seldom that artificial insemination is practiced with beef cattle. With the customary methods of beef herd management it is expedient to permit the bulls to run with the herd. Many advantages can be given for artificial insemination, but these seem to be overshadowed by the difficulties involved with its practice in beef herds. In dairy herds, with closer confinement and greater observation, it is a common practice (see page 299).

BEEF CATTLE BREEDS

The objectives of the purebred breeder are somewhat different from those of the commercial beef raiser. The latter is concerned only with characters that have to do with efficient beef making and high carcass value. The breeder of purebreds considers breed-distinctive features; and there is not a high correlation between many of the breed characters and economical production. The function of the purebred breeder is to maintain registered purebred herds of such merit that the commercial cattle raiser will be able to secure for his use bulls and some cows that will improve his herd.

PUREBREDS

Purebreds are the offspring of individuals that are recorded in the herd-book of a record association and that meet the requirements for registration. A breed is a group of animals having a common origin and possessing certain distinctive characteristics which are transmitted with reasonable uniformity and which are not common to other members of the same species. The number of registrations of the various breeds for a given period is shown on page 23. Genetically, breeds are not pure in the sense that they are "homozygous." However, purebreds are less heterozygous than the foundation stock from which they were derived. It has been estimated that cattle will lose about 10 per cent in the amount of heterozygosity in a century of time under usual breeding practices.

Most of our purebreds are of European origin, and when introduced they were used in commercial livestock production to grade up herds. Marked improvement followed the use of purebreds on the so-called "common" stock. Consequently, a period of rapid expansion in the purebred herds followed and continued into the 1920's. Since that period of rapid expansion, breed associations have given more attention to breed improvement or the raising of the merit of the breeds. We have in most breeds a sufficient number produced which can be sold at a profitable price. However, there are many commercial herds that could be improved by the use of a good purebred bull, and the supply of outstanding herd sires is far from sufficient to meet the needs of the purebred herds. Our means of identifying the sires of high merit are in need of improvement. There is a definite trend toward use of production-tested sires.

CHOOSING A BREED

Some cattlemen regard the choice of a breed in beef cattle as unimportant, for there is much variation within a breed. All biological material is variable. A range in any character that influences the merit of a breed is to be expected. However, there may be an actual difference between breeds in the average in merit. Likewise there may be within a breed groups such as families or strains of superior merit. In beef cattle it may be difficult to separate differences in beef qualities due to heredity or breeding from differences caused by nutrition and environmental factors.

The breed raised in the area is an important point to consider in making a choice of beef breeds. If selection is made of the popular or numerous breed in a community, breeding stock is available locally, methods of successful producers can be observed, and there may be advantages in disposing of the production of the herd. Such additional considerations as market requirements and demand for the kind produced, ability to graze and utilize roughage, adaptability to the environmental conditions, early maturity, and hardiness should be given consideration in choosing a breed. Personal preference or fancy should be secondary to features that affect economic value.

The breed selected is probably of less importance to the commercial cattle raiser than to the purebred breeder, provided the breeds are equally adaptable to the circumstances and of equal productive capacity. The purebred breeder is subject to the effect of expanding or contracting numbers of a breed. For example, there was a time when Galloway cattle were increasing in number in the United States, and during that time Galloway cattle breeding was profitable. At present this breed is quite uncommon.

BEEF CATTLE BREEDS

There follows a brief discussion of the common beef cattle breeds; their origins, native homes, early improvement, characteristics and adaptability.

ABERDEEN ANGUS

The northeastern part of Scotland, in the counties of Aberdeen Kincardine and Forfar, was the native home of this breed. The climate is cold and damp in that rolling to rough area, and the soil is not especially productive except in the valleys.

Fig. 69. A champion Shorthorn bull, Kleern Max Juggler, grand champion at the International Livestock Exposition. Owned by Clausen Bros., Spencer, Iowa.

The breed came about from the uniting of two or more local strains, the most noted of which were the "Buchan Humlies" and the "Angus Doddies." Not much progress was made with the breed until the last half of the eighteenth century.

In 1873, George Grant of Victoria, Kansas, a native of Scotland, imported four Angus bulls. These bulls were mated with the native cattle, largely of the Texas Longhorn kind, and the crossbreds were well received. Subsequent importations were made, and the cattle soon became popular with the feeders and on the livestock markets. Early importations were made to Canada.

Black color, polled heads and smooth-hair coats are characteristic of Aberdeen Angus cattle. White is objectionable, except on the underline behind the navel, and even there it is acceptable only if moderate in extent. A white scrotum in males is undesirable.

Although Aberdeen Angus are not so large as Herefords or Shorthorn, they are not much smaller; mature fitted bulls weigh about 2,000 and cows about 1,600. The very small or the large coarse kinds are not desirable. Angus cattle are more cylindrical in form than Hereford and Shorthorn, but they are typical of the beef type in conformation and fleshing.

Aberdeen Angus cattle have proven their worth in the feed lot and in interbreed competition for finished cattle. They are good rustlers and are well adapted to range conditions. The cows generally produce sufficient milk for their calves. In the feed lot Angus calves gain fast, reach market maturity at a young age, and produce highly acceptable carcasses.

BRAHMAN OR ZEBU CATTLE

The Brahman or Zebu cattle belong to the "Bos indicus" rather than the "Bos taurus," which includes the European originated breeds. There are four principal breeding stocks in the species which have been imported to this country. They are: (1) Nellore, (2) Gir, (3) Guzerat, (4) Krishna Valley. Distinctive characters are evident in each of these breeds. As in other cattle, some of these breeds have more pronounced dairy characteristics than others. There are numerous groups and breeds of Zebu cattle in India.[1]

In 1849 Dr. J. B. Davis of South Carolina made the first importation to this country of Brahman cattle (one bull and two cows) of which we have record.[2] He also brought over three bulls from Australia for a Mr. Barrow in 1861. In 1904, A. M. McFadden of Victoria, Texas, bought two head from the Hagenbeck Circus at St. Louis. In 1906 Abel P. Borden imported 51 head of various breeds and colors (gray, white, black, and

[1] N. R. Josh and Ralph W. Phillips, "Zebu Cattle of India and Pakistan," *Food and Agriculture Organization of the United Nations,* Rome, Italy, March, 1953.
[2] C. L. Douglas, *Cattle Kings of Texas,* C. Baugh, Dallas, Texas, 1939.

red), of which 33 head were taken to Texas. In 1954 registration of 17,010 head of Brahman cattle was reported by the American Brahman Association and the Pan-American Zebu Association recorded 1,980 head. This latter Association accepts offspring of Brazilian Brahman bulls recently brought to this country.

Fig. 70. A champion Shorthorn female, Golden Rule Luxury, grand champion at the International Livestock Exposition. Owned by Holz Bros., Grand Junction, Iowa.

Brahman cattle are different anatomically in that they have a hump over the shoulders, large, loose, pendulous dewlap, folds of skin along the underline, a slender whiplike tail, and large pendent ears. In color they vary from a cream or chocolate-brown to black, and the hoofs are black. The bulls roar rather than bellow, and the call of the cow is somewhat like a grunt. They cross readily with the common cattle, and the crosses are not infertile. Brahman cattle are resistant to ticks and tick fever. They are adapted to tropical and semitropical conditions. High temperature, humidity, and intense sunlight are withstood better by Brahmans and their crosses than by common cattle. In regions of high temperature Brahmans are especially suitable because of their resistance to diseases and insects and also their hardiness. Their heat tolerance is due to lower heat production, greater surface area per unit of weight, shorter hair, and other body-temperature regulating mechanisms not visually apparent.[3]

[3] Samuel Brody, "Climate Physiology of Cattle," *J. of Dairy Sci.,* Vol. 39, No. 6, June, 1956.

According to E. J. Warwick, Brahman crosses can be expected to perform rather well to weaning especially if there is Brahman blood in the dam.[4] Performance in the feedlot does not differ greatly between the two breeds, and carcass differences are much smaller than usually thought. It is pointed out that comparisons made have not taken disposition or calving percentages into account and that most experiments have been conducted in the far South, mostly in the coastal plain area.

Breeds of Brahman breeding developed in the United States

Santa Gertrudis. The Santa Gertrudis [5] breed was developed on the King Ranch in Southeast Texas by crossing the Shorthorn and the Brahman breeds, both of beef type. In attempting to develop a cattle breed most suitable for subtropical ranch conditions, a bull, Monkey, was produced. From that bull, by means of close inbreeding and selection, came all the present day Santa Gertrudis cattle.

The breed is a solid deep cherry-red in color. It is commonly horned although polled individuals occur. In size it is comparable to the larger of the beef breeds. Typical individuals have short straight hair and show slightly their Brahman ancestry by somewhat large dropping ears, a loose hide, and some skin folds along the dewlap and underline. Because of these qualities they are more heat tolerant than some other breeds.

The Santa Gertrudis has been widely distributed in the United States and in other countries. Individuals gain fast on grass, and do well on scant vegetation. Only selected or approved animals can be recorded.

Beefmasters. The Beefmasters were also developed in Texas, by the Lasaters. In color the Beefmasters are dun, brown, reddish-brown or red, with some white markings or spotting. The foundation came from the use of Brahman bulls of several beef breeds upon a large herd of Hereford and Shorthorn cows. It is estimated that the breed is one-half Brahman and one-fourth each of Hereford and Shorthorn. Selection and progeny testing were techniques used in developing the breed.

Brangus. The Brangus is a black, hornless breed developed in Oklahoma from a Brahman-and-Angus cross. In breeding they are three-eighths Brahman and five-eighths Angus. The program for development of the breed is similar to that used in the formation of the Santa Gertrudis.

Charbray. The Charbray cattle are another breed from a cross-bred foundation: the Charolaise and the Brahman. The Charolaise is from the province of that name in the prairie area of central France. A few have

[4] E. J. Warwick, 49th Annual Meeting of the American Society of Animal Production, Chicago, Illinois, November, 1952.

[5] Robert J. Kleberg, Jr., "The Santa Gertrudis Breed of Beef Cattle," Kingsville, Texas.

been brought to the United States via Mexico. To qualify as a Charbray an individual must be at least three-fourths Charolaise, and not more than one-fourth or less than one-eighth Brahman.

The Charbray is a large, muscular, horned, creamy-white breed. It shows but slight evidence of its Brahman breeding and few Brahman characteristics. Charbray cattle are popular in the south and west because they are vigorous and fast growing, graze well, and handle easily.

Braford. The Braford, a cross of Brahman and Hereford, is still in the formative stage.

GALLOWAY

The Galloway was developed in southwestern Scotland, in the counties of Kirkcudright and Widon, formerly the province of Galloway. In this area the climate is rigorous, being damp and cold much of the time. The land is rough but the grazing is good. At a comparatively early date this breed took form; it is considered one of the oldest of British breeds. This breed probably descended from the native cattle. In England there is a belted Galloway.

Galloways were first brought to this continent by the Graham Brothers of Ontario, Canada, in 1853. Importations were made to Michigan in 1870. Soon thereafter they became widespread in the central and western states.

The breed resembles Aberdeen Angus in that it is black in color and polled. It is distinguished by its characteristic curly hair coat which may develop a brownish tinge. Galloways are also smaller, slower growing, somewhat less prominent in the poll, longer bodied, and flatter of rib than the Angus.

Galloways are rugged, hardy cattle that do well as grazers. They have never been numerous in this country.

HEREFORD

The native home of Hereford cattle is in Hereford county which is in the west central part of England. The land is rolling and the climate favorable. Excellent crops and abundant pasture are produced. Very little is known about the origin of the breed, but the "white-faced" cattle were early known as being able to make maximum use of forage.

Henry Clay of Kentucky is credited with making the first importation of Hereford in 1817. About 1825 Admiral Coffin of the Royal British Navy presented a male and a female to the Massachusetts Society for Promoting Agriculture. Soon thereafter numerous importations were made.

The white face of the Hereford is distinctive. White is also present to

Fig. 71. A Polled Hereford bull, Domino Princo. Owned by Falklands Farm, Shellsburg, Pa.

Fig. 72. A champion Polled Hereford female, Domestic Larryette M 8. Owned by the Bridwell Hereford Ranch, Windthorst, Tex.

varying degrees on the underline, including the legs below the knees and hocks. The breast, flank, switch and crest are usually white. Extensive white on the back legs or flanks is objectionable.

Herefords are distinctly a beef breed, and have the typical general appearance of beef cattle, being broad, deep, and heavily muscled. Ample size and ruggedness of constitution typify the breed. They are one of the larger beef breeds; mature bulls weigh 2,200 pounds in fitted condition and cows similarly fitted weigh 1,800 pounds. Suitability for grazing under a wide range of conditions has been responsible for their popularity in range states. They are also highly acceptable under feed-lot conditions.

The Polled Herefords are similar to Herefords but are free from horns, or naturally polled. In 1901 Warren Gammon secured from various breeders 4 bull and 7 female purebred polled Herefords, to start the first double-standard Polled Hereford herd. Single-standard herds in which just one of the parents was naturally hornless had been started previously. The Polled Association handles the purebred registrations of polled cattle in its registry.

The natural absence of horns has many advantages both on the range and in the feed lot.

SCOTCH HIGHLAND CATTLE

This breed is also known as the West Highland. It was developed in West Scotland and the Hebrides Islands. Highland cattle have been bred for centuries in this very rough mountainous country. The rigorous climate and limited feed supplies of this area are responsible for the breed's ruggedness.

There is wide range of color; black, red, yellow, dun, and silver occur, but brown is preferred. Typical individuals have wide, branching horns and a very hairy, long, shaggy hair wat.

Several importations to this country have been made, but the breed to date has failed to compete successfully in beef production.

SHORTHORN

The Shorthorn came from the northeastern English counties: Durham, Northumberland, York, and Lincoln, especially from the Tees River Valley. Excellent pastures and crops are grown in that area. The breed evolved from the numerous cattle strains native to that section. As the cattle were improved they were called Shorthorns to distinguish them from the unimproved Longhorns. They were often called Durham cattle.

Miller and Gough of Virginia are given credit for bringing the first Shorthorns into the United States in 1783. There were some other importations made shortly thereafter. Col. Lewis Sanders of Kentucky imported 8 head

Fig. 73. Model Polled Shorthorn bull, Alpine Sensation, champion at the International Livestock Exposition. Owned by Paul Teagardin, Ashville, Ohio.

in 1817. Soon numerous importations were made, including three large groups by the Ohio Importing Company in 1834–36.

In color the Shorthorn is roan, red, white, or a combination of red with white spots. Dark red is the most popular color, followed by roan. Red is an incomplete dominant, white is recessive, and the roan is the heterozygous condition. Spotting is in the mixed red and white. A dark muzzle is very objectionable. Shorthorns are one of the largest of the beef breeds. Fitted bulls weigh 2,200 pounds and fitted cows 1,900 pounds. In form Shorthorns are somewhat more rectangular than Herefords or Angus.

There are two divisions of the breed: the dual-purpose type and the beef type, which is the Scotch strain developed by Amos Cruickshank. Shorthorns may be horned or polled.

Beef Shorthorns and their crosses are well adapted to farm, feed-lot, or range conditions. The cows are good milkers and produce fast-growing calves. They are widely distributed in the United States.

POLLED SHORTHORNS

The polled Shorthorn was developed in the United States. For a time it was called Polled Durham. In all respects the Polled Shorthorns are comparable to the original breed, and they are recorded in the same herd book.

Fig. 74. A model Polled Shorthorn female, a champion at the National Western Stock Show, Denver, Colo. Owned by the Lynwood Farms, Carmel, Ind.

OTHER BEEF BREEDS

There are other beef-type breeds, such as the Sussex Welch Black, and still others known in Great Britain but not common in this country.

BREEDING

PERCENTAGE OF BLOOD

Percentage of blood is used often to express the amount of pure breeding in a grade or a crossbred. A crossbred female mated to a male of a third breed will have offspring which is 50 per cent of the sire and 25 per cent each of the components of the crossbred female. Santa Gertrudis cattle for example are three-eighths Brahman and five-eighths Shorthorn, which of course would be true of an individual having five great-grandparents of the Shorthorn and three of the Brahman breed. It will be readily seen that this method can be used to express the inheritance of a grade or a cross and to evaluate an individual in a pedigree.

The percentage-of-blood idea, based on Galton's law of ancestral hered-ity, does not fit into the explanation of unit characters that involve one to three factors. For example, the behavior of horned and polled characters does not lend itself to explanation in terms of percentage of blood. The Mendelian law offers a more plausible explanation for the inheritance of unit characters. For example, the black of the Angus or Galloway is dominant to the red of the Red Polled. The crossbred between these two breeds is not midway between the two breeds in color. On the other hand, in such features as conformation, a cross may be midway between the parents, on the average, because conformation is due to many factors and their interaction.

BREEDING SYSTEMS

Breeding systems are based upon closeness of relationship between animals mated or on their similarity or dissimilarity in individuality. On the basis of relationship, we may have grading up, crossbreeding, and inbreeding. On the basis of resemblance, we may mate those which appear to be alike or those which are unlike. This is assortative mating or a form of selection.

Inbreeding, or the mating of closely related individuals, is not practiced to any great extent in commercial cattle raising. Its use is limited more to purebred herds for the establishment of lines or families, descendants of noted individuals. We do not have in cattle the situation that exists in commercial corn growing, where inbred lines are developed which respond favorably when crossed. Commercial corn growers use hybrid seed corn, which usually gives greater yields and greater resistance to wind, disease, and unfavorable conditions than open-pollinated varieties. The inbreeding to form inbred lines reduces vigor and fertility, which can be tolerated in corn because the reproductive rate is greater than it is in domestic animals. Beef herds have been developed from the progeny of one sire, but these are rare, and in practice cattle breeders often resort to an outcross in an attempt to gain vigor.

Crossbreeding or mixed breeding preceded the formation of many of our breeds of today, and this was followed in many instances by inbreeding.

Grading up

By successive use of purebred sires a herd may be graded up. The amount of blood of the common or scrub stock will be reduced by this process. It will readily be seen that each use of a purebred sire reduces by one half the remaining blood of the common stock. The first sire produces offspring of one half pure breeding if the dam is of scrub breeding. The amount of purebred blood increases successively to three fourths, to seven eighths, to fifteen sixteenths, and so on, by the use of purebred sires. The value of the offspring is enhanced over that of the parent roughly by one half the supe-

Fig. 75. A Brahman bull, Aristocrat Manso. Owned by J. D. Hudgins, Hungerford, Tex.

riority of the purebred over the grade. It is quite obvious that the amount of improvement is lessened by each step, and the high grades are little if any poorer than purebreds. Actually, the purebreds in most instances are increasing in merit, and the grades then tend to move upward in merit in the grading-up process in the same manner as purebreds improve. "Grading up" designates the process when confined to one breed. When grade females are mated to a purebred sire of another breed, it is crossbreeding.

Marked improvement in productive capacity has come about; in 3 decades there has been a 38 per cent increase in the beef produced per cow per year. Grading up is responsible for some of that improvement.

Crossing cattle of nondescript breeding with the beef breeds

Bulls of beef breeding, when mated to cows of nondescript breeding, will produce calves that are decidedly higher in quality of beef than those of straight nondescript breeding. This is essentially the grading-up process.

Native eastern Arkansas cattle were crossed with the Aberdeen Angus at the Arkansas Experiment Station.[6] These native cattle showed no evidence of immediate relationship to improved beef breeds and were small

[6] H. E. Dvorachek and Arthur T. Semple, "Beef Producing Qualities of Purebred Aberdeen Angus Cattle Compared with Arkansas Native Cattle," Arkansas Agri. Exp. Sta., *Bull. 247*, 1931.

sized, hardy, prolific, and accustomed to shift for themselves in large forested areas. During the trial the native cows doubled their weight; poor nutrition was, therefore, responsible to a considerable extent for lack of size. A study was made of the straightbreds, Aberdeen Angus and native, and also of the crossbreds and the second cross.

The native cows produced weanling calves at a lower cost than did the Aberdeen Angus cows or the crosses. This was due to the smaller size of the native cows and the resultant low feed for maintenance requirement. There was practically no difference in the birth weights of the calves, the daily gains, and the feed requirements per unit of gain. The purebreds and the second crosses dressed slightly higher than the crossbreds and the natives. In grade on foot and in the carcass, the purebreds and second crosses ranked first and second, with the crossbreds third and the native a low fourth. The higher selling price of the carcasses from the offspring of the purebred bull made possible a greater return over feed costs.

Crossbreeding

Crossbreeding is the mating of individuals that are dissimilar, that is, of different breeds, species, or family. Family crossing is referred to as "outcrossing."

In crossbreeding of beef cattle we may classify the crosses into three groups: (1) breed crosses within the beef type, (2) breed crosses between the beef and dairy types, (3) crosses between beef cattle and other species. The latter are referred to as "hybrids."

1. Crosses between various breeds of beef cattle. Some breeds were crossed in the formative period; for example, some Galloway supposedly was used with the Shorthorn. Also, beef breed crosses have been popular in the beef trade in England. Crosses of the Shorthorn with the Aberdeen Angus or the Galloway give a blue-gray color, which was popular on the English markets. Crossbreeding of beef cattle may be advantageous for the range producer when he is able to crossbreed systematically and when he either feeds his own steers or sells direct to the feeder. Buyers of feeder cattle tend to prefer those which are of uniform breeding, type, size, color, and quality. Therefore crossbred feeder cattle that are not uniform may sell for less than uniform straightbred cattle. This disadvantage does not exist on the market for finished cattle. Crossbred range cows have proved very satisfactory.[7] See page 216.

An eight year comparison of straightbreds and crossbreds, Angus and Herefords, in Ohio failed to indicate any significant effect of hybrid vigor.[8]

2. Breed crosses involving dairy-type breeds. These are not uncommon.

---

[7] Bradford Knapp, Jr., A. L. Baker, and R. T. Clark, "Crossbred Beef Cattle for the Northern Great Plains," *Circ. 810,* U.S.D.A., April, 1949.

[8] *Ohio Research Bulletin 703,* 1951.

When the outlook in dairy production is not favorable, dairymen are tempted to cross their dairy herds with beef bulls. What might be expected from such a cross may be judged from the following investigation.

Discrimination against dairy-type steers is mainly because the carcasses that they yield are inferior to those of the beef-type steers. The carcass of the dairy-type steer is less acceptable to the consumer, consequently they sell lower than beef-bred steers; also when offered as feeders or stockers they undersell beef-bred steers.

Straightbred Holstein calves were compared with those of straightbred Aberdeen Angus crosses between the two breeds in three trials at the Wisconsin Agricultural Experiment Station.[9] In these tests all the calves were finished at 12 to 15 months at a weight from 900 to 1,000 pounds. Following is a tabulation of the average for the 3 years for the fattening period, which was about 200 days. The calves were allowed to nurse until they were about 6 months old. Creep feeding of grain was practiced during the nursing period.

FATTENING CROSSBRED VERSUS PUREBRED CALVES FOR BABY BEEF

	HOLSTEIN CALVES	ABERDEEN ANGUS CALVES	CROSSBRED CALVES
Daily gain, pounds	2.37	2.19	2.05
Feed cost for 100 pounds gain	$11.27	$12.20	$13.30
Average selling price	$10.05	$13.00	$12.17
Dressing percentage	59	62	62
Carcass grade			
Prime		8	
Choice		12	12
Good	1	5	8
Medium	22		2
Fair	1		

The Holstein calves outgained the other group but sold much lower and had a lower carcass yield. This group also made gains on less feed cost than the other group, probably because they did not carry as much fat when the fattening period began. The carcasses of the Holsteins were lacking in flesh over the shoulder blades, ribs, and loin. Also, they were uneven in fleshing. The purebred Angus carcasses were smoother in finish than those of the crossbreds, but differences in the color of fat and lean, marbling of meat, and quality were difficult to detect. In the cooked beef there was no outstanding difference in the quality.

Observations that have been made on crosses made with dairy-type and beef-type cattle indicate that the beef-type characters are dominant in

[9] J. G. Fuller and B. H. Roche, "Fattening Crossbred vs. Purebred Calves for Baby Beef," *University of Wisconsin Pamphlet,* June 8, 1929.

the head and forequarters, while the dairy-type characters are dominant in the rear quarters.

3. Crosses between beef cattle and other species. Of the crosses between beef cattle and other species, too—with the Brahman and with the American buffalo—are worthy of discussion because of their value in certain environments.

A. BRAHMAN CROSSES. When used for commercial beef production it is common to limit the amount of Brahman blood to one fourth or one half. Cattle of Brahman breeding are common along the coastal region of the Gulf of Mexico from Mexico to southern Florida. A few of the Brahman crosses are raised in other range areas. These cattle usually are sold to the meat packers from the range, and are seldom fed very heavily on concentrates.

In a study[10] made on the feeding of heavy grain ration to Shorthorns

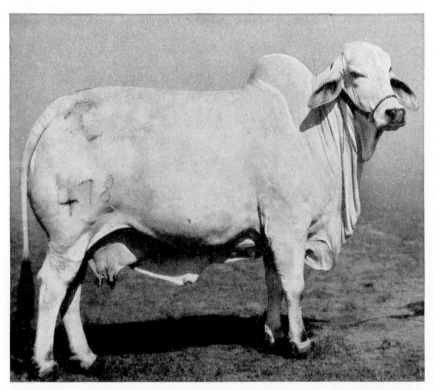

Fig. 76. A noted Brahman cow, Dutchess. Owned by J. D. Hudgins, Hungerford, Tex.

[10] W. H. Black, A. T. Semple, and J. L. Lush, "Beef Production and Quality as Influenced by Crossing Brahmans with Hereford and Shorthorn Cattle," *Tech. Bull. 417*, U.S.D.A., 1934.

and Herefords and crosses of these breeds with the Brahman, it was found that the straightbred steers were slightly or moderately superior in daily gain, economical use of concentrates, and appraised value of the carcass per 100 pounds. The steers of Brahman breeding had less shrinkage from feed lot to market and had a significantly higher dressing percentage. The Brahman crossbreds had smaller heads, larger hides, and smaller digestive tracts than the non-Brahman cattle. The carcasses of the Brahman crosses graded lower than those of the beef breeds. Brahman-beef crosses, fed and managed like beef-bred steers yielding carcasses that graded good, yielded instead carcasses that graded low good. In comparisons made of the meat of the Brahmans and non-Brahmans there were but slight differences, and considering the various qualities which affect cooked beef the two kinds are approximately equal in desirability.

Fig. 77. Santa Gertrudis cow, Mama Grande. Four years old; weight 1,820 pounds. Owned by the King Ranch, Kingville, Tex. (Santa Gertrudis Breeders' International, Kingville, Tex.)

After a two years' test in eastern Oregon,[11] it was concluded that the Brahman-Hereford crossbreds were inferior to straight Herefords in winter gain and carcass grade.

B. CROSSES OF CATTLE WITH THE AMERICAN BISON. Attempts have been made to form a breed by crossing the American bison with domestic

[11] Hubert Farris, Jr., *et al.,* "Brahman and Hereford Crossbreds," Oregon State College, *Bull. 549,* Corvallis, Oregon, June, 1955.

cattle. A bison bull is mated to cows, and the hybrid [12] is called a "cattalo." The cows have physical difficulties in giving birth to the hybrid calves. Also, the hybrid males have low fertility. The reverse cross, that is, mating domestic bulls to bison cows, has been quite successful at the Dominion Experimental Farm, Wainwright, Alberta, Canada. The crosses are superior in strength, vigor, cold tolerance, and survival ability, and may have commercial possibilities. Recently bison and Brahman crosses had been made.

Advantages of the crossbreds

Most of the characters, such as size and vigor, which are desirable and contribute to commercial value, are dominant. Crossbreds, therefore, gain from the accumulation of the dominant characters from the strains, breeds, or species crossed. This heterosis is greater in some crosses than others.

Crossbred females have greater heterozygosity, and, therefore, they may have offspring less uniform than offspring of straightbred cows. Buyers of feeder cattle sometimes object to mixed colors. This is because inferior bred animals of poor feed-lot response are often mixed or off in color; the same criticism does not hold for crossbred feeders of good beef breeding. If crossbred females are kept for the breeding herd they require, in most instances, more bulls, since the female breeding herd is replaced in about 2½ years time. Under normal conditions, cows of different breeding in the herd may require bulls of different breeds in a rotational program.

Crossbred females have proved themselves to be excellent range cows. They are high in fertility and producers of heavy calves at weaning time. These advantages seem to carry on beyond the first generation.

It should be pointed out that successful crossbreeding depends upon use of the best possible individuals in the crosses. If carried beyond the first stage or cross, a rotational crossing system is most desirable. In feed-lot tests it is commonly observed that the crossbreds make more rapid gains. However, there appears to be little or no difference in feed-lot efficiency between crossbred and straightbred feeder cattle of beef breeding.

BREEDING STOCK SELECTION

One of the prime essentials in the successful establishment and maintenance of a beef breeding herd is the selection of the individuals which compose the herd. Even in an established herd the choice of replacements for the individuals being removed demands careful judgment if the merit of

---

[12] Some confusion exists concerning the use of the term. A hybrid may be a species cross or merely the offspring of parents unlike one another in one or more characters that are inherited. In corn breeding, "hybrid" has still another use, for "hybrid corn" is the product of crossing inbred lines.

the herd is to be maintained or enhanced. The selection of a herd sire is likewise a problem worthy of much consideration since, in the usual herd where but one sire is used, the sire contributes one half of the inheritance to a crop of calves. With beef cattle 40 to 50 per cent of the females and 3 to 5 per cent of the males are needed for replacements to maintain cattle numbers.

BASIS FOR SELECTION

There are three bases for selection in beef cattle: (1) pedigree, (2) production records, (3) individuality. We decide what to add or to retain in the herd mainly by studying performance and appearance. It is quite obvious that all bases should be considered in making a selection, if possible. However, selection is often based upon individuality or appearance, because of the absence of production records and records of ancestry.

1. Selection based upon pedigree. A pedigree is a record of the ancestry of an individual; it gives also the names and addresses of the breeder and the owner and the individuals date of birth. Performance records of the animals, if available, may be given, as well as any special distinction of the sire or the dam. It is obvious that only favorable information will be given relative to production, for production records are not necessarily a part of the pedigree.

The pedigree may be a valuable and fairly reliable guide in selecting breeding herd members. Its value is dependent upon the information given. It may not be too helpful, because the individual inheritance is not known and is merely estimated from parents' or relatives' performance. The sample of inheritance from either parent may be average or above or below average. The usefulness of the pedigree, particularly of the sire and dam, is in supplementing the other bases of selection, that is, individual merit and performance.

2. Selection based upon production. The most reliable basis for selection is the production testing of the individual, its parents or other relatives. There has been a marked increase in production testing of all kinds of livestock. In beef animals the measuring of production is more difficult than with some other kinds of livestock. Beef sires and dams that produce offspring efficient in feed utilization, rapid-gaining and of desirable carcass quality are desired by cattle producers and beef consumers alike.

The herd manager can take advantage of the rather high heritability of rapidity and economy gains by selecting breeding stock better than average in these qualities. It has been shown that meat tenderness is inherited and that it can be passed to succeeding generations through selective breeding. Conformation is also to be considered. See production testing, page 220.

3. Selection based upon appearance. Knowledge of the prerequisites of good beef type is essential in the successful management of a beef breeding herd. It is possible to detect actual differences in animals on foot that are related to carcass value. A correlation of $+0.69$ has been found between grade as feeders and carcass grade. The heritability of grade and type of beef cattle is 30 per cent or higher, which would permit progress in this area by proper selection. If then the sire or the dam were better than average by 50 per cent in some character like grade and type it would be expected that offspring would average 15 per cent higher in that character. However, since the genotype may not be the same as the phenotype, we are not certain about the transmitting ability of a specific beef sire or dam. Certain requirements for breeding herd individuals include the qualities desired in an ideal market steer. For example, a market steer should be wide, deep, and low set, and we have found from experience that breeding individuals of that same conformation produce their kind rather consistently. That individuals of correct type are produced by individuals deficient in type is the exception rather than the rule. Following are the main items of individuality or appearance emphasized in selecting beef-type breeding cows and heifers; showring judging is on the same major considerations, with some emphasis upon breed characteristics as well.

A. SIZE.   In keeping with our desire for heavy weight for age in beef steers and the credit which weight advantage gives in judging beef steers, we demand heavy weight for age in our beef breeding stock. Extremely small, compact individuals are to be avoided in making selections. However, we can have breeding stock that is too large. Late maturity is a consequence of large mature size. Rapid gains are correlated with large size, and rapid gains in most instances are more economical than slow gains. Consequently, in our beef herds we want sufficient size to give rapid gains, but this should be consistent with the early maturity market requirement for finished cattle. Big, coarse, rough steers, unfinished at marketable weights, are not in demand on the cattle markets; small, dwarflike pony steers are not profitable to the feeder.

Size differences can be noted in breeding cattle. Aside from dwarfs, we recognize the large, intermediate or conventional, and small. The latter are often referred to as "comprest" or "compact." In most instances the intermediate is the practical size, considering economy of gains and desirability of carcass. The intermediate approach the large in gaining ability and the small in finishing ability. Steers from large breeding stock will not yield top grades of lightweight carcasses, for they pass the required weight before the desired condition or fatness is reached. It is evident also that steers from small stock will not profitably produce heavy carcasses. Large cattle arrive at a given weight at a younger age. It should be emphasized again that, with individuals of the same mature size, those which gain faster and mature earlier in a given environment are more efficient.

In a comparison of large cows with smaller, more compact cows, it was found that although the large cows had larger calves, there was no difference in proportion of calf weight to cow weight. The big cows, however, excelled in per cent of calf crop and in lifetime production or length of productive life in the herd. The big cows were more hardy and productive.

B. FORM.   In form the beef breeding cow or bull should be comparable to the ideal beef steer, which, briefly described, is wide, deep, low set, symmetrical, straight in lines, and not paunchy. The breeding animals must conform to the beef type, but there are differences due to sex. It is quite obvious that paunchiness is tolerated less in finished steers than in breeding cattle and that, even with the steer, efficiency of production dictates ample capacity for feed. Natural fleshing or thickness of flesh is estimated by thickness in the shoulder, crops, and round, or parts where the thickness of fleshing is not masked by a heavy fat covering.

C. CONDITION.   Fatness in excess is not desirable in breeding animals. A thick even covering of flesh without excess of fat is the goal. Overconditioning or high fitting is not an uncommon fault in show animals. It is a detriment to the animal and wasteful. Evidence of fat-storing ability is not to be minimized, because that ability is demanded in commercial cattle. Moderate fleshing is typical of the individuals kept for breeding.

D. QUALITY.   A reasonable degree of quality is desired. A moderate size to the head and bone, general smoothness, and a pliable hide indicate the quality preferred. Too much emphasis can be put on quality, especially in the refinement of the animal.

E. BREED TYPE.   Although conformity to breed characteristics may not be associated with economy of beef production, individuals typical of the beef breeds are desired because of their uniformity.

F. SEX CHARACTER.   When the bull is approaching maturity, attention is given to the development of the secondary sexual characters, as well as the primary sex organs. The maturing bull shows a heavier front quarter, a crest, a heavier head and horn, and a change in temperament. These qualities of masculinity are desired by cattle raisers, for they may indicate virility. Prepotency cannot be estimated by the appearance of masculinity in males.

Similar changes occur in the growth and development of the heifer. Femininity is stressed by cattlemen in selecting heifers and cows. In this connection mammary development is also considered. A beef breeding cow or heifer should produce calves regularly and yield enough milk to give its calves a good start.

G. CONSTITUTION.   A strong constitution is an important consideration in selecting beef breeding cattle. To the breeder this implies the ability of livestock to thrive under a wide range of conditions.

Additional considerations in beef breeding herd selections

Following are some further points to heed in making additions to the breeding herd.

1. Age.   Younger animals have longer periods of expected usefulness. Yet with very young individuals it is impossible to estimate development. Only with older individuals can breeding ability be appraised.

2. Freedom from disease.   In making herd additions precautions should be taken to prevent the introduction of cattle diseases. Tuberculosis and abortion disease tests and retests serve as safeguards against the introduction of those diseases. The herd from which purchases are contemplated should be investigated thoroughly for health and regularity of breeding.

3. Breeding history.   When individuals of breeding age are being selected, their breeding history should be examined. Only animals of regular breeding records are worth considering in purchasing beef breeding cows and bulls.

4. Reliability of the breeder.   Purchase of breeding stock should be made from those who have an established reputation for fair dealing. In sales of beef cattle all animals of breeding age sold are guaranteed to be breeders. Cows in calf or with calves at foot are taken as proved breeders and no further guarantee is given. Guarantees are often made also on retesting for tuberculosis and abortion disease.

5. Cost, including cost of delivery.   All herd additions should represent a forward step in herd improvement. In founding a herd or adding to it, the choice of the individuals is more important than the cost if it is within reasonable limits. In determining costs the expense of delivery is to be included.

Production testing with beef cattle

Milk and butter production can be determined by weighing the milk yielded and testing the butterfat content of the milk. Beef production is not so easily measured. A test to demonstrate differences with beef cattle must measure efficiency of gains in weight of feed consumed for a given increase, and must also measure the value of the carcass; for comparative purposes conditions of feeding must be comparable. Such tests require considerable time and are expensive. The calves at birth must be ear tagged or tattooed for identification, and their birth dates recorded. The calves are weighed at weaning time and at other periods, and their gains are recorded. By means of correction factors for weight and gain differences, allowances may be made for differences in tests, just as the dairyman has an age differential for dairy cows of different ages. For example correction factors are available for range cattle, so that weaning weights may be corrected for differences in age and sex of the calves, as well as the age of their dams.

Progency testing permits estimating the ability to transmit productive qualities by sires and dams. The difference in the progeny of a sire within a beef breed is illustrated by the following data.[13]

AVERAGE POUNDS FEED CONSUMED BY PROGENY TO PRODUCE 100 POUNDS GAIN

SIRE NUMBER	CONCENTRATES	HAY	TOTAL
1	504	297	801
2	643	351	994

A difference of 193 pounds of feed is noted in the progeny of the two sires in the feed consumed to produce 100 pounds gain in weight. In all probability, as much variation existed in the carcass value. This difference in economy of gain is impossible to predict from the conformation of the progeny.

Apparently, it is not necessary to feed out a large number of calves from a sire to determine his breeding ability. Three closely related beef bulls rated on 62 calves did not change materially in their ranking after the first 5 to 10 calves finished the record of performance test.

As both parents contribute equally to the inheritance of a progeny, it is necessary to test for performance not only the sires but also the dams. The fact that a mature sire may be used for a herd of 40 to 50 cows when hand mating is practiced (or 50 per cent less under pasture mating) emphasizes the greater influence of the sire. Since heredity is an important part in gaining ability it can be appraised by comparative feeding tests on prospective sires.

One factor that complicates measurement of the hereditary possibility of an animal is the fact that, although the sire provides 50 per cent of the genes for an offspring, and these genes carry only a sample of the inheritance. This explains why full brothers are not identical.

Individual merit testing is being carried out with beef cattle in the testing of beef bulls. The calves are placed in feed lots at weaning time and fed to a given weight, in some cases 900 pounds. The rapid and economical gaining individuals are saved for breeding bulls. There is a high correlation between the performance of the bulls in the feed lot and that of their offspring. In a survey [14] of the kinds of bulls used in range commercial herds, it was found that nearly 94 per cent of the cattlemen used purebred bulls and that 26 per cent were buying production test bulls. When production tested bulls are more widely available, their use will increase.

With the cow breeding herd, there are records which may be kept to identify the productive individuals. The most important records are: regu-

[13] Bradford Knapp, Jr., "Performance Testing in Beef Cattle," *Extension Animal Husbandman*, U.S.D.A., No. 58, June, 1940.
[14] M. E. Ensminger, *National Livestock Producer*, May, 1948.

larity of calving, and birth weights and weaning weights of the calves. Calf weights are highly heritable; consequently selection for these features could bring about herd improvement. Large, vigorous calves have a low mortality rate and make rapid gains.

"Bull grading," a form of selective breeding, has been found effective in the range states in the improvement of range cattle. Bulls are put in 4 classes. Only the top two classes are used regularly; included in these are bulls which would sire calves that would grade as choice feeders or, later, as choice slaughter cattle. Class 3 bulls are used occasionally and class 4 bulls are culled from the herd.

The lowest grade of bulls are described as [15] "Plain, upstanding, slow-maturing, thin-fleshed, lacking in quality and character, and having serious defects in conformation." The complete program not only includes evaluation of the bull, but also proper management, selection of cows, identification, weighing and grading calves after weaning, and checking the cow herd after weaning.

AMERICAN BEEF CATTLE PERFORMANCE REGISTRY ASSOCIATION [16]

This organization was formed in 1955 in order to encourage measuring and recording of performance and production of beef cattle and to encourage the use of records as an aid in selecting more productive breeding cattle. Adequate records, when employed in a sound breeding program, which gives proper emphasis to quality and beef conformation as well as to production, will give producers an opportunity to breed more profitable beef cattle in the future. The policy of the organization is to work through state Performance Testing Associations as they are organized. Individual memberships are available in states without organizations.

COMMUNITY BREEDING

In beef cattle we seldom find anything comparable to a dairy herd improvement association or to a stallion joint ownership group. Among dairy cattle breeders such organizations as bull circles have flourished; among beef cattlemen they are far less common. The advantages of a community breeding project are apparent. Following is a list of these advantages:

[15] Ruben Albough, Horace T. Strong, and F. D. Carroll, "Guide to Beef Cattle Improvement Program," *Circular 451,* California Agricultural Experiment Station and Extension Service, Davis, California, March, 1956.

[16] "General and Special Rules," American Beef Cattle Performance Registry Association, Canyon, Texas, May, 1955.

1. Sires of proved ability can be kept, for exchange of valuable sires is promoted.

2. Selections can be made from herds in the immediate vicinity, with more facts available and at less cost, instead of from herds at some distance away.

3. Line breeding without extreme inbreeding can be accomplished.

4. Breeders can acquire information from the experiences of others.

5. Buyers are attracted by the reputation of a community for breeding stock produced, and more sale stock is available.

6. Advertising, sale expenses, and other business costs of the breeders can be handled cooperatively, with lower costs.

7. By pooling resources and joint ownership, owners can purchase better sires.

In spite of their many advantages, community breeding enterprises and organizations have not become numerous.

Chapter 13

DAIRY CATTLE—GENERAL VIEW

With beef cattle, the main source of income is from the sale of steers, heifers, and cows for slaughter. With dairy cattle, on the other hand, the major income is derived from the sale of milk and milk products. However, considerable meat is obtained from dairy cattle, for finally milk cows and dairy bulls are marketed to the slaughterers, and veal calves are largely a dairy by-product. Also, a number of cows that would be classified as beef type are milked. In census reports the division is made not on type but on method of handling; that is, into milk cows and those kept for beef. In other words, the reports are based upon use, rather than adherence to the specification of a type.

DISTRIBUTION OF MILK COWS

Milk cows, which, in general, are dairy bred are more widely distributed on farms and ranches in this country than any other kind of livestock. There is a general demand for dairy products, and the dairy cow has great adaptability to climate and crop production. Dairying can be combined conveniently with almost every type of agriculture. Dairy products are sold from over 2 million of our farms. Many of our farms or ranches keep at least one cow that is milked. The keeping of a milk cow on the farm provides a home supply of essential human food.

With improved distribution of food supplies, including milk, many farm families have discarded the family milk cow. A more uniform supply is available through dealers, for the family cow's production seldom matched the desired quantity. As a consequence, there are now fewer family cows. Also, there are fewer specialized dairy farms. Farms selling milk have decreased, but sales per farm have increased. There are fewer milk cows on farms, but the increase in milk production per cow has offset the decline

224

in cow numbers. Milk cows have decreased slightly in numbers, but other cows, not kept for milk, have increased in numbers so that the number in each category now is about the same.

DAIRYING AND AGRICULTURE

In the permanent settling of our farms, grain farming was first developed, and this was followed by diversification. Dairy farming combined conveniently, and in most instances profitably, with general farming. As a consequence, the place of dairy farming was established in a permanent system of agriculture over the entire United States. Not only was dairying an economical source of nutritive material for human consumption, but it provided a practical means of fertility maintenance. The demand for dairy products, both for the farm and elsewhere, has been on the increase. The high nutritive value of milk and its products established by research has caused a great demand for dairy products.

COMMERCIAL DAIRYING DISTRIBUTION

Commercial dairying is concentrated in certain areas, but home dairying is quite widespread. Farms reporting dairying as their main activity are not numerous; in fact, less than 10 per cent were so reported in a recent classification. Each agricultural area uses its resources to produce those products for which its production costs are comparatively low. Then, too, since some dairy products are highly perishable, they are produced near the consuming centers. It is quite apparent that the distribution of the kinds of dairying is related to the agricultural characteristics of each area and its accessibility to markets.

Much change has taken place in dairy practices and in marketing methods. Not so long ago milk was used as fluid milk or made into butter or cheese. These are still important outlets, but more recently several new milk products have been developed and new marketing methods devised. Milk products have been standardized, and buttermaking and cheese making have been transferred from farms to factories. The factory system of dairy manufacture, which is now widespread, has had a marked influence upon the industry. The first cheese factory was established in New York in 1851; the first creamery was started in Iowa in 1871. Distribution and processing of milk have been shifted from the farmer to specialized groups.

GENERAL METHODS OF DISPOSITION

We readily recognize that the products of dairying or commercial milk may be disposed of as market milk, butter, cheese, or other dairy products. The farmer may sell the above products to the consumer direct, but processors have largely dominated the butter, cheese, and other dairy products fields. The farmer usually leaves even the distribution of milk to a milk dealer or a milk sales agency.

The disposition of milk from the farms by proportion is given in the table below.

From a survey of the data over a period of years it appears that the amounts of milk used on the farm have varied from year to year, but there seem to be some decided trends. The amount fed calves appears not to have changed materially. More is now consumed as milk or cream and less as farm butter. The amount of farm-churned butter has decreased. Also, there is a marked decrease in the cream delivered to plants and dealers. The amount of milk sold as milk for wholesale deliveries to plants, dealers, etc., has increased markedly.

YEARLY DISPOSITION OF MILK PRODUCED ON FARMS IN THE UNITED STATES [1]

Average, 1945–1954 inclusive

	MILLION POUNDS	PER CENT
Milk used on farms where produced		
1. Fed to calves	3,271	2.79
2. Consumed as fluid milk or cream	10.180	8.67
3. Used for farm-churned butter	5,378	4.58
4. Total utilized on farms	18,829	16.03
Milk marketed by farmers		
1. Delivered to plants and dealers		
a. As whole milk *	74,800	63.69
b. As farm-skimmed cream	19,530	16.63
2. Retailed by farmers as milk and cream **	4,281	16.63
3. Total in combined milk and cream marketings	98,611	83.97
Grand Total	117,440	100.00

* Estimates include milk delivered to market milk receiving and processing plants but excludes milk sold to other farmers for local delivery.
** Based on health officers' reports and information on sales by producer-distributors.

Roughly, about one-sixth of the milk produced is used on the farm where it is produced, and the remaining five-sixths enters into commercial channels.

In the territory adjacent to centers of population, market or fluid milk is the main dairy product and the region is termed "milkshed." Market cream is usually supplied by an area farther from the population center than the milkshed. Butter, cheese, and other dairy products almost always

[1] *Agricultural Statistics,* U.S.D.A., 1955.

come from still greater distances. The more concentrated and less perishable products are produced at greater distances from the center of demand.

FARMERS' OUTLETS FOR MILK

The milk sold from the farm as cream on the butterfat basis or whole-saled as whole milk may reach the consumer in one of the following forms.

Fluid milk

The fluid milk reaching the large urban centers is produced mainly on the specialized dairy farms. The sanitary conditions pertaining to its production are prescribed by the milk ordinances of the cities in which it is sold. It is sold mostly as pasteurized milk, which is graded (A, B, and Certified—"Certified" may be applied to unpasteurized milk.) Milk is pooled at plants where it is standardized, pasteurized, and packaged for delivery to the consumer. Market cream for consumption as cream is handled similarly. Milk in excess of the consumptive requirement for fluid milk is termed "surplus" and is used for various by-products. This brings a lower return to the producer than fluid milk. Surplus is often termed "manufacturing milk" and is used for butter, cheese, canned milk, and other dairy products. One reason, other than seasonal variation, for the existence of "surplus" milk is that consumption is not uniform from day to day.

Butter

Most of the butter is churned in modern factories. Cream or milk is gathered from the farms by trucks and hauled to the creameries. At the creamery, the milk is separated and the cream is pasteurized and churned into butter. Sour cream often is not wanted on the market. The butter-making process is carefully controlled and standardized to produce a high quality, uniform product. The buttermaker is of necessity technically trained because of the many principles involved in the manufacturing process.

Cheese

Cheese making has also become a process performed in factories rather than upon the farms. Skilled workmen are essential for the manufacturing and curing of cheese. Much cheese nowadays is processed or blended and reworked so that the process of manufacture is far more complex than when cheese was first made on the farm. Many varieties have stimulated new demands and increased the use of cheese in the American diet. In addition to cheddar cheese, also known as American, brick, and long-horn, and by other names, Swiss, Edam, Blue, Gouda, Provolone, cream, Camembert, cottage, and other varieties of cheeses are produced in the United States.

Condensed milk

Since milk has large volume because of its high moisture content, condensation is often practiced. Most of the moisture may be removed, as in dried milk, or less water may be removed, as in condensed milk. Such products are less voluminous than milk and can be stored for comparatively long periods of time. Condensed milk may be made from skim milk or whole milk, and it may be sweetened or unsweetened. Unsweetened condensed milk packaged in hermetically sealed cans is termed "evaporated milk." Consumption of evaporated milk has been going up; that of condensed milk has gone down.

Other dairy products

Ice cream accounted for 6.5 per cent of all the milk supply in the United States in 1953. Non-fat dried milk solids (dried skim milk) are by-products of butter manufacture, and their household use is on the increase. Casein, lactose, lactic acid, dried whey and other by-products of milk are being marketed. Many new and useful products are being developed from milk.

THE DAIRY AREAS

The dairy belt extends from New England, including New York, southeastern Pennsylvania, and central Maryland, across northeastern Ohio to

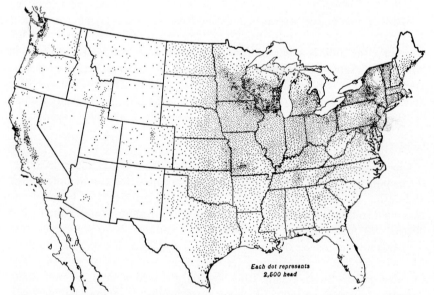

Fig. 78. Distribution of milk cows in the United States. Milk cows and dairy heifers are most numerous in the dairy belt and near large centers of human population. (*Misc. Pub. 269*, U.S.D.A.)

Michigan, Wisconsin, southeastern Minnesota, northern Illinois, and eastern Iowa. Heavy populations of dairy cows are near densely populated areas. The distribution of milk cows and heifers being kept for milk cows is shown in Figure 78.

Southern Wisconsin has the heaviest population of milk cows per square mile. Bulk cooling and hauling of milk, mechanization on the farm, and sanitary regulations have speeded up a trend toward larger and fewer herds.

Leading states in milk production

Milk production is not directly proportional to the number of cows milked, for the level of production is variable. Areas in which herds are small have tended to have the lowest production per cow.

The 15 states listed below had 67 per cent of the cows milked on farms in the country, and in one year produced over 70 per cent of the milk, excluding milk sucked by calves. There is shifting in rank from year to year among the states that are close together in numbers and production.

LEADING STATES IN NUMBER OF COWS AND HEIFERS 2 YEARS
AND OLDER KEPT FOR MILK AND MILK PRODUCTION

10-year average for numbers, 1-year for milk production [2]

STATE	KEPT FOR MILK, THOUSAND HEAD	MILK PRODUCTION, MILLION POUNDS
Wisconsin	2,485	16,550
Minnesota	1,606	8,615
New York	1,424	9,473
Iowa	1,288	5,887
Texas	1,266	3,184
Ohio	1,064	5,777
Illinois	1,057	5,631
Missouri	1,014	4,434
Michigan	991	5,631
Pennsylvania	974	6,156
California	859	7,014
Indiana	754	3,776
Oklahoma	692	1,877
Kansas	670	2,522
Tennessee	661	2,505
United States Total	25,135	123,502

Dairy cattle and human population

The number of dairy cows has tended to increase more or less regularly with the human population, but has grown less rapidly than the human population. We have less than 0.14 milk cow for each person in the country, whereas until 1890 we had about 0.25. In other words, the number of persons per cow is greater than it used to be. This is offset in part by

[2] *Agricultural Statistics,* U.S.D.A., 1955.

greater production per cow. Since 1900 the number of cows per capita has remained fairly stable, except in the feed shortage years following severe droughts. Beef cattle, on the other hand, have shown no decided trend in numbers, but are subject to more violent fluctuations than are milk cows.

The variation in milk cows is shown in Figure 79. Even though droughts and feed shortages have caused liquidation of milk cows and heifers kept for milk, the tendency has been upward. Since the productive period of the milk cow on the average is 3 to 4 years, the replacement rate is very high, and many of the calves are kept to go in the herd. Surplus calves are sold as veal calves.

MILK COW NUMBERS AND MILK PRODUCTION

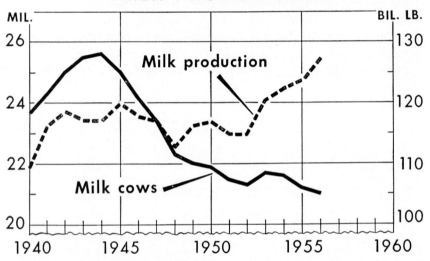

Fig. 79. Milk cows and milk production in the United States. Output per cow has continued its upward trend, reflecting heavy culling of low producers and high feeding rates. (U.S.D.A., Agricultural Marketing Service.)

Relative numbers of different breeds

About 60 per cent of the registered purebred cattle were classified as dairy cattle. Of the different breeds, the Holstein-Friesian led in numbers registered in the past decade, followed by the Guernsey, Jersey, Ayrshire, and Brown Swiss, in the order named.

BEEF FROM DAIRY CATTLE

All cows that are milked are not of dairy-type conformation. As the characters for each type are quite antagonistic, the highly developed dairy cow has the least acceptable beef carcass. In the meat trade dairy cattle compete with beef cattle, especially in the cow beef class. About one third of the beef supply of the United States is derived from cattle of the dairy

Fig. 80. Dairy cows on good pasture. Pasture provides economical feed for dairy cattle. (Babson Bros. Co.)

breeds, and most of our veal comes from calves of dairy breeding. Meat packers have been able by processing to improve the eating properties of beef from dairy cattle, but it cannot be made comparable to meat from cattle of beef breeding. Beef from the dairy cows which cannot be used for block or cutter beef is disposed of as meat specialties, such as bologna.

Some dairy breeds rank higher than others in their beef value. Some will fatten quite readily when put on a fattening ration and may carry a fair degree of finish. The fat of the Jersey and the Guernsey has a high yellow color; it is no less nutritious or edible than white fat, but is discriminated against by the butcher.

Value of milk cows and slaughter cattle [3]

Based upon the prices received by farmers, the average milk cow was worth the equivalent of a 1,480-pound cutter and canner cow on the Chicago market for a 30-year period. This was equivalent to what farmers were receiving for an average 936-pound animal for beef. It is apparent that the relationship changes with the demand for milk and beef.

When the outlook is favorable for dairying, herds are expanded in numbers; the reverse happens when dairying is unprofitable. In a recent period [4] of time, a milk cow was equivalent in price to what farmers were receiving

[3] *The Agricultural Situation*, U.S.D.A., July 1, 1941.
[4] *Agricultural Statistics*, U.S.D.A., 1955.

for 269 pounds of butterfat, or 4,246 pounds of milk (wholesale). Of more concern to the farmer producing milk is the price ratio between the product and the feed, because milk and butterfat is the form in which the dairyman markets feed. The dairy product-feed price ratios are given on page 232.

SHOW CLASSIFICATION OF DAIRY CATTLE

The classification of dairy cattle is somewhat simpler than that of beef cattle, since it includes only breeding animals. Individual and group classes are shown. The Purebred Dairy Cattle Association recommends the following classes:

BULLS

CALVES (born after June 30 of previous year and before March 1 of current year)
JUNIOR YEARLINGS (born Jan. 1 to June 30 of previous year)
SENIOR YEARLINGS (born July 1 to Dec. 31)
TWO-YEAR-OLDS
THREE YEARS AND OVER
SENIOR CHAMPION (2 years and older)
JUNIOR CHAMPION (under 2 years)
GRAND CHAMPION

FEMALES

HEIFER CALVES (born after June 30 of previous year and before March 1 of current year)
JUNIOR YEARLINGS (born Jan. 1 to June 30 of previous year)
SENIOR YEARLINGS (born July 1 to Dec. 31)
JUNIOR CHAMPION (from above three classes)
TWO-YEAR-OLD COWS
THREE-YEAR-OLD COWS
FOUR-YEAR-OLD COWS
AGED COWS (five years and over)
SENIOR CHAMPION (from above four classes)
GRAND CHAMPION
COW, IN MILK, any age, judged on udder alone

GROUP CLASSES

JUNIOR GET-OF-SIRE (consists of four animals under 2 years of age, none of which has freshened, either sex, the get of one sire, not more than two can be bulls.)

GET-OF-SIRE (consists of four animals either sex, the get of one sire; at least one must be 2 years of age or older, not more than two can be bulls.)

PRODUCE OF DAM (consists of two animals any age, either sex, the produce of one cow.)

DAIRY HERD (consists of four cows that have freshened, all to be owned by exhibitor.)

BEST THREE FEMALES (any age, bred and owned by exhibitor.)

Livestock shows publish premium lists which give the classes, as well as other rules and regulations.

Chapter 14

DAIRY TYPE

The dairy type differs from the beef type mainly in the amount of fleshing in the females and the mammary development. As previously pointed out, beef cows and dairy cows are quite similar in internal anatomy and skeletal structure. The correct type in the different dairy breeds has been set forth in the representations of the true type or the ideal cow for each breed. These different models are quite similar since they combine all the dairy characteristics plus the distinctive features of the breed. The models serve as ideals or standards of perfection, for each is a composite of the many desirable characteristics which form the basis for selection or judging. They have been exceedingly helpful to all interested in the breed.

GENERAL CHARACTERISTICS OF THE DAIRY TYPE

Angularity of form is typical of the dairy type. The fleshing which characterizes the beef animal is somewhat lacking in the dairy cow. In fact, excess fleshing is regarded as a fault in a dairy cow. It should be pointed out that a thin cow may not be a dairy cow and also that, in dairy cows, there is much variation in flesh, associated with stages of lactation. A good dairy cow may be well fleshed when heavily fed during the dry period and still not assume the form of a beef cow.

The great difference in the natural muscularity of the two types is shown in Figure 16. The carcasses shown in this figure are from very young calves about one week old when slaughtered; so feeding has not altered the shape. The difference in the thickness of the back loins, round, and other flesh parts is due to inheritance.

BASIS OF SELECTING DAIRY COWS

Form, type, or general appearance is but one basis of dairy cow selection. The dairyman also has the pedigree or the records of the parents and

234

sometimes the performance record of producing individuals in milk and butterfat. In practice, all of these means are used to decide what should be kept or added to the breeding herd. Following is a discussion of selection according to the different bases.

PRODUCTION RECORDS

High producers are generally more profitable than low producers, and the best way to distinguish between the two is to measure the production. This is the most reliable means of predicting future production. A lactation record is but one expression of a cow's ability to produce, and subsequent records may vary from the first. Then too, there may be circumstances which would affect one record and not another. Such very tangible factors as feeding, care, times milked per day, and physical condition may materially affect the milk and butterfat yield in a lactation period. Consequently, in interpreting records the conditions under which the record was made should be considered.

Production records are highly reliable for predicting, but in their absence selections must be made on the basis of pedigree, production of the parents, or the individuality or general appearance.

In the management of a dairy herd the continuance of an individual cow in the herd should be based upon her production. If she is not yielding a reasonable profit over and above feed and other costs, neither pedigree nor conformation should cause her retention.

PEDIGREE

The parents are listed in the pedigree; the descendants are known as the progeny. Mere statement of the names of the parents or the offspring may have little meaning. Actual records are, of course, necessary to evaluate a progeny test. The pedigree is not an infallible measure of an individual's productive capacity because the pedigree does not indicate the inheritance passed on by the parents.

Herd sires are often selected on the basis of pedigree combined with other means. The pedigree may be a helpful guide to selection.

GENERAL APPEARANCE OR CONFORMATION

It is often necessary to pass judgment upon or select dairy animals upon their physical appearance alone. Certain characteristics that are rather typical of high production in dairy cows are considered in making such selections. This is not an accurate method of determining the productive ability of a dairy cow. Differences between high producers and low producers are often evident in conformation, yet all cows of relatively good dairy type may not be highly productive.

The approved dairy type is the result of breeding and selection to perpetuate a certain form or conformation. Individuals which did not come up to the usual standard set for approved type were discarded, and those which met the requirements won in the show ring and were in demand for breeding. Experience has shown that this conformation is not always an indication of producing ability. Yet, when type is scored and compared with production, the two appear to be related.

A most striking illustration can be cited of the correlation of type and production, from the study of Holstein cows with known production records that had also been officially classified for type under the Selective Registry program of The Holstein-Friesian Association of America.[1] Under the classification program, which is based upon type alone, cows are given ratings of excellent, very good, good plus, good, fair, or poor. The following tabulation gives the averages of the production records for each of these classification groups.

CLASSIFICATION & PRODUCTION CORRELATION

A summary of 59,642 animals having classification breakdowns and production records in the files of The Holstein-Friesian Association of America (1953)

CLASSIFICATION	AVE. LBS. MILK M.E. BASIS	2x—305 DAYS % FAT	AVE. LBS. FAT M.E. BASIS	NO. OF ANIMALS
Excellent	14,034	3.62	507.8	860
Very Good	13,267	3.60	477.5	10,371
Good Plus	12,688	3.59	455.9	23,697
Good	12,150	3.58	435.4	19,161
Fair	11,621	3.56	413.7	5,403
Poor	10,970	3.49	382.4	150

High classification was accompanied by high actual production of the cows. It may be impossible actually to predict production by physical appearance, but apparently appearance is related to production and can be used in grouping individuals. In several of the dairy cattle breeds, herds may be officially scored or rated on type and the individuals classed into groups.

DETAILED DESCRIPTION OF THE IDEAL DAIRY TYPE

THE DAIRY COW SCORE CARD

The score card is helpful in teaching the desired conformation of the dairy cow and the relative importance of the different parts. It is a condensed de-

[1] *Holstein-Friesian Judging Manual of The Holstein-Friesian Association of America.* Brattleboro, Vt., 1956.

scription of the ideal conformation. Breeders of dairy cattle have long used the score card not only to describe the ideal type but also to describe breed type. The different parts of a dairy cow are illustrated in Figure 81.

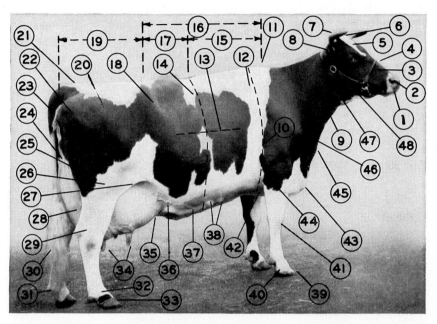

Fig. 81. Parts of a Dairy Cow (Listed on the illustration)

1—Muzzle	13—Ribs	25—Thigh	37—Mammary Veins
2—Nostril	14—Barrel	26—Stifle	38—Milk Wells
3—Face	15—Chine	27—Rear Flank	39—Sole
4—Bridge of Nose	16—Back	28—Rear Udder	40—Heel
5—Forehead	17—Loin	29—Hock	41—Knee
6—Poll	18—Hip	30—Switch	42—Chest Floor
7—Horns	19—Rump	31—Dewclaw	43—Brisket
8—Ear	20—Thurl	32—Pastern	44—Point of Elbow
9—Neck	21—Tail Head	33—Hoof	45—Dewlap
10—Heart Girth	22—Pin Bones	34—Teats	46—Point of Shoulder
11—Withers	23—Tail	35—Fore Udder	47—Throat
12—Crops	24—Rear Udder Attachment	36—Fore Udder Attachment	48—Jaw

A composite dairy cow score card became available in 1943 and was revised in 1957. It has been approved by The American Dairy Science Association and copyrighted by The Purebred Dairy Cattle Association. The score card is given below, followed by the characteristics of the different breeds and a guide to evaluation of defects in judging cows. The ideals of type and breed characteristics must be considered in the application of this score card.

DAIRY COW UNIFIED SCORE CARD [2]
Breed characteristics should be considered
in the application of this score card

Order of Observation Score

1. GENERAL APPEARANCE—30 points

Attractive individuality with femininity, vigor, stretch, scale, harmonious blending of all parts, and impressive style and carriage. All parts of a cow should be considered in evaluating a cow's general appearance

BREED CHARACTERISTICS—(See Chapter 19.) 10

HEAD—clean cut, proportionate to body; broad muzzle with large, open nostrils; strong jaws; large, bright eyes; forehead, broad and moderately dished; bridge of nose straight; ears medium size and alertly carried

SHOULDER BLADES—set smoothly and tightly against the body 10

BACK—straight and strong; loin, broad and nearly level

RUMP—long, wide and nearly level from *hook bones* to *pin bones;* clean cut and free from patchiness; *thurls,* high and wide apart; *tail head,* set level with backline and free from coarseness; *tail,* slender

LEGS AND FEET—bone flat and strong, pasterns short and strong, 10
hocks cleanly moulded. *Feet,* short, compact and well rounded with deep heel and level sole. *Fore legs,* medium in length, straight, wide apart, and squarely placed. *Hind legs,* nearly perpendicular from hock to pastern, from the side view; and straight, from the rear view

2. DAIRY CHARACTER—20 points

Evidence of milking ability, angularity, and general openness, without weakness; free from coarseness; giving due regard to period of lactation

Neck—long, lean and blending smoothly into shoulders; clean cut 20
throat, dewlap, and brisket. *Withers,* sharp. *Ribs,* wide apart, rib bone wide, flat, and long. *Flanks,* deep and refined. *Thighs,* incurving to flat and wide apart from the rear view, providing ample room for the udder and its rear attachment. *Skin,* loose and pliable

3. BODY CAPACITY—20 points

Relatively large in proportion to size of animal, providing ample capacity, strength, and vigor

BARREL—strongly supported, long and deep; ribs highly and widely 10
sprung; depth and width of barrel tending to increase toward rear

[2] Copyright, 1957, by The Purebred Dairy Cattle Association, Peterborough, New Hampshire.

Fig. 82. The true type Holstein-Friesian cow. (Holstein-Friesian Association of America.)

HEART GIRTH—large and deep with well sprung fore ribs blending   10
  into the shoulders; full crops; full at elbows; wide chest floor

4. MAMMARY SYSTEM *—30 points

  A strongly attached, well balanced, capacious udder of fine texture indicating heavy production and a long period of usefulness

UDDER—long, wide, symmetrical and of moderate depth, strongly   10
  attached, showing distinct cleavage between halves, no quartering
  on sides; soft, pliable, and well collapsed after milking; quarters
  evenly balanced

FORE UDDER—moderate length, tending to carry forward uniformly   6
  the width of rear udder, and strongly attached

REAR UDDER—high, wide, slightly rounded, fairly uniform width   7
  from top to floor, and strongly attached

TEATS—uniform size, cylindrical, of medium length and diameter,   5
  squarely placed under each quarter, plumb, and well spaced
  from side and rear views

MAMMARY VEINS—large, long, tortuous, branching   2

TOTAL POINTS—100

---

* Because of the natural undeveloped mammary system in heifer calves and yearlings, less
emphasis is placed on mammary system and more on general appearance, dairy character,
and body capacity. A slight to serious discrimination applies to overdeveloped, fatty udders
in heifer calves and yearlings.

EVALUATION OF DEFECTS [2]

In a show ring, disqualification means that the animal is not eligible to win a prize. Any disqualified animal is not eligible to be shown in the group classes. In slight to serious discrimination, the degree of seriousness shall be determined by the judge.

EYES

1. Total blindness: Disqualification
2. Blindness in one eye: Slight discrimination
3. Cross-eyes: Slight discrimination

WRY FACE

Slight to serious discrimination

CROPPED EARS

Slight discrimination

PARROT JAW

Slight to serious discrimination

SHOULDERS

Winged: Slight to serious discrimination

TAIL SETTING

Wry tail or other abnormal tail settings: Slight to serious discrimination

LEGS AND FEET

1. Lameness—apparently permanent and interfering with normal function: Disqualification
   —apparently temporary and not affecting normal function: Slight discrimination
2. Bucked knees: Slight to serious discrimination
3. Evidence of arthritis, crampy hind leg: Serious discrimination
4. Boggy hocks: *Slight to serious discrimination*

ABSENCE OF HORNS

No discrimination

LACK OF SIZE

Slight to serious discrimination

UDDER

1. Blind quarter: Disqualification
2. Abnormal milk (bloody, clotted, watery); Possibly disqualification. A slight to serious defect
3. Udder definitely broken away in attachment: Serious discrimination
4. A weak udder attachment: Slight to serious discrimination
5. One or more light quarters, hard spots in udder, obstruction in teat (spider): Slight to serious discrimination
6. Side leak: Slight discrimination

DRY COWS

Among cows of apparently equal merit: Give strong preference to cows in milk

FREEMARTIN HEIFERS

Disqualification unless proved pregnant

OVERCONDITIONED

Slight to serious discrimination

TEMPORARY OR MINOR INJURIES

Blemishes or injuries of a temporary character not affecting animal's usefulness: Slight discrimination

EVIDENCE OF SHARP PRACTICE

1. Animals showing signs of having been operated upon or tampered with for the purpose of concealing faults in conformation, or with intent to deceive relative to the animal's soundness: Disqualification
2. Uncalved heifers showing evidence of having been milked: Serious discrimination

Fig. 83. The ideal type Guernsey cow. (American Guernsey Cattle Club.)

Score-card points

The parts of the score card will be discussed separately.

1. General appearance. In general appearance the dairy cow is quite different from the beef cow. A thin beef cow is not an acceptable dairy cow. Attractiveness in individuality and carriage has been stressed in the development of the dairy type. A balance or symmetry of parts is desired which, combined with style, femininity, and vigor, makes for beauty of conformation plus productiveness.

The *breed characteristics* have been previously enumerated. The various features required in the different breeds are not utilitarian qualities, but they constitute breed type. Score cards of the various breeds are available from the different breed record associations. These describe the characters wanted by breeders as well as the requisites of dairy type. A head that is clean cut and shows refinement and femininity is desired on the ideal cow. Coarseness or heaviness of the head and neck are regarded as faulty. The dairy cow head is longer, narrower, and finer than that of the beef cow. Eyes which are quite prominent, moderately large, full and bright, and which denote alertness are desired. A wide face and forehead is suggested. A broad muzzle with open nostrils is required. The jaws should be strong and well muscled. Ears that are of medium size and carried alertly are preferred.

There are distinct breed differences in the head, which may be regarded as minor since they do not detract or add to the dairy character of the head. Horns vary with the breeds, but medium fineness and medium length are, in general, wanted in the horns.

The shoulder blades are set smoothly against the body and moderately thin at the withers in the model individual. Winged shoulders are definitely objectionable.

Fig. 84. An excellent Jersey cow, Sir's Standard Bright Beauty, 1940 national grand champion Jersey cow. Bred by H. V. Amason of Rayle, Ga. Owned and shown at the 1940 National Dairy Show by J. L. Hutcheson, Sr., of Greenfields, Rossville, Ga. (Photograph by Harry Strohmeyer, courtesy of the American Jersey Cattle Club.)

A. BACK, LOIN, AND RUMP. These are given less emphasis in the dairy cow than in the beef cow. This difference of emphasis merely illustrates the divergence of the two types. That which goes with milk production is important in the dairy type, and in the beef cow the back and loin are prime essentials since they yield high-priced beef cuts. A back that is strong and straight and a loin that is broad and strong are requisites for ideal dairy form, also a rump that is long, wide, and level, with a smooth, fine tail setting and thurls wide apart. Extreme thickness or beefiness of the top such as would be present in a beef cow is not wanted in the dairy cow.

B. LEGS AND FEET. The front and hind legs are to be well set and fairly wide apart. Straight legs of medium length are preferred. Bones, including the joints, of ample size and free from coarseness are stressed. A dairy cow cannot perform satisfactorily under average conditions unless she has ample underpinning. Cows are kept to convert pasture, as well as other feed, into dairy products. Good feet and legs are needed for ability to graze. Hocks carried close and knees too close together are rather common in dairy cows; such conformation interferes with normal rear udder development. Narrowness in front is associated with a lack of chest capacity and resultant impaired vigor.

2. Dairy character. In estimating dairy character the time of the lactation period is to be considered. In general, angularity and freedom from excess fleshing are stressed.

A clean-cut, lean, fairly long *neck* blending smoothly into the shoulders and brisket is desired. The withers of the dairy cow should be sharply defined, for they form the apex of the wedge or angular conformation. Heavy fleshing or coarseness of the withers is objectionable. One indication of the general openness of conformation suggested for the dairy cow is the width between the ribs. Wide, flat, and long ribs are desired.

The *thighs* are different from those of the beef cow; they are flat and lean rather than thick and plump. As the udder is of primary importance, the thighs should not interfere with its size or attachment.

The skin is important in selecting dairy cows; it must be medium in thickness, loose, and pliable. A good hide indicates good nutrition, for the hide's pliability, secretions, and hair are affected by the circulation.

3. Body capacity. A capacious middle or barrel indicates consumptive capacity and ample space for the vital organs. Large body capacity permits utilization of much feed and chest capacity is indicative of strength and vigor. A *barrel* that is deep and wide, and increasingly so toward the rear meets the requirement. The middle needs to be strongly supported, with well-sprung ribs that are wide apart. Much emphasis is given to the heart girth on dairy cows. Long, well-sprung ribs, width at the chest floor, and fullness at the point of the elbow will give the large heart girth desired.

4. Mammary system. The characteristics indicating well-developed milk-secreting organs constitute the most important part of the score card. A cow may have all of the other qualifications required, but if she lacks mammary development or a strongly attached, capacious, good-quality udder, she is not suitable for the dairy herd. Heavy and persistent production are essential for a profitable dairy cow.

A large-sized *udder* high in quality and symmetrically shaped is preferred. It should be long, wide, and moderately deep. A shapely, well-carried udder will stand up under successive lactations. It should extend well forward and be well attached both in front and in the rear. Misshaped

Fig. 85. An excellent Ayrshire cow, Alfalfa Farm Ann 2nd. A grand champion cow, and also a winner in the milking contest, Eastern States Exposition. (Ayrshire Breeders' Association.)

Fig. 86. A model Brown Swiss cow. (Brown Swiss Cattle Breeders' Association.)

udders, pendulous, unevenly balanced, asymmetrical, or otherwise deformed, will become worse with advancing age; such conditions may inhibit production.

An udder large because of fibrous tissue is less productive than one composed mainly of secretory tissue. A high-quality udder is soft, pliable, elastic, free from excess fibrous tissue, and high in secretory tissue. Such an udder will be well collapsed after milking.

Milk or mammary veins which carry venous blood have long been stressed in judging cows, and large, long, crooked, and branching veins were preferred. Investigations have revealed that there is no significant relationship between the extent of the visible milk veins and milk production. *Teats* convenient in size, uniform, well placed, and shapely are essential for ease in milking.

THE DAIRY BULL

The qualities wanted in the dairy cow are also desired in the herd sire, yet the dairy bull is rarely selected on individuality alone. Since the value of a herd sire is determined by the individuality of the offspring and their productiveness, it is no wonder that all considerations which might be helpful in his selection are used. The pedigree and the productiveness of his ancestry are valuable aids in choosing a bull.

There is great diversity of opinion as to just what constitutes correct type in the dairy bull. The bull's individuality is certainly less reliable in predicting value than the external character of a cow. The value of a sire is known only when his heifers are in production.

Since there is relationship between the individuality of a sire and that of his produce, we have true-type models of dairy bulls as we do for cows. In general, bulls showing angular dairy form are preferred to smoother bulls which are less angular and more thick and fat.

DAIRY BULL UNIFIED SCORE CARD [3]

Breed characteristics should be considered
in the application of this score card

Order of observation   Score

1. GENERAL APPEARANCE—40 points

Attractive individuality, with masculinity, vigor, stretch, and scale, harmonious blending of all parts, and impressive style and carriage. All parts of a bull should be considered in evaluating a bull's general appearance

[3] Copyright, 1957, by The Purebred Dairy Cattle Association, Peterborough, New Hampshire.

Fig. 87. The true type of Holstein-Friesian bull. (Holstein-Friesian Association of America.)

BREED CHARACTERISTICS—(See Chapter 19.)   15

HEAD—clean cut, proportionate to body; broad muzzle with large, open nostrils; strong jaws; large, bright eyes; forehead, broad and moderately dished; bridge of nose straight; ears medium size and alertly carried

SHOULDER BLADES—set smoothly and tightly against the body   13

BACK—straight and strong; *loin,* broad and nearly level

RUMP—long, wide, and nearly level from *hook bones* to *pin bones;* clean cut and free from patchiness; *thurls,* high and wide apart; *tail head,* set level with backline and free from coarseness; *tail,* slender

LEGS AND FEET—bone flat and strong, pasterns short and strong,   12 hocks cleanly moulded. *Feet,* short, compact, and well rounded with deep heel and level sole. *Fore legs,* medium in length, straight and wide apart, squarely placed. *Hind legs,* nearly perpendicular from hock to pastern, from the side view; straight, from the rear view

2. DAIRY CHARACTER—30 points

Angularity, general openness, without weakness; free from coarseness

Neck—long, lean, with medium crest, blending smoothly into 30
shoulders; clean-cut throat, dewlap, and brisket. *Withers,* sharp.
Ribs, wide apart, rib bone wide, flat, and long. *Flanks,* deep and
refined. *Thighs,* incurving to flat, wide apart from the rear view.
Skin, loose and pliable

3. Body Capacity—30 points

Relatively large in proportion to size of animal, providing ample
capacity, strength, and vigor

BARREL—strongly supported, long, and deep; *ribs* highly and widely 15
sprug; depth and width of barrel tending to increase toward
rear

HEART GIRTH—large and deep with well sprung fore ribs blending 15
into the shoulders; full crops; full at elbows; wide chest floor

Total Points—100

EVALUATION OF DEFECTS[3]

In a show ring, disqualification means that the animal is not eligible to win
a prize. Any disqualified animal is not eligible to be shown in the group classes.
In slight to serious discrimination, the degree of seriousness shall be determined
by the judge.

Fig. 88. The ideal type of Guernsey bull. (American Guernsey Cattle Club.)

EYES
1. Total blindness: Disqualification
2. Blindness in one eye: Slight discrimination
3. Cross-eyes: Slight discrimination

WRY FACE
Slight to serious discrimination

CROPPED EARS
Slight discrimination

PARROT JAW
Slight to serious discrimination

SHOULDERS
Winged: Slight to serious discrimination

TAIL SETTING
Wry tail or other abnormal tail settings: Slight to serious discrimination

LEGS AND FEET
1. Lameness—apparently permanent and interfering with normal function: Disqualification
—apparently temporary and not affecting normal function: Slight discrimination
2. Bucked knees: Slight to serious discrimination
3. Evidence of arthritis, crampy hind leg: Serious discrimination
4. Boggy hocks: Slight to serious discrimination

ABSENCE OF HORNS
No discrimination

LACK OF SIZE
Slight to serious discrimination

TESTICLES
Bull with one testicle or with abnormal testicles: Disqualification

OVERCONDITIONED
Slight to serious discrimination

TEMPORARY OR MINOR INJURIES
Blemishes or injuries of a temporary character not affecting animal's usefulness: Slight discrimination

EVIDENCE OF SHARP PRACTICE
Animals showing signs of having been operated upon or tampered with for the purpose of concealing faults in conformation, or with intent to deceive relative to the animal's soundness: Disqualification

Score-card parts

The various items of the score cards are discussed in the following

1. General appearance. In general appearance the dairy bull should be representative of the breed in all respects; also vigor, masculinity, attractiveness, and balance or symmetry are demanded. Size should be ample, breed differences considered. The head that is definitely masculine, clean cut, moderately long, wide, and broad on the muzzle with open nostrils is specified. Lean, strong jaws and fairly large, bright eyes are preferable. The ears should be medium in size and well carried. Horns, if present, should be medium in size and not too spreading.

A strong, straight back that is fairly wide and long is required in the model, as is a loin that is broad and level and a rump that is long, wide, and level. Width is stressed in the hips, thurls, and pinbones. The tailhead

Fig. 89. An outstanding Jersey bull. Brampton Standard Sir, classified as an excellent gold and silver medal bull and also a superior sire. An outstanding sire of productive and high-classifying daughters. (American Jersey Cattle Club.)

Fig. 90. An excellent Ayrshire bull, Vista Grande King, classified double-approved and excellent. (Ayrshire Breeders' Association.)

should be neat and well carried. A tail that is rather long and tapering with a well-developed switch is desired.

2. Dairy character. A typical bull should show evidence of the transmission of milk rather than beef qualities. Angular conformation plus freedom from beefiness is typical of *dairy character*. In this connection we emphasize a long, masculine-appearing neck with a moderate crest, smoothly blended with the shoulder, and clean cut. The withers are less sharply defined than in the cow, yet the vertebrae should rise above the shoulder blades and be fairly fine and free from fleshiness. The openness of conformation desired is indicated by the ribs of the dairy bull, which should be wide apart. Plump thighs are not typical of the dairy bull; rather they should be flat, trim, wide apart as viewed from the rear, and well cut up between the thighs. Teats or rudimentaries that are wide apart and well placed are desired. Testicles that are uniform and normal in size are a requisite. Hide should be medium in fineness, pliable, and loose, with a fine hair coat.

Fig. 91. An excellent Brown Swiss bull, Blankus Baronet of Walhalla. (Brown Swiss Cattle Breeders' Association.)

3. Body capacity. A capacity that is great, the size of the bull considered, is demanded. This provides ample space for the consumption of feed and also denotes strength and vigor.

A long, deep, wide barrel and a well-developed heart girth give the capacity requisite for dairy production. Width as well as depth should be stressed for chest capacity.

4. Feet and legs. Ample underpinning is necessary for ruggedness, vigor, and animation. Squarely set legs that are clean cut and ample in bone are essential for normal activity. The legs should be straight, quite wide apart, and medium in length, with the pasterns strong and springy. A well-developed set of shapely feet is also a requisite.

Dispositions of dairy bulls

Dairy bulls are active and often less tractable than beef bulls. Some are rather difficult to handle. Ample equipment is needed to handle a dairy bull safely; bulls should always be handled with care even though they may appear gentle.

EXAMINATION OF DAIRY CATTLE

It has been found advisable to study a dairy animal first at some distance away, probably 20 to 30 feet. It is always desirable to move dairy cattle, for faults not observed when an individual is poised or standing usually become evident when he moves. After the individual or class has been made to stand, the student should make a closer inspection from the front, sides, and rear. Lastly, handling is resorted to in order to examine points or parts not discernible to the eye and to confirm what has been previously observed. Handling permits an estimate of hide quality and flesh covering. It is also resorted to for determination of the quality and soundness of the udder and perhaps to examine the milk veins.

Fig. 92. A well-developed udder. Cows that rank high in milk production have large and well-developed udders.

The novice is inclined to be unsystematic in his examination, depending too much upon handling and inspecting the individual at too close range. Many important features are properly appraised at a distance, and close inspection fails to give the proper evaluation of the animal as a whole. The main considerations in physical selection are best evaluated at some distance from the individual.

SIZE OF DAIRY CATTLE

LARGE COWS PRODUCE MORE MILK

That large cows are more productive than smaller cows is shown by an analysis of data concerning 554 dairy herds in New York State.[4] For each 100-pound increase in the size of the dairy cows there was an annual in-

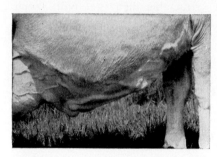

crease of approximately 800 pounds of milk per cow. A tabulation of the data is given below. The heavy cows produced more milk and had a higher estimated value per cow than the lighter cows. The decrease in milk production is quite regular from the heaviest to the lightest. Although the two lightest groups were the youngest, age does not appear to be related to size in the other groups.

Fig. 93. A well-developed mammary system.

Even though the larger cows may give higher average yields of milk and butterfat, a smaller cow may be more efficient because of low maintenance needs. In selection production ability rather than size should be emphasized.

RELATIONSHIP BETWEEN SIZE OF COW, MILK PRODUCTION PER COW, AND VALUE PER COW

554 Herds in Five New York Counties, 1940

	AVERAGE WEIGHT PER COW, POUNDS	AVERAGE MILK PRODUCED PER COW POUNDS 3.7 MILK	AVERAGE ESTIMATED VALUE PER COW	AVERAGE AGE PER COW YEARS
1. 10 per cent of herds with heaviest cows	1,140	7,886	$109	5.5
2. Next lighter 10 per cent	1,061	7,614	93	5.6
3. " " " " "	1,026	6,948	88	5.5
4. " " " " "	992	6,439	84	5.7
5. " " " " "	964	6,654	87	5.4
6. " " " " "	935	6,123	80	5.6
7. " " " " "	908	5,935	82	5.3
8. " " " " "	876	5,737	82	5.6
9. " " " " "	842	5,535	76	5.2
10. 10 per cent of herds with lightest cows	792	5,070	70	5.0
Range between groups 1 and 10	343	2,816	39	0.5
Per cent increase from lightest to heaviest	43.9	55.5	55.7	10.0

[4] *Farm Economics,* No. 125, May, 1941, New York State College of Agriculture, Cornell University, Ithaca, N. Y.

SIZE OF DIFFERENT BREEDS

There is a rather large difference in size as indicated by weight among the common dairy breeds. Based upon the suggested weights for mature individuals, the breeds rank in order: Holstein-Friesian, Brown Swiss, Ayrshire, Guernsey, and Jersey. In all the breeds there is a wide range of weight; consequently there is considerable overlapping and little difference in the average.

Suggested weights for average mature individuals of both sexes, taken from breed score cards and other sources are given in Chapter 19 in discussion of the various dairy breeds. Weights for heifer calves are given below.

There are advantages and disadvantages of large size. As maintenance requirements are proportional to size, it will require more feed to keep larger cows. Large individuals are also slower in maturing and may come into production older than small ones. Size, however, has the advantage of vigor and ruggedness, and large animals bring more income when sold as beef. Large size gives greater consumptive capacity and consequent greater production.

Weights of dairy heifers of different breeds at various ages

The normal weights of heifers of different breeds at various ages is given in the table below.[5]

WEIGHTS OF WELL-GROWN HEIFERS AT VARIOUS AGES

AGE	BREED				
	Ayrshire	Brown Swiss	Guernsey	Holstein	Jersey
months	lbs.	lbs.	lbs.	lbs.	lbs.
Birth	71	90	65	91	54
1	86	105	79	113	68
2	114	147	105	150	92
4	190	340	177	250	164
6	281	385	267	365	250
8	371	460	350	474	331
10	451	575	427	568	402
12	518	662	490	653	462
14	592	727	556	725	518
16	635	785	605	795	568
18	690	855	663	861	615
20	743	935	712	928	658
22	790	1,000	763	999	702
24	845	1,050	818	1,075	750

[5] *The Midwest Farm Handbook,* Iowa State College, 1954.

The above weights are attained by normal individuals fed and cared for so that they will develop towards the upper limit of their inheritance. It has been found that well-grown heifers develop into cows with large capacity for feed consumption and with consequently high production capacity.

WEIGHT ESTIMATES FROM MEASUREMENTS

With dairy cattle, cows, and heifers, the heart-girth measurement is commonly used to estimate weight. In computing the ration it is necessary to know the approximate live weight. If scales are not available weight can be estimated from the measurement of heart girth. There are several tables of weights and heart girths given for dairy cows and heifers in various textbooks on dairy husbandry. The individual to be measured should be standing squarely on all four legs. The measurement is made just in back of the shoulders or in the region of the smallest girth.

Breed and age affect the relation of weight to measurement. Consequently actual heart girth is modified according to the following table in order to take the differences into account. Actual heart girth is increased by the inches indicated for age and breed differences. To use the table for estimating the weight of a Holstein cow less than three years old, for example, 6 inches should be added to the actual girth measurement. This table is based upon the investigations at the Nebraska and Illinois Agricultural Experiment Station.[6]

INCHES TO ADD TO ACTUAL HEART GIRTH
FOR BREED AND AGE DIFFERENCES *

AGE	BREED			
	Jersey	Guernsey	Ayrshire	Holstein
	in.	in.	in.	in.
Less than 3 years old	0	2	2	6
3 to 4 years old	2	4	4	8
5 years or over	2	5	5	9

* The equation is $W = 0.342 \ (G + g)^{1.85}$
where W is live weight in pounds.
      G is heart girth in inches.
      g is girth modifier in inches for age and breed.

The table below gives the relationship between heart girth and approximate weight. The modified heart girth is the actual girth plus the amount added because of age and breed. A Holstein cow less than three years of

[6] W. L. Gaines, H. P. Davis and R. F. Morgan, "Estimation of Initial Live Weight at Each Lactation of Dairy Cows." *J. Dairy Sci.,* vol. 24, 1941.

age with an actual heart girth of 76 inches would have, for the purpose of estimating weight, an 82-inch girth and would weigh approximately 1187 pounds. This table is based upon probable weight 31 days after calving.

ESTIMATED LIVE WEIGHTS OF DAIRY COWS FROM
MODIFIED HEART GIRTHS

Mod. heart girth	Weight	Mod. heart girth	Weight	Mod. heart girth	Weight	Mod. heart girth	Weight	Mod. heart girth	Weight
In.	Lbs.	In.	Lbs.	In.	Lbs.	In.	Lbs.	In.	Lbs.
50	475	60	666	70	886	80	1134	90	1411
51	493	61	687	71	910	81	1161	91	1440
52	511	62	708	72	934	82	1187	92	1469
53	530	63	729	73	958	83	1214	93	1499
54	548	64	751	74	982	84	1242	94	1529
55	567	65	773	75	1007	85	1269	95	1559
56	586	66	795	76	1032	86	1297	96	1589
57	606	67	817	77	1057	87	1325	97	1620
58	626	68	840	78	1082	88	1353	98	1651
59	646	69	863	79	1108	89	1382	99	1683

The live weights of female dairy heifers may be estimated from actual heart girth measurement by the use of the following table.

ESTIMATED WEIGHTS OF DAIRY HEIFERS HAVING VARIOUS
HEART GIRTHS [7]

Heart girth	Weight	Heart girth	Weight	Heart girth	Weight
In.	Lbs.	In.	Lbs.	In.	Lbs.
25	52	35	135	45	274
26	58	36	146	46	292
27	64	37	157	47	311
28	71	38	170	48	330
29	78	39	183	49	350
30	87	40	196	50	370
31	95	41	211	51	392
32	104	42	226	52	414
33	114	43	241	53	436
34	124	44	257	56	460

[7] H. P. Davis, R. F. Morgan, Samuel Brody and A. C. Ragsdale, "Relation of Height at Withers and Chest Girth to Live Weight of Dairy Cattle of Different Breeds and Ages," *Nebraska Research Bulletin* 91, July, 1937.

Chapter 15

MILK SECRETION

Milk is synthesized and secreted by the mammary glands in the udder of the cow. This is characteristic of all animals included in the zoological class *Mammalia*. Milk is produced in the udder of the female after she gives birth to young. Rudimentary mammary glands are present in the male, but these are comparatively small and rarely active. Milk is derived for human

Fig. 94. Ayrshire cow with excellent mammary system. A well-developed udder is of first importance in selecting any dairy cow.

use from several species of the Mammalia class, but the dairy cow is distinctive because of the volume and persistency of her production. In the improvement of dairy cattle milk production has been the main objective.

THE UDDER

The mammary glands of the cow are included in the one structure, the udder. A large udder is a prerequisite for a productive cow. A well-attached udder will retain its shape and carriage with advancing age. An ideal udder has a level floor and has teats squarely placed at ample distance apart. The fore udder should extend well forward on the abdomen and the rear udder should extend well up between the hind legs. Breaking away of the udder attachments and relaxing of the median and lateral suspensory ligaments cause a pendulous, poorly carried udder. As age advances this becomes more distinctly quartered and more pendulous.

The udder of the cow is made up of four quarters, each a mammary gland, and is halved along the median line. The median suspensory ligament separates the halves. The quarters are also separate, for each quarter is independent in secretory tissue and milk ducts. An udder injected with a stain and sectioned will show a definite division between the fore and rear quarters. The division between the quarters on a side is not obvious from external examination, but a distinct groove separates the sides on the median line.

THE INTERNAL STRUCTURE OF THE UDDER

In examination of an udder being dissected it will be observed that each half is enclosed in a fibrous capsule, and extension of the suspensory ligaments. Exclusive of the fibrous connective tissue and the overlying skin, there are secretory tissue, a duct system, a blood and lymph system, and also nerves. Each of these will be briefly considered separately. (See Figure 95.)

Secretory tissue

At the termination of each small milk duct are found three to five saclike structures called *alveoli*. A single layer of nucleated epithelial cells lines each alveolus, and these cells are responsible for the secretion of milk. Outside of these are the structural connective tissue, blood, lymph vessels, and nerves. The circulatory system, blood, and lymph provide the materials from which milk is made, and the milk is taken up by the epithelial cells and passed into the lumen or opening of the alveolus. Espe [1] has likened the mammary gland to innumerable bunches of grapes freed from gravity but

[1] Dwight Espe, *Secretion of Milk*. Collegiate Press, Inc., of Iowa State College, Ames, Iowa, 1941.

attached to a hollow-trunk system. The grapelike bunches of alveoli form the lobules, and the loaded branches, the lobes. The "grapes" are so numerous in the more highly efficient glands that, except for the collecting system,

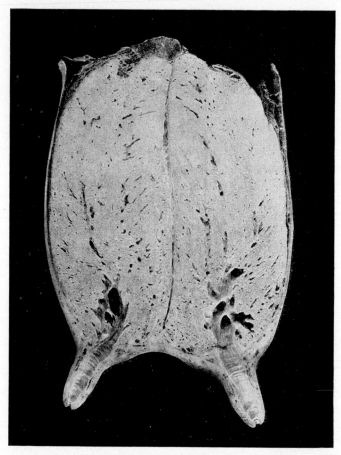

Fig. 95. Vertical transverse section through the rear udder of a lactating Holstein cow. (U.S.D.A., Bur. of Dairy Industry.)

or ducts, and the blood vessels, practically all of the available space is occupied by the alveoli and thin connective tissue septa. In less "milky" udders the connective tissue septa are thicker and more pronounced.

Duct system

The duct system has its termination in the teat, and it extends to secretory tissue in the alveoli. The teat is comprised of the connective-tissue wall which is covered with skin that is practically hairless and is usually darker colored than the skin on other parts. (See Figure 96.) The central part is a cavity termed the "teat cistern," and this is drained through the streak canal. This canal is from 8 to 12 millimeters long and is lined with folds which close the opening. Sphincter muscles keep the folds pressed together to close the opening. In milking pressure is applied from the upper part downward, forcing the milk out of the teat.

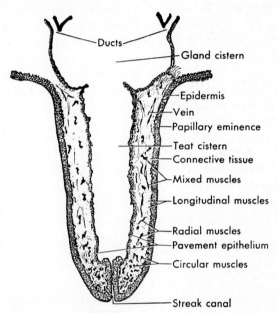

Fig. 96. A longitudinal section of a cow teat and the lower part of the milk cistern. (From *Dairy Science,* by W. E. Petersen, J. B. Lippincott Company, Philadelphia, Pa.)

Immediately above the teat cistern in the body of the udder is the gland cistern. This serves for milk storage. The gland cistern is variable, but it generally has a capacity of about 1 pint. About 12 to 50 rather large ducts enter the gland cistern. Each large duct drains a portion of the gland called a "lobe." The ducts branch into the many small ducts which drain the alveoli.

Circulatory system

The udder receives its main supply of blood from an artery running to each half. A branch from the iliac artery, known as the "external pudic artery," passes through the inguinal canal to the udder. There are two main branches of this artery in the udder, the cranial, which goes to the fore quarter, and the caudal, which goes to the rear quarter. The surface circulation is from the general peripheral circulation.

Three different routes carry the blood away from the udder. They are the external pudic veins, the subcutaneous abdominal veins, and the perineal veins. The subcutaneous abdominal veins are commonly called the *milk veins,* and they are a continuation of the mammary veins of the udder. The place where the milk vein penetrates the abdominal wall is called a "milk well." The size of milk veins is dependent upon the stage of lactation; they are largest at the peak of lactation. The greatest volume of blood is returned to the heart by the milk veins; consequently, they are large in heavy producers. However, since blood may be returned to the heart by other than the milk veins, their size is not a reliable index to volume of production. There is also a lymphatic circulation in the udder. The lymph comes from the blood and then is carried away from the tissue in lymph vessels which join together to form larger vessels. Lymph vessels pass up the inguinal canal and enter the lumbar lymph trunk.

Nerve system

The udder is innervated by sympathetic nerves which pass to the udder through the inguinal canal.

DEVELOPMENT OF THE UDDER

The tissue from which the udder develops is differentiated quite early in the fetal development. When born, the heifer calf has a well-developed teat cistern and gland. As the heifer grows, the fatty tissue in the udder is replaced by a developing duct system. With pregnancy, there is a very rapid development of the duct system which is practically complete at the end of five months of pregnancy. As pregnancy advances, there is a great growth in the size of the udder, owing to the formation of alveoli. At parturition milk secretion begins.

HORMONAL CONTROL OF SECRETION

Certain hormones influence the development of the udder. *Estrogen,* an ovarian hormone, causes the development of the duct system. *Progesterone,* a secretion of the corpus luteum, is responsible for the development of the alveoli and epithelial cells. *Prolactin,* a secretion of the anterior pituitary body, causes secretion of milk. Thyroxin from the thyroid gland functions in milk secretion. The adrenal gland secretions also have to do with maintenance of milk flow. These and other hormones have to do with the growth and functioning of the mammary glands. Each apparently has a definite function, and they act in sequence. The mechanism of milk secretion is not understood completely. Lactation is linked with reproduction, and the activities of the organs concerned with reproduction in the female are interrelated with milk production. It is known, for example, that pregnancy, after the fifth month, inhibits milk production. Estrus also appears to affect lactation.

As milk production recedes, the udder shrinks in size because of the reabsorption of the alveoli. The alveoli develop again on subsequent pregnancy.

MILK SECRETION

Although the structure of the mammary gland has been studied and is quite well understood, we do not understand just how milk is formed. Therefore, we have several theories as to how milk is synthesized. The most widely accepted theory is that, in general, milk is formed by true cell metabolism. In other words, milk is a synthetic product of the epithelial cells in the alveoli. The materials for milk are taken from the blood stream and changed to make the various constituents of milk. Some materials are unchanged in passing through the cell; they are filtration products from the blood. This is largely true of such things as water, minerals, and vitamins. Milk globulin, one of the milk proteins, is identical with the globulin found in the blood. On the other hand, such substances as the milk proteins, casein, and lactalbumin have for their precursors the amino acids in the blood, which are synthesized into proteins by the cells. Milk then contains some quite complex materials that are not found in the blood but are elaborated from the blood constituents. While the secretion of milk is mainly a matter of cellular metabolism, normal milk contains the products of cell degeneration and also infiltration products from the blood.

TIME OF MILK SECRETION

Milk secretion is a continuous process. No rapid increase occurs in secretion during the act of milking. The milk drawn at a regular period of milking is in the udder at the time. An udder removed from a slaughtered milk cow would give the normal amount of milk.

As milk is secreted in the udder, pressure accumulates and causes a decrease in the rate of secretion. If an udder is not milked the secreted milk may be resorbed. The fact that udder pressure affects milk secretion explains why it may be necessary to milk high-producing cows more than twice per day.

MILK LET-DOWN OR HOLDING UP MILK

Suckling by a calf or other "conditioned" responses such as those caused by rattling of milk pails, starting the milking-machine engine or massaging the udder with a damp towel cause a let-down of milk already manufactured in the udder. The milk in the gland cistern may be withdrawn but the remainder is not obtained unless the let-down occurs.

Response to the conditions mentioned causes a nerve impulse to travel to the cow's brain. The brain signals the pituitary gland, which releases the hormone, oxytocin, into the blood. The blood carries it to the udder, where it causes a contraction of smooth muscles surrounding the milk storage places in the udder.

The let-down of milk is effective for only a few minutes. If milking is delayed the milk is resorbed into the blood and lost. If milking is done too slowly, part of the milk will remain in the udder.

NATURE OF MILK

Milk is a secretion of the normally functioning mammary gland. Whole milk contains a mean of approximately 9 per cent milk solids not fat, and not less than 3.8 per cent fat. It is a very complex material and contains some rather complex substances. It is the natural food for young mammalia; consequently, it must contain the many needed nutrient materials in order to be adequate. Milk is regarded as being our best single food.

Milk contains sizable quantities of protein, fat, lactose, and mineral matter. It also contains small amounts of the vitamins, pigments, enzymes, and other organic compounds.

Milk is opaque and ranges in color from bluish white to yellowish white. It has a sweetish odor when freshly drawn. The taste is sweet. Fresh milk is very slightly acid, having a pH of 6.5 to 6.62. It is amphoretic to litmus paper; that is, it will turn red litmus blue and blue litmus red. Feeds may influence both the odor and the taste of milk.

The water in milk forms the continuous phase in which materials are held in solution. Sugar or lactose of milk, as well as some of the minerals, albumin, and globulin, are in true solution. There is also a colloidal phase which includes some of the protein compounds in the form of minute particles. Further, there is a suspension phase, which includes the fat globules, particles of microscopic size. The specific gravity of milk ranges from 1.026 to 1.034, the average being about 1.032 at 15°C. A quart of milk weights 2.15 pounds.

COMPOSITION OF MILK

The composition of milk varies with the breed and with the individual. It may be affected by such factors as condition of the cow, stage and period of lactation, environmental conditions, feeding, and management. These factors and others affect not only the quality of the milk but also the quantity.

The fat content may vary 30 per cent from day to day, but there is usually less variation in the protein, sugar, and minerals. There may also be a 20 per cent variation in the quantity of milk. As lactation advances, the milk flow declines, the content of fat rises, and the lactose declines.

Composition of milk varies greatly among cows. Therefore, the butterfat test is highly important in a comparison of cows. Much difference exists in the persistency of production. Cows having about the same initial production may show as much as 50 per cent difference in yearly production.

The table from Petersen [2] which follows gives the variation in the composition of cows' milk and also the mean or average composition.

VARIATIONS IN COMPOSITION OF COWS' MILK

CONSTITUENT	MAXIMUM, PER CENT	MINIMUM, PER CENT	MEAN, PER CENT
Water	90.32	80.32	87.27
Protein	6.40	2.07	3.55
Casein	6.29	1.79	3.02
Albumin	1.44	0.25	0.53
Fat	10.00	1.20	3.80
Lactose	6.12	2.11	4.90
Ash	1.21	0.35	0.71

A big difference is found in the composition of the milk from representative individuals of the dairy breeds. Following is a tabulation of milk composition by breeds.

COMPOSITION OF MILK BY BREEDS

BREED	TOTAL SOLIDS, PER CENT	FAT, PER CENT	PROTEIN, PER CENT
Jersey	14.80	5.36	3.80
Guernsey	14.50	4.96	3.75
Brown Swiss	13.00	4.00	3.50
Ayrshire	13.00	4.00	3.50
Holstein	12.30	3.42	3.30

The breeds giving the least milk have the highest fat and protein content. As the fat content of milk increases, the percentages of protein and of ash also increase but the lactose content decreases. Of the various ingredients in milk, lactose seems to be the least variable, that is, within cattle and among species.

THE FAT IN MILK

The fat particles in milk vary in size from 1 to 10 microns in diameter. The Guernsey breed has the largest fat particles; those of the Ayrshire and

2 W. E. Petersen, *Dairy Science,* J. B. Lippincott Company, Philadelphia, Pa., 1950.

Holstein are comparatively small. The fat content does not remain constant during milking. The first-drawn milk is lower in fat than that which is drawn last, and fat content also varies from one milking to the next. Of all the constituents of milk, the fat content is the most variable. There may be seasonal variation in the fat test, for as the amount of milk decreases, the fat content usually rises. Season may affect the feed supply and therefore change the amount of milk produced. Many other conditions may have similar influence. Fat content of milk is higher in the winter because of the effect of lower temperatures.

The color in milk is due to the carotenes—fatlike substances; these materials are precursors of vitamin A. Since vitamin A is colorless, milk which is highly pigmented because of its carotene content may not have more vitamin-A value than lighter-color milk. Guernseys produce milk and butter high in yellow color or carotene. Holsteins have the least carotene.

COLOSTRUM MILK

The milk yielded immediately after calving is vastly different in composition from normal milk, if the cow has had a rest period prior to calving. This first-produced or colostrum milk changes to normal in a few days. Ordinarily, milk produced in the first three or four days after calving is not used for human food. Colostrum milk is much higher in total solids than normal milk because of its high protein, mainly globulin, content. Colostrum milk is higher in ash, more variable in fat (0.15 to 12.0 per cent), and lower in lactose than regular milk. Cows milked up until calving yield colostrum less different from normal milk than do cows with a precalving rest period. Colostrum milk is somewhat laxative and very high in vitamin A and antibodies, making it particularly beneficial for the newborn calf.

FACTORS THAT INFLUENCE MILK YIELDS AND COMPOSITION

As previously indicated, breed and calving affect both the quantity and quality of milk. Other conditions also affect milk flow. Some of the more important of these will be discussed separately.

STAGE OF LACTATION

A normal lactation curve based upon the amount of milk produced has been extensively studied. Production increases until about the fiftieth day of lactation, and thereafter gradually declines. Much difference is manifest in the continuance of milk flow or persistency of production. Fat production is more constant than milk yield, because as milk yield decreases, the fat content increases. Protein content increases after the third month of lactation.

NUMBER OF MILKINGS

Since pressure built up by milk retards secretion, frequent milkings will give greater production than the usual twice-a-day milking. The expense of more frequent milkings is seldom justified, except with high-producing cows.

FEED AND STATE OF NUTRITION

Inadequate nutrition will affect the amount and quality of milk yielded. The composition is likewise altered—fat, protein, ash, and total solids increase, but lactose decreases. A satisfactory ration must contain the dietary essentials and must also be sufficient in amount to sustain milk production. Deficiencies in the ration will cause greater changes in milk volume than in most milk constituents. Since the specific effect of different feeds and feed constituents upon the quantity and quality of milk is rather completely discussed in some of the textbooks on dairy cattle listed at the end of this book, it will not be included here.

SEASONAL EFFECTS

Seasonal variation in the quantity and quality of milk is influenced by the temperature. Fat content is lowest in August and highest in January. Cows calving in the fall normally produce the maximum amount of milk and butterfat. Winter calving is superior to spring and summer calving, milk and butterfat yields considered.

CONDITION OF THE COW

The condition of the cow at calving time affects the yield and the fat content of milk. A heavy yielding cow is in negative nutritive balance when lactating; so an accumulation of flesh is helpful in sustaining milk production. Increased production follows a dry period of 6 to 8 weeks.

AGE

A cow will attain maximum production at about 7 years of age under normal conditions. At 10 years production begins to decline.

A heifer calving as a two-year-old will produce from 70 to 77 per cent of her mature production. A three-year-old with her second calf will yield from 80 to 87 per cent, and a four-year-old with her third calf from 90 to 95 per cent of mature production. A five-year-old is usually just a little short of maximum production. Age is taken into consideration in the requirements for the advanced registration of cows.

FACTORS FOR STANDARDIZING RECORDS TO MATURE-EQUIVALENT BASIS [3]

(Multiply the records started at various ages by the factors given)

AGE Yr.–Mo.	BREED					
	Ayrshire	Brown Swiss	Guernsey	Holstein	Jersey	Milking Shorthorn
2–0	1.30	1.45	1.24	1.31	1.27	1.42
2–6	1.24	1.35	1.18	1.24	1.21	1.30
3–0	1.18	1.23	1.12	1.18	1.15	1.24
3–6	1.13	1.16	1.08	1.12	1.09	1.18
4–0	1.10	1.10	1.06	1.08	1.06	1.13
4–6	1.06	1.07	1.04	1.04	1.03	1.10
5–0	1.03	1.04	1.02	1.02	1.02	1.04
5–6	1.02	1.02	1.01	1.02	1.01	1.04
6–0	1.00	1.00	1.00	1.00	1.00	1.0;
7–0	1.00	1.00	1.00	1.00	1.00	1.00
8–0	1.00	1.00	1.01	1.00	1.01	1.01
9–0	1.02	1.01	1.02	1.02	1.02	1.02
10–0	1.03	1.02	1.04	1.04	1.04	1.04
11–0	1.04	1.04	1.06	1.06	1.06	1.08
12–0	1.06	1.06	1.08	1.09	1.08	1.08
13–0	1.07	1.08	1.10	1.12	1.10	1.10
14–0	1.09	1.10	1.12	1.15	1.12	1.12

MISCELLANEOUS FACTORS IN MILK SECRETION

Health is a major factor in milk and butterfat production. For example, mastitis or digestive disturbance may affect milk yields and quality. Some drugs inhibit or stimulate milk flow.

[3] *B.D.I.–Inf.*–162, October, 1953, Bureau of Dairy Industry, U.S.D.A.

Chapter 16

MILK PRODUCTION
AND MILK RECORDS

The breeding, feeding, and management of the specialized dairy cow has been directed toward heavy milk production. The costs of feed and other items are increased as production is stepped up; however, they are not directly proportional to the gain in production. With cows that are handled as milk cows, high production is stressed, because it is usually economical and necessary for profit from the enterprise. There is a point beyond which additional production may not be economical, but under most conditions the efficient near-maximum yield is seldom reached. Many cow herds are below the level of most economical production.

MILK PRODUCTION ON FARMS AND
AVERAGE PRODUCTION

For a 10 year period there were on the average 22,633 thousand milk cows on farms. Each cow had a yearly production of 5,191 pounds, which gives a total of about 117,440 million pounds of milk per year. This includes all cows milked; there are many other than specialized dairy cows. On the basis of our average human population this would be a production of about 734 pounds of milk per capita.[1]

For a period with production of milk per cow as indicated and testing 3.94 per cent butterfat, there would be an annual yield of 204.6 pounds of butterfat. This estimate excludes the milk sucked by calves and the milk produced by cows not on farms. The production per cow seems to be

[1] *Agricultural Statistics,* U.S.D.A., 1955.

increasing. The drought year of 1934 was an exception, but production in the other years has shown an upward tendency since 1924, the year of the initial estimate. The heaviest milk-producing cows in 1954 were in the states of California, New Jersey, Rhode Island, and Wisconsin, where the annual production was above 7,000 pounds per cow annually. States with relatively low milk production per cow were Louisiana and Mississippi, where the annual production was below 3,000 pounds per cow per year.

For the conversion of butterfat to butter it is usually assumed that butter is approximately 85 per cent butterfat. On this basis the average milk cow for the decade yielded about 240 pounds of butter.

PRODUCTION NEEDED FOR PROFIT

The profit made from dairying lies in the margin between the cost of keep of the cow and the price received for her production. Dairy cows also provide a home market for farm-raised feeds and bring an indirect return through the maintenance of fertility and the resultant improved crop yields.

Since considerable expense is involved in keeping milk cows, a certain level of production must be maintained. Illinois studies indicate that cows producing 4,000 pounds of 4 per cent milk or less during a year yielded no profit. As the yield was extended beyond 4,000 pounds, profit was

Fig. 97. A Holstein-Friesian cow. Haven Hill Crescent Gewina Count. The Official World's Record fat producer. In 365 days she produced 1,523 pounds of butterfat and 38,878 pounds of milk. Classified excellent. Owned by Rock River Farms, Mr. & Mrs. R. B. McLaughlin, Byron, Ill.

shown. Since the average production is only slightly in excess of the 5,000 pounds, it is apparent that many unprofitable cows are being milked. Costs of production are not uniform throughout the country. In the South, for example, costs for housing and certain feeds are lower; therefore, a profitable level of production may be below 4,000 pounds.

Cows that are low producers should be identified early and culled, because a poor dairy cow is not a dual-purpose cow and is a poor competitor with one. It is apparent that is, 160 pounds of butterfat is just on the verge of profit and if the average annual production is just over 200 pounds, many cows being milked are in the unprofitable class. Rapid herd improvement will follow the culling of cows of low productive capacity.

ECONOMY OF HIGH PRODUCERS

The fact that the amount of milk and butter fat produced is related to economy of production has been demonstrated many times. In the table below, the records from herds in the dairy-herd-improvement association for one year are placed in various average milk production groups.

RELATION OF PRODUCTION TO INCOME OVER FEED COST [2]

A Summary of Records of Herds in Dairy-Herd-Improvement Associations

Range of Average Milk Production	Herds		Average per Cow							Value of Product Over Feed Cost	Return for $1 Spent for Feed	Feed Cost for 100 Pounds of Milk
			Production				Feed Cost					
			Milk	Test	Butterfat	Value	Roughage Including Pasture	Grain	Total			
Lb.	No.	Pct.	Lb.	Pct.	Lb.	Dol.	Dol.	Dol.	Dol.	Dol.	Dol.	Dol.
2,500–3,499	14	0.1	3,184	4.7	148	194	51	54	105	89	1.85	3.30
3,500–4,499	84	.4	4,165	4.7	194	244	63	65	128	116	1.91	3.07
4,500–5,499	421	2.3	5,117	4.7	241	290	71	68	139	151	2.09	2.72
5,500–6,499	1,420	7.6	6,076	4.7	284	341	77	78	155	186	2.20	2.55
6,500–7,499	2,683	14.5	7,029	4.6	320	383	82	85	167	216	2.29	2.38
7,500–8,499	3,091	16.7	7,994	4.3	345	423	87	93	180	243	2.35	2.25
8,500–9,499	2,936	15.8	8,998	3.9	353	441	91	96	187	254	2.36	2.08
9,500–10,499	2,919	15.7	9,994	3.7	371	468	92	101	193	275	2.42	1.93
10,500–11,499	2,388	12.9	10,973	3.6	400	500	94	107	201	299	2.49	1.83
11,500–12,499	1,510	8.1	11,939	3.6	431	539	97	115	212	327	2.54	1.78
12,500–13,499	747	4.0	12,918	3.6	465	585	99	126	225	360	2.60	1.74
13,500–14,499	244	1.3	13,911	3.6	498	622	101	132	233	389	2.67	1.67
14,500–15,499	68	.4	14,823	3.6	538	658	100	148	248	410	2.65	1.67
15,500–16,499	20	.1	15,963	3.6	579	726	114	168	282	444	2.57	1.77
16,500–and over	11	.1	17,287	3.6	615	786	122	205	327	459	2.40	1.89
Total	18,556	100.0	..	..	..	..	..	..	..	..	..	..
Average *	..	..	9,109	4.0	361	447	89	97	186	261	2.40	2.04

* Average is for 18,556 herds that completed a full 12-month testing period.

[2] *Agricultural Statistics*, U.S.D.A., 1955.

It should be pointed out that the above information is for a selected rather specialized group in herd improvement association and that the average is not for all herds in the country.

It will be noted that in all cases the value of the product was more than the feed cost. Since feed is but just one of the costs involved, herds in the lower levels of average milk production were not profitable to their owners. In general, the return for each dollar spent for feed increased and the feed cost for 100 pounds of milk decreased with increasing production. As production becomes greater the overhead expense becomes relatively less, leaving a greater proportion for profit. High production obtained by economical methods is essential for profitable dairying.

The main difference in cost between high and low producing cows would be the greater concentrate (grain) consumption of the more productive cows. The roughage and pasture cost is a little higher for more productive cows but labor, housing, bull service, interest, taxes, depreciation and veterinary would not be vastly different from less productive cows.

INDIVIDUAL VARIATION OF PRODUCTION

As milk and butterfat production have been developed in dairy cows, there has been greater variation in the amount produced. Cows at the level of production sufficient to give a calf a good start and no more do not vary much. Within the groups given in the previous table there is a large variation of production, more in the groups at the upper levels than in the lower brackets.

A striking example of this variation is one case of two cows sired by the same bull that were kept under comparable conditions and given equal opportunity. For an average of 2 years the high producer yielded 7,192 pounds of milk and 388 pounds of fat yearly, while the low-producing half sister produced but 2,695 pounds of milk and 124 pounds of fat.

Cause for wide variation in production

It has been found that the low-producing cows are no less efficient in utilization of feed than high producers. In fact, it has also been found that the ability to digest feeds is not related to breed, age, or milk-producing capacity. Likewise, the requirements for maintenance are not significantly different. The principal difference between high and low producers is the capacity for feed consumption and ability to convert it to milk. The reason for this is apparent; if there is no difference in the ability to use the feed or maintenance, there must be a difference in the amount used. With greater feed consumption there is a larger proportion available for making milk. This explains why capacity for feed consumption, or the size of the barrel, is given considerable emphasis in dairy cattle selection. A cow with large capacity can consume more feed, and a large amount may be used for milk production.

Eckles [3] compared two somewhat similar cows kept under comparable conditions. One cow produced about three times as much milk as the other and as a consequence consumed more feed. The higher-producing cow used but 35 per cent of her feed consumption for maintenance, but the lower producer required 56 per cent of the feed she consumed for that purpose.

A high-producing cow has a relatively large amount of the milk-secreting hormone. This endocrine secretion stimulates milk secretion. Also in high-producing cows there is a large amount of secretory tissue. Since the materials for the milk come from the food intake directly or indirectly, the lactating cow has a good appetite and consumes great quantities of feed.

Fig. 98. A Jersey cow, Imp. Wonderful Snowdrop. An outstanding individual with a noteworthy production record of 14,234 pounds of milk and 833 pounds of fat. Many times grand champion, classified as excellent. (American Jersey Cattle Club.)

It should be pointed out that the urge for secretion may be so great that body accumulations of nutrient material are somewhat depleted by lactation. As it is impossible to estimate the extent of milk-producing hormone

[3] Clarence H. Eckles and Ernest L. Anthony, *Dairy Cattle and Milk Production.* The Macmillan Company, New York, N.Y., 1950.

secretion, we cannot be certain about the milk production. Good milk cows will put on flesh in the dry period and lose it when milking. It does not pay to feed heavily cows that do not milk heavily, as poor dairy cows are not efficient beef makers. However, it is usually economical to feed good cows well. As milk production is inherited, we select for breeding those cows which come from highly productive parents.

DAIRY HERD RECORDS

One of the essentials of successful management of the dairy herd is the keeping of adequate records. This involves the identification of the individuals in the herd so that individual records may be kept. Without records it is impossible to tell which are the productive and profitable cows in the herd. A record of production will enable the dairyman to make proper selections for the breeding herd, eliminate unprofitable cows, and feed his cows intelligently.

The most important record on the individual cow is the amount of milk produced. The range of production within a breed is five times as great in the volume of milk as in the butterfat test. The amount of milk is therefore more important than the test for butterfat in determining production. In practice, 1 or 2 days' weights of the milk are made once a month or in some cases every 2 months. Such weights form the basis for fairly accurate estimates of yearly production. Daily weights of the milk are of course more accurate, and inform the dairyman more promptly of changes in production. Butterfat tests are commonly made monthly, and the estimate of monthly production of butterfat from such tests will be accurate within 5 per cent.

DAIRY HERD IMPROVEMENT ASSOCIATIONS

The purpose of the dairy herd improvement association is to provide means for recording the production of cows in the organization. In 1955 there were 2,288 such organizations, with over 41 thousand herds on test and more than a million cows enrolled. The associations are cooperative, usually consisting of about 26 dairy farmers, and a man is employed to keep the records under state college supervision. The supervisor visits each herd each month, and weighs the milk yielded by each cow. In some associations bimonthly testing is used, and the membership may be twice as large as where monthly testing is done. A composite sample is made of the milk of each cow, and the butterfat is determined by the Babcock test. From these data the monthly production for each cow is determined and recorded in the owners herd book.

The associations value extends beyond breeding and improvement, since the supervisor aids the farmer in feeding and management problems. The average yearly production of cows in the associations is 375 pounds of fat and 9,502 pounds of milk,[4] nearly twice that of the average for the country. Through the culling of low producers and the improvement of production methods, production has been nearly doubled.

Owner-sampler and weigh-a-day

An Owner-Sampler plan offers the dairy farmer an economical means of getting milk and butterfat production records on his cows. Under this plan the owner makes the weights and takes the samplers on an assigned day. The butterfat tests are made and the production records calculated by the D.H.I.A. supervisor.

The Weigh-A-Day-Month plan is a low-cost milk recording service. The owner weighs the milk from each cow in his herd for a 24-hour period near the middle of each month. The records are computed by a central office and reported back to the owner. The Owner-Sampler and Weigh-A-Day-A-Month records are for the owner's information and are not used in advertising.

Fig. 99. A Guernsey cow, Adohr Eldor Pearlette. A grand champion cow, also winner of trophies for best A.R. cow and best-uddered cow. (American Guernsey Cattle Club.)

[4] *Agricultural Statistics,* U.S.D.A., 1955.

Official testing

The breed registry organizations have set up standards which are the basis for selective registration of individuals meeting a certain minimum of production. Sires are admitted on the basis of the production of their daughters. Advanced registry is available in the dairy and dual-purpose breeds. Records increase the value of tested cows and sires. Also, they serve as a basis for improvement of the average excellence of dairy cattle.

Official testing is under the general direction and supervision of the breed registry organization superintendent of advanced registry. The states have superintendents of official testing at the state agricultural colleges who have charge of the tests and appoint the supervisors. The latter visit monthly the farms under the testing program where they weigh and test for butterfat content all of the milk produced by the cows on test for a 24- or 48-hour period. Their reports are sent to the state college and are forwarded to the breed registry organization.

Unified general rules for official testing approved by the Purebred Dairy Cattle Association and the American Dairy Science Association are followed. Some variations from the general rules permitted by the various breed organizations.

Fig. 100. A Brown Swiss cow, Jane of Vernon, owned by Judd's Bridge Farm, New Milford, Conn. In 3½ lactations this cow produced 76,254 pounds of milk and 3,574 pounds of butterfat. She is regarded as having one of the most perfect mammary systems to be found in any dairy cow.

There are two systems of production testing provided by the breed registry organizations for the breeders of registered dairy cattle.

1. Advanced registry.   In this system one or more selected cows may be entered at any time for lactation records of either or both 305 or 365 days in length. Daily milk weights must be kept, and test periods are preceded by a preliminary dry milking.

2. Herd improvement registry.   In this system the entire herd is tested. The test is for 1 year and may be started on the first of any month. No daily milk weights are required of the farmer. The tests are 24 hours in duration, and there is no preliminary dry milking prior to the test period.

RECORDS OF CHAMPION PRODUCERS

Some phenomenal records have been made by dairy cows. Formerly short-time records such as 7-day and 30-day periods were used for measuring production, but they have been found to be less reliable than records for longer periods. Lactation records of 365 days in length are commonly given. More emphasis is being put on lifetime records, since a yearly record is only one expression of production.

Perhaps too much emphasis has been placed upon the top yearly records since they are sometimes made under forced conditions. Economy of pro-

NATIONAL MILK AND BUTTERFAT RECORDS FOR EACH BREED
(OCT. 15, 1956)

Breed	Length of Record	Times Milked Daily	Pounds Milk	Pounds Fat
Ayrshire				
Neshaminy Miss Phett	305d.	2x	20,946	1036
Garclaugh May Mischief			25,329	895
Brown Swiss				
Royal's Rapture of Lee's Hill	365d.	3x	34,669	1465
Guernsey				
U. of A. Lubas Eldorene	365d.	3x	20,277	1350
Welcome-In Forward's Clara	365d.	3x	26,672	1120
Holstein				
Haven Hill Crescent Gewina Count	365d.	3x	38,878	1523
Green Meadow Lily Pabst	365d.	3x	42,805	1246
Jersey				
Opal Crystal Lady	365d.	2x	23,725	1237
June Volunteer Fantasy	365d.	3x	20,097	1319
Milking Shorthorn				
Ruth B.			21,641	957
Hastoe Barrington 30th (Canadian)			22,483	851
Red Poll				
Jean Duluth Beauty			20,281	892

duction and sometimes the future usefulness of the individual are secondary in making a high record. However, such records at least point out the potentiality of production.

A list of the record cows in milk and fat production of the various dairy and dual-purpose breeds in the United States is on page 275.

There are several phenomenal examples of long-term production by dairy cows of the different breeds. Some of the outstanding long-time records are listed below.

Most cows remain in the dairy herd a comparatively short period of time; as a consequence, their record of production is but a small proportion of their potential production. Disease, infertility, and other conditions result in short periods of productivity for individual cows in the average herd. The records that follow have been made by heavy producers over a comparatively long period.

BREED	NAME	LENGTH OF RECORD	PRODUCTION OF MILK, POUNDS	PRODUCTION OF BUTTERFAT, POUNDS
Holstein-Friesian	Panco Hazel	13 lactations 4919 days	281,193	10,599
Holstein-Friesian	Genodale Pride Ormsby	13 lactations 5193 days	271,903	9,229
Holstein-Friesian	Ionia Ormsby Queen	12 lactations 4790 days	267,304	8,601
Guernsey	Caumsett Ida	11 Records	194,280	8,508
Guernsey	Reveller's Fanny	14 Records	180,558	8,804
Guernsey	Ideal's Peter's May Jewel	8 Records plus 274 days	177,906	9,343
Ayrshire	Delchester Audacious Netty 2nd	5439 days	219,891	8,676
Ayrshire	Crusader's Joyce of Windy Top	6537 days	206,593	8,709
Jersey	Silken Lady Ruby	Lifetime	184,883	10,226
Jersey	Radiant Romance Storrs	Lifetime	154,327	7,706
Brown Swiss	Lady's Gypsy Girl F.	4431 days	248,125	10,576
Brown Swiss	Royals Rapture of Lee's Hill	3491 days	234,828	10,079
Milking Shorthorn	Trixie 3rd	Lifetime	132,142	6,030
Milking Shorthorn	Lady Blackwood	Lifetime	138,234	5,300

Fig. 101. An Ayrshire and calf, Crusader's Joyce of Windy Top, at 19 years of age with her 15th living calf. She has a lifetime record of 206,888 pounds of 4.2 per cent butterfat milk or 8,725 pounds of fat in 6,550 days. (Ayrshire Breeders' Association.)

MILK COWS—ECONOMICAL PRODUCERS OF HUMAN FOOD

The dairy cow is a very efficient converter of farm feeds into human food. A comparatively large proportion of the nutrient material consumed by efficient cows is converted into milk nutrients. The milk cow produces more human food from the feed she consumes than does any other farm animal. The cow is followed by the hen as a converter of protein into human food; the hog is about on a par with the cow in efficiency as a converter of energy.

Comparisons among various farm animals, for efficiency in converting nutrients in feed consumed into human food, does not give the entire story of economy of production. In the first place, the feeds consumed by different kinds of livestock are not comparable, and second, feed is just one item in production cost.

Although there are differences in recovery of food value from feed and in providing it for human use, there is a place for all of our domestic animals. All edible animal products are used in the human diet. For example, milk and meat are not directly competitive as foods. Each kind of livestock fills a place in a balanced farming program, and each is suited to a particular situation. Dairy cattle might be a logical choice under certain circumstances, that is, with an ample feed supply and a suitable market, but beef cattle would be more adaptable to range feeding conditions and greater distance from markets.

Chapter 17

CONSUMPTION OF MILK
AND DAIRY PRODUCTS

The various outlets for milk available to the dairy farmer have been previously discussed. Milk may reach the ultimate consumer in many forms, depending upon demand, which is an expression of consumer's preference. The total amount of milk and milk products consumed appears to shift from year to year.

MILK AS A FOOD

Milk is our best single food. It is the natural food of young mammals and therefore quite well suited to their needs. Milk is not a nutritionally complete food; it needs supplementation to form an adequate and ample diet. However, milk is particularly good to supplement the cereal grains which normally provide the bulk of the energy value in our diet. Because of the quantity and quality of its protein and its content of essential vitamins and minerals, it is valuable in most diets, especially for the young. Milk is regarded by many as an absolute essential in the human diet. It is commonly referred to as the "most nearly perfect food."

Milk may be fortified in certain ways to make it a more complete food. One addition is that of Vitamin D. This is the antirachitic vitamin which is involved in normal bone growth. Rickets, a bone disease, may be due to an inadequate supply of Vitamin D. Milk fortified with this vitamin will prevent rickets. Three methods of fortification are in use: (1) direct exposure of the milk to ultraviolet light; (2) feeding cows irradiated yeast or other material high in Vitamin D; (3) adding Vitamin-D concentrates to the milk. The usual method is to add 400 U.S.P. units of D_2 or D_3 per quart of milk.

In volume as well as quality, milk and milk products rank high. It has

279

been estimated that about one quarter of the food consumed by the average person is milk and its products.

UTILIZATION OF TOTAL MILK PRODUCED

The uses of milk yearly for several decades are shown in Figures 102 and 103. It will be noted that about one-half of the milk produced is consumed as fluid milk and cream on farms and in cities and villages. The milk sold in cities and villages by distributors is largely standardized by mixing the milk taken in from the different farms. Milk that enters the market milk trade is a fairly uniform product generally prepared by pasteurization. About half of the milk produced is used for manufactured dairy products, including butter made on the farms.

PER CAPITA CONSUMPTION OF DAIRY PRODUCTS [1,2]

The milk equivalent of all of the dairy products used per person for a recent 10-year period is about 734 pounds. The consumption of milk and the milk equivalent of cream consumed per capita is higher on farms than in cities. The average consumed in this form was about 362 pounds per person yearly.

The balance of the consumption was in the following dairy products and in the amounts given.[2] Butter, 9.88 pounds; cheese, 7.14 pounds; evaporated milk, case goods, unskimmed, 18.45 pounds; commercial ice cream, 18.3 pounds production weight; nonfat dry-milk solids, 3.59 pounds.

Milk consumption is the heaviest on a per person basis in the north Atlantic region, followed by the north central, the western, the south Atlantic, and the south central in the order named.

CHANGES IN CONSUMPTION OF DAIRY PRODUCTS

Recent changes in consumption of dairy products are due to the declining demand for milk fat or products containing milk fat.

Milk and cream consumption increased during the 1920's until 1929. A temporary decline followed in the middle 1930's, probably mostly among city populations. A rise in consumption took place in the late 1930's, and in 1941 consumption was almost up to the 1929 level. Since then, there has been a gradual increase in production and consumption, followed by a slight decline. The increased consumption during the last decade has been due to greater per capita consumption of city populations.

[1] In the conversion of dairy products to whole-milk equivalent, the following factors applied in 1949: butter, 20.0 pounds; American cheese, 10.0 pounds; other cheese, 9.6 pounds; evaporated milk, 2.14 pounds; condensed milk, 2.4 pounds; and dry whole milk, 7.5 pounds.

[2] *Agricultural Statistics,* U.S.D.A., 1955.

CONSUMPTION PER PERSON OF MAJOR DAIRY PRODUCTS

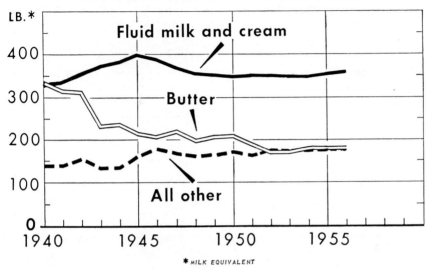

Fig. 102. Consumption per person of major dairy products. About one-half of our dairy products are consumed as milk and cream. Total milk production has shown an upward tendency, but consumption per person has not changed much in the past few years. (U.S.D.A., Agricultural Marketing Service.)

Butter consumption during the 1940 decade was about 12.8 pounds per person. A decline in consumption was coincident with World War II. Following the war period there were increases in consumption of butterfat and in whole-milk products; however there was a decline in numbers of cows in the butter-producing areas.

Manufactured dairy products have steadily increased in consumption. Development of processed cheese and improvement in its packaging and distribution have stimulated consumption, which has shown a gradual increase during the past decade. Similar progress has been made with a variety of other dairy products. Consumption of evaporated and canned milk has increased more than twofold since 1920. This increase has been due to the improvement of processing and the relative prices of the condensed products and fresh milk and cream.

Consumption of ice cream per capita has increased more than twofold since 1920. During the depression of the early 1930's ice cream consumption was quite low, but by 1937 the rate was back to its former level. There was a high point in consumption for the year of 1946, following which there has been a drop, and then a leveling off in consumption.

The change in consumption of dairy products since 1920 is shown in Figure 103.

Per Capita Output and Use

MILK PRODUCTS

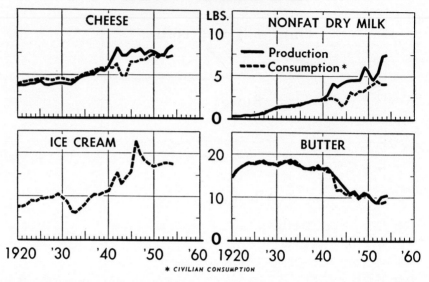

Fig. 103. Milk products, per capita output, and use in the United States. There has been a marked increase in the consumption of nonfat dry milk. Consumption of ice cream has also increased since the depression, then leveled off. Cheese consumption has increased slightly; butter consumption has decreased. (U.S.D.A., Agricultural Marketing Service.)

GRADES OF MILK

The grades and their meanings vary according to local regulations. The Standard United States Public Health Service milk ordinance has been adopted by nearly 1600 municipalities and over 400 counties.[3]

Grades of market milk are determined by local requirements, and these depend in part upon the demands of the trade. Milk grades are based upon conditions under which milk is produced as well as on indications of quality such as bacterial count, sediment or cleanliness, and other factors. Roughly, milk is divided into two classes—raw and pasteurized. Raw milk is not prepared in any way except that it is cooled. In this class is included "certified milk," which is the highest quality raw milk obtainable, produced under very exacting conditions. The term has been registered in the U.S. Patent Office, and milk designated "certified" must conform with strict regulations for production and distribution.

Two other grades of raw milk in general use are Grade A Raw and Grade

[3] "Marketing," *The Yearbook of Agriculture,* U.S.D.A., 1954.

B Raw. Grade A is higher in quality. Other grade terms for raw milk are not uncommon.

Pasteurized milk is not so generally graded, although in certain localities Certified, Grade A, and Grade B are common.

Homogenized milk is whole milk processed in such a way as to break up the fat globules so that the fat remains evenly distributed in a fine emulsion throughout the milk.

BUTTER GRADES

There are several market class terms applied to butter offered for sale. For example, we have sweet or ripened cream butter, depending on whether sweet cream or ripened cream was used in its manufacture. We also have creamery butter which is factory made, and farm or dairy butter made on the farm. There may be another classification based on the use of salt. Butter without salt is referred to as sweet or unsalted butter; the usual butter contains about from 2.0 to 3.5 per cent of common salt. Renovated or process butter is melted, refined, and reworked. Butter can be made from the cream separated from whey, and this is designated as whey butter. Low-grade butter is known as packing stock and is used for making renovated butter.

Market grades of creamery butter are based upon the flavor, body, color, salt content, and packaging of the butter. These constitute the major divisions of the butter score card and are weighed in the order named—that is, flavor is the most important item in butter grade. On the market, butter seldom scores more than 93 or 94 points.

The usual grades and scores for creamery butter are given below.

GRADE	SCORE	QUALIFICATIONS
Special	93 or above	Clean, sweet, creamy, with no off flavors
Extras	92	Clean, sweet; lacking somewhat in rich, creamy flavor
Firsts	88 to 91½	Has a slightly objectionable flavor
Seconds	83 to 87½	Possesses off flavors, such as fishy, stale, unclean, rancid, or cheesy
Thirds	80 to 82	Lowest grade butter, seldom used for human food

PASTEURIZATION OF MILK

Milk is treated with heat or pasteurized in order to destroy pathogenic or disease-producing organisms. Milk is pasteurized by two methods. *The holding process* requires the heating of the milk to 143–145°F for 30 minutes and then cooling rapidly. *The flash process* is accomplished by heating the milk to 160–180°F and then cooling. The holding process is more generally used. States and cities specify the requirements for pasteurization.

Pasteurization has only a minor effect upon the constituents of milk, and it renders milk safe for consumption, since less than 1 per cent of the organisms which it contains survive the process. Apparently, none of the disease-producing organisms are resistant to pasteurizing. The composition is not markedly changed by this treatment, but the cream line may not be so deep in the pasteurized milk, especially if the cooling is not rapid.

It has been estimated that more than 90 per cent of the market milk is sold as pasteurized. Not only is pasteurized milk made safe, but its keeping qualities are improved.

MILK PRICES

PRICES FARMERS RECEIVE FOR MILK [4]

The milk dealers' average buying price per 100 pounds for standard grade milk testing 3.5 per cent butterfat, which is used for city distribution as fluid milk, is reported. Such milk brought the producer $4.70 per 100 pounds on the average in a 10-year period f.o.b. the local shipping point or country plant. The range in the yearly price has been from $3.26 to $5.46 per 100 pounds. Market milk must meet certain standards of quality in addition to butterfat content. The conditions on the farms where it is produced and in the processing plants must meet certain standards. City and state regulations set these standards, and minimums are prescribed for such features as bacterial count and sediment test. Such milk is therefore more costly to produce than milk produced under conditions which do not comply with equal sanitary regulations. Milk so classified shows very little seasonal variation in price.

There is a seasonal variation in other milk prices, with a low in summer and a high in winter, as would be expected.

As production is higher in the summer months, milk prices are lower then. At the same time costs are lower in the summer, because of lower feed cost, less housing, and less labor.

Milk sold to condenseries for evaporated milk brings less to the producer than the average milk sold. In a comparable period 100 pounds of milk, testing 3.5 per cent butterfat, brought about $3.29, or about $1.41 less than the average milk used for city distribution as milk and cream. Some seasonal variation in the price of such milk occurs, and it is the same general pattern as for average milk. The milk used for this purpose is much more seasonal in production than that disposed of through other channels.

It is evident that, as compared with the usual outlets for milk, that which

[4] *Agricultural Statistics*, U.S.D.A., 1955.

is standard grade and used for city distribution is sold at a premium, while that which is sold to condenseries brings lower prices.

COST OF DISTRIBUTION OF MILK

There have been many new developments in the marketing of milk. On many markets homogenized milk has replaced regular milk and home-delivery routes have been losing out to dealers' wholesale outlets, including retail stores. Fiber or paper containers have been replacing glass containers. Containers of various sizes are available; however, the 1-quart glass container is the most widely used at present.

Distribution costs have been increasing and the farmer's share of the consumer's milk dollar has been decreasing. Less than one-half of the cost of milk to the consumer is received by the original producer.

A U.S. Department of Agriculture [5] survey for a recent year indicates a distribution of the consumer's milk dollar as follows:

		PER CENT OF TOTAL COST
To the farmer		45
Marketing costs		55
Distribution	23	
Processing	18	
Assembly	5	
Profits	5	
Management	4	
Totals	55	100

In an 8-year period the farmer's share of the milk dollar has decreased 10 per cent.

The cost of delivery accounted for about one-fourth of the cost of the milk to the consumer and is more than one half of the cost of the milk to the distributor. It is quite obvious that milk can be sold to the consumer several cents cheaper per quart on a cash-and-carry basis than when it is delivered. Delivery in most cities is now on a 3 days a week basis and costs the consumer about 1 cent more per quart than milk sold in retail stores.

MILK PRICES RETAIL

Prices for milk vary greatly from city to city. For example, for the year 1954 the dealer retail price of standard milk delivered to the family trade in Milwaukee, Wisconsin, was 19.6 cents per quart, while in Jacksonville, Fla., it was 27.0 cents per quart. These two cities presented the extremes

[5] *Agricultural Marketing*, U.S.D.A., vol. 1, No. 4, November, 1956.

in price for 25 cities for that year. Milk prices appear to be higher in the largest cities in the East and South.

Marked year-to-year differences also appear. In Chicago, for example, the average yearly retail price per quart delivered to the family trade has ranged from 16.5 to 25.3 cents in a 10-year period. During that time the average price for milk in 25 cities was 20.3 cents per quart.[6]

MILK AS COMPARED WITH OTHER FOODS IN COST

The economy of the dairy cow as a converter of farm feeds into human food has been pointed out previously. Since the value of a food cannot be expressed in a single term, it is not possible, for example, to compare foods like milk and meat. These two foods are not comparable in composition, and we have no way of converting the different nutrient materials to a common basis for comparison. Since energy is the greatest single nutrient essential provided by foods, this may be used as a basis of comparison. Yet this only gives an energy comparison, and does not give credit for such food essentials as protein, minerals, and vitamins. Milk, because of its composition, furnishes most of the essential constituents in adequate amounts. On the basis of cost, lard may be a more economical source of energy, and lean meat may be a more economical source of protein. Milk is an excellent and economical food and in recent years milk has been cheap as compared with beef.

OLEOMARGARINE AND BUTTER

The consumption of table fats and butter substitutes moves about in the same fashion as the margin between the price of butter and margarine. Oleomargarine consumption was increased during World War II, and since then it has shown some tendency to increase further.

In a recent 5-year period on the Chicago market, the wholesale price of grade B butter was 67.6 cents per pound, and white domestic oleomargarine was 30.6 cents per pound, a margin of 37 cents. The per capita consumption of margarine ranged from 3.8 to 8.4 pounds, with an average of 5.1 pounds during a recent 9-year period. Cottonseed oil and soybean oil are the principal products used in the manufacture of oleomargarine.

Butter consumption is higher among the people in the higher income brackets. Because of its lower price, oleomargarine is substituted for butter as family incomes decrease.

[6] *Agricultural Statistics,* U.S.D.A., 1955.

Chapter 18

DAIRY CATTLE FEEDING
AND MANAGEMENT

The largest problem confronting the dairyman is that of feeding the herd of cows that are milking. Economical rations that are ample in required nutrients are essential for success. Raising dairy calves, feeding the herd sire, and feeding the dry cows are problems which may be troublesome to the dairyman, but his big job is to feed intelligently the cows in milk. Attention to feeding and management alone does not ensure success in milk production. The efficiency of the cow is an all-important item in profit from the enterprise. Not only is it unprofitable to feed a cow lacking in dairy breeding the way dairy cows are fed, but among those selected and bred for milk production some are inefficient and unprofitable.

The feeding of dairy cattle has been studied extensively. Several excellent textbooks on the subject are listed at the end of this book. Further, in most states where dairying is an important enterprise, the subject of dairy cattle feeding is covered in at least one publication from the state agricultural college and experiment station. There are also several publications available on this subject from the U.S. Department of Agriculture. It is not the purpose of this textbook to cover in detail dairy cattle feeding; rather, a survey of the nutritive requirements and feeding and management practices is given.

Dairy cattle are kept under a wide range of conditions. However, it is impossible to maintain a dairy herd under circumstances such as prevail on the range. Specialized milk production requires feeding and handling that are not possible with a range herd. Pasture is the natural feed for the dairy cow and under most conditions it retains a place in the ration. As production has been stepped up in the milk cow, nutrient needs have increased so that pasture alone will not suffice the heavy producer. In the evolution of dairying we have more closely confined our milk cows and their ration of necessity has come to include other feeds.

Even though dairy cows are not suitable for extensive ranging, they are kept under quite divergent circumstances. The extreme range of production affects actual requirements and, as a consequence, feeding. Cow herds kept at some distance from centers of population, for most of them have ample pasture and relatively low-priced farm-grown feeds. On the other hand, a dairy enterprise near a dense human population has high-priced land which makes for expensive pasture and farm feed. Such farms purchase more feed than do the farms farther removed, but they have the advantage of nearness to the market for the sale of their products.

NUTRITIONAL REQUIREMENTS OF DAIRY COWS

In the dairy cow we recognize such productive needs as maintenance, growth, reproduction, and milk secretion, all of which demand certain nutrient materials. In practice it is difficult and impractical to separate the nutritional needs, with the exception of milk production. It has proved feasible and economical to alter the feed in quantity according to the quantity and quality of the milk produced by the cow. Feeding standards included under maintenance provide sufficient surplus to permit normal reproduction and some growth.

There are numerous feeding standards for the dairy cow. Also available are the Recommended Nutrient Allowances of the National Research Council. They are much the same in general but vary slightly in suggested amounts of nutrients. The requirements are commonly given in terms of digestible protein and total digestible nutrients, or net energy, or some adaptation of these values of feeds. The requirements as now given include some of the inorganic nutrients and some of the vitamins. Cattle, being ruminants, can elaborate some of the needed nutrients like the B-complex vitamins from other materials in the feed.

✕ A 1,000-pound dairy cow should have for maintenance alone the daily amounts of nutrients shown in the table on page 289, according to the Morrison Feeding Standard. The suggested amount of nutrients for milk production is also given.

The maintenance requirement is in proportion to the 0.73 power of the live weight, for the needs are not directly proportional to the weight. The nutrients for milk production are varied in accordance with the butterfat content.

The requirements for maintenance are not so different from those suggested for a 1,000-pound beef cow that is pregnant and being wintered, except that the total digestive nutrients are less and the nutritive ratio is narrower. The basal needs for the two are comparable, and a satisfactory ration for one would be ample for the other.

Individual feeding is generally used for dairy cows in milk, in contrast with beef cows, which are group fed. Rations for dairy cows are based on needs of the individual cow; in beef cattle an average ration for an entire lot is commonly used. It is economical to have dairy cows consume all of the good-quality roughage they will take. If at least one-third of it is leguminous in winter feeding, this intake will meet maintenance needs, and if the roughage is of good quality, it will be nutritionally complete. During the summer, good pasture is a valuable and economical addition. Concentrates are fed then to provide for the milk produced.

DAILY REQUIREMENTS, MORRISON FEEDING STANDARD [1]

DIGESTIBLE PROTEIN		TOTAL DIGESTIBLE NUTRIENTS					NET ENERGY	
Mini-mum Allow-ance, Pounds	Recommended for Good Cows under Usual Conditions, Pounds	Mini-mum Allow-ance, Pounds	Recommended for Good Cows under Usual Conditions, Pounds	Cal-cium, Pounds	Phos-phorus, Pounds	Caro-tene, Milli-grams	Mini-mum Allow-ance, Pounds	Recommended for Good Cows under Usual Conditions, Pounds
For maintenance, 1,000-pound cow								
0.60 — 0.65		7.0 — 7.9		0.022	0.022	60	5.6 — 6.3	
For milk production—per pound of milk								
3.5 per cent milk								
0.038 — 0.046		0.28 — 0.30		0.0022	0.0017	..	0.26 — 0.28	
4.0 per cent milk								
0.041 — 0.049		0.31 — 0.32		0.0022	0.0017	..	0.29 — 0.30	

BALANCED RATIONS

Various meanings have been attached to the term "balanced ration." A ration may be balanced according to a feeding standard when the nutrients in the feed allowance balance the daily requirements for the individual. Most feeding standards set the requirement for dry matter, digestible protein, total digestible nutrients or net energy, some of the inorganic nutrients, and vitamins, which does not include *all* of the dietary essentials. For the maintenance of a 1,000-pound cow the minimum allowance advised would be met if we fed 31.6 pounds per day of wild oats as green roughage. In other words, the intake of digestible protein and total digestible nutrients

[1] F. B. Morrison, *Feeds and Feeding,* 22nd ed., The Morrison Publishing Company, Ithaca, N. Y., 1956.

would meet the prescribed minimum allowance. It is quite evident that such a ration is impractical and would not be satisfactory. It may be lacking in some of the essentials. An adequate ration would contain all the factors needed, and some authorities use this term synonymously with a balanced ration. It is evident that such rations, to be adequate, must contain: (1) ample protein of proper quality, (2) sufficient total digestible nutrients or net energy,' (3) ample amounts of calcium, phosphorus, sodium, chlorine, iron, and other essential minerals, (4) abundant quantities of vitamins A and D and other essential vitamins, (5) enough of the essential fatty acids and other dietary essentials.

In practice the dairyman uses the balanced ration. By giving attention to the general requirements of a satisfactory ration, an adequate combination of feed is made. The feeding standard is at best only an approximate guide. The composition of feed is based upon averages, as are the animal requirements, although the latter have a considerable margin of safety. It is, therefore, evident that values given for feeds or the requisites given for animals are not absolute.

GENERAL REQUIREMENTS OF SATISFACTORY RATIONS

Certain general precautions are taken in combining feeds into rations suitable for dairy cows in milk. These general requirements are listed below.

Variety

In formulating rations it is suggested that at least two roughages and three concentrates be included for a good cow and that still more variety be given a heavy producer.

Palatability

Feeds including both concentrates and roughage should be palatable and therefore readily consumed by the cow.

Succulence

Cows almost always produce more milk in winter if succulent feeds are included in the ration. In the absence of succulent feed like silage in winter, the best quality of roughage and constant access to a water supply are suggested to maintain milk flow.

Bulkiness of the concentrated mixture

It is thought to be of value to have some bulky feeds in the concentrate mixture, especially for cows heavily fed on concentrated feeds. Light feeds, such as ground oats, wheat bran, and beet pulp, are desirable for this purpose. Their use provides a more porous mixture.

Laxative feeds

Slightly laxative feeds are preferred for the ration, since it has been found that rations of that effect are more efficient.

Effect upon the milk

Some feeds affect the flavor of the milk. Such feed should be avoided in compounding a ration.

Effect upon the cow

Feeds that have a harmful effect upon the cow, because of the physical nature or chemical composition, are also to be avoided. Some feeds cause digestive disturbances, while others contain toxic materials such as ergot in rye.

Cost of the ration

Lastly, the matter of cost is given as one of the general requirements. Perhaps it should be the major consideration, since profit from the enterprise depends upon costs involved and the income from the product. Feeds make up about one half the cost of milk production. It is, therefore, evident that the cost of the nutrients in the feeds is an important consideration in feed selection.

GENERAL RULES FOR FEEDING

Certain general rules have long been in use for setting rations for milking cows. At best they are rough estimates as compared with computations according to a feeding standard. But these "thumb rules" are fairly accurate and easily applied; therefore we list them:

1. Allow all the roughage a cow will eat.
2. Feed 1 pound of concentrates per day for each 2½ to 4 pounds of milk, depending upon the richness of the milk and the quality of the roughage fed—or
3. Feed 1 pound of concentrates per day for each pound of butterfat the cow produces a week.

1~3 in Jersey
1~4 in others

Modifications have been made in the above rules, mainly to adjust the concentrate intake to the butterfat content of the milk and to the quality of the roughage consumed.

In following these general rules there is a distinct tendency to underfeed the high producer and overfeed the low producer.

WINTER FEEDING

The dairy cow has less natural protection than the beef cow, and in the wintertime in many sections barn feeding is a necessity. Dry, well-ventilated, and well-lighted barns are essential for comfortable housing of the dairy herd. The common method of handling in the winter is to feed in the stall or stanchion. In the loose-stabling method, the cows are fed roughage outside or in an open shed. The cows are confined in the barn for feeding of concentrates and for milking. Stabling in an open shed that is dry, well-bedded, and not drafty has proved satisfactory.

When leguminous hay is available for roughage, the feeding problem is comparatively simple, for the usual allowance of 2 pounds per day per 100 pounds live weight will more than meet maintenance needs. Further, such roughages work well with combinations of home-grown grains. With nonleguminous hays, a grain mixture higher in protein is indicated and protein concentrates are needed.

Silages are very extensively used in the ration. On most farms silage is

Fig. 104. Barn feeding of dairy cows in winter by the loose-housing or stabling method. (Babson Bros. Co.)

an economical feed, for in nutritive value 3 pounds replace about 1 pound of hay. Silages are made from many different plants. Corn silage is a variable feed depending upon the grain yield of the corn from which it is made. Silage should be compared with other rougages on the basis of cost of nutrient value. It has many advantages in the dairy ration, but it is not indispensable and its use should depend upon relative cost.

Roughages are commonly cheaper sources of nutrients than grain, even though they are less digestible. Concentrates have at least 25 pounds more total digestible nutrients in 100 pounds of feed than roughages. This is because the nutritive energy in concentrates ranges in digestibility from 75 to 100 per cent, while digestibility of roughages ranges from 30 to 75 per cent. It is evident that a ration of roughage alone would be insufficient for a highly productive cow. On the other hand, cattle do not thrive on grain alone. Since roughage is economical and essential, a combination of roughage and concentrates is used for the milk cow.

The best procedure appears to be to select the feeds for the cow so that the necessary minerals and vitamins are supplied. Common salt, and under some conditions, phosphorus, calcium, iodine, and perhaps some other minerals must be added to the natural feeds.

If we take, for example, a 1,200-pound cow producing 30 pounds of 3.5%-butterfat milk daily, the winter ration could be made up of about 24 pounds of mixed hay, like clover and timothy, plus about 10 pounds of a suitable concentrate mixture. Such a mixture could consist of 600 pounds of corn and cob meal, 200 pounds of ground oats and 200 pounds of high protein feed like soybean meal. In addition, salt and other minerals should be supplied. Concentrate mixtures are varied in their components to compensate for different protein levels in roughage combinations.

SUMMER FEEDING

Summer feeding differs from winter feeding in that pasture is available and less housing is needed. Pasture should be a part of the dairy cow's feeding program, for it appears to be necessary for fertility and economical production. Good pasture provides an abundance of carotene, the precursor of vitamin A, and other dietary essentials not too plentiful in winter rations. Also, cows that are pasture fed are exposed to sunlight, which gives vitamin D. Pasture supplies many of the essentials lacking in barn feeding, and therefore prevents diseases and inefficient response to feed caused by deficiencies. On pasture, reserves are built up which are carried over into the winter feeding period. The pickup in production which attends the turning of the cows on pasture is proof of its high value.

The great difficulty with pasture is that in general it is poorly managed and good-quality pasture grass is not available throughout the season. High-producing cows cannot maintain production on pasture alone, and many pastures are insufficient for average production. Young pasture grass is high in protein and low in fiber, and will supply an ample amount of nutrients to sustain a cow yielding about 40 pounds of milk daily. Cows may consume up to 150 pounds of pasturage per day. One to three acres are required to provide ample pasture for one cow, depending upon growing conditions. In fact, pasture under some conditions may be luxuriant enough to pasture two cows per acre.

Cultivated land can be used for pasture, and under favorable conditions the production of nutrients will be comparable to that of other crops. Permanent pasture, too, may yield a good return if pastured by dairy cows. Such pastures are often abused by grazing too early and too heavily. Strip grazing and rotational grazing will increase the returns per acre from pasture land. Green feeding, or bringing the pasture grass to cows confined in dry lots, is increasingly practiced. This method increases the returns from the land and provides more uniform grass supplies to the cows. On the other hand, it involves more labor and machinery.

Fig. 105. Feeding cut pasturage on dry lot. Bringing cut pasture to cows confined on dry lots is a practice that has been increasing. (Babson Bros. Co.)

Pasture improvement by weed control, suitable seeding, and fertilizing will be reflected in sustained production of nutrients.

In management there is a general tendency not to supplement pasture properly with other feeds. Soilage crops, concentrates, hay, silage, and supplementary pasture may augent declining regular pastures. If milk prices are low, supplemental feeding with concentrates may not be advisable.

FEED EQUIVALENT IN PRICE TO 1 POUND OF MILK OR BUTTERFAT

Under most conditions feed makes up the greatest proportion of the cost of milk production. Labor is another large item in costs. The feed cost may range from 50 to 75 per cent of the cost of production. Over a period of years, 1 pound of butterfat has been equivalent in price to 23.0 pounds of concentrate ration.[2] This is a comparison on average prices received by farmers for both butterfat and concentrate feed, mostly grain. One pound of milk was equivalent in price to 1.28 pounds of concentrate feeds such as corn and linseed meal or soybean meal. It is obvious that, when butterfat sells for much less than the above equivalents, the sale of butterfat may not be a profitable outlet for feed.

CALF RAISING

Since the productive life of the average cow is less than 5 years, many of the calves must be raised for replacements. This is a major item of expense in dairying and a feature in which many dairy herds are inefficient. It goes without saying that only the better calves should be kept for replacements. It costs as much to raise a poor calf as a good one. Therefore, only calves of good individuality and parentage should be retained. Diseases are quite prevalent in young calves; for best results calves should be raised under sanitary conditions and fed only nutritionally complete rations.

Nearly all of the calves raised on the dairy farms are raised by hand. A dairy calf is commonly given its dam's (colostrum) milk the first 3 to 4 days, whole milk until it is 2 weeks of age, and then skim milk. On farms selling cream the skim milk is used for calf feeding; where whole milk is the main product, the use of milk substitutes is prevalent; and whey feeding is common in cheese-producing areas. Milk feeding continues until the calf is about 2 to 3 months old, but supplementary feeding begins when the calf is about 2 weeks old.

When the calf has been changed to dry feeds and is well started on them, the problem of raising it is comparatively easy. Good roughage, plus suitable concentrate supplementation, ample in amount, will permit proper growth and development.

MANAGEMENT OF THE DAIRY HERD

Careful planning and management are prerequisites to success in the dairy enterprise. Management includes all of the practices in the production

[2] *Agricultural Statistics*, U.S.D.A., 1955.

of milk. Milk production is limited, first by the capacity of the cows to produce, and second by the proper feeding, care, and attention for the herd. Phenomenal records of production have resulted in large measure from improvement in management, which includes feeding, breeding, and care.

The following considerations present managerial problems to the dairy farm operator.

THE FEED SUPPLY

A dairy herd is kept on a farm to use a supply of feed. This home supply is supplemented with purchased feeds. Good management involves planning for an ample feed, including the pasture crop, and securing economical feeds to complete the rations. On usual farms dairy cows are kept to utilize home-raised feeds, and the size of the herd should depend upon the amount of feed grown on the farm. A cow producing 300 pounds of butterfat per year will require the feed and pasture from nearly 4 acres.

BUILDINGS AND EQUIPMENT

A dairy barn that provides ample protection and is equipped so that it is convenient and sanitary is a requisite. Facilities are needed not only for housing the dairy herd and for production of clean milk, but also for raising the calves and young stock, and for housing the herd bull.

LABOR REQUIREMENTS

A dairy herd involves considerable labor—more than is needed for a beef herd or a sheep flock. Dairy herds are kept on many farms to utilize available labor.

THE MARKET OUTLOOK

The demand for milk and milk products has been quite constant and is increasing. Expansion and contraction of production should be planned according to the market outlook. Market requirements are continually changing, and good management requires a knowledge of consumer demands.

KEEPING RECORDS

The importance of production records of individual cows has been stressed before. Other records are needed by the operator, so that he may know what parts of the enterprise are profitable. Records of the various items of cost will permit analysis of the phases of production. For example, good records may show that raising of replacements is more costly than necessary.

PROPER HANDLING OF THE COWS

Dairy cows require considerable care, and the man-labor requirement is relatively high. Cows respond to regularity, comfortable surroundings, and gentle handling. A good herdsman concerns himself with proper watering, exercising, grooming, and bedding of the herd. Comfortable surroundings, free from the annoyance of flies and other parasites, help to sustain milk yields.

PROPER CARE FOR CALVES, YOUNG STOCK, AND THE HERD BULL

Replacements are needed and may be costly if proper attention has not been given to the rearing of young stock. Dry, draft-free pens are needed for wintering calves.

The herd bull should be well quartered, safely handled, and well fed.

MAINTAINING HEALTH

Numerous diseases may affect the dairy herd. Strong, healthy, vigorous individuals are most profitable in the herd. Strict sanitary conditions need to be maintained to prevent infectious diseases.

HIGH QUALITY OF MILK

Quality milk sells higher than an inferior product. Most consumers will willingly pay a little more for good-quality milk free from objectionable materials. Our market milk is commonly regarded as among the best in the world because of its quality, its widespread distribution, and the safeguards used in its preparation.

Chapter 19

DAIRY CATTLE BREEDS
AND BREEDING

DAIRY CATTLE BREEDING

Much of the material on the reproductive process in beef cattle in Chapter 12 applies to the breeding of dairy cattle. Therefore, in this chapter the discussion will be limited to the breeds, breeding systems, breeding stock selection, and certain features in which dairy cattle differ from beef cattle in the control of the reproductive process.

THE REPRODUCTIVE PROCESS

Some dairy heifers mature sexually earlier than do beef heifers, especially those of the smaller breeds. In actual practice early calving of dairy cows is due to a more uniform level of feeding during growth. Beef cattle use grass mainly, and often in the winter period receive restricted rations which may retard development. Dairy heifers are generally fed quite liberally during the winter.

For well-grown heifers it is not uncommon to breed at 15 months of age. Stage of development affects the time of breeding. Size at maturity is apparently not affected materially by difference in time of first calving, provided good feeding is practiced. As a rule dairymen plan to have their well-grown heifers calve when they are about 2 years of age. Delay in calving beyond 2 years may lead to a little more milk production in the first lactation, but the cost is increased since this practice involves a longer feeding period before freshening. Dairy bulls may be used for light service when they are about 1 year old. From 2 years until 7 or 8 years old a bull may be used heavily. Since the breeding in most dairy herds is seasonal, with

298

natural service one exceptionally active bull is kept for every 50 to 60 cows.

Fall calving is much more widely practiced with dairy cattle than with beef cattle; a dairy calf can be well started on skim milk with grain and roughage during the fall and winter, then turned on pasture the next spring.

There is no particular advantage in feeding skim milk to calves beyond 2 or 3 months of age. Fall calving of cows in most instances brings increased production during the time of higher prices and results in higher production per cow.

ARTIFICIAL INSEMINATION

A very rapid increase in the use of artificial insemination with dairy cattle has occurred. This practice has been used to some extent in a practical way with sheep and horses. Its use with swine has been largely experimental.

In 1955, a total of 5,413,874 cows was artificially bred by the artificial breeding associations in the United States, in addition to many bred artificially within the herd or between herds to other than association bulls. In some states as high as 40 per cent of the dairy cows were bred artificially. The Holstein-Friesian Association of America reported that 40.8 per cent of its registrations in 1955 were for animals resulting from artificial insemination.

A summary compiled by the United States Department of Agriculture for 1955 showed 1,476 artificial breeding units using 2,450 sires of which 36 per cent were officially proved. Their proved sire records had an average of 11,265 pounds of milk and 476 pounds of butterfat for their dams. During the year an average of 2,210 cows were bred per sire in artificial service.

For success of artificial breeding a skilled technician is necessary. Also, the semen must be collected and cared for properly. Most failures result from improper time of insemination, which comes from failure of the herd owner to identify the cows in heat.

REPRODUCTION AND MILK PRODUCTION

Milk production in a cow will decrease as time of subsequent calving approaches. The usual goal is to have a cow produce a calf every 12 months, which would require conception on the eighty-fourth day after calving with a normal gestation period of 281 days. It has been found that cows bred and conceiving between 75 and 110 days after calving will give the greatest average daily milk production.

Dry periods have been found to be advantageous, considering the long-time production of the cow. With high-producing dairy cows, a dry or rest period of 6 to 8 weeks is regarded as ample. When rest periods are included in the management plan, the heavy-milking cow can build up her body reserve depleted during lactation. A high-producing cow often yields more nutrient material than she is taking in. Persistent milkers are dried up by increasing the interval between milkings and then stopping entirely.

Fig. 106. First prize Guernsey Get of Sire, Waterloo Dairy Cattle Congress, St. James Farm, Naperville, Ill.

DAIRY CATTLE BREEDS

Our dairy cattle breeds are of European origin, some coming from the continent and some from the British Isles and Channel Islands. The common beef breeds all came from the British Isles, as have the dual-purpose breeds. We have developed no breeds of dairy or dual-purpose cattle in this country.

It is the function of the purebred cattle breeder to raise seed stock or maintain the purebreds that can be used in the improvement of the common dairy herds. The task of improving the inferior herds is still unfinished, and there are many herds of nondescript breeding that could be materially improved by the use of a good purebred bull. For an exceptionally productive herd it may be very difficult to find a sire that would increase the production of the daughters over their dams in the herd. Consequently, the problem of choosing a herd bull becomes more difficult as the herd is improved.

CHOOSING A BREED

The differences among dairy breeds are not highly related to efficiency of production. Success in dairying is much more dependent upon the management of the enterprise than on the breed chosen. Yet real differences occur in size, maturity, butterfat content of the milk, and other features which may be pertinent to the choosing of a breed for a specific situation.

The problem of breed selection is affected by the following:

1. The breeding stock available in the locality, also its cost and the probable demand for surplus animals.

2. The adaptability of the breed to local conditions, such as climate, feed, and grazing conditions.

3. Requirement of the available markets for milk and butter.

4. The capacity and economy of a breed to produce—and this should include vigor and constitution for growth as well as for milk and butterfat production. Growing ability is of importance, considering the beef and veal value.

5. The personal preference of the operator.

Fig. 107. An outstanding Holstein-Friesian bull, Sir Ormsby Skylark Barbella, owned by Pabst Farm, Oconomowoc, Wis.

COMPARISON OF BREEDS IN PRODUCTION

The differences in the production of the dairy breeds can be determined from the records made under the advanced register, or register of merit, and

AVERAGE YEARLY PRODUCTION OF MILK AND BUTTERFAT OF COWS OF DIFFERENT BREEDS FROM OFFICIAL RECORD[1]

	ADVANCED REGISTER OR REGISTER OF MERIT RECORDS			Butterfat		HERD-TEST AND HERD-IMPROVEMENT RECORDS			Butterfat	
BREED	Records up to	Cows and Heifers with Completed Records	Milk, Pounds	Quantity	Test Per Cent	Records up to	Cows and Heifers with Completed Records	Milk, Pounds	Quantity	Test Per Cent
Ayrshire	Jan. 1, 1941	7,129	10,469	416	3.98	Jan. 1, 1948	66,554	9,016	368	4.08
Brown Swiss	Oct 1, 1951	5,924*	12,562	511	4.06	Oct. 1, 1951	28,708	9,711	390	4.01
Guernsey	June 15, 1952	171,282*	9,816	484	4.9	June 15, 1952	97,312	8,175	397	4.80
Holstein	Dec. 31, 1951	94,925†	15,636	545	3.49	Dec. 31, 1951	341,161	11,329	400	3.53
Jersey	Apr. 1, 1947	78,226*	8,636	463	5.36	Past 10 years	171,365	7,120	379	5.32

* Official yearly and 305-day production records.
† Official yearly and 10-month production records.

[1] Data from Dairy Cattle Breeds, FARMERS BULLETIN 1443, U.S.D.A., 1925. Revised 1954.

the herd improvement test. These tests have been summarized and are reported in the table on page 302.

As would be expected, the average production is higher in the advanced register, or register of merit, tests than in the herd improvement test, since the latter includes all of the cows in a herd. However, there is a rather close agreement in the butterfat test. Yet there was a difference of 100 pounds in the quantity of butterfat produced.

Fig. 108. A milk cow of nondescript breeding. Note the lack of dairy temperament and the small udder.

In making comparisons of breeds from these data it should be noted that in some instances the numbers are not great, and the averages are the composite of many herds. There is no great difference among breeds in the quantity of butterfat produced. The relative size in different breeds is a factor to consider, as mentioned on pages 252 and 253.

DAIRY BREEDS DISCUSSED

Following is a brief discussion of the common dairy breeds, their origins, native homes, early improvement, characteristics, and adaptabilities.

AYRSHIRE

This breed was originally from the county of Ayr, which is located in southwestern Scotland. Comparatively, the Ayrshire is a young breed, developed in the later part of the eighteenth century. Ayrshire is a hilly area having a heavy clay soil with but moderate fertility and abundant rainfall which produce good pasturage. The climate is moderate, but severe storms occur. The principal use of the milk is for cheese making. The breed was founded from crosses of local strains plus several breeds from elsewhere. Shorthorn, West Highland, Dutch or Flemish cattle (Holstein) and also stock from the Channel Island (Jersey and Guernsey) were imported for improvement of the native cattle. The extent to which the various stocks were used is not a matter of record, but the Shorthorn is thought to be the principal imported breed. Careful selection is regarded as the main method by which improvement was accomplished by a small number of noted breeders.

In 1822 the first importation was made to this country. Numerous importations have been made subsequently from both Canada and Scotland. The breed is widespread but it is most numerous in the New England states. For a time the descendants of the Early Imported Ayrshires were known as the New England type but these have been practically replaced by the imported or Scottish type.

The breed characteristics as given by the Purebred Dairy Cattle Association are as follows:

GENERAL. Strong and robust, showing constitution and vigor, symmetry, style and balance throughout, and characterized by strongly attached, evenly balanced, well shaped udders.

COLOR. Light to deep cherry red, mahogany, brown, or a combination of any of these colors with white, or white alone, distinctive red and white markings preferable, black or brindle objectionable.

SIZE. A mature cow in milk should weigh about 1,200 pounds, mature bull about 1,850 pounds.

HORNS. Inclining upward, small at base, refined, medium length and tapered toward tips. No discrimination for absence of horns.

Ayrshire cows are outstanding in style and grace. Deep, rounded, stocky bodies are typical. They may be inclined more toward muscularity and have less dairy wedge than the smaller dairy breeds. The cows have excellent udders which extend well forward and are strongly attached high in the rear. Although the horns as described are common, polled individuals occur and are accepted in the showring.

This breed early (1925) established the herd test, the purpose of which was to test an individual. The advanced registry testing, which tested a few was dropped in 1941. There are various designations for meritorious sires and dams. There is a type classification plan as well as a selective registration plan.

The main criticisms of the breed are that short-bodied, blocky cows tend to lack persistency in milking and that some individuals have short teats. Ayrshires are excellent grazers, especially under adverse conditions, both climatic and nutritional. They use roughage and pasturage well and maintain high milk production on limited concentrates. The calves are of good size (60 to 80 pounds) at birth and are strong and vigorous. The milk yielded is about average in butterfat test, but it does not have much yellow color and the fat globules are small. Ayrshires are well adapted to economical milk production even when conditions are not the best.

BROWN SWISS

Switzerland, a rugged, mountainous country, is the original home of the Brown Swiss breed. The cattle are pastured on the mountain slopes as the season permits. Herders stay with the moving herds and deliver the milk to cheese factories. In winter the cattle are returned to the valleys and are barn-fed on roughage with turnips, potatoes, and some concentrate feed, usually oil cake. The Brown Swiss is one of our older breeds; it came from the northeastern part of Switzerland. Originally the triple-purpose ideal was desired, for the cattle were used for milk, meat, and draft. High standards for breeding and selection have long been maintained by the Swiss cattle breeders.

The initial importation of Brown Swiss cattle to the United States was made in 1869, the second in 1882. Numerous other importations were made, but in the past fifty years but few have been imported because of the embargo due to foot-and-mouth disease in Europe.

The general characteristics of the Brown Swiss cattle as given by the Purebred Dairy Cattle Association are as follows:

GENERAL. Strong and vigorous, but not coarse. Size and ruggedness with quality desired. Extreme refinement undesirable.

COLOR. A solid brown color varying from very light to dark preferred. White or off-color spots are objectionable. Females with any white or off-color markings above the underside of the belly, or with white core in switch, do not meet the color standards of the Brown Swiss breed, and shall be so designated when registered. Pink noses and light streaks up the side of the face are objectionable.

SIZE. The minimum weight for mature cows should be about 1,400 pounds, for mature bulls about 2,000 pounds.

HORNS.   Incurving and inclining slightly up. Of medium length, lacking coarseness, tapering toward refinement at tips. Polled animals are not barred from registry.

Typical individuals of this breed are strong and vigorous. Size and ruggedness with quality is desirable but extreme refinement is undesirable. The breed has been described as being rugged, substantial, well-proportioned and rather muscular. Rapid improvement has been made by the Brown Swiss breeders. This applies to the mammary system, which is usually well-developed with a shapely, well-carried udder.

The Brown Swiss breeders established a Register of Production in 1911 and a Herd Improvement Test in 1932. There is also a Farmers division in the Register of Production for cows milked not more than twice daily except the first 15 days of lactation when three times daily milking is permitted. The breed also has a type classification program.

Even though Brown Swiss are large cattle they are excellent grazers and do well on ordinary pastures. Because of their large size they are somewhat late maturing, but the size is advantageous in the new born calves, which are big (75 to 95 pounds) and rugged. Brown Swiss are comparatively long-lived and have a relatively long productive life. The calves are excellent for veal production because of their size, meatiness and white fat. The milk of the Brown Swiss is about average in butterfat, has small fat particles, and is rather low in yellow color.

GUERNSEY

This breed originated in the Channel Islands, mainly Guernsey, which is near the north coast of France. The origin was from a cross of two stocks: the large brindle cattle of Normandy and the smaller native cattle from Brittany, France. All of the Channel Island cattle were much the same in form and color, but, after importation of cattle from France and between Jersey and Guernsey was prohibited, two distinct breeds took form. The Guernseys included the cattle on the islands of Alderney and Sark. A "Scale of Points" was adopted in 1830, which marked the beginning of great improvement in the breed.

The farms and cow herds are small on the Channel Islands and the type of agriculture is intensive. Green feed is available throughout the year. Hay, roots, and some grain are fed.

It is thought that Guernseys were first brought to the United States in 1830, although some Alderneys were brought here at an earlier date. Numerous importations have been made. Guernseys have long been a popular and numerous breed in this country.

Guernsey characteristics are given as follows by the Purebred Dairy Cattle Association:

GENERAL. Size and strength, with quality and character are desired.

COLOR. A shade of fawn with white marks clearly defined. Skin should show golden yellow pigmentation. When other points are equal, a clear or buff muzzle will be favored over a smoky or black muzzle.

SIZE. A matured cow in milking condition should weigh at least 1,100 pounds. By milking condition is meant: that state of flesh in which cows are commonly found under good dairy-farm conditions after they have been in milk from 3 to 6 months. A bull in breeding condition should weigh about 1,700 pounds.

HORNS. Inclining forward, incurving, refined, and of medium length. No discrimination for absence of horns.

The Guernsey is often compared with the Jersey, for they are comparable in many respects. Guernseys are larger than Jerseys and are somewhat more rugged and slower maturing. Calves at birth range from 55 to 85 pounds in weight and are regarded by some as difficult to raise. The breed has been criticized for lack of symmetry of the udder, weak backs, low loins and roughness over the rump, coarse shoulders and lack of barrel capacity. Much progress has been made in overcoming these faults. The Guernsey has an excellent temperament, is wide-awake, alert and quite tractable. Because of their smaller size and yellow pigmented body fat, Guerseys are outranked by some of the other dairy breeds in veal and beef production. Guernseys appear to have longer gestation periods than most of the other breeds of dairy cattle.

This breed early (1901) established an excellent system of cow testing for their advanced register, on a weekly or yearly basis. The testing is now on the long-time basis. Currently the cows are enrolled in the advanced register on the single, double, or triple letter basis, these classes depending upon age, length of test period, and calving requirements. Sires are admitted if they have two qualifying daughters. A herd improvement division was established in 1930 with certification of records by officials in charge of advanced register testing.

Guernsey milk is second only to the Jersey in butterfat and has an average butterfat content of about 4.98 per cent. The milk and butterfat are extremely high in carotene, which accounts for their yellow color. "Golden Guernsey" milk is a copyrighted trade mark of the association. Guernsey fat particles are comparatively large. The milk is in strong demand for market milk, and is also well adapted for butter manufacture rather than for cheese making or condensed milk.

THE JERSEY

This breed takes its name from the Channel Island of its native home, Jersey. Its origin, like that of the Guernsey, was from the Normandy and Brittany cattle of France. In 1789 a law was enacted that prohibited the importation of cattle to the island except for immediate slaughter. The climate is mild and pasturing throughout the year is practiced. During the winter hay and roots are fed, with a small amount of concentrate feed like oil cake, bran and some grain.

A scale of points was made available in 1834 and covered both sexes. This was followed by marked improvement in conformation. In selection special emphasis is placed upon butterfat production. Compared with the Jerseys in this country, the cows in their native homes are smaller and less productive, probably because of more limited feeding. There is selective registration in Jersey based upon examination and acceptance by judges.

Several Jersey cows were imported in 1850. This was followed by numerous importations to this country after 1870 and up to the present time, except for the war years.

The characteristics of the Jersey, as given by the Purebred Dairy Cattle Association are, as follows:

COLOR.   A shade of fawn, with or without white markings.

SIZE.   A mature cow in milk should weigh about 1,100 lbs. A bull at maturity should weigh 1,500 pounds in breeding condition.

HORNS.   Inclining forward, incurving, small at base, refined, medium length, and tapering toward tips.

There is considerable variation in color. While fawn is the common color, the range may be from yellow to nearly black. White spots are not uncommon. There is some preference for the solid-colored fawn, which is considered most typical.

It will be noted that the Jersey is the smallest of the common dairy breeds. The calves at birth weigh 50 to 75 pounds. Breeders in this country have increased the size; as a consequence an American type was developed, larger than the Island type. The Jersey is typical of the wedge shape, has a well-developed barrel and udder, and, except when dry, does not commonly carry excess fleshing. The outstanding cows are nearly ideal in dairy character and general appearance.

Jerseys are noted for long productive lives, reproductive capacity, and early maturity. The calves are smaller at birth than those of other breeds and are considered by some difficult to raise. As would be expected, the Jersey, because of its small size and yellow fat color, is the lowest ranking of the dairy breeds in veal and meat production.

The milk of the Jerseys averages 5.3 per cent in butterfat and they are well above other breeds in total milk solids. The fat is high in carotene, which gives it its characteristic yellow color. The fat globules are comparatively large. Because of its composition, Jersey milk is noted for the "Jersey Cream Line" and is well adapted for the special milk market, and for butter production. The Jersey is an active breed and that, combined with its comparatively small size, accounts for its high rank in grazing ability. This breed does well under adverse conditions, but responds in productivity to good feeding conditions. In this country it is widespread, but it seems to be especially adapted to the southern sections. Jerseys have a highly developed nervous system and a nervous temperament. This accounts for their favorable response to careful handling, as well as their reaction to mistreatment.

The breed started seven-day butter tests in 1884, and their Register of Merit in 1903. Later the seven-day tests were dropped and the records put on a yearly basis. There are three classes in the Register of Merit based on age and calving requirements. The Herd Improvement Registry, based on records for the entries, was adopted in 1928. A herd classification program is also available in which the entire herd is officially classified by a Jersey Cattle Club designated official.

Jerseys rank high as butterfat producers; they make efficient use of concentrates, good pasture, and roughage. This breed is especially adapted for warmer sections, either dry or humid.

THE HOLSTEIN-FRIESIAN

This breed originated in the two northern counties of Holland, West Friesland and North Holland. The breed is commonly known here as the "Holstein," but in other countries it is called "Friesian." The joint or official name was established when the two associations were combined in this country in 1885. The origin of the breed is obscure, but it is an old breed, having been selected for milking qualities for more than 2,000 years. Its homeland has a fertile soil, abundant rainfall, and excellent pastures. Pasture feeding prevails during the summer, and barn feeding is practiced in winter.

Cattle from Holland were brought to this country by the first Dutch settlers. The first importation of Holsteins was made in 1795, but Holsteins bred as such here were imported in 1852. For a time numerous other importations were made, but 1905 marked the last time Holsteins were imported from Holland.

The Holstein characteristics described in the score cards prepared by the Purebred Dairy Cattle Association follow:

GENERAL. Rugged feminine qualities in an alert cow possessing Holstein size and vigor.

COLOR. Black and white markings clearly defined. Color markings which bar registry are solid black, solid white, black in switch, black belly, black encircling leg touching hoof head at any point, black from hoof to knee or hock, black and white intermixed to give color other than distinct black and white.

SIZE. A mature cow in milk should weigh 1,500 pounds or more. A mature bull in breeding condition should weigh about 2,200 pounds, or more.

HORNS. Inclining forward, incurving, small at base, refined, medium length and tapering toward tips.

Holsteins are a rugged breed with great capacity for feed consumption and milk production. The Holstein has more size than most of our cattle breeds. The calves weigh 80 to 105 pounds at birth. There is some difference in the dairy conformation; some individuals quite angular and others tend to be muscular. The Holsteins in Holland are more beefy in conformation than those in this country. The Holland Holstein may have red and white markings; in recent years, however, the black and white has been preferred. Occasionally red colors occur in the United States Holstein. Our present day Holstein is generally of the approved dairy type, having wide, deep, long body, smooth shoulder, wide loin and hips. Large, capacious udders with well-formed and well-spaced teats are typical. In some cases the udder lacks symmetry.

The Advance Registry is of long standing in this breed. The first entries in its record of dairy performance plans were made in 1856. The Babcock test was first accepted by Holstein; at first tests were for 7, 30-day, and longer periods. Currently only 305-day and 365-day semi-official and herd tests are recognized. The breed also has a herd inspection and classification plan.

The Holstein commonly produces more milk at lower cost than other breeds. Holstein milk averages about 3.5 per cent of butterfat, the lowest of the dairy breeds. The average butterfat in milk of a herd may be below that required for a given market. The proportion of fat to solids not fat makes Holsteins especially well-suited for cheese making and evaporated milk production. Holstein milk and butter are low in carotene and, consequently, they lack yellow color. Colorless Vitamin A occurs in the milk and fat instead of the yellow precursor carotene. Fat globules are rather small in size. The Holstein outranks the other dairy breeds in meat and veal production, because of its large size, meatiness, and white body fat.

The Holstein is ranked as the highest dairy breed in disposition and temperament. This breed is less nervous than the other breeds, reflecting many years of selection for docile individuals. Some other breeds excel Holstein in grazing on scant pastures. Holstein is adapted to liberal feeding and luxurious pastures.

OTHER DAIRY BREEDS

Several other breeds are classified as dairy type. These include Dutch Belted, French Canadian, Kerry, Dexters, Red Danish, and others. The numbers of these breeds in the United States are not great.

DAIRY BREEDING ORGANIZATIONS

THE AMERICAN DAIRY CATTLE CLUB

This organization was started in 1936 for the purpose of improving the dairy cattle of the United States, regardless of color or previous breeding, through the practice of continually testing production of females and proving bulls.

THE PUREBRED DAIRY CATTLE ASSOCIATION [2]

This association was organized in 1940. Membership is limited to recognized clubs, societies, and associations engaged in maintaining registers of purebred dairy cattle.

The object of the association in general is to increase the interest of all dairymen in purebred dairy cattle, first, by cooperatively making available data showing the economic need for and the value of the registered dairy animal; secondly, by cooperating with and assisting agricultural educational institutions in the United States in such projects and programs as will encourage the breeding of better dairy cattle through the use of purebred seed stock; and, thirdly, by originating or participating in activities which will advance the interests of purebred registered dairy cattle.

Some of the major projects which the association has sponsored or adopted are: (1) uniform rules for official testing; (2) classification for each breed of dairy cattle at state fairs; (3) rules and regulations governing artificial insemination in purebred dairy herds; and (4) code of ethics for public and private sales.

The membership of this association on July 1, 1952, consisted of five national breed associations representing the following breeds: Ayrshire, Brown Swiss, Guernsey, Holstein-Friesian, and Jersey.

[2] "Dairy Cattle Breeds," *Farmers' Bull. 1443*, U.S.D.A., July, 1954.

BREEDING SYSTEMS

We have various systems of breeding: grading up, crossbreeding, in-breeding, line breeding, and outcrossing. To some extent these various systems have been tried out. Experimental evidence is not conclusive as to what may be expected from the methods other than grading up. The grading-up process is a rather elementary step. Steps for further improvement are not too clearly defined. With fairly accurate means of evaluating the producing capacity of individuals, records are secured which are helpful in making selections and planning matings. The proper use of in-breeding or the milder form, line breeding, for establishing superior strains with high milk and butterfat production has not been clearly demonstrated.

A consideration of the various breeding systems and their probable use follows.

GRADING UP OF DAIRY CATTLE

The classic experiment at the Iowa Agricultural Experimental Station clearly demonstrated the value of a purebred sire of the various dairy breeds in improving the production of the daughters over that of the dams. Scrub cows mated with good purebred Holstein, Guernsey, and Jersey bulls produced daughters which yielded 64 per cent more milk and 52 per cent more fat. The granddaughters, which were but 25 per cent scrub breeding, yielded 130 per cent more milk and 109 per cent more fat than their grandams of nondescript breeding. Through successful use of purebred bulls scrub breeding is decreased by one half in each generation. Very high grades may resemble purebreds in many respects, but they are not accepted for registration on the grounds that the fraction of scrub breeding may carry undesirable characters.

High grades may be nearly up to purebreds in productivity. A survey [3] in New York State indicated that in 553 herds, registered herds had the highest average milk production per cow, and the grade herds were below herds in which both grade and registered stock were kept. Such a difference would be due only in part to breeding, for feeding and management of the purebred herds might be superior to that of grade herds.

In grading up, if different breeds were used we would have crossbreeding as well. Generally, grading up is restricted to one breed because of the uniformity secured.

[3] *Farm Economics,* No. 125, May, 1941, New York State College of Agriculture, Cornell University, Ithaca, N. Y.

CROSSBREEDING OF DAIRY CATTLE

Crossbreeding in dairy cattle is not uncommon. This practice is said to have had its beginning with the demand for milk of a golden-yellow color. This color, it will be recalled, is due to carotene or provitamin A. Another stimulus to crossbreeding was the specifying of a minimum butterfat content of market milk above that typical for some breeds. Since the results of crossing are uncertain and the market demands transitory, it appears unsound to attempt to produce milk of color and test to meet a market demand. For example, in the crossing of Jerseys and Holsteins, the crossbred cows would tend to be intermediate in butterfat content of milk, milk color, and volume produced. However, there is no assurance that the inheritance will be blended in any one case. Evidence rather indicates that the crosses approach the high-yielding breed in milk production and the low-testing breed in butterfat content.

The use of crossbreds for breeding is attended with segregation from the intermediate. The number of heifers that must be kept in the herds for the maintenance of herd numbers is usually more than half those produced. Continued crossbreeding and vealing the calves is therefore impractical, except for a limited number in the herd.

Crossing animals of two breeds may produce offspring of greater vigor. Three-breed and four-breed crosses, using proved sires of pure-breeding, have maintained high production levels.

INBREEDING AND LINE BREEDING

In these two systems there is mating of related individuals. When the mating is between individuals rather distantly related it is termed "line breeding"; mating of closely related animals is termed "inbreeding." Through line breeding, relationship to some desired individual or group is kept high by mating descendants not closely related to each other. The mating of double first cousins would commonly be called line breeding. The confusion between the two terms "line breeding" and "inbreeding" is illustrated by a comparison of the case just given with another in which half brother and sister are mated. The latter is commonly referred to as "inbreeding," yet the intensity of inbreeding is no higher than in the mating of double first cousins. Line breeding is actually a mild form of inbreeding.

Line breeding with judicious selection has been the means of establishing some prominent families of dairy cattle. It can be practiced without loss of vigor and vitality if attended with proper selection, and by its means uniformity can be attained. Dairymen have generally accepted line breeding as a useful tool in breed improvement, but they have shied away from more intense inbreeding.

Inbreeding has been shunned by dairy cattlemen because it may be attended with loss of vigor, size, and productivity. Inbreeding will uncover recessive characters. Therefore, it may be useful in determining the presence or absence of recessive characters which may be objectionable. Since inbred individuals are more homozygous, a herd in which inbreeding is practiced would become more uniform if cattle with undesirable characters were culled.

BREEDING STOCK SELECTION

The ideal form or physical appearance of the dairy cow and the dairy bull have been discussed in Chapter 14. Selection may be on the basis of type or form, production, or pedigree. In dairy cattle, methods of measuring merit have been devised to form a basis for breeding stock selection. In livestock used mainly for slaughter there is some difference between the form ideals of the finished slaughter animal and of the individual for the breeding herd. Such a situation does not exist in dairy cattle; breeding and market ideals are one and the same. However, some other considerations that relate to dairy breeding stock selection are discussed in the paragraphs which follow.

Fig. 109. Outstanding Guernsey sire, Ideal's Superior. Bred and owned by Jacob Tanis, Augusta, N. J. See the extended pedigree with notes in Figure 110, on pages 316–317. (The American Guernsey Cattle Club.)

NUMBERS NEEDED FOR REPLACEMENTS

As compared with beef cattle, a larger proportion of the females must be kept in order to maintain dairy herd numbers. It is estimated that from 50 to 65 per cent of the females produced are needed to perpetuate the breeding herds. The average interval between generations, or the average age of the parent when the offspring are born, is 4 to 4½ years. The period of usefulness of an individual cow in the average dairy herd is comparatively short.

PEDIGREE

Quite generally the use of the word "pedigree" is reserved for purebred animals, or those registered in the recognized herdbook of the breed. The word in its broadest sense may be applied to any individual, for it is a statement of the ancestors. A pedigree reveals those related to the individual through its parents. It is a statement of the sire and the dam, and their sires and dams, and so on. To be useful in selection more than the mere name and registration number must be shown, since these alone give no indication of merit—though to one familiar with a herd or breed the name of the sire and dam may have much meaning. Dairymen have attempted to give more meaning to pedigree by including certain pertinent information. For example, the sire may have a number of advanced register daughters and some advanced register sons. The records of some of the individual daughters may be given, and also the average of all daughter A. R. records. The records may be of such distantly related individuals or collateral relatives that they are of little value in evaluating the animal.

The use of the pedigree in selection is helpful but, since it is not infallible, it should be used to supplement other means of evaluation such as appearance and performance.

PRODUCTION RECORDS

In the breeding of dairy cattle much attention has been placed upon production records. (See also Dairy Herd Improvement Associations, page 272.) It has been assumed that high producers would have offspring which in turn would yield well. This is not always the case. The producing ability of a cow is what she herself will yield and not what she will transmit. In other words, a cow may be productive because of a heterozygous genetic make-up, or dominant factors overshadowing recessives, in which case she is not pure, genetically, for milk production. The recessives may combine to give low production rather than high production to her offspring. It is

GARDENVILLE SUPREME

Sold 1947 for $7600
18 PR Sons, 48 Tested Daughters
2 over 1000, 4/900, 14/800,
20/700, 28/600, 38/500 lbs.
7 Daughters Classified
3 Very Good, 3 Desirable
Ideal's G.S. Rosette
16510-#1013-Jr3 365 3x
#20282-#1157-Sr4 365C 3x
Ideal's G.S.' Susie
15673-#962-Jr2 365 3x
18825-#1130-Sr3 365 3x
Ideal's G.S.' Marnetta
16394-#977-Jr2 365 3x

IDEAL'S SUPERIOR

3 PR Sons, 24 Tested Daughters
6 over 900, 12/800, 18/700,
20/600, 21/500 lbs.
2 Daughters Classified
2 Desirable
Ideal's Superior's Girlie
16413-#971-Jr2 365 3x
Ideal's Superior's Cordelia
16334-#931-Jr2 365 3x
Sold 1954 for $5200
Ideal's Superior's Queenie
1646-#928-Jr2 365C 3x
Ideal's Superior Odetta
#16895-#906-Jr2 365C 3x
Ideal's Superior Susanne
#17742-#905-Jr2 365C 3x
Ideal's Superior Netoria
#17008-#901-Jr2 365 3x
Sold 1954 for $2900

IDEAL'S NORANDA'S SUSIE

13029-655-G-1095
16582-#894-Sr3 365 3x
18540-1004-5yrs. 365C 3x
19277-1026-7yrs. 365 3x
1 AR Son, 2 Tested Daughters
Ideal's G.S.' Susie
15673-#962-Jr2 365 3x
18825-#1130-Sr3 365 3x
Ideal's Whitman's Susie
15684-#869-Jr2 365 3x

The Sire Summary on this bull, IDEAL'S SUPERIOR, shows:
  34 Daus., 4 yrs., or older
  21 Tested Daughters
  27 Records
  12,846 lbs. milk average, M.E.*
  5.2 average test (% fat)
  676 lbs. fat, average, M.E.*
  2 Classified daughters
  82.5 Avg. Classificat'n Rtngs.
* Mature Equivalent—305 days—2×

RIEGELDALE MELBA'S EMORY

Private Sale 1946—$30,000
86 PR Sons, 182 Tested
Daughters
1 over 1000, 2/900, 6/800,
22/700, 71/600, 129/500 lbs.
132 Daughters Classified
3-E, 44-VG, 59 D
Riegeldale Emory's Virginie
19716-1005-7yrs. 365C 3x
Classified Very Good '49, 51
Riegeldale Emory's Bobolink
16848-966-8yrs. 365 3x
Very Good '48
Sold in '47 for $2250
Riegeldale Emory's Bette
15157-865-8yrs. 305 3x
Sold 1952 for $1600

DOUGLASTON BARONESS DARLING

13717-671-GG-1094
15755-701-AA-1095
Very Good 1947
Sold 1942 for $8800
3 AR Sons, 4 Tested Daughters

IDEAL'S SUSIE'S NORANDA

5 PR Sons, 22 Tested Daughters
1 over 1000, 4/800, 7/700,
10/600, 16/500 lbs.
Ideal's Noranda's Carrie
16194-765-Jr3 365C 3x
17556-875-Sr4 365 3x
19224-841-5yrs. 365C 3x
Ideal's Noranda's Jenny
16635-839-5yrs. 365 3x
Ideal's Noranda's Arvella
14805-815-6yrs. 365 3x

IDEAL'S KING GEORGE SUSIE

11989-588-Jr2
14127-735-AA-3x
14371-694-AA-3x
11286-548-9yrs. 365 2x
3 Tested Daughters

HIS MAJESTY OF BOURNEDALE

19 PR Sons, 40 Tested Daughters
2 over 900, 2/800, 6/700,
18/600, 31/500 lbs.
24 Daughters Classified
1-E, 8—VG, 11-D
Bournedale Bellona
1419-751-D; 17871-921-A-3x

GREEN MEADOW MELBA

15341-#963-Sr2 365C 3x
Very Good 1948 at 15½yrs.
Private Sale—$8600
2 AR Sons, 7 Tested Daughters
Riegeldale Melba's Betsey
16914-814-8yrs., 365 3x

DOUGLASTON CROWN PRINCE

29 PR Sons, 98 Tested Daughters
6 over 800, 21/700, 48/600,
74/500 lbs.
43 Daughters Classified
2-E, 20-VG, 16-D
Douglaston Baroness Camrose
17125-888-5yrs. 365C 3x
Very Good 1951, Excellent 1952

DOUGLASTON KING'S CHARLOTTE

15228-#828-Sr2 365C 3x
19751-988-AA-3x
Very Good '48
Sold 1947—$11,000
3 AR Sons, 2 Tested Daughters

IDEAL'S NORAWYN'S GARDENIUS

1 PR Son, 1 Tested Daughter
Ideal's N.G.'s Ramona
10317-473-7yrs. 305 3x

IDEAL'S EMPEROR'S SUSIE

Winner of Skyline Trophy 1951
Average Lifetime Production 12
records: 15324-728 including
21500-1014-7yrs. 365C 3x
2 AR Sons, 5 Tested Daughters

IDEAL'S KING GEORGE

20 Tested Daughters
1 over 800, 2/700, 7/600,
18/500 lbs.
Ideal's King George's Risbecq
15934-844-5yrs. 365C 3x
15661-828-6yrs. 365C 3x

IDEAL'S EMPEROR'S SUSIE

Winner of Skyline Trophy 1951
Average Lifetime Production 12
records: 15324-728 including
21500-1014-7yrs. 365C 3x
2 AR Sons, 5 Tested Daughters

clear, then, that in order to know the ability to pass on factors for high production, the genotype must be known. In our breeding, therefore, we endeavor to establish pureness or homozygosity for the factors which give high production.

Observations on the production of dams and their daughters indicate that the offspring of high or low producers tend to regress toward the average.

PROGENY TESTING

The transmitting ability of an individual may be measured by testing a sample of its offspring or descendants. Such tests are confounded by the fact that each individual represents a sample of inheritance from both the sire and the dam. This is overcome by making several combinations, for example, by testing the daughters of a bull out of several different cows. Another condition which may affect the interpretation of progeny tests is "nicking," which is due to the heterozygous condition in which the dominant characters prevail. It has been observed that sires may improve the production in one herd but actually cause a decrease in another herd. The explanation is, no doubt, in the inheritance passed on by the herd of cows and how it compensates with that of the sire.

BULL INDEXES

Daughter and dam comparisons are made to arrive at a bull index. Direct credit is given to a sire in such indexes for raising the production of his daughters over that of their dams. This is based upon the assumption that the dam's production and her transmitting ability are the same, which is not so. Such indexes may be helpful in identifying a bull capable of transmitting high production, but they are not infallible guides.

Chapter 20

DUAL-PURPOSE CATTLE

In many situations the specialized dairy type or beef type is not so adaptable to the needs of the farm or ranch as the intermediate or dual-purpose type. As would be expected, this type is not so economical in milk production as the dairy type, nor so efficient in quality beef production as the beef type. Investigations have indicated that herds of dual-purpose cows have higher feed costs than dairy herds of equal milk and butterfat productivity, and one investigation indicated that dual-purpose steers require a larger amount of digestible nutrients for weight increases than beef steers must have. This kind of cattle raising is centered in the north central states and is adapted to the nonspecialized farms in that area. Dual- or all-purpose cattle have never been numerous in the ranching sections where extensive grazing is practiced, except as a source of the family milk supply. In the eastern and far western states specialized dairy farming generally prevails, but some dual-purpose and beef herds are maintained.

A surprisingly large number of cows of beef or dual-purpose breeding produce dairy products used on the farms in the corn belt. This is because such cows are available on the farms, and specialized dairy cows are not needed to produce the home supply of milk. Although a sizable number of cows are handled on the dual-purpose plan, relatively few of the registered purebred cattle are of the dual-purpose breeds.

ADAPTABILITY OF THE FARM FOR DUAL-PURPOSE CATTLE PRODUCTION

Dual-purpose cattle are well suited for medium-sized farms, where the equipment and labor available are inadequate for specialized dairy farming. The farm-raised feeds are used for the breeding herd and the calf crop in the dual-purpose plan. If the feeds raised are mainly pasture and forage, the calves are usually marketed as feeders. When sufficient concentrates are

319

grown on the farm, the calves are fattened or finished, generally as yearlings. Farms best adapted for the milk and beef herds are those which have insufficient labor and equipment to warrant the maintenance of a dairy herd and insufficient production of feed, both roughage and concentrates, to justify a specialized beef breeding herd. Beef cattle are best suited to farming conditions where a large amount of feed is available in proportion to labor supply. If a corn-belt farm is not sufficiently large or productive to permit profitable production with a beef herd, a dual-purpose herd of profitable size may be adaptable. A farmer can care for a herd of 10 dual-purpose cows and receive a good labor return for full-time employment during the winter months, whereas a larger herd of beef cows would be needed for the same employment.

Compared with the strictly dairy-type cows, the dual-purpose cows are more valuable for beef, more rugged, and require less attention and less protective housing. Also the dual-purpose cows make greater use of roughage and require less concentrated feed.

Dual-purpose cattle permit diversification and are suitable to medium-sized farms, where they will provide for the utilization of farm-grown feeds and surplus labor. Because of this use they are called general farm cows.

FLEXIBILITY OF DUAL-PURPOSE CATTLE RAISING

Since neither beef nor milk is the main production, greater flexibility is possible with the dual-purpose type. To some extent it is practical to stress dairying when milk and butterfat are profitable and beef and perhaps veal production when slaughter animals are in demand. Shifts in production may cause the main objective of the breeding program (an intermediate kind) to be altered, and the dual-purpose herd so altered may be less profitable than the specialized beef or dairy herd. The tendency to lean either toward beef or dairy conformation is one of the difficulties to overcome in breeding dual-purpose cattle. A considerable portion of the cost of producing dairy products, milk and butter, is labor. When the income for labor is insufficient, milk production may be used by the calf crop directly and labor may be reduced. With a specialized dairy herd, the proportion of cows being milked is relatively high and the feed of the farm is marketed principally through the cows. With a dual-purpose herd, more of the feed is marketed through cattle other than milk cows. Beef cattle use nutritive material over that needed for maintenance for gain in weight; dairy cattle use this for milk. Dual-purpose cattle stress both purposes.

DUAL-PURPOSE HERD MANAGEMENT

Some, or all, of the dual-purpose cows are hand milked, and their calves are raised on skim milk. Cows so managed require the same shelter, care,

Fig. 111. Model-type Milking Shorthorn bull. (American Milking Shorthorn Society.)

Fig. 112. Model-type Milking Shorthorn cow. (American Milking Shorthorn Society.)

and feeding as specialized dairy cows. Fall calving is the common practice with such herds for the following reasons:

1. Greatest production is during the winter, the time of highest prices for dairy products.

2. The greatest amount of labor is required during the winter when the labor requirement for other farm work is low.

3. Cows and calves can make the greatest use of pasture when it is available. In some situations spring freshening may be preferable because then cows produce most of their milk while on grass and there is less heavy feeding during the winter. Furthermore, on some farms more labor may be available during the summer months.

Methods of Management of a dual-purpose herd

There are many possibilities in the handling of a dual-purpose herd of cows because it is not common to milk the entire herd. Some raisers milk only the best cows and practice double nursing with the calves, while others practice partial milking once a day in the morning after the cows have been separated from the calves since the previous evening, and then allow the calves to run with the cows during the day.

DUAL-PURPOSE BREEDS

There are three common breeds of dual-purpose type: the Milking Shorthorn, Red Polled, and Devon. In the 1930 census the enumeration of the registered purebreds indicates that the dual-purpose made up less than 2 per cent of the total for all cattle.

MILKING SHORTHORN

Formerly the Milking Shorthorns were registered in the same herdbook as the beef Shorthorns (American Shorthorn Breeders' Association). The only special designation of the registry certificate was that it bore the words "Milking Shorthorn." In March, 1948 the American Milking Shorthorn Society began recording Milking Shorthorns, and that association maintained a separate office. The original association, however, continues to register calves as Shorthorn or Polled Shorthorn, regardless of whether the parents are recorded as of milking type. The Shorthorn breed was, at its beginning, dual-purpose in type rather than beef. Soon after this formative period separation became evident. Thomas Bates, who started in Shorthorns in 1800, stressed milk qualities and developed the two-purpose type. Later beefiness was again emphasized with the development of the "Scotch Shorthorn." Amos Cruickshank, the greatest of all Scotch breeders, began with beef Shorthorns in 1837 and he is credited with being the "refounder" of the breed. Dairy Shorthorns in England are more numerous than the specialized dairy breeds and are the source of a considerable portion of the country's milk.

Fig. 113. Milking Shorthorn cow, Mountain Majorette, Grand Champion female at the National Milking Shorthorn Show.

A "grading up" system was adopted in 1948 by the association to aid those with grade herds to grade up by using Milking Shorthorn bulls to final purebred registration for cows with approved conformation and production.

Milking shorthorn characteristics

In color the Milking Shorthorn is similar to other Shorthorns. Likewise they may be horned or polled. Large size is desired in this breed—mature bulls in good flesh weigh over 2,000 pounds and mature dry cows weigh 1,500 to 1,700 pounds; greatest weight takes place during lactation. Commonly the Milking Shorthorn is larger in frame, more upstanding, longer bodied, more angular, and with less natural flesh than the beef Shorthorn. As would be expected, dairy temperament is more highly developed in the dairy Shorthorn, and they may be less lymphatic than the beef type.

The tendency has been to put more emphasis on milking qualities than on the characters typical of beefiness. Milking Shorthorn cows have good mammary development, and there have been many outstanding production records in this breed. The udder should be large, well carried, and properly attached and should carry good-sized, well-placed teats.

Fig. 114. Beef steer of Milking Shorthorn breeding, Red Lad. Shown by the Clampitt Farm, New Providence, Iowa. On-foot winner, 1955 National Steer Show, Waterloo, Iowa. Weight 1,125 pounds, dressing per cent 63.2, loin muscle area 11.2 square inches.

As would be expected, there is considerable variation in type, ranging from typical body conformation to the extreme in dairy conformation.

RED POLL

This breed was developed in the eastern middle coastal area of England in Norfolk and Suffolk counties. The cattle of Norfolk were horned and rather beefy, whereas the Suffolk cattle were polled and good milk producers. The Red Poll, which came from crossing these two foundation stocks and perhaps some other breeds, originated about 1815. In 1862, after the two stocks had been merged for several years, they were first recognized as a breed by the Royal Agricultural Society. The Great Britain Red Polled Society was organized in 1888. The "ed" was dropped from the original name "Red Polled" by the American Club in 1940.

Red poll characteristics

The breed name indicates two of the outstanding characteristics: red color and hornlessness. Any shade of red is permissible, but deep to dark red is preferred. There is slight discrimination against too light or too dark red approaching black. The switch may be red, white, or mixed. There may be a limited amount of natural (born) white on the underline back

Fig. 115. A mature Red Poll bull of the correct type; weight 2,475 pounds. Six times international grand champion. Undefeated on the 1940 State Fair circuit. (Red Poll Cattle Club of America.)

of the navel. Any natural white above the underline, above the switch of the tail, or on the legs is a disqualification for registration. The nose should have a clear color and the interior of the ears a yellow waxy color. A solid black or solid blue (cloudy) nose is a disqualification.

Comparatively, the Red Poll is medium in size. When in moderate flesh the mature cow should weigh from 1,200 to 1,500 pounds and the bull 1,800 to 2,000 pounds. In conformation the Red Poll is more angular and longer-legged than the typical beef type, somewhat approaching the true dairy type, but more thickly fleshed than the latter. In the Red Poll score card the fleshing is described as a moderately thick, smooth covering.

THE DEVON

This breed is classified as a dual-purpose breed, although it inclines strongly toward the beef type. In England Devon cattle are called a dark

Fig. 116. A mature Red Poll cow of the correct type. Undefeated in class for 2 years. (Red Poll Cattle Club of America.)

Fig. 117. A 3-year-old Red Poll heifer of the correct type. Undefeated in class on the 1940 State Fair circuit. Twice grand champion. (Red Poll Cattle Club of America.)

red beef breed and are known by some as the "Red Rubies." The origin of the Devon is quite obscure, but it is an old breed valued more than a century ago for working, fattening, and milking. In this country they are less numerous than the two other dual-purpose breeds and are confined mostly to the Eastern States.

Great size and substance typifies this breed. As would be expected, fast gains are common with Devons. During World War II in England this breed demonstrated that it could make excellent beef in a comparatively short time in ordinary farmers' hands under austerity conditions.

Devons are red in color, occasionally with dapple markings and with a skin of an orange-yellow tinge. The breed is horned; the horns of the bull are thick, straight, and comparatively short, those of the female longer and curving upward and outward.

RECORDS MADE BY DUAL-PURPOSE COWS

The outstanding records of dual-purpose cows made in the United States are included with dairy cow records on pages 275 and 276.

Some phenomenal records have been reported from other countries. Melba 15th of Darbalara, a Shorthorn cow in Australia, for many years held the world's record with a yearly record of 32,522 pounds of milk and 1,614 pounds of fat. Cherry, a grade Shorthorn cow in England, is credited with a yearly milk record of 41,645 pounds of milk.

While records comparable to dairy-type individuals are possible, individuals making such records approach or actually are strictly of dairy type. Average milk and fat production are more in keeping with dual-purpose type.

For advanced registry for cows there are four different single-letter records indicating the type of supervision: (A) official, (B) semi-official, (C) private [1] and (CT) Dairy Herd Improvement. Double-letter records are on the same supervision basis, but they are limited to 305 days of lactation and it is required that a living calf be produced within thirteen months after freshening. The milk and fat minimum requirements are reduced by 10 per cent for the 305-day records.

Bulls to be recognized in the advanced register must have daughters which meet certain production and type requirements.

The American Milking Shorthorn Society, established a system of advanced registry in 1912. To be eligible for the advanced record of merit, a cow at mature age (5 years) must produce 300 pounds of fat and 8,000 pounds of milk in 1 year. The requirements are adjusted for age; that is, younger cows have a lower requirement than mature cows. The association reported in 1955 that 35,924 cows have fat records averaging 311.9

[1] Discontinued by Milking Shorthorn Association, April, 1955.

pounds, average butterfat 3.92 per cent. Also 38,863 cows had an average yearly milk production of 7,959 pounds.

Fig. 118. Red Poll cow, R. L. Josephine, owned by Reynolds, Lybrook Farms Company, Advance, N. C. This cow produced 15,310 pounds of milk and 772 pounds of butterfat in 1 year. (Red Poll Cattle Club of America.)

The Red Poll Cattle Club adopted an advanced register system in 1908. The requirement for entrance for a mature cow is 300 pounds of fat and 6,000 [2] pounds of milk in a year. A 10-year average [3] of all advanced registry records on an actual production basis indicates a yield of 7,631 pounds of milk, 312 pounds of butterfat, and an average butterfat test of 4.08 per cent.

MANAGEMENT OF DUAL-PURPOSE COWS

MINIMUM PRODUCTION

It is obvious that dual-purpose cows must make a certain level of production if they are to be generally profitable for milking. A minimum of 200 pounds of butterfat for the first lactation period and 250 pounds for mature cows is suggested as a lower limit based on a 10-month lactation period. Individuals which fall below such performance should be culled from the breeding herd. It is evident that a record of milk yields and butter-

---

[2] The minimum for milk production has been discontinued by the Red Poll Cattle Club.

[3] *Red Poll News,* July–August, 1956.

fat test is needed to determine yearly production, which may furnish a basis for selection.

FEED AND LABOR REQUIREMENTS FOR THE BREEDING HERD

A standard of feed and labor requirements based upon a study of farm records has been formulated by Crickman et al.[4] In formulating this standard for the beef system, it is assumed that the cow calves in the spring and suckles the calf 6 to 7 months. The standard set for the milk and beef system is for a single cow milked by hand.

It is assumed that the pasture will consist of 1½ acres of average bluegrass pasture or its equivalent, cornstalk pasture, for 1 month, and also that straw will be fed.

It will be noted that where the meat and milk plan is followed, more feed (hay and fodder and concentrates) is needed per cow. Also considerably more man labor is needed.

STANDARD AMOUNTS OF FEED, LABOR, AND CASH COSTS
PER HEAD PER YEAR FOR BREEDING HERD

	BEEF SYSTEM	MILK AND BEEF SYSTEM	BULL
Number of head per farm	20–30	10–20	1
Weight of calf at weaning, pounds	400		
Butterfat produced per cow, pounds		160	
Grain, pounds		1,000	730
Hay and fodder, pounds	3,000	3,750	3,000
Pasture, including cornstalks, days	225	225	225
Man labor, hours	20	110	30
Horse work, hours	3	4	2
Veterinary, medicine, salt, etc., cents	20	20	20

RELATIVE PROFITS FROM DUAL-PURPOSE AND DAIRY CATTLE

The loss of milk production in "beefy" cows must be offset by the greater beef value of the calf crop if such cows are to make as good returns for the feed consumed. If the calves are not fattened out or finished, this higher sale price because of beef value will not be attained. This was shown by a recent study in Iowa involving dairy and some dual-purpose herds. In several of the dual-purpose herds the calves were carried to the long yearling stage mainly on roughage and then sold as feeders or as medium-grade slaughter cattle. From this study it was apparent that calves without grain cannot make as profitable use of roughage as milk cows. Even the low-producing dairy herds had a higher return for feed consumed than the dual-purpose herds. Studies made on farms indicated that the specialized

[4] C. W. Crickman, George A. Sallee, and W. H. Peters, "Beef Cattle Production in Minnesota," Bull. 301, University of Minnesota, 1934.

beef or dairy cattle herds gave a larger net return than the dual-purpose herds. One investigation indicated that the feed cost averaged somewhat higher on dual-purpose herds than on specialized dairy herds in the same production range.[5]

Fig. 119. Milking Shorthorns in the pasture. Powell Farm, Ionia, Mich.

CHARACTERISTICS OF THE DUAL-PURPOSE TYPE

The ideal of the dual-purpose cattle breeders is midway between the dairy and beef types. Briefly stated, the typical dual-purpose bull or cow should be less thick than the beef type and not so lean and angular as the dairy type. In *size* the ideal is intermediate. Extremes in either direction are to be avoided. For mature individuals in moderate flesh a breeding cow should weigh about 1,200 pounds, and about 1,800 pounds is desirable for the bull. A *form* which is straight of line, deep, moderately wide, and with medium length of legs is desired. Off-type beef cattle that are shallow bodied and long legged do not have the true dual-purpose form. *Quality* or refinement is typical of the desired type. Smoothness of form and fleshing is stressed, and a clean-cut appearance of the head is desired. Coarseness, as indicated by heavy bone in the shanks, is undesirable. *Fleshing and condition* are less pronounced than in the beef type. Yet a fleshing of moderate thickness throughout is demanded for the ideal. Greater covering of flesh on the shoulder, rib, loin, thigh, and twist than is carried by the dairy type

---

[5] W. H. Peters, J. B. Fitch, H. R. Searles, and W. E. Morris, "Dual-Purpose Cattle," *Extension Bull. 203,* Agr. Ext. Div., University of Minnesota, 1939.

typifies the dual-purpose kind. *Dairy qualities* are demanded, as the dual-purpose cow must indicate capacity for milk production. A good dual-purpose cow is expected to yield up to 20 pounds of milk daily on pasture, or roughage, in addition to maintaining her weight. The cow, to comply with the dairy requirement, must have an udder of good size, well carried, balanced, and shapely, and with even, moderate-sized teats.

INVESTIGATIONS WITH MILKING SHORTHORN CATTLE. U.S. DEPARTMENT OF AGRICULTURE

Milk production, as well as beef production, has been studied extensively by the U.S. Department of Agriculture on a herd of milking Shorthorn cattle. It would seem from the data presented that the milk production is highly hereditable. When determined by the intra-sire daughter on dam regression method, production heritability appeared higher than when determined by the paternal half-sib correlation method. In either case there was a definite correlation.[6]

In the study of the beef characters it was found that all three of the beef characters: slaughter grade, carcass grade and dressing per cent were highly hereditable; therefore, prospects for their improvement by selection appear to be good.[7]

When the Milking Shorthorn steers were fed out with a maximum use of roughage and compared with beef steers fed and handled under the same conditions, Milking Shorthorn steers outgained the beef steers. The beef steers did have a higher degree of finish at the end of the feeding trials than the steers with dual-purpose breeding. A study was made of the proportion of weight carried on the front and the hind legs. A high correlation ($+0.66$) was found between the weight carried on the hind legs and the weight of the carcass hind quarters. In other words, steers carrying more of their weight on the hind legs would dress out with carcasses having a greater proportion of their weight in the hind quarters. The beef-bred steers tended to have a little higher proportion of their weight on their hind legs than the Milking Shorthorn steers but the differences were not statistically significant. The fatter of the steers also had a greater proportion of their weight carried on the hind legs.

The progress report mentions that there was an occurrence of low-producing cows and that some progress seems to have been made in reducing the incidence of such low production from the herd.

[6] T. S. Yao, W. M. Dawson, and A. C. Cook, "Heritability of Milk Production in Milking Shorthorn Cattle," *J. Animal Sci.,* Vol. 13, No. 3, August, 1954.

[7] W. M. Dawson and R. E. Davis, "Progress Report of Work with Milking Shorthorns by the U.S. Department of Agriculture," *Milking Shorthorn Journal,* March, 1956.

Part II–SWINE

Chapter 21

SWINE—GENERAL VIEW

The word "swine" is used to designate all domestic animals commonly referred to as pigs and hogs. Often "hogs" is used synonymously with swine. Hogs originated in the Old World and were domesticated before the time of historical accounts. The hog has followed civilized man over the entire world. In some countries swine exist in a semiwild stage, roaming free the year around and feeding mainly on mast in the forests. By domestication, which included confinement and feeding, man was provided with a more uniform supply of meat. John Ashton [1] says of man's use of the hog:

Bred and reared since immemorial time by Nordic and Latin races alike, he has proved a source of inestimable food value to the public, and made riches for his breeders and feeders through the centuries.

Indeed it is no exaggeration to affirm that the energy, initiative, courage, strength, and resistance to fatigue and hardship displayed by the great colonizers, pioneers and explorers of the past has been due in great measure to their liberal use of pork products as food.

ORIGINS

TIME OF DOMESTICATION [2]

In all probability man's first use of swine occurred during the Neolithic Age or before written history, when swine of the type known as turbary or Asiatic pigs were found. They were small and much valued for food and, be-

---

[1] John Ashton, "A History of Hogs," *Monthly Bull.*, Missouri State Board of Agr., January, 1923.

[2] W. G. Coates, "Pigs and Pig Keeping," *Pig Breeders Annual*, 1936–1937.

335

cause they could exist on a woodland diet, they were able to go through the winter much better than other stock. Domestication of swine traces back to about 4900 B.C., for Chinese history relates that hogs were domesticated at that early period. Swine are mentioned in Biblical historical writings as early as 1500 B.C., and legendary and historical accounts mention the keeping of swine in Great Britain as early as 800 B.C.

Fossil remains of the ancestors of the present-day hog have been found in the Pliocene strata of Europe and Asia and in the Eocene strata of North America and Europe. Fossil remains of a prehistoric relative of modern pigs have been found in some western states. The domesticated hog today is closely related to the wild hogs found in various parts of the world. These wild hogs are of various types, including the pygmy hog of Nepal, the bush pig of Africa, and the peccary of North America. There is reason to believe that the domestic hog originally looked much like the wild hogs of today. These early hogs were gregarious, often forming large herds. They were very muscular and their meat was rather inferior in quality. They were fierce fighters, having very large tusks. The young pigs were almost invariably striped with bands of dark brown on the body, much as young wild pigs are today. The food of the wild hogs consisted mostly of root, acorns, and such forage as they were able to secure in the forest.

The domesticated hog seems to have had an origin that involved several distinct races or species, which were crossed. It also appears that swine were domesticated in different regions. Some types of the wild hog became extinct, and it is impossible to say when man first domesticated those which remained. It is known that some of the early explorers found domesticated hogs in the South Sea Islands. The domestication of hogs seems to have been almost universal, for nearly all countries possessed them, and each section developed a characteristic type of hog.

ZOOLOGICAL CLASSIFICATION

Swine belong to the mammals and to the *Ungulata* group, which includes hoofed animals. The order is that of the *Artiodactyla* or those with even toes, and the suborder is the *Suina*. The family is that of *Suidae,* which includes the domesticated hog and the wild hogs. Following are listed the various groups of the *Suina* or swinelike ungulates.

SUINA. Swinelike Ungulates
Family *Hippopotamidae.* Hippopotamuses

This family contains the hippopotamus and the pygmy hippopotamus, both from Africa. The latter is a dwarf species found only in a restricted area on the west coast.

Family *Dicotylidae*. Peccaries or Javelinas

This family includes the peccaries, which are found only on the American continent. They differ from the pigs of Europe in that they have three toes on the hind feet. Their stomachs are more complicated, and they possess a dorsal gland which is lacking in the *Suidae*.

The "peccaries" of America, common to extreme southern United States, Mexico, and other Central American countries, would appear to be a degenerate type of the wild hog. They are small ratlike pigs and do not respond to domestication.

Family *Suidae*. Pigs

This *Suidae* or pig family contains several interesting pigs, such as the wild boar of Europe; the babirusa from the Celebes which has tusks in both jaws, and the wart hog from Africa. This also includes our domesticated swine Sus scrofa domesticus discussed in the next few paragraphs.

ORIGIN OF THE DOMESTICATED HOG

Although the exact origin is veiled in obscurity, it is generally accepted that the domesticated hog of today descended from the European wild boar *Sus scrofa,* and that the first improvement was brought about by Neapolitan, Siamese, and Chinese crosses *(Sus indica).*

1. Sus scrofa. The wild boar, *Sus scrofa,* has been known in Europe, Africa, and Asia. Varieties existed on every continent except Australia and America.[3] They have become extinct in Great Britain. They varied greatly in different localities. The wild boar is noted for strength, vigor, activity, slow maturity, and long life. It has a large, coarse, long head and snout, heavy shoulders, short back and loin, light hams, and long legs. The color is a dusty brown or rusty gray with black spots or streaks. A russet-gray color is common in the young, and as age advances this becomes a dark chestnut brown with the hair tinged with gray at the ends. The skin is very thick, the hair bristly, with a soft woolly undergrowth. The young have light-colored longitudinal bands, giving a striped appearance. Prolificacy and apparent immunity to most diseases are outstanding features of this species.

2. Sus indica. One of the other species of swine is the *Sus indica,* a wild parental form of which little is known. It has a different-shaped skull and different teeth from the *Sus scrofa.* This species includes swine of China, Japan, and eastern Asia. In general, they are small in size, fine, short legged,

[3] In 1912, 25 head of this species were imported from the Harz and Ural Mountains of Europe to Eastern Tennessee. From these the number increased to 600 to 700 head in 1946.

and blocky, early maturing, rapid fattening, smooth coated, quiet and gentle in disposition. This group is a marked contrast to the *scrofa* in quality, being less coarse and more refined; fine bone, very fine thin hair, and absence of bristles were characteristic features. This species was not prolific and had but a small proportion of lean to fat in the carcass.

Two divisions of this species have been noted:

A. CHINESE.　White and black and white.
B. SIAMESE.　Black and plum color.

3. Sus wadituaneus. The Neapolitan, from the *Sus wadituaneus,* a grayish-black breed from Italy, was introduced into Great Britain about the twelfth century for the purpose of improving the English swine. No doubt the Neapolitan carried a good deal of the *Sus indica* in addition to some *Sus scrofa.* Two breeds took form in Great Britain—the old English hog and a breed which originated in the Scottish Highlands. These breeds were modified by foreign blood. The white breeds resulting supposedly owe their characteristics to the Chinese; the black breeds were dominated by the influence of the Neapolitan hogs. There is some evidence that these two breeds were used in this country.

Present-day breeds

Our present-day breeds vary in color and color patterns, size, general conformation, appearance of head and ear, and other points. Prolificacy, early maturity, symmetry, quality, size, feeding qualities, quality of meat, and carcass yields have been the main points improved. Careful breeding, feeding, and selection have been the main factors in the development of our domesticated hog, though very often inbreeding has been practiced.

The domesticated hog will quickly revert to the old type if placed in a suitable environment. Large numbers of wild pigs may be found in the more remote districts of southern United States. Queensland, New South Wales, and New Zealand. In each instance they have reverted from the domestic type. The so-called "razorback" is a typical example of this retrogression.

INTRODUCTION OF SWINE TO AMERICA

Columbus was the first man to bring hogs to the North American continent. In the second voyage made by Columbus in 1493, hogs as well as other domestic animals were brought from the Canary Islands to Haiti in the New World. Later, hogs were taken by many of the early Spanish explorers to Mexico to the Spanish settlement. Hernando De Soto is credited with the introduction of hogs into what now is the United States. In May, 1539, De Soto's expedition landed in Florida with 13 head of hogs which later developed into a large drove.

Hogs were brought to this continent by the first settlers from England. The colonists along the Atlantic coast brought hogs with them, as did those who settled in Nova Scotia and Newfoundland.

Fig. 120. A champion Chester White barrow, at the National Barrow Show. The carcass of this barrow had a length of 30.1 inches, a backfat depth of 1.4 inches, and a loin eye of 4.25 square inches. Shown by the Gunderson Bros., Beloit, Wis.

GROWTH OF SWINE PRODUCTION

The early colonists in America brought hogs with them to supply meat for the diet. Soon production exceeded domestic needs, and pork and lard became available for export. The Connecticut Valley early became a center of hog production. Very early, pork packed in the northern colonies was exported to the West Indies, where it was exchanged for sugar and rum. The first data on exports were for 1790, and that year 6 million pounds of pork and lard were exported.

As agriculture developed west of the Allegheny Mountains, corn was marketed chiefly through hogs and cattle. Cincinnati developed into a large pork packing center. The midwest grew rapidly as a hog-growing area, and many packing plants were established. With the extension of the railroads, pork packing plants were started at the central or terminal markets. At the time of the first United States census, 1840, the important hog-production centers were in the corn-growing areas of Tennessee, Kentucky, and Ohio. The use of ice made summer packing possible about 1857, and this facilitated shipping of pork instead of live hogs.

Hog production expanded rapidly after the Civil War, and prices were very low in the early 1870's. Heavy exportation followed. Our export market was partially closed in 1881 when several European countries prohibited imports from the United States because of alleged infestation with *trichinae*.

Hog production in this country expanded from 1867 to 1923. The expansion was not one of gradual accumulation. There were years when the estimate of hog numbers was lower than that of the previous year, but the general tendency was upward. Since 1923 extreme fluctuations have occurred, and the drought of 1934–1935 drove hog numbers down to the lowest point in 59 years. The changes in number of hogs on farms are shown in Figure 121.

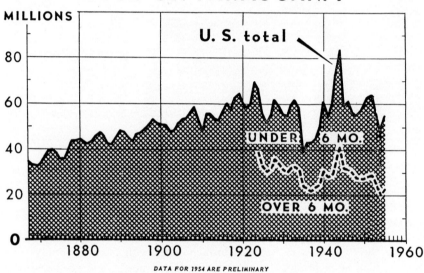

Fig. 121. Hog numbers on farms. Hog numbers change markedly from year to year. There was an upward tendency until 1923, then a decline until 1935, and a rise to an all-time high in 1945. (U.S.D.A., Agricultural Marketing Service.)

"Production cycles," that is, expansion and contraction of numbers, occur in swine as in cattle. The cycle is much shorter in swine than in cattle because of the greater production rate and the shorter period of time required to produce a marketable pig.

AREAS OF HOG RAISING

The growth of hog production in this country was due mainly to increases in the north central states or corn belt states. The great increase in number of hogs was in the corn belt along the border of the Great Plains. Hog raising has followed corn raising, for hogs furnish a profitable market for the corn. The cornbelt states produce nearly three fourths of the corn grown in the United States. The increase in dairying in the west north central states may also account for the concentration of hog numbers in that area. It appears that the increase in available feeds caused by reduction of horses and mules has gone largely to swine and dairy cattle.

The distribution of hogs in the United States is shown in Figure 122. The north central states have more than 60 per cent of the total hog population.

The center of swine numbers, as determined from census reports, has moved westward in each decade. For a time the center moved toward the South, but since 1880 it has usually moved northward, following the northern extension of the corn belt.

Hog production is materially influenced by corn yields. When supplies for feeding are short in a section, hog raising is reduced, and when there is a surplus of corn hog raising is increased. It has been estimated that over one half of the corn produced in the commercial corn-growing states is fed to hogs.

Farms and ranches raising hogs

Hogs are widely raised in our country. The 1954 agricultural census reported hogs on 49.5 per cent of the farms. The states in the west north

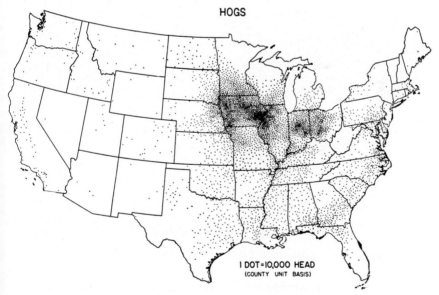

HOGS

I DOT=10,000 HEAD
(COUNTY UNIT BASIS)

Fig. 122. Swine are concentrated in the corn belt but are quite widely distributed in farming areas. There are comparatively few in the range areas. (U.S. Dept. of Commerce.)

central division (Minnesota, Iowa, Missouri, North Dakota, South Dakota, Nebraska, and Kansas) have the largest proportion of farms with hogs, 58.2 per cent. Iowa is the state with the largest percentage of farms with hogs, 78.5 per cent. The geographic division with the greatest number of hogless farms and ranches was the Pacific, where only 14 per cent of the farms have hogs. California is the state with the lowest proportion of hog-raising farms, about 9.4 per cent. On the basis of the census report there were 30 hogs for every 100 inhabitants of the United States.

Although hogs are found in every state, in very few regions outside of the corn belt are they raised in sufficient numbers for more than local needs. Our commercial supply of pork is mainly from the corn belt.

Leading states in hog production

Iowa is the leading state in hog numbers and has had that position since 1880. The other states have shifted around considerably in rank. Nebraska, for example, ranked second for one 10-year period. Then extreme droughts caused heavy reduction in that and other of the western corn-belt states. A ranking of the states on the basis of a recent period follows. The numbers given are the average of the January 1 estimate for a 10-year period.

HOGS—NUMBERS IN LEADING STATES

Yearly Average—10 Years 1944–1953 [4]

STATES	THOUSAND HEAD
Iowa	11,705
Illinois	6,328
Indiana	4,005
Missouri	4,063
Minnesota	3,726
Ohio	3,169
Nebraska	2,854
Texas	1,850
Wisconsin	1,837
Georgia	1,736
South Dakota	1,721
Kentucky	1,466
Kansas	1,395
Tennessee	1,328
Alabama	1,230
United States	61,166

TYPES OF AGRICULTURE AND HOG RAISING

There are three types of agriculture in which hogs play an important part.

1. Corn. In the corn-producing areas of the world, hog raising is profitable because the corn is marketed through hogs. Such is the case with

[4] Agricultural Statistics, 1955, U.S.D.A.

our corn belt in the central part of the United States. Corn is also raised extensively in the La Plata region of South America and in the Danube Basin of southern Europe. In these corn-growing areas, hogs comparable to the so-called "lard-type" hogs are raised. In the United States the muscular "meat type" is desired.

2. Dairying. Dairy by-products have long been highly regarded as feed by hog growers. Hogs are quite common in dairying areas, where they are kept to consume skim milk, buttermilk, and whey, as supplements to the usual basal feeds. This is the case in the northeast central United States and also in parts of Canada, Ireland, Denmark, Holland, South Sweden, and Latvia. A lean type of hog known as the "bacon type" is often raised in dairy sections.

3. Potatoes. A third type of agriculture in which hogs are involved is associated with the growing of potatoes. Germany and Poland are examples of this relationship. In this country we use hogs to some extent to utilize cull and surplus potatoes.

Fig. 123. A Yorkshire gilt of the desired type. Winner at the Yorkshire Type Conference.

LEADING SWINE COUNTRIES

The world hog population is located mainly in the temperate zones. Originally, swine were found almost entirely in tropical countries. Now they are not numerous in most of the tropical and subtropical countries because of unfavorable production conditions and because available vegetable oils are used to supply the needed fats. China has the largest hog population; production in that country, however, is largely for domestic consumption and only small quantities enter into world trade. The most important countries in the world trade, because of their exportable supplies or inadequate supply for domestic consumption, are Denmark, United Kingdom, United States, and Holland.

A list of the leading countries in respect to number of swine appears below. The numbers are based upon best recent estimates.

HOGS: NUMBER IN LEADING COUNTRIES

1952–1956 Average [5]

COUNTRY	THOUSANDS
China	72,000
United States	52,910
U.S.S.R.	41,767
Brazil	31,999
Germany, Western	13,627
Mexico	7,717
France	7,414
Canada	5,372
Philippine Islands	5,273
Yugoslavia	4,183
Denmark	4,146
Estimated World Total	355,000

CLASSIFICATION OF SWINE

ORIGIN OF BREEDS

Most of the swine breeds raised in the United States were developed in this country. Of the breeds given on page 345, four originated in Europe and the remainder in the United States. The foundation for most of our swine breeds came from England, with some from China, through England, and also some from Spain and Portugal. Differences between breeds in prolificacy, early maturity, and rapidity of gain have been demonstrated. A more detailed presentation of the swine breeds is given in Chapter 27.

SWINE TYPES

Formerly, swine were divided into lard-type and bacon-type breeds. This distinction was based upon the principal objective in the development of each kind. The typical individuals of each type are distinctive in general

[5] *Foreign Agriculture Circular, U.S.D.A.,* 1956. Average of 5-year period if available, otherwise for any year or years within the period.

conformation, yet the one is not wholly a producer of lard or the other of bacon.

The difference in general conformation between these two types is far less pronounced than it once was. Since heavily fattened or lardy hogs have been discriminated against on the market, the proponents of the swine breeds have stressed leanness and the meat-type hog.

The lard type was originated in this country to meet a need. Changed conditions, including a lessened domestic demand for fat pork, a decrease in export demand for lard, and an increased use of lard substitutes, have forced a change toward a less lardy hog.

The swine producers have also used the word "type" for description of size in lard-type hogs. Accordingly, we have small-, medium- or intermediate-, and large-type hogs. There was also the so-called "meat type" and the contrasting "fat type" used with reference to market hogs. The former is comparable to the new market grade U. S. No. 1 and the latter to U. S. No. 3. The intermediate in size is the most desirable for all interests concerned.

As the domestic market has been the first consideration of the hog grower in the United States, efforts to establish the bacon-type breeds and to produce English bacon or Wiltshire sides have not been very successful.

Lard-type and bacon-type breeds

The breeds in the United States are as follows:

Old Breeds	New Breeds
Berkshire	Landrace
Chester White	Minnesota No. 1, No. 2, No. 3
Duroc	Hamprace—Montana No. 1
Hereford	Beltsville No. 1, No. 2
Hampshire	Maryland No. 1
OIC	San Pierre
Poland China	
Spotted Poland China	
Yorkshire	
Tamworth	

The Landrace is a new breed in this country. The other new breeds have been created within the past 2 decades.

NUMBER OF DIFFERENT BREEDS

In the last census that enumerated the livestock breeds, the leading swine breeds in numbers of registered purebreds were, in the order named: Duroc, Poland China, Chester White, Spotted Poland China, Hampshire, Berkshire, Tamworth, and Yorkshire. However, relatively few hogs were classed as registered purebred. At that time about 1 farm in 54 which raised hogs reported registered purebreds. This does not include the many that could qualify in breeding but were unrecorded. In a recent report on yearly registrations the swine breeds ranked as follows: Duroc, Hampshire,

Fig. 124. A Hampshire junior sow pig of the approved type. A champion at the National Barrow Show.

Spotted Poland China, Poland China, Berkshire, Chester White, Yorkshire, Tamworth, OIC, Hereford, and Inbred.

SHOW-RING CLASSIFICATION OF SWINE

The livestock shows and expositions have two main divisions for swine—breeding, and market or slaughter hogs. In the latter division the showing is usually limited to barrows, specially for individuals and pens of three. Litters and carloads of market hogs are comprised of both barrows and gilts. The breeding classes are for purebreds; in the market classes purebreds, grades, and crossbreds compete. Classification by weights is common, although not universal, in the market classes, and usually there is a limitation on age. There have been some attempts made to broaden swine show classifications by the addition of more classes. In some cases combination classes for groups have been introduced in which both breeding and market individuals are included. Also, in some cases on-foot and carcass placings are made. Recently some of the group classes have been deleted from some shows.

With breeding classes, age classes are used, and the base dates are February 1 and August 1. There are six classes for boars and the same number for sows. Below is a listing of the usual classes.

Fig. 125. Slaughter barrows and gilts in the stock yards. Crossbreds, straightbreds and grades of the various breeds are among the receipts.

SHOW-RING CLASSIFICATION OF BREEDING SWINE

BOARS

1. Aged boar (farrowed before August 1, 2 years previous).
2. Senior yearling boar (farrowed on or after August 1, 2 years previous and before February 1 the previous year).

3. Junior yearling boar (farrowed on or after February 1 the previous year and before August 1 the previous year).
4. Senior boar pigs (farrowed on or after August 1 the previous year and before February 1 current year).
5. Senior spring boar pig (farrowed on or after February 1 and before March 15 of the current year).
6. Junior spring boar pigs (farrowed on or after March 15 of current year).

sows

7. Aged sow (farrowed before August 1, 2 years previous).
8. Senior yearling sow (farrowed on or after August 1, 2 years previous and before February 1 the previous year).
9. Junior yearling sow (farrowed on or after February 1 the previous year and before August 1 the previous year).
10. Senior sow pigs (farrowed on or after August 1 the previous year and before February 1 of current year).
11. Senior spring sow pig (farrowed on or after February 1 and before March 15 of the current year).
12. Junior sow pigs (farrowed on or after March 15 of current year).
13. Senior champion boar, between the first-prize winners of classes 1, 2, and 3. Senior champion sow, between the first-prize winners of classes 7, 8, and 9.
14. Junior champion boar, between the first-prize winners of classes 4, 5, and 6. Junior champion sow, between the first-prize winners of classes 10, 11, and 12.
15. Grand champion. The grand championship is between the junior champion and the senior champion both in the boar classes and in the sow classes.
16. The reserved grand champion is included in some show-ring classifications of swine. It is the second-best individual in the breed of its sex of the show, and it may be the animal second in class to the grand champion.
17. Young herd bred and owned by exhibitor. A boar and three sows, farrowed after August 1 the previous year.
18. Get of sire. Four animals, either sex, any age, get of one sire. At some shows, the get need not be owned by the exhibitor.
19. Produce of sow. Consists of four animals, either sex, any age, produce of one sow.
20. Breeder, feeder litter. Consists of one boar, one get and one barrow, the property of the exhibitor, farrowed on or after February 1 of the current year all from one litter.

Chapter 22

TYPES OF AMERICAN HOGS

The word "lard" apparently is a persistent one with reference to types in hogs. As has been previously indicated, this term is far less apt than when it was first applied to our hogs. Present-day market hogs yield about 15 per cent of their live weight in lard. The dietary habits of our first settlers and the demands of our early export trade led to the development of a lardy hog. When our first midwestern farmers developed hog production on a commercial scale, lard and fat pork cuts were in relatively strong demand. A large, well-finished hog that would yield large amounts of lard and heavy pork cuts suitable for barrel pork or dry salt pork was the ideal market hog. Such hogs could profitably convert corn and other feeds into pork products, highly desirable at that time. Our first developed hogs were vastly different from the English market ideal—suitable for Wiltshire-side processing—and consequently the words "lard" and "bacon" were used to distinguish the two kinds, then quite different in form.

American farmers created breeds of hogs because the bacon-type hog of England failed in several respects to meet American requirements. The so-called "lard type" was modified, as time went on, to meet changing conditions. Drastic changes were made in the generally desired type, and the pig responded remarkably to the needs of the times. The capacity for change of swine type or form has been demonstrated time and time again.

What were the forces which caused a shifting from one type to another? The demand for pork and lard is the biggest factor, although the requirements of the hog raisers were not wholly ignored. Such factors as the development of refrigeration, the improvement of curing and processing pork, and foreign and domestic demand for lard have caused changes in the desired type of hog. The producer was concerned with such factors as productiveness and economy of production. The lard type shifted to less lard,

349

more meat and the current "meat type" hog. Since 1900 it has also passed through the small-, large-, and intermediate-size type stages. We now have the intermediate-size type. Before 1900 hogs were generally big; a few small-type herds, however, have existed since rather early days of pork production in the midwest.

PRESENT-DAY TYPE

The desired type of hog of the present day is neither large nor small, but intermediate or medium. This type suits most of the various interests concerned with swine type. It has been modified to suit present conditions. Consumer desires, reflected through meat dealers to meat packers, have shown a strong preference for small pork cuts that are meaty, firm, and not lardy. The producer wants an efficient, rapid-growing, productive hog which will sell well on the market. These specifications are fulfilled to a high degree by the intermediate-size type. Demands or preferences for pork products are not static or uniform. They vary with localities and change with time. It is therefore evident that there will continue to be fluctuations in the ideal, but for the most part the "middle-of-the-road" type will be in greatest demand.

The most desirable market type has been defined as "one which can be produced most efficiently and economically and for which the packing industry will pay a price preference because of a higher carcass value in terms of yield and quality of pork products."

An Illinois study [1] report on the various size types of hogs prompted these conclusions.

None of the types of animals included in this study meets effectively the present pork market demands. The intermediate type approaches the ideal most nearly, with the chuffy, the rangy, and the very chuffy following in the order named. The ideal hog would have the quality and plumpness of the intermediate type, the length of the rangy, and the early maturity of the chuffy.

A more recent study [2] of the influence of type of hog on production efficiency by the U.S. Department of Agriculture led to the following conclusions:

1. Intermediate-type hogs, in general, are superior to those of small or large type from the standpoint of the swine producer.

2. Small-type hogs are less efficient in general performance, even when slaughtered at approximately 150 pounds, than those of the other two types.

[1] *Bull. 415,* Ill. Agr. Exp. Sta., 1935.
[2] *Circ. 698,* U.S.D.A., March, 1944.

3. Large-type hogs must be fed to weights of more than 225 pounds, under good feeding management practices, to attain sufficient finish to be graded as choice.

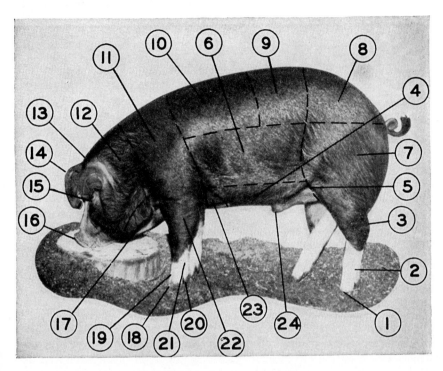

Fig. 126. Parts of a market hog.

1—Pastern	7—Ham	13—Poll	19—Pastern
2—Hind Leg	8—Rump	14—Ear	20—Dewclaw
3—Hock	9—Loin	15—Eye	21—Knee
4—Belly	10—Back	16—Snout	22—Foreleg
5—Hind or Rear Flank	11—Shoulder	17—Jowl	23—Fore Flank
6—Side	12—Neck	18—Foot–Toe	24—Sheath

Such was the situation in 1944, after there was some market decline in the value of lard and fat pork cuts in relation to the lean pork cuts. Since then breeders have gone even more definitely to the intermediate size "meat type" hog. By breeding and selection the type of hogs can be changed markedly, and swine are modified to suit current demands in so far as these are compatible with economical production. With the present-day type of hog we have sufficient finish at the common marketable weight of 200 to 225 pounds. To such weights this type is unexcelled in economy of gain.

DETAILED DESCRIPTION OF THE IDEAL MARKET-TYPE HOG

The following description applies to market hogs. A description of the requirements of pigs or hogs for the breeding herd is included in Chapter 27.

The market barrow score card

The purpose of the score card is to describe an ideal individual on foot. The score card is helpful in teaching the student the parts of a market pig and their comparative value. Likewise, the nomenclature for the description of the parts may be acquired from the score card. From the hog score card we learn, for example, that the back and loin should be fairly wide, slightly arched, rather flat from side to side, and covered with thick, smooth, firm flesh—that is, muscle rather than fat—and that in value these parts represent 12 per cent of the entire hog. Some similarity in names or parts appears between the animal on foot and in the carcass, as can be observed from the figures of the parts of the hog, Figure 126, and of the parts of the carcass, Figure 158. However, they may not be identical and this causes confusion; for example, the shoulder of a hog on foot usually includes more than the pork cut "shoulder."

Suggested student score card for a market barrow

The score card which follows is suitable for a finished market barrow (or gilt) of the intermediate type. It is a description of an ideal market pig which under usual conditions would top the market. The range of weight which will bring the top market price depends upon many circumstances. Supply in proportion to demand causes the top-price kind to vary. At times packing sows have sold for higher prices on the market than correctly-finished young pigs. This would happen only when packing sows are scarce on the markets and when there is a strong demand for that class. It is quite obvious that pork cuts and lard yield would be quite different in a market pig at 200 pounds and a packing sow at 350 pounds. To a degree, they are interchangeable, but they differ widely in size, weight, and leanness of the loin, bacon belly, and ham. The pork cuts from pigs marketed at weights from 200 to 220 pounds are most acceptable to the trade.

The market barrow is taken as the ideal for the score-card description because it represents the top market class. Actually, barrows and gilts at comparable weights and quality sell at the same price, much as do ewe and wether lambs in market mutton sheep.

The score card is used mainly in teaching, because through its use the entire animal may be studied, and a systematic consideration of the various parts may be made. Seldom are score cards used in selection or judging.

MARKET BARROW

Scale of Points

GENERAL APPEARANCE—42 points:
1. WEIGHT—according to age
   5 to 6 months   200 to 225 pounds
2. FORM—moderately long, deep, fairly wide; top line slightly arched; under line and sides straight; trim middle, balanced, stylish; legs squarely placed
3. QUALITY—smooth in form and fleshing; free from wrinkles or flabbiness; head and ear medium fine; bone medium size; hair not coarse, bristly, or curly
4. CONDITION—degree of fatness, indicated by a moderately thick, firm covering of flesh over all parts of the body, not excessively fat
5. DRESSING PER CENT—or carcass yield—indicated largely by condition and trimness of middle

HEAD AND NECK—5 points:
6. SNOUT AND FACE—medium length, wide, clean cut, not coarse
7. EYES—wide apart, open, not small
8. EARS—medium size, fine texture, wide apart
9. JOWL—smooth, neat and trim, not flabby
10. NECK—medium length, smooth, blending neatly with the shoulders and head

FOREQUARTERS—9 points:
11. SHOULDERS—smooth, blending smoothly into the sides, not wider than back and hams, compact on top, well fleshed
12. CHEST—wide, deep, full
13. FRONT LEGS—medium length, straight, bone medium size, pasterns strong

BODY—28 points:
14. BACK AND LOIN—wide, slightly arched, rather flat from side to side, covered with thick, smooth, firm flesh
15. SIDES—moderately long, deep, smooth; free from wrinkles; flanks well let down
16. BELLY—straight, trim, free from flabbiness

HINDQUARTERS—16 points:
17. RUMP—long, wide, slightly arched but not drooping, rather flat from side to side
18. HAMS—wide, deep, full, heavy, firm, shank short
19. HIND LEGS—medium length, straight, bone medium size, pasterns strong

Score-card points

The detailed points of the score card and a brief description of each follow. For the most part, it would seem that the points of the score card pertain to the carcass and that the standard of perfection is a statement of the meat packer's requirements. However, the twofold ideal is considered in its making, and the resulting ideal is highly acceptable to the raiser. In the main, the hog raiser can produce a top meat type hog as cheaply as an inferior one, and if the pig is up to standard in weight for age, efficiency of production is generally assured.

1. General appearance. The general-appearance rating is divided for convenience into weight, form, quality, condition, and dressing per cent. Nearly one half of the value of a market hog is determined by general appearance. Perhaps this is an undervaluation, because, as compared with sheep and cattle, more of the value of the slaughter pig is appraised by visual examination, and this in a general way rather than by critical examination of each part. The swine judge or hog buyer does not handle market animals to determine fleshing as do cattle and sheep judges.

A. WEIGHT. Weight for age is the most important single point on the score card from the producer's viewpoint. Rapid gains are generally economical gains, and hogs are sold in weight groups rather than on the basis of other considerations. It has been found that the feed required for 100

Fig. 127. Chester White barrow of the desired present-day type. An International Livestock Exposition Grand Champion, shown by Donald Brown, Battle Ground, Ind.

pounds gain decreases as the average daily gain increases. In other words, slow gains require more feed than fast gains. A pig making a gain of 1 pound a day from weaning time to a weight of 225 pounds will require about 430 pounds of feed (concentrates) to make 100 pounds of gain in dry lot. If the gain is speeded up to 1.5 pounds per day, the requirement would be reduced to 375 pounds of concentrates.

Slow-gaining pigs are less attractive to the packer than fast-gaining pigs. The former are generally long legged and lean in conformation. Fast-gaining pigs are usually plump, meaty, and healthy appearing, and are relatively young when finished.

Weight is a factor in market price, as previously indicated, yet it is usually more economical to have a fast-gaining heavy pig than a slow-gaining light pig, even though the light pig may be in a weight range quoted at the higher price. This is, of course, with pigs of comparable ages.

There are breed differences in weight for age; also the gilts are slightly lighter than the barrows. For a minimum standard a weight of 200 to 225 pounds is suggested for the 5- to 6-months-old pig. A good pig should weigh, after 4 months of age, nearly 1.2 pounds for each day of his age—that is, if full feeding has been practiced.

B. FORM OR CONFORMATION. Type, as used in swine, is mainly a matter of form; for example, a pig may be described as being long, tall, narrow, and shallow or, at the other extreme, short, low set, wide, and deep. The first terms describe the rangy or extremely big type; the second describe the small type. As the intermediate is the desired type, we stress moderation of the specifications. Therefore, when finished, the market barrow is moderately long, deep, and wide. A slightly arched top line, straight side lines and bottom lines, with resultant trimness of middle, and balance are included in the description of form. Stylishness and well-set legs are also desirable.

C. QUALITY. To comply with the ideal in quality, smoothness of form and fleshing, and absence of wrinkles, creases, flabbiness, or unevenness in the fleshing or skin are stressed. Refinement of the bone, head, and hair are also required. In its descriptive use, quality means refinement, or lack of coarseness. On the markets, quality is a more widely used term and implies general goodness.

D. CONDITION OR FINISH. The fatness or finish desirable depends upon the relative price for lean cuts and the fat cuts and lard. Lean cuts are much higher priced than the fat cuts, but a certain amount of finish, or fat is needed to make the lean cuts acceptable. Within limits, the fat improves the quality and cooking properties of the meat and it increases dressing per cent. A certain amount of fat is essential for the best cured pork cuts such as bacons and hams. Overfat hogs may be penalized less on the market than are underfinished hogs, largely because fat can be trimmed off, but cuts too lean cannot be improved. The fat from hogs has a higher value than that of other farm animals, yet heavy yields of lard may be objectionable and the lean cuts of pork are in the greatest demand.

Fig. 128. A champion Duroc Barrow at the International Livestock Exposition. Shown by Purdue University, Lafayette, Ind.

A moderately thick, firm covering of flesh over all parts of the body is ideal. Width of body and plumpness of the hams, jowls, and flanks indicate condition. Pigs lacking in meatiness are narrow and shallow and show insufficient covering.

Hog carcasses of the top grade are required to have a uniform layer of back fat about 1½ inches or less thick; which can be readily observed when hog carcasses are split. (See page 394.) The fat back can be determined on the live animal by a live animal probe, see pages 476, 478.

E. DRESSING PER CENT.   The carcass yield determines to a degree the value of a slaughter hog. A trim-middled, highly-finished hog has a high carcass yield. When killing tests on slaughter hogs go no further than the yield, the overly fat hog has an advantage, for a fat hog dresses high, but overly fat carcasses are worth less than leaner carcasses.

2. Head and neck.   The head and neck are far less important on the score card than the other divisions. The packer wants a minimum of head and neck because these are largely cheap meat and by-products. Therefore, medium size of the head and neck is desirable, and coarseness is decidedly objectionable. The head should not be long and narrow. Eyes that are fairly prominent, clear, and bright are desired. The ears are to be medium in size. Trimness and neatness of the jowl are stressed. Very heavy, coarse jowls are not wanted, for these are the source of a relatively cheap pork cut. The neck should be of medium length and well blended with both the head and the shoulders.

3. Forequarters. The forequarters are divided into the following parts on the score card: shoulders, chest, and front legs. Of these parts the shoulder receives the greatest emphasis. Briefly, a smooth shoulder, blending smoothly into the sides and neck and not wider than the back or hams, compact on top and well fleshed, is wanted. A wide, deep, full chest indicates a strong constitution, as does a fullness or lack of depression just back of the shoulders. Front legs, to be highly acceptable, are to be medium in length and size of bone. Straight legs with strong, rather short pasterns are desired.

4. Body. In aggregate value the body is exceeded in credit only by general appearance. It is the source of the higher priced cuts and is the heaviest part of the carcass. A back and loin which is straight or slightly arched, wide, and which carries a smooth covering of thick, firm flesh, is in demand, because from it comes a good pork loin. The loin area of a carcass is measured in the certified meat hog program, and a minimum of 3.5 square inches for the loin eye muscle is required. The fat back should not be excessive. Sides that are moderately long, deep, smooth, free from wrinkles, and having flanks well let down make high-class bacon if they are of the right weight and sufficiently lean. A straight, trim belly free from wrinkles adds to the bacon cut.

As would be expected, length of body is emphasized. Without ample

Fig. 129. A purebred Hampshire barrow, Grand Champion at the International Livestock Exposition. Shown by George McGuire, Wisner, Neb.

length leanness cannot be secured. Proper balance between length, width, and depth is desirable. A market pig between 200 and 225 pounds in weight should be 14 to 15 inches deep and 11 to 12 inches wide at the heart girth. To have ample length such a pig should be 40 to 42 inches long from the poll to the root of the tail, measured along the side; this would be about 46 inches long measured over the top. (See carcass measurements, page 417.)

5. Hindquarters. The ham is the most important part of the hindquarter. The rough pork cut on the carcass comprises both the ham and the rump. A long, wide rump continuous with the conformation of the back and loin and blending into a wide, deep, plump, short-shank ham is desired. Excess fat or flabbiness on the ham is to be avoided. Hind legs properly set, of medium length and with medium-sized bone, meet the requirements.

The word description of the market hog is helpful in establishing a conception of that ideal. Properly to establish the ideal and to have it more generally understood, illustrations, drawings, photographs, and live animals are essential.

Fig. 130. Berkshire barrow of the present-day meat type. Grand Champion, 1956 International Livestock Exposition. Shown by Boys Town, Omaha, Neb.

Additional characters emphasized in breeding hogs

Market classes are placed according to their perfection as a profitable market hog; breeding hogs are selected for the main objective, which is the ability to produce good market hogs. In breeding hogs less emphasis is placed on finish and dressing percentage, and constitution, feet and legs, and breeding qualities are given relatively more emphasis.

The selection of boar and gilts for the breeding herd is discussed in Chapter 27.

SWINE-JUDGING OBSERVATIONS

Properly to evaluate an animal we must know the various parts and also their relative value. The score card is helpful in becoming familiar with the parts and their merit. In evaluating an animal, it is best to consider it first as a whole and then consider the different parts. Observation of swine should be made from some distance—12 to 25 feet. The inspection should cover not only the side view but also the front and rear views. Closer examination should follow to make a detailed and careful study.

OTHER SWINE TYPES

The type previously described—that is, the intermediate size "meat type"—is preferred in our country, but we have other rather well-developed types, some of which border on the intermediate.

THE SMALL TYPE

This type prevailed from 1895 to 1912. Its main disadvantages for our general use are:

1. Lard yields of finished hogs are relatively high.
2. Very small hogs may be unsuited for average farm feed-lot conditions, where size and ruggedness are worth-while attributes.
3. The sows lack in prolificacy.

Fig. 131. A small-type market pig. Such pigs are finished at light weights but have a high lard yield.

On the other hand, this type has certain points in its favor, some of which are:

1. They are finished for the market at light weights.
2. The sows are small and require less feed for maintenance and less space in housing.

THE RANGY OR LARGE TYPE

When there is strong pressure for poundage of pork, large hogs come into prominence. This tendency was pronounced after World War I. Of course there are various degrees of bigness. The demand from 1920 to 1923 was for the extremely big type; since that subsided, the emphasis has shifted to the intermediate hog. Some of the advantages of big hogs are:

1. They can be carried to heavy weights when necessary.
2. At lighter marketable weights their lard yield is comparatively low.
3. The sows are prolific.

Some of the objections to the big-type hog are:

1. They are unfinished at desired marketable weights. Extremely large pigs continue to grow for a longer time and are slow to finish.
2. The pork cuts from the pig of sufficient finish are too large for the general demand. For example, at the desired size, the bacon belly may lack finish, firmness, and thickness.

Fig. 132. A large- or rangy-type market pig. Such pigs must be carried to rather heavy weights to have sufficient finish.

3. The breeding stock is of large size, requiring a relatively large amount of feed for maintenance and a large amount of housing space.

4. Some of the pork cuts are poorly proportioned for the trade. This is especially true of the long-shanked "banjo" ham.

BACON-TYPE HOGS

Bacon-type hogs have a distinctive conformation readily distinguished from the common types on our markets. We raise some strictly bacon-type hogs, and there have been several attempts to establish this type, especially in our dairy states, but as yet the numbers raised have been comparatively small. In the slaughter hog schedule in our market classes and grades of swine, there is no longer a class for bacon hogs, as there was once.

Bacon hogs are of especial importance in Canada, Denmark, Great Britain, and Ireland. The main demand for bacon of this type has been from the English market. The Wiltshire requirements are very exacting as to both qualities of the side and method of curing. England produces about one half of the pork that its people consume. The most popular cut of pork on the English market is the Wiltshire side or Wiltshire bacon. A Wiltshire side is a half of a dressed hog carcass with the backbone, aitchbone, shoulder blade, and feet removed. The entire side is given a mild cure and is smoked in one piece. There is some variation in the manner of cutting a Wiltshire side.

The hogs raised in England may be used for fresh pork or cured for bacon. The pork pig is slaughtered at lighter weights, usually about 80 to 100 pounds, and is disposed of as fresh pork. This production is mainly from the home pig industry, and the demand for such pork is more limited than the demand for bacon. The English demand for Wiltshire bacon is for the most part supplied by imports from Denmark and other countries. In recent years very little pork has been exported from Canada to England. In England the early-maturing breeds suitable for killing at light weights, such as the Middle White and the Berkshire, are preferable for fresh pork; the Large White and Tamworth are suitable for bacon and are usually slaughtered at a live weight of 200 pounds. The bacon type has been defined as that suitable for Wiltshire-side production.

BACON TYPE AND INTERMEDIATE TYPE

The leaner kind of intermediate hogs, or those that would class as meat type on our market, will produce a large proportion of acceptable Wiltshire side. To qualify, such hogs must be between 200 and 220 pounds in weight and of suitable conformation and finish. Intermediate-type hogs,[3] with

[3] R. E. Hutton and E. Z. Russell, "Production of Hogs Suitable for Wiltshire Sides," *Circ. 532,* U.S.D.A., 1939.

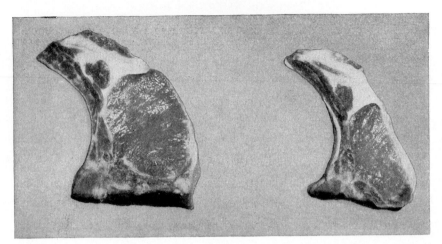

Fig. 133. A good pork chop and a poor one. The chop on the left has a loin eye measurement of 6.9 square inches, the one on the right a measurement of 3 square inches. The meaty pork chop is from a 232 pound purebred Hampshire barrow, just under 6 months of age. The carcass was 31.12 inches long, the fatback was 1.42 inches thick, and the four main lean cuts made up 55.97 per cent of the carcass weight. The pig was Grand Champion of the Waterloo Meat Animal Show. (Rath Packing Company, Waterloo, Iowa.)

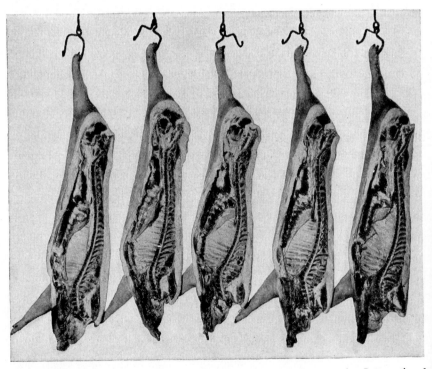

Fig. 134. Market barrow carcasses, sweepstakes carcasses at the International Livestock Exposition.

Fig. 135. A model Poland China barrow, champion middleweight barrow, International Livestock Exposition. Shown by Ben Kelly, Dallas Center, Iowa.

Fig. 136. Champion crossbred barrow, National Barrow Show. Owned by Owen Olson, Newhall, Iowa. (Photograph from Geo. A. Hormel & Co., Austin, Minn.)

good length, smooth shoulders, plump hams, and a considerable degree of smoothness and quality, if marketed at the proper weight and finish, will yield a good percentage of carcasses suitable for conversion into Wiltshire sides. This type of hog can be found in practically all the American breeds.

Fig. 137. A champion Tamworth barrow at the International Livestock Exposition. Shown by Floyd Hoffer, Aledo, Ill.

DRESSING THE BACON HOG

Hogs dressed for Wiltshire sides will yield about 60 per cent of exportable bacon with a usual range from 56 to 64 per cent. A 200-pound pig will therefore yield two sides weighing about 60 pounds each. The yield is lower than for regular dressing, packer style, because of the greater trimming needed for the Wiltshire.

Hogs used for making Wiltshire are singed on the killing floor after dressing. This is done by a torch arrangement, and the side is evenly singed but not burned. A properly singed skin is a light golden-brown color and tender enough so that it can be readily punctured with a toothpick. Often hogs suitable for the export trade are called "singers" or "Canadian singers." The side, when dressed for a Wiltshire, has the foreleg cut off at or above the knee joint and the hind leg at or above the hock joint. The shoulder ribs, neck bone, backbone, aitchbone, skirt, and loose fat are removed. The breastbone is sawed or cut down smooth and even with the face of the side. The belly is neatly trimmed, and the side is squared on the neck.

The Wiltshire side is placed in a brine solution for about 4 days for curing. After it has been in the cure, the side is allowed to drain for 3 or 4 days.

Fig. 138. A Yorkshire barrow, grand champion at the International Livestock Exposition. Shown by The Ohio State University, Columbus, Ohio.

WILTSHIRE REQUIREMENTS

In Canada the requirements for the grading of hog carcasses are very well defined. Government grading of carcasses is mandatory and, since September 30, 1940, this has applied to the carcasses of hogs at all establishments slaughtering 3,000 or more hogs per year. Prior to that time, about 60 per cent of the hogs slaughtered were graded on the rail by government graders and settlement was made on weight and grade of the carcass. The carcass grading was started in 1934 on a voluntary basis.

Canadian grade standards are based on the requirements of the export market for Wiltshire sides. The type and quality of hog suitable for this trade was found to be highly acceptable for their domestic trade. There are five grades of carcasses. The top grade is "A," commonly called "selects." There is only one class in this grade, and the carcass weight range is from 140 to 170 pounds. The minimum length is 29 inches, and the measurement for length of the carcass is taken from the front edge of the first rib to the aitchbone. The maximum fat on shoulders is 2 inches; this measurement is taken at the point of maximum fat thickness on the shoulder, except for any small fat infiltration into the lean. The maximum fat on the loin is 1½ inches; this measurement is taken at the point of maximum fat thickness on the loin between the last rib and the tail.

The carcasses in grade A are described as follows: All carcasses shall be of best quality. Shoulder—shall be balanced in weight in relation to the ham. Belly—thick and of even width throughout, with full flank. Ham— full fleshed, evenly covered with fat, and of good shape. Back—fat firm and of even thickness within variation allowed. Quality—fat trim and white with proper balance of fleshing and fat in carcass throughout.

Firmness of fat is very important in grading Wiltshires. A slight softness will disqualify a carcass from grade A for Wiltshire sides. Lack of maturity, lack of finish, or too much softening feed, such as soybeans, will cause softness. Unbalanced rations, such as too much corn, lack of exercise, or unthriftiness, may cause the carcass to lack sufficient hardness. The other grades are for carcasses less acceptable to the trade. Grades B, C, and D have three classes each, which are weight divisions, and grade E includes carcasses that are unfinished or oily, rejected or condemned, with physical injuries, stags, or ridglings. Grade B, like A, is a "bacon grade for export" while C, D, and E are "pork grades" for the domestic market.

The predominating hog breed in Canada is the Yorkshire. It has been estimated that over 90 per cent of the hogs of that country are of Yorkshire breeding. New breeds from crosses and using Landrace breeding are being developed.

Fig. 139. Tamworth barrows of the proper finish for marketing. A champion pen of Tamworths at the International Livestock Exposition.

DANISH HOG PRODUCTION

Normally about 80 per cent of Denmark's total slaughter of hogs is exported in the form of bacon, and in some years nearly all of the pork exports have been shipped to England. The hog industry expanded with dairy production. Hogs were increased in Denmark with the introduction of the cream separator, to make use of skim milk. The principal concentrate feed is barley; however, some corn, oats, rye, and wheat, especially of low grade, are used. Milk by-products are used in quantities. Indoor feeding in well-constructed permanent buildings prevails, for pasture and roughage are used mainly for cattle.

The hog production in Denmark was developed to supply the British market with bacon. For a time exports to Germany caused a fat type of hog to be developed, but as this trade was frequently restricted, the Danes concentrated upon a lean bacon type that would suit the English. Since 1895, England has taken the bulk of Denmark's surplus hog production. When import quotas on pork were imposed by England, more than 60 per cent was allotted to the Danes.

Two breeds have been used: the domestic breed, the Danish Landrace, and the bacon breed imported from England, the Large White or Yorkshire. The cross between these two breeds was found to be best for producing the type of bacon desired on the English market. More recently the Landrace has tended to overshadow the Yorkshire, for the bacon qualities of the Landrace have been greatly improved.

BACON-HOG RAISING IN THE UNITED STATES

The northern states, including Wisconsin, Minnesota, Montana, North Dakota, and South Dakota, are in the best position to supply this type of hog. In the corn belt, where corn predominates in the swine ration, bacon hogs tend to become too lardy for Wiltshire.

Although we can, apparently, grow bacon hogs and produce Wiltshires, this has never developed into a large business. American meat packers have not been successful in meeting the competition from European Wiltshires on the English market. American-made Wiltshire sides are generally criticized by the English for excessive saltiness.

Feeding hogs for Wiltshires

In U.S. Department of Agriculture investigations [4] it was found that, in contrast with the intensive European methods of swine production, self-

---

[4] R. E. Hutton and E. Z. Russell, "Production of Hogs Suitable for Wiltshire Sides," *Circ. 532*, U.S.D.A., November, 1939.

feeding simple rations on alfalfa pasture in large groups produced a large proportion of suitable Wiltshire sides. Yorkshires, Chester Whites and their crosses, and a few Duroc Jerseys were used in this series of experiments. A few of the carcasses were overly fat for export bacon but were highly satisfactory for domestic consumption. Wheat and barley were the grain components of the ration; tankage and minerals, and alfalfa pasture supplemented the grain.

Pork export cuts

In addition to Wiltshire sides, we have exported Cumberland sides, and regular long clears, which are cut differently from our regular pork cuts. Briefly described they are as follows: Cumberland sides include the side and shoulder in one piece, cut square on the ham end with the leg cut off below knee joint; regular long clears comprise the side of a carcass with the ham off and the backbone, shoulder bones, and ribs out, foreleg cut off close to the breast, and the aitch- and breastbones cut down smooth with the face of the side.

There are other less well-known export cuts which from time to time enter into the export trade. Our export trade is not limited to the so-called export cuts. Considerable quantities of hams and lard are also sold abroad at times.

DESCRIPTION OF THE BACON TYPE

As compared with our common hogs, the so-called bacon hog is not so wide, somewhat longer, deeper in the side, smoother at the shoulder, somewhat longer in the head, neck, and legs, and less plump in the ham. Even when finished, the bacon hog is less fat or wide than our intermediate hog of the meat type. The bacon hog is more muscular and less lardy than our usual top market hog. In temperament the bacon hog is less lymphatic and more active and animated.

The description of an ideal bacon-type pig that would satisfy the market requirements as previously set forth would also depict, within limits, the ideal breeding gilt and boar. The ideal individual for breeding is of course one that will produce the kind which will yield the Wiltshires in demand on the critical and discriminating market. This does not imply that the producing of suitable products is merely a matter of breeding, since feeding and processing are also important.

Since the same general type is applicable to both the market hogs and those for the breeding herd, one short description follows. It should be pointed out, however, that many characteristics are given emphasis in the breeding herd which are disregarded in the market hog.

Size. In size the bacon hog should be well developed for its age. The market weight limits are rather narrow: 140 to 170 pounds for grade A class carcasses. Size for age to secure rapid and economical gain, and reasonably early maturity are emphasized.

Fig. 140. A Yorkshire sow, P. Nora. (Curtiss Candy Co.)

Form. The form of the bacon hog is typical. Briefly, a form that is long and in which all parts are proportionately developed so as to have a well-balanced, strongly built individual is perfection. The top line is slightly arched and carried strong, and the side lines and under lines are straight.

Quality. Quality is indicated by fine hair and smooth skin which shows no tendency to wrinkle. In individuals of high quality, the flesh is firm and smooth with no flabbiness at the jowl, foreflank, belly, or ham.

Condition. In general, bacon hogs have less finish than our common market hogs. A good covering of firm flesh especially along the back and loin is needed, but overfatness is to be avoided.

Style. Canadian score cards for bacon hogs include style, under which they specify that the ideal should be active and sprightly, walking without a swaying movement.

HEAD. The head will vary a great deal with the breed. Within the Yorkshire breed, which is the predominating bacon breed of Canada, much variation exists. Moderate length and width of head are desired. A face that is broad between the eyes and at the poll is required. Good size, bright eyes, and moderately fine ears are specified. A jowl that is of fair width, muscular, neat, and not flabby and a neck that is muscular and of medium length are emphasized.

FOREQUARTERS. In the forequarters the shoulder is the most important single part. It is to be smooth, somewhat rounded from side to side over the top, very compact, no wider than the back, and not extending back onto the side. The breast and chest should be wide, deep, and full.

BODY. The body is made up of several very important parts; back and loin of moderate width, rising slightly above a straight line but not unduly arched, are wanted. Weak, sagging backs are discriminated against. A uniform width and fleshing with a slight arch is the description of the proper back and loin. The side that is deep, long, smooth, well fleshed, and straight between the shoulder and ham meets the requirement of the Wilt-

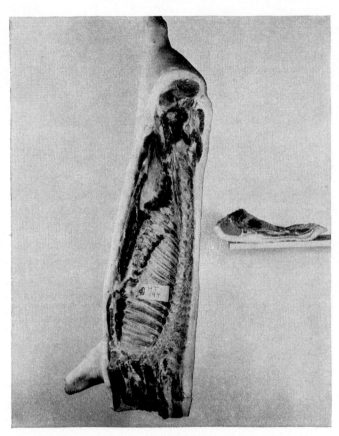

Fig. 141. A Wiltshire side and a cross section made from the other side of the carcass. (Dept. of Agri., Canada.)

shire. Ribs of good length, moderately arched, are essential for a good side which should be the same width as the shoulders and hams throughout. Fullness at the fore and rear flank is needed for a deep side.

HINDQUARTERS. The hindquarter on the usual United States market hog carcass is mainly ham, but on the bacon carcass, it is the gammon, which is further divided into two parts. On the live hog these are the rump and the ham. A desirable rump is the same width as the back; long and slightly rounded from a point above the hip to the tail and somewhat rounded from side to side over the top. A ham that is full without flabbiness, somewhat tapering to the back but carrying flesh well down toward the hock, and without wrinkles or folds is desired.

LEGS. The front and hind legs should be well placed so that the individual stands squarely upon them. They should be medium in length, straight, and with pasterns upright.

Fig. 142. A Landrace gilt. This breed, developed in Denmark, is used to produce Wiltshire sides or bacon for the British Market.

The live hog and the carcass

Since in countries such as Canada and Denmark, which produce bacon for export, the grading is done on the carcass rather than on foot, the appraisal of the market pig on foot is of less importance than it used to be. Under the carcass grade system, instead of an estimate of the condition of the live hog, a measurement can be made of the fat covering.

Selection of the breeding individual, however, continues to be a consideration of importance in production of bacon hogs. Live hog grading has the advantage of setting before the producer the on-foot specifications for a desirable market hog. The characteristics specified will guide him in the selection of breeding hogs.

Fig. 143. A Yorkshire boar of the approved conformation. A Type Conference champion.

Feeding affects size type and fatness

The type, small, intermediate, or large, is affected in part by feeding and management. The pattern for type is set by inheritance, but the fulfillment depends upon nutrition. The size and weight a hog will attain at maturity are set by its heredity but may be affected by feeding. Pigs fed heavily are finished at lighter weights than pigs fed limited rations. Large-type or rangy pigs may yield quite acceptable carcasses when they are self-fed, especially if corn is the basis of the ration. Pigs closely confined may have fatter carcasses than pigs having range or pasture and taking more exercise.

Chapter 23

HOG MARKETS

Hogs are marketed by the same methods as those used for cattle. Hog men, however, usually have more market outlets, and there has been a greater increase in direct marketing of hogs than of other livestock. As compared with cattle and sheep, there are relatively few hogs taken out from the market for further feeding.

Decentralization has been more marked in hog slaughter than in slaughter of other livestock. A relatively small amount of the hog slaughter is being done at the public stockyard centers, for there has been a big growth of slaughter at the interior packing plants. There has been a great increase in the number of hogs trucked to market.

These changes have caused marked alterations in our hog markets and methods of marketing; and it is apparent that one of the characteristics of our marketing system is its changeableness. Hogs, like other livestock, may pass through several hands before they finally reach the slaughterers, or these agencies may not be used and the sale may be made by the producer to the packer. There are such well-established agencies as farmer cooperative associations, community auctions, country dealers, assembly points or concentration yards, and public markets through which livestock may pass en route from the producer to the slaughterer.

METHODS OF MARKETING

A raiser of hogs may sell to a local buyer, concentration yards, local auction, or local packer, any of which by definition represents a direct sale. He may also ship to a public stockyard market and use the services of a livestock commission agent who in turn would sell to a packer, shipper, or trader. For purposes of selling, the producer may join with a cooperative which would sell to any of the buying agencies or consign to a centralized cooperative commission association. There is also some home slaughter and direct selling of the pork products.

There has been a great growth of direct marketing or sale to slaughterers at places other than recognized public stockyard markets where the owner is represented by a commission agent. The direct buying of hogs increased until 1946. During the 1940–1949 period 57.8 per cent of hogs were classified as "directs." The livestock purchased direct are shown in Figure 144.

According to a federal study,[1] the principal reasons for the rapid increase in direct marketing of hogs in recent years may be found in the competitive situation as between local or interior packers on the one hand and public market packers on the other, associated with the expansion of corn and hog production in the western corn belt. The chief reasons for this competitive situation are found in the transportation developments, both rail and motor truck, as they affect convenience and cost of moving livestock direct and through public markets and of transporting live animals as compared with livestock products; in comparative labor costs among packers in different areas; in differences between direct and public market channels with respect to costs of marketing including shrinkage, commission charges, yardage fees, and other marketing costs; and in producer preferences, which play a part in the farmer's choice of market outlet.

SLAUGHTER LIVESTOCK: PERCENTAGE PURCHASED DIRECT IN THE UNITED STATES, 1923-50

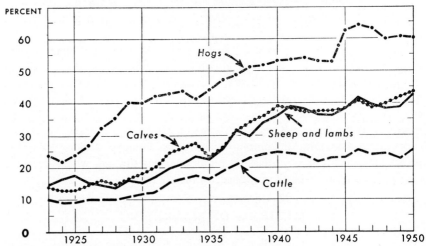

Fig. 144. Slaughter livestock purchased direct. More hogs are purchased direct than any kind of livestock. (U.S.D.A.)

[1] "The Direct Marketing of Hogs," *Misc. Pub. 222,* U.S.D.A., 1935.

From this study it was concluded that the causes of increased direct marketing of hogs and other livestock are closely associated with the economic development of the country and particularly of its livestock industry. It is shown that the sharp decline in the level of hog prices since 1926 has been due to the drastic reduction in consumers' income incident to the depression and the decline in foreign demand for American hog products. ✗

It does not appear that direct marketing has restricted competition among slaughterers and distributors and enabled them to exact a wider margin. In fact, the principal widening in margins occurred prior to the years of rapid increase in direct marketing and was not confined to hogs or to meat animals generally, but appeared also with respect to other products outside the influence of direct marketing of livestock. The conclusion that direct marketing has not caused a widening of the margins between the price of a given weight of live hogs and the wholesale or the retail price of the products derived therefrom is also supported by the fact that these margins declined materially during recent years of rapid increase in direct marketing. This decline, however, was due largely to reductions in labor charges and some other costs during the depression.

Data on price differentials among markets show that no one market, and no particular type of market, sets the level of hog prices. The distribution of the volume of hogs consigned to public markets among the different grade classifications was shown to be approximately the same as the distribution of the hogs marketed direct; that is, the public markets on the whole were not receiving more than their proportionate share of low-grade hogs. This, together with the fact that no one market or group of markets sets the price for all markets, leads to the conclusion that the growth of direct marketing has not impaired the price-registering function of the public markets or caused the prices at the interior markets to be lower than if direct marketing had not increased.

Moreover, this study shows that the growth of direct marketing has not caused the returns to producers of hogs to be less than they would otherwise have been. This was contrary to the opinions of some who were interested in the question.

Although this study shows that the growth of direct marketing has not been to the disadvantage of the producer, it also shows that there is need for correction of some practices and the development of additional services to improve the marketing of hogs.

LEADING HOG MARKETS

The large hog markets are located in or near the corn belt, the area of our densest hog population. The pork-packing plants have tended to move toward the areas of hog raising, and local or interior packers have increased their slaughter. In this decentralization the packers at the central markets have established buying points in the producing areas. The hogs moving direct are a part of the receipts on the markets, but it is obvious that the central markets secure a smaller proportion of the total hogs marketed than formerly.

Chicago is still the leading hog market of the country in numbers. For the decade 1930–1939 yearly receipts have averaged over 5 million head, more than twice the number at the next largest market. The markets are continually changing in rank as receipts fluctuate markedly. St. Louis National Stockyards, Illinois, or East St. Louis, South St. Paul, Omaha. Indianapolis, and Sioux City are very large central hog markets. A listing of large hog markets based upon a recent 5-year period follows.

With the rapid increase of population in the Pacific states and Texas the westward movement of market hogs has turned farther back East. This is more extreme in the case of hogs than other livestock. (See Figure 23, page 55.) As a consequence, western markets have increased in receipts.

HOGS, YEARLY TOTAL AND SALABLE RECEIPTS AT PUBLIC MARKETS

Average of 5 Years—1951 to 1955 [2]

MARKET	TOTAL AVERAGE	SALABLE AVERAGE
1. Chicago, Ill.	3,446,677	2,557,038
2. St. Louis NSY., Ill.	3,003,996	2,572,177
3. South St. Paul, Minn.	2,902,243	2,616,983
4. Omaha, Nebr.	2,850,491	2,137,309
5. Indianapolis, Ind.	2,288,356	2,272,820
6. Sioux City, Iowa	2,136,775	1,936,265
7. St. Joseph, Mo.	1,692,238	1,284,851
8. Peoria, Ill.	1,134,465	1,063,157
9. North Salt Lake, Utah	969,259	30,897
10. Denver, Colo.	891,849	174,036
11. New York, N. Y.	885,263	2,169
12. Cincinnati, Ohio	838,567	763,279
13. Sioux Falls, S. D.	760,263	759,599
14. Kansas City, Mo.	666,910	557,658
15. Fort Worth, Tex.	654,048	142,733
TOTAL	33,924,815	24,109,506

SEASONAL VARIATION IN HOG RECEIPTS

Farrowings are peaked in the spring and fall, and it is obvious that marketings will be the heaviest when these crops are ready for market. Some farmers full feed, making possible a finished market pig at 6 months of age or slightly under, while others follow a limited feeding plan for a longer

[2] From reports of Livestock Division, Agricultural Marketing Service, U.S.D.A., based on reports submitted by stockyards companies.

time. Circumstances may alter the time of marketing and desirable marketable weights.

Peaks in market receipts of hogs occur in the late fall, when the spring pigs predominate in the receipts. There is another slight peak in May and June from the marketing of fall-farrowed pigs. Since feeder and stocker pigs are but a small fraction of the receipts, hog slaughter follows market receipts very closely.

Below is a tabulation of the salable receipts of hogs by months for a recent 10-year period.

The months of January, December, November, and February are those of very heavy receipts. These are also months of comparatively low prices. Months with low receipts, like August and September, are generally months in which hog prices are relatively high. The seasonal variation is due, then, to the natural movement of the finished pigs to market. Spring pigs, more numerous than fall pigs, are marketed from late August on and reach the peak of movement in December or January. Marketings then decline until April and May, when fall pigs appear in number on the markets. Low receipts prevail in the summer because of the absence of new-crop pigs. The receipts, as a consequence, are made up of a relatively large proportion of packing sows.

SALABLE RECEIPTS PER CENT BY MONTHS AT 12
PUBLIC STOCKYARD MARKETS

Average for 10 Years, 1945–1954 [3]

MONTH	PER CENT PER MONTH
January	10.94
February	8.11
March	8.07
April	7.65
May	7.63
June	7.52
July	7.13
August	6.68
September	6.36
October	8.33
November	10.29
December	11.29

In the northern section of the corn belt marketings are more seasonal and the winter movement is more pronounced than in the southern corn belt, where the two-litter-a-year plan is more extensively followed. In the specialized hog producing areas there has been a shift toward spaced or

[3] *Livestock Market News Statistics,* Agricultural Marketing Service, U.S.D.A., 1955.

multi-farrowing, which tends toward a more even distribution of market receipts.

SEASONAL VARIATION IN HOG WEIGHTS

Heavy hogs predominate on the markets in the summer and early fall. It is not unusual for one third of the receipts during August to be packing sows. The average weight is less when the younger hogs make up the largest proportion of the receipts.

The average live weights by months of hogs slaughtered under federal inspection follow.

AVERAGE LIVE WEIGHT OF HOGS SLAUGHTERED UNDER FEDERAL INSPECTION

Average for 8 Years, 1948–1955 [4]

MONTH	AVERAGE WEIGHT, LBS.
January	248.1
February	243.0
March	239.7
April	240.7
May	248.9
June	264.7
July	270.6
August	252.8
September	233.0
October	229.5
November	237.0
December	242.8
Average of Total	245.88

FEEDER PIG MARKETS

Actually, a comparatively small number of feeder pigs pass through the central markets. Such pigs are usually moved direct from the grower to the feeder or are marketed through local buyers, auction sales, and truckers. In some areas feeder pigs are available from "pig hatcheries" or specialized feeder pig growers (see page 398). The greatest movement of feeder pigs is in September and February, but it is spread quite uniformly in the other months.

Of the central stockyards, South St. Paul, Sioux City, Kansas City, and East St. Louis have fairly large receipts. Memphis, Wichita, Omaha, Springfield (Mo.), Oklahoma City, and St. Joseph also have numbers of feeder pigs offered for sale. The above order is the rank in number of receipts of feeder pigs for a recent period. The feeder-pig trade is quite variable from

[4] "Livestock Market and News Statistics," *Statistical Bulletin,* No. 178, Agricultural Marketing Service, U.S.D.A., 1955.

year to year. It is markedly affected by the pig crop in an area and by available feed supplies.

Fig. 145. A movable loading chute. A loading chute like this with a cleated floor is a safeguard against injuries in loading. (Harry J. Boyts, National Livestock Loss Prevention Board.)

The trade in feeder and stocker pigs is comparatively small, as indicated by the total receipts at 67 markets of less than 500,000 head a year.

SHRINKAGE OF HOGS IN SHIPPING

There is a normal loss of weight, called "shrinkage," from the time of weighing at the point of origin to the time of weighing after the sale on the market. As feeding is interrupted and there is an excretory loss of urine, feces, and moisture in expired air, home weights are higher than market weights. "Filling," or feeding and watering at the yards before selling, will recover some of the loss of weight. The weight at arrival is spoken of as the "shrunk-out" weight. It will be recalled that it is recommended that hogs not be filled by feeding before selling.

Numerous investigations have been made on the subject of shrinkage in hogs being marketed, and there is much disagreement in the actual amount of weight loss or shrink.

Following is a tabulation of the usual range of shrinkage.[5]

[5] Information from Edward N. Wentworth, Armour and Co., August, 1950.

| | TRUCK | | RAILROAD | | |
	50 Miles	100 Miles	400 Miles	1,000 Miles	2,000 Miles
Barrows and gilts	2–3%	4–6%	6–8%	8–10%	8–11%
Sows	4–5%	5–6%	6–8%	7–10%	8–11%

The highest rate of shrink occurs in loading and in the first few miles of the trip. Total shrinkage increases with distance and time of shipping, and it is greater in mixed shipments (more than one kind of livestock loaded together) and with lighter hogs. Hogs shrink less than other farm animals en route to the market. There appears to be some seasonal variation in hog shrinkage; there is less in winter than at other seasons of the year.

A study of "fills" or weight gain at the market from water and feed, on hogs [6] indicated that hogs would take on about 5.5 pounds of fill or 2.5 per cent of their live weight. Of this fill 65 per cent was corn and 35 per cent water. Feeding at the market tends to equalize shrinkage, for hogs with the greatest shrink will usually take the largest fill.

TRANSPORTATION TO THE MARKET

A larger proportion of hogs are transported by motor truck than any other class of livestock. Only 2 per cent of the total receipts on 17 markets in 1916 were trucked in. In 1940 about 75 per cent of the hog receipts at these same markets were "truck-ins." [7] At 62 markets the percentage of trucked hogs was 86.3 per cent for 1953–1955.[8]

For hauls to market under 100 miles, costs for trucking are usually less

Fig. 146. Hogs in the stockyards. Note the variety of hogs in the first pen.

[6] *Monthly Letter to Animal Husbandmen,* Armour and Co., Vol. 10, No. 4, July, 1929.

[7] *Drive-in Receipts of Livestock,* U.S.D.A., 1941.

[8] *Agricultural Statistics,* U.S.D.A., 1955.

than rail costs. On long hauls rail shipping may be advantageous. Farmers generally prefer trucks, especially for shorter hauls, for several reasons. First, less time is needed to get hogs to the market, which usually is a big advantage. Second, smaller loads are taken, which gives greater adaptability. Hogs can be topped out and marketed as finished. Third, more market outlets are available to trucks. Fourth, shrinkage, crippling, and death losses are no greater than in comparable rail shipments. Fifth, the truck picks up the hogs at the farm, but for rail shipment it is necessary to get the hogs to the local stockyards.

Number of hogs per truck

The number of hogs or calves per truck for maximum safe loading is given below.

HOGS OR CALVES PER TRUCK

Single-Deck Trucks

FLOOR LENGTH, FEET	AVERAGE LIVE WEIGHT, POUNDS								
	100	150	175	200	225	250	300	350	400
8	27	21	19	18	16	14	13	11	9
10	33	26	24	22	20	18	16	14	12
12	40	31	28	26	24	22	19	17	14
15	50	39	36	33	30	27	24	21	17
18	60	47	43	40	36	33	28	25	21
20	67	52	48	44	40	35	32	28	24
24	80	62	57	52	48	44	38	34	28
28	93	72	67	61	56	51	44	39	33
30	100	77	72	66	60	55	47	42	35
32	107	83	76	70	64	58	51	44	38
36	120	94	86	79	72	66	57	50	42
42	140	109	100	92	84	77	63	55	49

Double-Deck Trucks *

FLOOR LENGTH, FEET	AVERAGE LIVE WEIGHT, POUNDS								
	100	150	175	200	225	250	300	350	400
8	43	33	31	29	27	24	21	18	16
10	53	41	38	36	33	30	26	23	20
12	63	50	46	43	40	36	31	28	24
15	79	62	56	54	50	45	39	34	30
18	95	75	70	65	60	55	46	41	36
20	105	83	77	72	67	61	52	46	40
24	127	100	93	87	80	73	62	55	48
28	148	116	109	101	93	86	73	64	56
30	158	125	116	108	100	91	78	68	60
32	169	133	130	115	107	97	83	73	64
36	190	150	140	130	120	110	94	82	72
42	220	172	164	151	142	128	109	96	80

* Divide equally.

Number of hogs per railroad car

The number of hogs commonly shipped per railroad car depends upon the size of the car and the weight of the hogs. Hogs may be shipped in

HOGS PER RAILROAD CAR PER DECK [9]

CAR SIZE, FEET	AVERAGE LIVE WEIGHT, POUNDS											
	100	*125*	*150*	*175*	*200*	*225*	*250*	*275*	*300*	*325*	*350*	*400*
36	130	115	100	89	79	73	68	62	59	56	53	47
40	140	127	110	98	88	82	76	69	65	62	59	52

double-deck cars, and in loading fewer hogs are put in the upper deck, especially during warm weather. Overloading and underloading are to be avoided, since these are contributing factors to injury and death. On page 383 is a statement of the limits of total weight which should be shipped in railroad cars of the two common lengths.

Shipping losses

The National Livestock Loss Prevention Board investigation indicates the following ratio of death and crippling among hogs received at the markets.

PERCENTAGE OF HOGS DEAD AND CRIPPLED ON ARRIVAL BY RAIL
AND TRUCK AT KANSAS CITY, ST. JOSEPH, OMAHA,
SIOUX CITY, AND ST. PAUL

Average, recent 2-year period

PER CENT DEAD		PER CENT CRIPPLED	
Rail	*Truck*	*Rail*	*Truck*
0.088	0.174	0.174	0.291

The death loss is higher for trucked hogs than for those shipped by rail, partly because some disabled hogs are shipped by truck that could not be shipped by rail. Poor loading conditions and improper handling are no doubt more prevalent in truck than in rail shipments. These losses are quite tangible. Other damage, such as bruising, is evident only upon slaughter. The causes of handling bruises in marketing are somewhat different for hogs than for cattle, for hogs are slower-moving and less sure-footed. A survey by Livestock Conservation Inc.[10] indicated the following distribution of causes of bruising:

[9] *Bull. 20,* Swift & Company, May, 1941.
[10] "Livestock Conservation Handbook," Livestock Conservation, Inc., 1955.

Canes, whips and clubs—42 per cent
Kicking and prodding—20 per cent
Crowding and trampling—15 per cent
Fork and nail punctures—12 per cent
Spreaders—2 per cent
Other causes—9 per cent

Practices recommended in shipping hogs

By following certain shipping practices it is possible to reduce death and crippled losses in shipping hogs to market. Based on a study of shipping hogs to market, Wiley [11] has made the recommendations given below.

1. Do not feed hogs in cars during warm and hot weather, or when the maximum temperature during transit is 60 degrees or higher.

2. Clean cars before loading, particularly during warm and hot weather, or from April to October, inclusive, for the corn-belt shipping territory.

3. Bed cars with sand during cool, warm, and hot weather (40-degree maximum temperature and above), and with straw or sand and straw during cold weather.

4. Shower hogs during warm and hot weather when the cars are bedded with sand.

5. Load a 36-foot single-deck car less than 18,000 pounds during cold and cool weather and less than 17,000 pounds during warm and hot weather. Load a 40-foot single-deck car under 20,000 pounds during cold and cool weather and under 19,000 pounds during warm and hot weather.

6. Partition large hogs like sows and stags away from smaller hogs, especially when they are not accustomed to running together.

[11] James R. Wiley, "Death and Crippled Losses in Shipping Hogs to Market," *Bull. 318*, Purdue University Agr. Exp. Sta., 1927.

Chapter 24

MARKET CLASSIFICATION
OF HOGS AND HOG PRICES

In this chapter there are two divisions, the first dealing with the groups of hogs on the market and the second with prices of market hogs. The discussion of price pertains only to market hogs, which are mainly slaughter hogs.

MARKET CLASSIFICATION OF HOGS

The hogs on the market present a wide range in weight, form, finish, and quality. On our early markets, a one-price system was used and hogs of all kinds were sold for the same price per pound. As consumer preferences became manifest, differentiation in hogs became prevalent. The factors related to desirability from a consumer standpoint were weight, sex condition, conformation, finish, and quality.

Hogs are sorted into various lots based upon characters that affect carcass value. Such sorting permits transactions in groups or lots quite similar in all essential respects. The general process of dividing swine into classes, subclasses, and weights is termed "classifying." The term "grading" applies to the last step in the sorting process and results in rather uniform groups of lots which are offered for sale. (See page 76.)

DIFFERENT MARKET CLASSIFICATIONS

There is some variation in the market classifications for swine and in the nomenclature used to designate the classes, weights and grades. The market standards of the United States Department of Agriculture are widely used. Fixed standards permit the producer to understand market information which he may get from newspapers, livestock papers, special reports, radio, television, and other media. Language understood by the producer is prerequisite to interpreting the happenings on the livestock market.

The first system of classifying and grading market hogs was used by the Livestock Market Reporting Service in 1918. Changes in production and marketing conditions have been responsible for modification of standards. Recently the standards for barrows and gilts have been changed and the degree of finish or fatness was reduced for each grade.[1]

BENEFITS OF CLASSIFYING AND GRADING

A standard or uniform classification would be of value to all concerned in hog production and marketing. With a uniform system direct or order buyers could buy the class, weight and grade they could use. Grading simplifies buying. Buyers and sellers can trade on a basis that more nearly reflects current market value. Grading also facilitates market reporting and provides a more accurate basis for statistical data for market analysis.

The producer is helped, for market quotations become meaningful in planning his production and marketing program. Also, complete, accurate market quotations help in determining where and when to sell.

MARKET CLASSES AND GRADES OF SWINE

A study of a rather complete report of the hog market will indicate groupings by sex, use, weight, and grades. No attempt is made to bring age into the classification directly as in the case of cattle, for a weight division effects the same purpose when combined with sex. Market hogs are mainly for slaughter, though a few are sold as feeders and a very few are disposed of for breeding. Following is a tabulation of the market classes and grades of swine [2] which may be on the market.

In comparing the schedule with that used for cattle, it will be observed that there is one less use selection and one less grade, as well as no age division. Also there is, in swine, a classification breakup of the choice grade

---

[1] "Official United States Standards for Grades of Slaughter Swine (Barrows and Gilts)," *Service and Regulatory Announcement 172*, U.S.D.A., July, 1955.

[2] "Swine" is used to designate both hogs and pigs. Hogs weigh 120 pounds and over, and may be of either sex or unsexed. If sexed, a hog has attained sufficient age or maturity to make reproduction possible. Pigs are under 120 pounds, either sex or unsexed, with insufficient age or maturity to make reproduction possible. *Circ. 569*, U.S.D.A., Sept., 1940. On the Chicago market "pigs" are swine weighing 130 pounds or less; light hogs are in the range of 135 to 195 pounds, and heavy hogs are 255 pounds and over. Actually, in the trade, the term "hogs" is used to cover all swine.

MARKET CLASSES AND GRADES OF HOGS

| | | BASIS FOR GROUPING | | |
	Sex	Use Selection	Weight	Grades
Divisions within each group	Barrows and gilts Sows Stags Boars Pigs	Slaughter Feeder and stocker	Different in various classes	U.S. No. 1 * U.S. No. 2 * U.S. No. 3 * Medium Cull

* For barrows, gilts, and slaughter sows.

in "barrows and gilts." In market usage this division is upon the proportion of fat to lean and yield of the different lean cuts—ham, loin, picnic, and butt. The U.S. No. 3's have a higher proportion of fat to lean, especially in the bacon bellies and regular hams, U.S. No. 1's have the most lean and U.S. No. 2's are intermediate between 1 and 3. See page 415 for a comparison of the yields of these three grades.

MARKET CLASSES OR SEX CLASSES OF SWINE

As previously indicated, a market class includes individuals of the same sex condition. Five classes of swine are recognized—"barrows and gilts," sows, stags, boars, and pigs. The sex condition is related to certain physical characteristics which influence conformation, finish, and quality. Because of these differences and the fact that they are related to the carcass and its use, we have division or group. A description of each class follows.[3]

Barrows

A barrow is a castrated male hog that shows no pronounced indications of sex development similar to those in an uncastrated male. As a rule the animal is castrated when only a few weeks old.

The animal usually has developed physical characteristics that are peculiar to its class. As a class, barrows are more evenly developed and balanced in conformation than stags, sows, and boars. The natural fleshing or muscular development of the various parts such as neck, shoulders, loins, and hams is more evenly developed and balanced. The difference between barrows and gilts in these respects, however, is very slight.

Gilts

A gilt is a young female hog that has not produced pigs and that has not reached an evident stage of pregnancy.

The animal has usually developed physical characteristics that are pe-

[3] *Circ. 569,* U.S.D.A., Sept., 1940.

culiar to its class. Gilts are very nearly the equal of barrows in evenness and balance of muscular development and conformation, although they tend, as a class, to be slightly lighter and less developed through the shoulders than barrows of corresponding weight and grade. The bacon sides from gilts usually require more trimming on the belly side than the bacon from barrows, because of the more pronounced so-called "seeds," thus slightly reducing the percentage of bacon bellies which rank high in market value. Furthermore, a varying percentage of gilts when marketed usually have reached a stage of pregnancy, which materially reduces their dressing percentage or carcass yield. Although this condition may not be detected in the live animal, it does cause a slight price discrimination against gilts on the part of practically all packer buyers and may in time lead to separation of barrows and gilts into distinct market classes.

Sows

A sow is a female swine that shows evidence of having produced pigs or that is in an evident stage of pregnancy.

Sows, as a class, are somewhat unevenly developed and lack balance in their muscular development and conformation. As a rule, they become relatively lighter in the shoulder and narrower through the fore part of the body as they increase in age and weight. Almost without exception the bacon sides from sows require more trimming on the belly side than do the bacon sides from barrows and gilts. Pregnancy, although not noticeable in the live animal, materially reduces dressing percentage. Sows, as a class, carry a larger proportion of fat than the corresponding grades of the other classes of slaughter hogs. Usually the fat covering is somewhat thicker than that of other classes of slaughter hogs.

Stags

A stag is a castrated male swine that shows pronounced sex development or physical characteristics peculiar to the adult uncastrated male.

Stags, as a class, are unevenly developed and lack balance in their muscular development and conformation. As a rule the neck and shoulders are overdeveloped and heavy, as related to other parts of the animal. As a class stags have relatively thick skins, coarse hair, and large bones, and are rough and heavy at the joints. They are not marketed in sufficient numbers to make the buying and selling of animals of this class on the basis of grade either practical or desirable. Hence, grade descriptions for stags, although possible and logical, theoretically at least, are commonly omitted.

Boars

A boar is an uncastrated male swine. Boars, as a class, show a greater development of masculine characteristics than do the class termed "stags."

Compared with other parts of the body, the neck, shoulders, and bones of boars are overdeveloped, causing the general conformation of the animal to be uneven and its parts to lack balance. Boars have less thickness of fat covering than other classes of hogs; sex condition does not affect the distribution of fat covering to any noticeable extent. They are very thick skinned, coarse haired, and heavy boned. As a class, they are the least desirable of all swine from a market standpoint. Boars, particularly those that have attained sufficient weight to be termed "hogs," should never be sent to market as such but should be castrated and fed a month or longer before marketing. The market value of boars as slaughter animals is low, since a considerable percentage are condemned, because of odor, as unfit for human consumption.

Barrows and gilts one market class

Barrows and gilts of the same weight that are typical of any given grade have practically the same conformation, finish, and quality, because sex condition in these two classes does not materially affect the characteristics on which the grade is based.

Hence, in actual market practice, barrows and gilts of the same weight selection and of the same grade almost invariably sell together. For all practical purposes they are one market class and are so recognized by practically all members of the trade. The relative number of barrows and gilts in any specific lot, however, does affect the price of that lot to some extent. Barrows usually yield a slightly higher percentage of carcass and a slightly higher percentage of bacon bellies than do gilts of the same weight and grade.

WEIGHT DIVISIONS OR SELECTIONS

There are numerous weight divisions of hogs, especially barrows and gilts. Sometimes the top price is paid for a rather narrow range in weight, but when heavy hogs are scarce in proportion to demand, many weight brackets are quoted at the same prices.

Hogs, the same in all respects but weight, will vary in dressing percentage, weight of carcass, size, and proportion of wholesale cuts. As the weight is increased in hogs the lard yields increase, and also the amount of the fat cuts, such as bacon bellies, clear plates, and fat backs. Lean cuts such as loins, hams, shoulders, and Boston butts make up a smaller proportion of the heavy carcass than of the light carcass.

Lard yields increase markedly as weights increase. A pig with a live weight of 200 pounds yields about 24 pounds of lard, a 300-pound pig about 47 pounds, and a 400-pound pig about 80 pounds. As would be expected heavy barrows and gilts are discounted in price because of their greater lard yields. Light weight sows of comparable grades sell at higher prices than heavy sows.

MARKET GRADES

The market grade of a hog is determined by the excellence of conformation and the degree of finish and quality. These factors give a basis for grading into four or five groups. *Conformation, finish, and quality are the important factors which affect market grade.*

Conformation

Conformation is the form, shape, outline, or contour of the hog and its different parts. It is important as a grade factor because it influences to a considerable extent (1) the amount or percentage of carcass weight as related to the live weight of the animal, commonly referred to as "dressing percentage"; (2) the amount or percentage of the various standard wholesale cuts of pork that the carcass will produce; and (3) the percentage of lean meat, fat, bone, and skin in the standard wholesale cuts of pork obtained from the carcass.

The ideal conformation in swine indicates that the animal, when slaughtered, will have a high dressing percentage and will produce a carcass with a proportionately thick covering of flesh throughout. The highest possible percentage of total weight should be in the higher priced cuts, such as loins, Boston butts, hams, and bacon bellies.

Finish

Finish is the amount and quality of fat, including fat on the outside of the animal's body and that on the inside of the abdominal and thoracic cavities, as well as intermuscular and intramuscular fat that surrounds and permeates the muscle fiber. In the live animal the interior fats can be judged only by analogy. Finish depends somewhat on inherited tendencies or breeding and somewhat on sex condition and age, but it depends largely on the quantity, kind, and quality of feed consumed by the animal and on methods of handling and care.

Finish is important because, more than any other single factor, it influences (1) the dressing percentage of the animal, (2) the weight and percentage of the various standard wholesale cuts of meat produced, (3) the percentage of lean, fat, bone, and skin in the standard wholesale cuts of pork obtained, (4) the percentage of connective tissue, intermuscular and intramuscular fat in the muscle or lean meat of the animal, and (5) the quality or character of all the fat. Since fat is worth less than lean, an excessive amount is highly undesirable.

Ideal finish in swine indicates that the proper thickness and firmness of external and internal fat is smoothly and evenly distributed.

Quality

Quality, defined as a livestock grade factor, is a characteristic of the muscle or lean meat and the fat of the animal. Quality varies with age and to some extent with sex condition and methods of handling and care. Quality is important because it is considered to be an indication of the varying percentages and character of the connective tissue in the lean meat, the size of the muscle fiber, that is, the grain or texture of the lean meat, and the percentage of intermuscular and intramuscular fat and dry matter contained in the lean meat. Experience indicates that these characteristics influence the tenderness, palatability, juiciness, and flavor in the lean meat of the cuts of pork which the animal will produce.

Quality in the live animal is thought to be indicated by its degree of refinement, condition of hair, smoothness and thinness of skin, smoothness of the joints of the legs, and size of the bones of the legs as related to the size and weight of the animal.

OFFICIAL MARKET CLASSIFICATION

The official grade standard is the basis for the market news service reports of the U.S. Department of Agriculture. It is now used rather completely on all markets. In this separation sex condition, weight, conformation, finish, and quality are considered as determinants of class and grade of slaughter swine. These factors are related to the value of a slaughter swine because of their relationship to the kind, size, quality, and yield of the wholesale pork cuts.

The new grades of the slaughter hog on foot (page 391) are directly related to the carcass grades which in turn is a reflection of the yield and grade of pork cuts. The pork carcass grades, which are the foundation for the slaughter swine grades, are based on differences in the ratio of lean to fat and the quality of cuts.

In market quotations there may be a bracketing of the smaller divisions. Some terms that have been used for years continue in spite of their absence from the federal government schedule. For example, it is quite common to use the term "butcher hog" for a part of the federal standard class of barrows and gilts.

A detailed description of the different grades is given for barrows and gilts. The poor grades merely deviate from the better grades in the extent to which they fail to meet the specifications; the top grades set the standard. In barrows and gilts we have five grades; a description of each follows.[4]

[4] "Official United States Standards for Grades of Slaughter Swine (Barrows and Gilts)," *Service and Regulatory Announcement No. 172,* U.S.D.A., July, 1955.

SLAUGHTER HOG SCHEDULE

CLASSES OF HOGS	WEIGHT GROUPS, POUNDS	GRADES
Barrows and gilts	140 to 160	
	160 to 180	
	180 to 200	U.S. No. 1
	200 to 220	U.S. No. 2
	220 to 240	U.S. No. 3
	240 to 270	Medium
	270 to 300	Culi
	300 to 330	
	330 to 360	
Packing sows	270 to 300	
	300 to 330	U.S. No. 1
	330 to 360	U.S. No. 2
	360 to 400	U.S. No. 3
	400 to 450	Medium
	450 to 550	Cull
	550 and up	
Stags	All weights	Ungraded
Boars	All weight divisions	Ungraded
Pigs	(See page 397.)	

U. S. No. 1. Slaughter barrows and gilts in this grade have an inter-mediate degree of finish. Hogs of the minimum finish for U. S. No. 1 are moderately wide over the top, and width of body over the top appears nearly equal to that at the underline. The back, from side to side, is moder-ately full and thick and usually appears well-rounded and blends smoothly into the sides. Width through the hams is usually nearly equal to width through the shoulders. The sides are moderately long, slightly thick, and usually smooth; the flanks are slightly thick and full. Depth at the rear flank may be slightly less than depth at the fore flank. Hams tend to be moderately thick and full with a slightly thick covering of fat. Jowls are moderately full and thick but are usually trim. Barrows and gilts in this grade produce U. S. No. 1 carcasses. Barrows and gilts with apparent degree of finish typical of the fatter one half of the U. S. No. 1 grade but with the evidences of meatiness, firmness of fleshing, and distribution of finish more nearly typical of the U. S. No. 2 grade shall be graded U. S. No. 2.

U. S. No. 2. Slaughter barrows and gilts in this grade have a moderately high degree of finish. Hogs of the minimum finish for U. S. No. 2 are wide over the top, and width of body appears slightly greater over the top than at the underline. The back, from side to side, is full and thick and often appears slightly flat with a noticeable break into the sides. Width may be slightly greater through the shoulders than through the hams. The sides

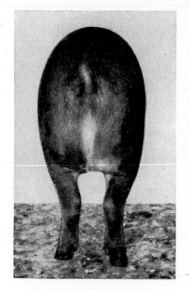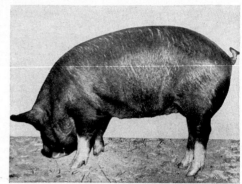

U.S. NO. 1

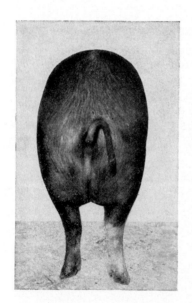

U.S. NO. 2

Fig. 147. U.S. Grades for slaughter barrows and gilts. The cull grade is not shown. There are similar grades for slaughter sows. (U.S.D.A., Agricultural Marketing Service, Livestock Division.)

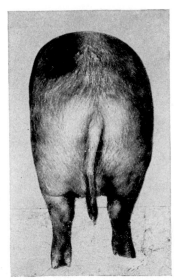

U.S. NO. 3

MEDIUM

are slightly short, moderately thick, and smooth; the flanks are moderately thick and full. Depth at the rear flank is nearly equal to depth at the fore flank. Hams tend to be thick and full with a moderately thick covering of fat, especially over the lower part. Jowls are usually full and thick, and the neck appears rather short. Barrows and gilts in this grade produce U. S. No. 2 carcasses. Barrows and gilts with apparent degree of finish typical of the fatter one half of the U. S. No. 2 grade but with the evidences of meatiness, firmness of fleshing, and distribution of finish more nearly typical of the U. S. No. 3 grade shall be graded U. S. No. 3. Those with apparent degree of finish typical of the thinner one half of the U. S. No. 2 grade but with the evidences of meatiness, firmness of fleshing, and distribution of

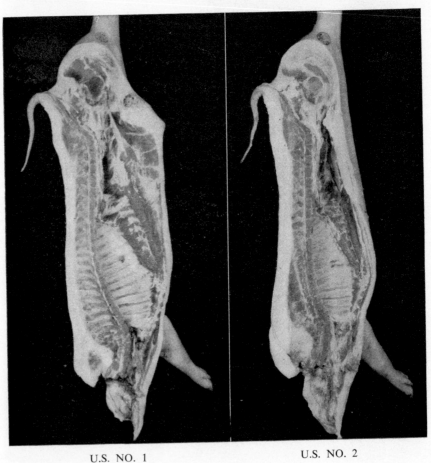

U.S. NO. 1   U.S. NO. 2

Fig. 148. Grades of hog carcasses, U.S. No. 1 and 2. Hog carcasses are not graded by government inspectors, for pork is sold as cuts, not by the carcass. (U.S. D.A., Agricultural Marketing Service.)

finish more nearly typical of the U. S. No. 1 grade shall be graded as U. S. No. 1.

U. S. No. 3.   Slaughter barrows and gilts in this grade have a high degree of finish. Hogs possessing the minimum finish for U. S. No. 3 are very wide over the top, and width of body appears somewhat greater over the top than at the underline. The back, from side to side, is very full and thick and often appears nearly flat with a pronounced break into the sides. Width may be greater through the shoulders than through the hams. The sides are short, thick, and smooth; the flanks are thick and full. Depth at the rear flank is equal to depth at the fore flank. Hams tend to be very thick and full with a thick covering of fat, especially over the lower part. Jowls are very

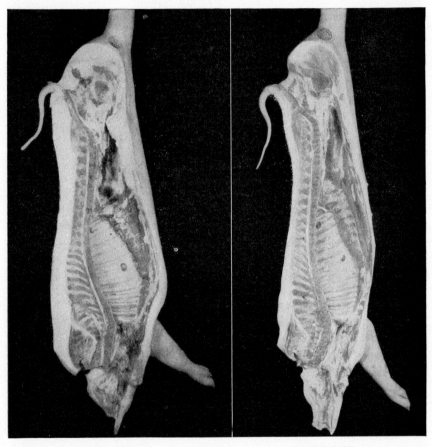

U.S. NO. 3   MEDIUM

Fig. 149.   Grades of hog carcasses; U.S. No. 3 and Medium. Note the difference in the depth of the fat back. The No. 3 is decidedly over-finished or too fat and the Medium is under-finished. (U.S.D.A., Agricultural Marketing Service.)

thick and full, and the neck appears short. Barrows and gilts in this grade produce U. S. No. 3 carcasses. Barrows and gilts with apparent degree of finish near the minimum for U. S. No. 3 grade but with evidences of meatiness, firmness of fleshing, and distribution of finish more nearly typical of the U. S. No. 2 grade shall be graded U. S. No. 2.

Medium. Slaughter barrows and gilts in this grade have a low degree of finish. Hogs of the minimum finish for the grade are moderately narrow over the top, and width over the top appears less than at the underline. The back, from side to side, is slightly thin and appears rather peaked at the center, especially at and immediately behind the shoulders, with a distinct slope toward the sides. Hips may appear slightly prominent. Width may be slightly less through the shoulders than through the hams. The sides are long, moderately thin, and wrinkled; the flanks are thin. Depth at the rear flank is less than depth at the fore flank. Hams tend to be thin and flat with a slight taper toward the shanks. Jowls are usually slightly thin and flat, and the neck appears rather long. Barrows and gilts in this grade produce Medium grade carcasses.

Cull. Slaughter barrows and gilts in this grade have a very low degree of finish. Hogs with the fleshing typical of the grade are narrow over the top, and width of body appears somewhat less over the top than at the underline. The back, from side to side, is thin, lacks fullness, and appears peaked at the center with a decided slope toward the sides. The hips are prominent. Width may be somewhat less through the shoulders than through the hams. The sides are very long, thin, and wrinkled; the flanks are very thin. Depth at the rear flank is considerably less than depth at the fore flank. Hams are very thin and flat with a decided taper toward the shanks. Jowls are usually thin and flat, and the neck appears long. Barrows and gilts in this grade produce Cull grade carcasses.

Slaughter sows

Grades of slaughter sows are also based upon the ratio of lean to fat and quality of the cuts. Specifications which include the per cent carcass yield of lean cuts and measures for back fat thickness are available.

In normal years, sows other than gilts constitute about 12 per cent of the total receipts. More than 30 per cent of the packer and shipper purchases in August are packing sows; in the first four months of the year the percentage is usually under 4 per cent.

Slaughter pigs

Swine under 120 pounds are classed on the market as pigs. Since their weights would permit their sale as feeder and stocker pigs, they are slaughtered only when the slaughter demand exceeds the demand for feeders. There are two market classes of slaughter pigs: (1) boars, (2) barrows and gilts. Very few boars are marketed as pigs, and when they are sold weighing over 60 pounds, they are discriminated against sharply. The slaughtering pig schedule follows.

SLAUGHTER PIG SCHEDULE

CLASS	WEIGHT GROUPS, POUNDS	GRADE
All classes	Under 30 30–60	Ungraded
Barrows and gilts	60–80 80–100	Good Medium Cull
	100–120	Choice Good Medium Cull

Feeder and stocker swine

This group is relatively small, as previously indicated. Feeder and stocker swine at the public stockyards are subject to federal inspection by employees of the U.S. Department of Agriculture. Those diseased and rejected as feeders and stockers are sold for immediate slaughter. Feeder and stocker swine are vaccinated against hog cholera, and then dipped as a precautionary measure to prevent the carrying of disease germs or parasites that may have come in contact with the hair or feet of the animals in the yard.

The trade in these pigs and hogs is heavy when the feeding ratio is favorable. This group includes hogs and pigs that show ability to take on, economically, additional weight and finish. They lack sufficient thickness and firmness of finish or fat to qualify for the better grades of slaughter hogs.

Following is the schedule for hogs and pigs sold as feeder pigs.

FEEDER AND STOCKER SWINE SCHEDULE

CLASS	WEIGHT GROUPS, POUNDS		GRADE
Barrows and gilts	Hogs	120–140 140–160 160–180	Choice Good Medium Common
	Pigs	80 down 80–100 100–120	

Choice-grade feeder and stocker barrows and gilts have excellent conformation and quality. Choice feeder pigs comply with the previously given specifications for top hogs, but lack size and finish.

Many feeder pigs go directly from the producer to the final feeder and do not pass through the central market. There is no uniform system for classifying or grading such pigs. They may be handled by a feeder pig dealer or organization. They may go through auction sales. Often the sale is made direct from the producer to the feeder.

Hog raisers who, because of various difficulties, cannot produce pigs economically find it cheaper to buy from the producer. Throughout the year producers sell weaning pigs to farmers, who feed them from the time they are purchased until they are ready for market. An establishment at which pigs are produced is sometimes called a "pig hatchery." It is a common practice for specialized pig raisers to sell pigs at about eight weeks of age when they weigh 30 to 35 pounds. The pigs are usually castrated and vaccinated, and treated for external and internal parasites.

There are also specialized areas in the country from which farm-raised pigs are sold at light weights; these commonly go to the areas where there is a liberal supply of feed.

Miscellaneous hogs

On the hog market there are some special groups not included in the regular classification. These are of very small numbers, and the usual market quotation does not include the miscellaneous group. Following are listed some that are included in the miscellaneous class.

Roasting pigs. Such pigs weigh from 15 to 50 pounds and are dressed shipper style, that is, with the head on. They are sold as whole carcasses. A thick, short, blocky pig that is well proportioned is required to qualify as a roasting pig. They are in demand during the holiday season, and they go chiefly to hotels, clubs, restaurants, and steamships, and frequently through meat dealers to consumers.

Governments. Pigs and hogs which fail to pass the regular ante-mortem inspection are retained, tagged, and killed under special government supervision. This includes swine that are crippled, are badly bruised, or show abscesses, and sows very heavy with pig.

Dead hogs. Hogs arriving dead at the market are disposed of by the tanking process, in which they are converted to grease and feeding or fertilizer tankage or meat scraps.

Roughs. Included in this group are the "throw outs" or hogs sorted out of other loads. These are coarse, rough hogs of all weights which are very inferior.

Soft or oily hogs. Carcasses that are soft or oily, either because of softening feeds or immaturity, are less desirable than firm carcasses. It is impossible to determine the softness or hardness on foot. Where soft hogs are numerous, packers buy hogs subject to meeting hardness requirements and settlement is based on the hardness of the carcass. Hogs yielding soft pork are docked 2 cents or more per pound. Market quotations except soft or oily hogs from the general price range for a given weight and grade.

HOG PRICES

Prices of hogs show much variation by days, months, and years. The wide range of variation is illustrated by the yearly average price at Chicago. Since 1880 the high year was 1947, when the average price per 100 pounds at Chicago for all weights was $24.65. The low was reached in 1932 with a $3.85 average.

The by-products from hog slaughter are worth very little as compared with the carcass. Of the slaughter animals, hogs have the lowest by-product value and the highest carcass yield. Since production in swine is so changeable, there are wide movements in prices.

The chief factors causing hog prices to change in this country, according to U.S. Department of Agriculture [5] findings, are:

1. Changes in the buying power of domestic consumers
2. Variations in hog production
3. Changes in the charges for processing and distributing
4. Changes in the foreign demand for American hog products

This investigation also indicated that changes in hog prices were due to causes other than changes in marketing methods.

The buying power of domestic consumers is a dominant factor in meat prices. This is apparent in Figure 150 which shows that the retail value of meat consumed tends to move with the disposable income.

KINDS OF PRICE CHANGES

In behavior, hog prices tend to change with some regularity, depending upon the various factors that affect the prices. Price changes may be classified into the following kinds:

1. Long-time trend
2. Cyclical changes
3. Seasonal changes
4. Irregular fluctuations

The long-time trend or secular movement has, in general, been the same for all kinds of slaughter animals. The prices tended downward from the

[5] *Misc. Pub. 222,* U.S.D.A., 1935.

close of the Civil War until about 1896, and then the tendency was upward until shortly after World War I. Since that time there has been a drop in prices, followed by an irregular trend.

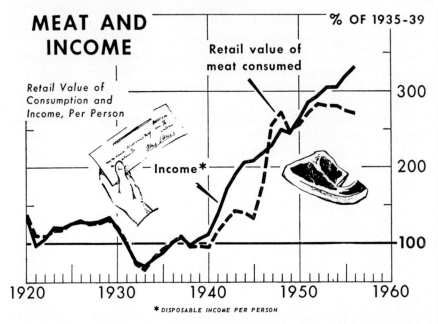

Fig. 150. Retail value of meat consumed and disposable income per person. These tend to move together. (U.S.D.A., Agricultural Marketing Service.)

Cyclical movements in prices are largely the result of the variations in hog production. Prices are high when numbers are low, and low when numbers are high. These cycles are the result of over-expansion by producers when the relation of hog prices to feed prices is favorable. Likewise, there is a tendency to curb hog production too much when the price ratio is unfavorable. Returns to producers of hogs are largely dependent upon the balance between volume of production and the demand for pork and lard.

Seasonal variations are also due to numbers on the market. When the volume of receipts is low, higher prices prevail; for there is an inverse relation between marketing and prices. As farrowings are quite seasonal, there is a marked seasonal variation in prices.

Short-time fluctuation in prices is also marked. The market price for hogs changes rapidly from day to day and even during a marketing day. The price paid at any given time is about that which will move the available supply, and it will be at or above what the lowest seller will take.

The hog price cycle

The more or less regular cycles in hog prices are shown in Figure 151. In that figure heavy hog prices at Chicago are adjusted to the 1910–1914 price level. Monthly prices are charted, as is also the price trend, which is

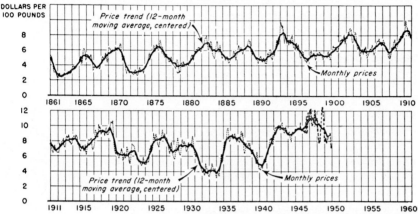

Fig. 151. Prices of heavy hogs at Chicago. There are regular cycles in prices which coincide with production cycles. When hogs are numerous prices are low, and when hogs are scarce prices are high. (U.S.D.A., Bur. of Agri. Economics.)

a 12-month moving average. The regularity in the swings of hog prices since 1860 is quite startling. The prices move in one direction for about 2 years and then in the other direction for an equal length of time. The cycle may take 5 years or as little as 3 years. We may also recognize alternate major and minor cycles. The major cycles with greater swings are 4 to 6 years long; the minor cycles are 3 to 4 years long.

These cycles of prices are due to corresponding swings in production.

Hog prices by classes

There is little spread in the market for hogs, as compared to the other kinds of slaughter animals. The two large classes, barrows and gilts, and packing sows, sell remarkably close together. In fact, at times (rarely) the latter group has outsold the former. On the eight markets [6] for the 1951–55 period,[7] combined barrow and gilts averaged $21.62 in cost per

[6] Chicago, Indianapolis, Kansas City, Omaha, St. Louis National Stockyards, Sioux City, South St. Joseph, and South St. Paul.
[7] *Livestock Market News Statistics, 1955*, U.S.D.A., 1956.

100 pounds and weighed an average of 228 pounds. Sows on the same markets for the same period cost an average of $15.55 per 100 pounds and weighed 386 pounds. The packing sows made up 12.0 per cent of the receipts for the 5 years.

For the year 1955 [8] the average price for all grades of hogs and pigs on the Chicago market was $14.95; hogs classified as heavy had an average price of $15.15, light hogs $16.10, packing sows $13.65, and pigs $11.00. Although this is but 1 year's average, it is fairly representative in that pigs were lower in price than hogs, and the light hogs outsold the heavier ones.

Prices of swine by months

The extent of the seasonal swing in hog prices is illustrated by the tabulation of the average price by months on the eight markets. In comparing prices with receipts by months, see page 377 and the table below. It will be noted that months of heavy receipts are months of low prices.

The average prices of hogs on the eight markets for a recent 10-year period follow. Also given is the seasonal variation in prices of hogs, expressed as a per cent of the average.

MONTHLY AVERAGE HOG PRICES, BARROWS AND GILTS AT EIGHT MARKETS,[9] FOR 10 YEARS (1946–1955) AND PER CENT VARIATION FROM THE 10-YEAR AVERAGE [10]

	AVERAGE COST PER 100 POUNDS	PER CENT OF AVERAGE
January	$19.82	95.9
February	$20.07	97.1
March	$20.15	97.5
April	$19.77	95.6
May	$20.46	99.0
June	$21.27	102.9
July	$22.57	109.2
August	$22.98	111.0
September	$21.72	105.0
October	$20.84	100.8
November	$19.29	93.3
December	$19.17	92.7
Average	$20.68	100.0

There are two peaks in hog prices. The spring rise in March occurs when most of the spring pigs have been marketed and fall pigs are not

[8] "Yearbook of Figures," *Chicago Daily Drover Journal,* 1956.

[9] Eight markets include Chicago, Indianapolis, Kansas City, Omaha, St. Louis National Stockyards, Sioux City, South St. Joseph, and South St. Paul.

[10] "Livestock Market News Statistics—1955," *Stat. Bull. 178,* Agricultural Marketing Service, U.S.D.A., 1956.

being marketed in volume. A summer peak occurs in July, August or September before most of the spring pigs have been marketed. With light hogs the summer peak is the highest; with heavy hogs the peak in the spring may be about the same as that of the previous fall. With expanding production, the summer peak is lower than the spring peak of that year, but when hog numbers are decreasing, the reverse is usually true. It will be noted that the months of heaviest receipts, November, December, and January, are the months of the lowest prices.

MARKETING MARGINS

Hog prices and pork prices do not maintain a fixed relationship to each other. The difference between the two is due to the cost of marketing services and the profits to the agencies providing the services. Marketing margins have been going upward as the cost factors in marketing service, such as labor, supplies, equipment, transportation, rent, and depreciation, have become more costly.

The farmer receives for 1.82 pound of live hog the same price that the consumer pays for 1 pound of pork. This difference or margin includes all the costs and profits from the feed lot to the final consumer. It therefore includes the charges for marketing, slaughtering, processing, wholesaling and retailing.

It has been found in a study of prices and margins during a 7-year period that there is seasonal tendency for margins to narrow in the first half of the year and widen in the latter half.[11] Also, there is a tendency for changes in retail prices to lag behind changes in farm prices.

As hog supplies vary seasonally, it is expected that the hog price would vary. It appears that hog prices are more sensitive to supplies than they once were. Marketing margins widen with increases in hog slaughter and the farm prices of hogs fall more rapidly than retail pork prices.

Hog-corn price ratio

The number of bushels of corn equal in price to 100 pounds of live hog is termed the hog-corn price ratio. This is not the corn required to produce a hog or 100 pounds gain on a live hog. It is merely a ratio that is helpful in determining the profitableness of marketing corn direct as compared to feeding it to hogs. As the ratio narrows, farmers sell the corn and their hogs. With a wide ratio, hogs are fed to heavier weights, and hog production is expanded.

The price of corn and hogs at Chicago is shown in Figure 152 as well

[11] "Pork Marketing Margins and Costs," *Misc. Pub. 711,* Agricultural Marketing Service, U.S.D.A., April, 1956.

as the hog-corn price ratio. The average hog-corn ratio is about 12. In other words 100 pounds of live hogs will sell for about the same amount of money as 12 bushels of No. 3 yellow corn at Chicago.

HOG-CORN PRICE RATIO AND HOG SLAUGHTER

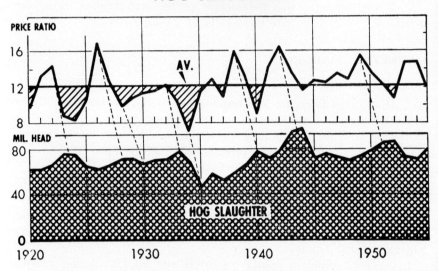

Hog-corn price ratio: Bushels of corn equal in value to 100 pounds of live hog.

Fig. 152. Hog-corn price ratio and hog marketings. When the hog-corn price ratio is favorable, there is expansion of hog production, which is followed by an increase in hog marketings. When the price ratio is unfavorable, there is reduction in hog numbers. (U.S.D.A.)

Chapter 25

HOG SLAUGHTER—PORK
AND LARD BY-PRODUCTS

HOG SLAUGHTER

As the interior packers have expanded, there has been a major shift in the location of hog slaughter. The amount of hog slaughter in the northwestern corn-belt states (Minnesota, Iowa, North Dakota, South Dakota, and Nebraska) has changed more than in other areas. In 1920 about 22 per cent of the slaughter was in those states, and by 1930 it was up to 30 per cent. Expansion in the northwest corn belt was accompanied by retraction elsewhere, especially in the southern corn belt.

With the westward shift in swine production there has been a marked tendency to decentralize pork packing. A few new plants have been built in the northwestern corn belt, but in the main the change has been merely a shift in the volume of slaughter at existing plants. Slaughter at points other than the principal markets is heaviest in the northwestern corn belt. More plants in that area and also more farms are slaughtering hogs than other livestock.

A classification of total hog slaughter for 10 years showed that 68 per cent of the hog slaughter was federally inspected and done in establishments conducting a wholesale business. Other wholesale and retail establishments or retail dealers accounted for 18 per cent of the total slaughter, and slaughter on farms for the remaining 14 per cent. Since 1900 there seems to have been no great change in hog slaughter by types. There was a slight increase in farm slaughter during the depression years, and more recently there has been a slight decrease in farm slaughter. The four large national packers handle a smaller proportion of hogs than other kinds of livestock. In 1954 there were 262 establishments operating under federal inspection which slaughtered hogs and had an output of more than 300,000 pounds of live weight per year.

Hog slaughter is unique in that the carcasses are seldom sold as such, as are carcasses of beef, veal, mutton, and lamb. Most hog carcasses are reduced to wholesale cuts at the place of slaughter. Of these cuts, roughly 15 to 20 per cent of the carcasses are sold to consumers as fresh pork, and the remainder are cured, rendered into lard, or made into meat products before being retailed.

Centers of hog slaughter

There are several large centers of hog slaughter. The slaughter by stations merely gives the number slaughtered at those points and in the immediate area; in some cases it is exceeded by the slaughter at some of the interior points. Some of the interior packers slaughter over a million hogs in a year. The slaughter under federal inspection by stations is given on page 407.

This table gives the number of head slaughtered at a station, which in some cases includes more than those at the stockyards market in that area. For example, the number slaughtered at Kansas City is more than the receipts at the Kansas City public stockyards market. The list on page 376 includes a selected group of slaughter points based upon all kinds of livestock; several large hog slaughter centers are not included. For example, nearly a million hogs are slaughtered annually at St. Joseph, Indianapolis, and Cincinnati. The eight slaughter centers listed on page 407 account for a little over one half of the slaughter under federal inspection. As mentioned previously, interior packers slaughter large numbers of hogs. The hog kill in Iowa and southern Minnesota has

Fig. 153. Slaughtered hogs on the overhead carrier. As the hogs move along the rail at 20 feet a minute, the steps in dressing take place. (The Rath Packing Co.)

been 15 million head in one year. Hog slaughter has moved toward the hog producing areas.

HOGS—ANNUAL SLAUGHTER UNDER FEDERAL INSPECTION, BY STATIONS

1945–1954 Average [1]

STATION	THOUSANDS
Chicago, Ill.	3,866
St. Louis, Mo.	3,434
Omaha, Neb.	2,577
South St. Paul, Minn.	2,467
New York, N. Y.	2,053
Kansas City, Mo.	1,746
Sioux City, Iowa	1,432
Denver, Colo.	521
All other stations	34,433
Total	52,829

Hog slaughter by months

Of all the kinds of livestock, the slaughter of hogs is the most seasonal. Slaughter parallels receipts by months, as previously given, for nearly all hogs marketed are slaughtered and there is but little trade in feeder pigs.

December and January are the months of heaviest federally inspected slaughter; these months each have 10 to 12 per cent of the yearly slaughter.

The lowest prices occur with the heavy receipts in December and January, but this is offset in part by the demand for storage. Heavy storage, on the other hand, tends to have a depressing effect upon hog prices the following summer.

Hog slaughter, proportion by classes

Sows, including gilts, usually predominate slightly in the hog slaughter under federal inspection, although in some years barrows outnumber the sows and gilts in the kill. In years of expanding hog numbers more sows are retained on the farm, and the proportion slaughtered is lowered. When liquidation is taking place, sows predominate, but the percentage in the slaughter is seldom over 52 per cent. Considering sows, those that have farrowed and raised pigs, and excluding gilts, only 12 to 13 per cent of the total slaughter are of this class. Less than 1 per cent of the slaughter is made up of stags and boars. Barrows and gilts make up over 87 per cent of the total slaughter.

[1] *Agricultural Statistics*, U.S.D.A., 1955.

Fig. 154. Government inspectors at work. Each carcass is carefully examined for signs of disease. Those unfit for food are rejected. (The Rath Packing Co.)

SLAUGHTERING HOGS

In the driving of hogs or pigs, care should be taken to see that they are not unduly rushed. Sticks or clubs are to be used with caution as they make bruises which affect the value of the carcass. Flat canvas straps are effective and harmless. Pigs are driven to the packing plant and are held in a small pen for shackling.

The hogs are shackled just above the hoof on the hind leg and then hoisted to an overhead rail. They pass along suspended from the rail to the "sticker" who sticks the pig with a knife in the center of the neck just ahead of the sternum. At some plants the pigs are immobilized by exposure to carbon dioxide and are stuck while anesthetized. This is referred to as "prone sticking," and in one plant it is combined with the immobilizer practice. After bleeding for about 10 minutes the hogs are dropped into the scalding vat in which the water temperature is about 140°F. Next is the dehairing process in which the hog is passed by chain through a dehairing machine. In some plants a process for removing hair, stubble, and roots is in use. After dehairing, the carcass is dipped into a hot solution of rosin and cottonseed oil. That which adheres to the carcass is permitted to harden; then it is stripped or peeled off, leaving a clean, white carcass. Following this, the gamb cords of the hind legs are exposed, hooks or a gambrel are placed in the cords, and the hog is again hung from the rail. Further cleaning and scraping by hand and washing are essential, and finally they are subjected to singeing by means of gas torches playing on all parts of the body. The animal must be absolutely and completely dehaired before it can be opened except for sticking and baring the gamb cords.

As the hog is moved along, suspended on a trolley which moves on an overhead track, the various steps in dressing take place and, finally, the cleaned dressed carcass is moved into the cooler. The various steps in dressing are:

1. Heading, or removing the head
2. Opening the carcass
3. Cutting free the bung, which is then tied and dropped down
4. Removing the viscera, which include the liver, heart, lungs, large and small intestines, pancreas, spleen, stomach, bladder, and their fat coverings
5. Splitting down the center of the backbone
6. Removing the leaf fat
7. Facing or trimming the inside of the hams
8. Washing the carcass and sending it to the coolers

During the dressing process inspections are made of the head, viscera, and carcass by inspectors from the U.S. Department of Agriculture Bureau of Animal Industry.

Two styles of dressing are common. The two methods are described below.[2]

1. The packer style is the one most generally used. The carcasses of all classes of slaughter hogs that are to be converted into primal cuts of pork are usually dressed in this manner. The carcasses are opened from crotch to neck and the backbone is split full length through the center. The ham facings, leaf fat, and kidneys, as well as the head, without the jowls, are removed.

[2] Don J. Slater, "Market Classes and Grades of Swine," *Circ. 569*, U.S.D.A., September, 1940.

2. The shipper style is the one usually used for slaughter pigs, which are most often sold as whole carcasses in the wholesale trade. The carcass is opened from the crotch to the tip of the breastbone, the backbone is left

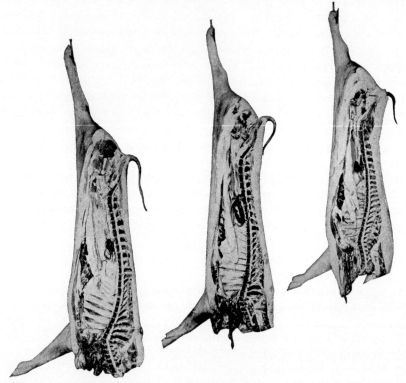

Fig. 155. Dressed carcasses of large, intermediate, and small types of hogs slaughtered at approximately 225 pounds. Note the great length of the large type on the left, as compared with small type on the right. (O. G. Hankins, Bureau of Animal Industry, U.S.D.A.)

intact, and the leaf fat is left in, as a general rule. The entire head is left attached. Those that weigh under 30 pounds are also "squatted," that is, placed on their bellies in a trough with the front legs doubled back from the knee joint and the hind legs extending straight back from the hams. They are sold for roasting whole, usually during the winter holiday season, and are generally considered a delicacy.

DRESSING PERCENTAGE

The hog is dressed with the skin and the shanks on. The barrel and chest cavity are relatively smaller than on other slaughter animals. As a consequence, hogs dress high.

Following are some typical yields and the usual range of yields for several classes of slaughter barrows and gilts dressed packers style.[3]

	DRESSING PER CENT	
BARROWS AND GILTS	*Range*	*Average*
U.S. No. 1	67–71	69
U.S. No. 2	68–72	70
U.S. No. 3	69–73	71
Medium	65–69	67
Cull	63–67	65

For an 8-year period the average dressing yield of hogs slaughtered (shipper style) in the United States was 76.1 per cent, based on a monthly survey of wholesale slaughterers by the U.S. Department of Agriculture. The average live weight for the same period is given as 244.6 pounds.[4]

Packer-style dressed carcasses yield about 7 per cent less than shipper-style dressed carcasses, because of the removal of head, leaf fat, kidneys, and ham facings.

Yields are usually calculated on the dressed weight of the carcass when chilled. The warm dressed weight is higher than the chilled dressed weight, for there is a "cooler shrinkage" which amounts to about 2.5 per cent.

Fig. 156. A champion Spotted Poland China barrow at the International Livestock Exposition. Shown by Byron Meach, Beloit, Wis.

[3] Information from C. L. Strong, Agricultural Marketing Service, U.S.D.A., January, 1957.
[4] *Livestock Market News Statistics,* Agricultural Marketing Service, U.S.D.A., 1956.

FEDERAL MEAT INSPECTION OF SWINE

The number of hogs and pigs condemned in the ante-mortem inspection is relatively small. In fact, 99.75 per cent of the hogs pass the on-foot inspection. Of those passed on foot, carcass condemnations are also low, for 99.78 per cent pass the inspection. In the classification of causes of condemnation, arthritis, pneumonia, or pleurisy, and abscess or pyemia are credited with the greatest number, followed by septicemia, icterus, tuberculosis, enteritis, and hog cholera. Sexual odor is also a condemnation cause; this is not common in other slaughter animals. In the inspection of swine carcasses there is a sizable condemning of carcass parts because of tumors and abscesses, tuberculosis, and injuries that show up in the meat.

PORK AND LARD

MEAT FROM SWINE

Pork is the meat derived from swine; it is sold as "fresh meat," which has undergone no substantial change in character since the time of slaughter, and "cured meat." The latter is the clean, sound product obtained by subjecting meat to a process of salting, by the employment of dry common salt or of brine, with or without the use of one or more of the following: sodium nitrite, sodium nitrate, potassium nitrate, sugar, sirup, honey, or spice.

DISPOSITION OF THE SWINE CARCASS

Almost all hog carcasses are cut up at the slaughtering plant and sold in the form of wholesale cuts. There is a small trade in roasting pigs and slaughter pigs, sold in carcass form. Not more than from 1 to 2 per cent of the hog carcasses from a large packing plant are sold whole. A large part of the carcass is cured as ham, bacon, or salt pork, or rendered for lard.

MARKET CLASSES AND GRADES OF PORK

Since the hog carcass is not sold fresh to the extent that lamb and beef carcasses are, the classification is somewhat different. There is not the same general use of standards for hog carcasses and pork cuts that there is for beef, veal, and lamb. Grading is not extended to the retail cuts as it is for beef, veal, and lamb. One carcass may excel for fresh pork, another for smoked meats, and still another for dry salt curing. Pork carcasses and cuts are graded on the three fundamental characteristics applicable to all kinds of meat cuts: conformation, finish, and quality. Weight is not a grade factor, but it is important in market value, since it is related to size of the pork cuts and to ratio of lean to fat.

Fig. 157. Large and small types of pig. Pigs between these two in length produce carcasses of greatest acceptability to the consumer.

A description of the terms "conformation," "finish," and "quality" follows: [5]

Conformation

The term "conformation" refers to the general build, form, shape, and contour or outline of the carcass, side, or cut. Conformation is determined by the skeleton, the depth or thickness of lean meat, and the thickness and distribution of external fat. It involves plumpness and blockiness or stockiness on the one hand and ranginess, lankiness, and angularity on the other. These terms refer to the extreme limitations of conformation, between which are placed all the modifications and degrees that apply to the various grades.

Because of economic conditions in the pork industry, resulting largely from a pronounced trend of consumer demand toward leaner pork cuts, together with the development of competition between lard and vegetable-oil products, new standards for grades of slaughter barrows and gilts and pork carcasses have been developed. The most desirable conformation in pork carcasses is represented by finished meat-type carcasses which involve smoothness, moderate fullness, thickness or meatiness, and adequate, uniform fat distribution, thickness of back fat averaging about 1½ inches

[5] From *Circ. 288,* U.S.D.A., Oct., 1933, "Market Classes and Grades of Pork carcasses of greatest acceptability to the consumer.

with variations above and below, depending upon the size and weight of the carcass.

Finish

Finish in pork refers to the thickness, color, character, and distribution of fat. The internal indications of finish are generous quantities of firm white fat in the crotch, around the kidneys, over the ribs, and along the breastbone. A moderate degree of finish may add to the attractiveness of the carcass or cut, but its chief significance lies in the fact that there is evidence that up to a certain point intermuscular and intercellular fat is associated with palatability. Furthermore, finish without waste serves as an excellent index of the degree of quality in the meat. Thick or wrinkled skin, lack of fat in the crotch, poorly covered kidneys and ribs, and general scarcity of fat along the breastbone are indications of poor finish.

Quality

Quality is a characteristic of the lean flesh and of the fat included therein. It pertains primarily to the thickness, firmness, and strength of both the muscle fiber and the connective tissue. It also involves the quantity, consistency, and character of juices or extractives that surround and permeate the muscle fiber and connective tissue. Color is not actually a factor in quality, but it is an excellent indication of the quality of a given piece of meat. Color in meat is of special commercial importance and influences market value.

Best quality in pork implies full, well-developed, firm, muscular tissue, with a minimum of strength in fiber and connective tissue. The best carcasses or cuts usually have a thin, smooth skin and are free from wrinkles. The most desirable color in fresh pork is grayish pink. The flesh is relatively firm and fine grained and is free from excessive moisture. The cuts, when chilled, hold their natural shape. The difference in color among pork carcasses and cuts of different grades, although considerable, is not so great as, for instance, in beef, veal, and lamb of different grades.

DRESSED PORK CARCASS CLASSES AND GRADES

Because of marked uniformity in the age at which most hogs are slaughtered, there are ordinarily only moderate differences in color of flesh, except in carcasses of old sows, boars, and stags. Firmness of flesh is always an indication of quality. High quality in pork carcasses is also indicated by firm, thin, smooth skin, free from wrinkles; low quality is indicated by harsh, rough, coarse, and wrinkled skin.

Most pork produced in the United States is more uniform in quality

than any other class of meat; therefore there is need for fewer grades. Instead of being divided into six or seven grades like beef, lamb, and mutton, pork carcasses are divided into not more than four grades, which are
sufficient for all commercial purposes. In fact, three grades cover all major
pork cuts except a small percentage of regular hams and bellies from cull-
grade carcasses, which, although possessing unusually low quality characteristics, have been found satisfactory for certain classes of trade. A fourth
grade, referred to as "cull," is provided for these hams and bellies. The
terms used to designate most of the grades of pork carcasses are No. 1, No.
2, No. 3, and cull. Barrows and gilt carcasses have a prefix of U.S. for the
first three grades, the fourth grade is medium, and the bottom grade is cull.
Carcasses soft or oily because of feed are specially identified as soft or oily,
as well as graded.

The dressed pork carcass schedule is as follows.

DRESSED PORK CARCASS SCHEDULE

CLASS	USE SELECTION OF CARCASSES	WEIGHT RANGE, POUNDS	GRADE
	Roasting pork	10–30	No. 1 No. 2 No. 3 Cull
Barrows and gilts	Meat- and fat-type pork	80–240	U.S. No. 1 U.S. No. 2 U.S. No. 3 Medium Cull
Sows	Sow (packing) pork	200–320	No. 1 No. 2 No. 3 Cull
Stags	Processing or manufacture	200–400	No. 1 No. 2 No. 3
Boars	Manufacture (inedible)	All weights	Ungraded

Official specifications for grades

Following are the official Agriculture Department descriptive specifications and carcass measurements of various weights and grades of barrow
and gilt carcasses.[6]

The standards for grades of barrow and gilt carcasses include carcass

---

[6] "Official United States Standards for Grades of Pork Carcasses (Barrow and
Gilt)," *Service and Regulatory Announcement No. 171,* U.S.D.A., July, 1955.

measurements and descriptions of carcass characteristics which indicate the lean and fat yields and imply the quality of meat typical of the minimum degree of finish of each grade. Visual estimates of fat thickness normally alleviate the necessity for measuring carcasses in the grading operation. In addition to the measurement guides to grade differences, the standards also provide the basis for consideration of other characteristics. While carcass measurements furnish a reliable general guide to grade, the final grade of borderline carcasses may vary from that indicated by measurements due to consideration of other characteristics such as visual evidences of quality; meatiness; conformation of hams, loins, bellies, and shoulders; and fat distribution. However, application of these additional factors is limited to borderline carcasses, and in no case may the final grade be more than one half of the width of a grade different than that indicated by carcass measurements. The standards describe carcasses typical of each grade and no attempt is made to describe the nearly limitless number of combinations of characteristics that may qualify a carcass for a particular grade.

U.S. No. 1

A description of the top grade for barrows and gilts follows.

Carcasses in this grade have near the minimum degree of finish required for the production of acceptable quality cuts. Meatiness based on yield of lean cuts in relation to carcass weight is slightly high; yield of fat cuts is slightly low. The ratio of total lean and fat to bone is slightly high. Carcasses possessing the minimum finish for U.S. No. 1 grade are slightly wide and moderately long in relation to weight. The back and loins are moderately full and thick with a well-rounded appearance. Hams are usually moderately thick, plump, and smooth and are slightly full in the lower part toward the hocks. Bellies are moderately long and smooth, slightly thick, and moderately uniform in thickness; the belly pocket is slightly thick. Shoulders are slightly thick and full but usually blend smoothly into the sides. The carcass is moderately well-balanced and smooth with moderately uniform development of the various parts. There are moderate quantities of interior fat in the region of the pelvis, a slightly thin but fairly extensive layer of fat lining the inside surface of the ribs, and a slightly small quantity of feathering. The flesh is firm. Both exterior and interior fats are firm, white, and of excellent quality. Carcasses with fat thickness typical of the thinner one-half of the U.S. No. 1 grade but with the firmness, quantity and distribution of interior fats, and belly thickness typical of the Medium grade shall be graded Medium. Carcasses with fat thickness typical of the fatter one-half of the U.S. No. 1 grade but with the fat distribution, meatiness, and thickness and fullness of hams, loins, shoulders, and bellies typical of the U.S. No. 2 grade shall be graded U.S. No. 2.

Grades and measurements

Measurements of average back fat thickness in relation to carcass weight or length are closely related to yields of cuts and the quality of the cuts. The following table of measurements provides an objective guide in determining the barrow and gilt carcass grades.

WEIGHT AND MEASUREMENT GUIDES TO GRADES FOR BARROW AND GILT CARCASSES

CARCASS WEIGHT OR CARCASS LENGTH *	AVERAGE BACK FAT THICKNESS (INCHES) † BY GRADE				
	U.S. No. 1	U.S. No. 2	U.S. No. 3	Medium	Cull
Under 120 pounds or under 27 inches.	1.2 to 1.5	1.5 to 1.8	1.8 or more	0.9 to 1.2	Less than 0.9
120 to 164 pounds or 27 to 29.9 inches.	1.3 to 1.6	1.6 to 1.9	1.9 or more	1.0 to 1.3	Less than 1.0
165 to 209 pounds or 30 to 32.9 inches.	1.4 to 1.7	1.7 to 2.0	2.0 or more	1.1 to 1.4	Less than 1.1
210 or more pounds or 33 or more inches.	1.5 to 1.8	1.8 to 2.1	2.1 or more	1.2 to 1.5	Less than 1.2

* Either carcass weight or length may be used with back fat thickness as a reliable guide to grade. The table shows the normal length range for given weights. In extreme cases where the use of length with back fat thickness indicates a different grade than by using weight, final grade is determined subjectively as provided in the standards. Carcass weight is based on a chilled, packer style carcass. Carcass length is measured from the forward point of the aitch bone to the forward edge of the first rib.

† Average of measurements made opposite the first and last ribs and last lumbar vertebra.

WHOLESALE PORK CUTS

In dressing hogs the carcass is moved to the cooler very soon after dressing, and it is chilled as rapidly and thoroughly as possible. The temperature at which the cooler is kept depends upon the time used for cooling. The carcass may be chilled in 1 day, that is, 24 hours, or in 2 or 3 days. Refrigerator temperatures are generally about 34°F, but the coolers to which warm carcasses are moved are kept at 25°F or lower.

After chilling, the carcasses are brought to the cutting floor and reduced to wholesale cuts. There is much variation in cutting because of variation in demand.

The common wholesale pork cuts are shown in Figure 158.

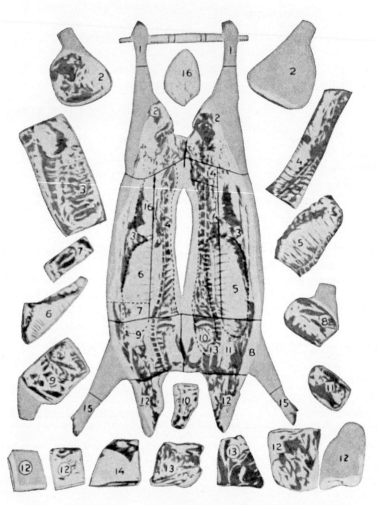

WHOLESALE CUTS—PERCENTAGE OF CARCASS

1—Hind Feet	1.00%	7—Brisket	2.25%	⑫—Jowl Butts	2.25%
2—Hams	19.00	8—Picnic	7.50	(Trimmed)	
3—Clear Bellies	16.50	9—N. Y. Style		⑬—Boneless Butt	3.05
4—Pork Loins	12.75	Shoulder	16.00	13—Boston Butt	5.20
5—Spare Ribs	2.50	10—Neck Bones	.95	14—Loin Butt	4.00
(Full Side)		11—Picnic Butt	3.02	15—Fore Feet	.92
6—Spare Ribs	1.50	12—Jowl Butts		16—Leaf Fat	3.52
(Half Side)		(Untrimmed)			

Fig. 158. The wholesale cuts of pork and their percentages of the carcass. (U.S.D.A.) *Courtesy National Livestock and Meat Board, Chicago, Ill.*

The main divisions of the carcass for domestic use are hams, shoulders, and sides. These divisions are further divided into wholesale cuts. Size of the carcasses and method of curing, as well as demand, influence the exact cutting methods. For example, hog carcasses of sufficient size have fat backs which can be cured by the dry salt method; lighter carcasses have thinner fat backs that must be rendered into lard.

The four lean primal pork cuts are the ham, shoulder, loin and Boston butt. Because of their relatively high value per pound these cuts make up about three quarters of the value of the carcass. Hogs with a weight range of 180 to 200 pounds have nearly one half of their carcass weight in these cuts. The yield of primal cuts is sometimes referred to as "cut out" value. It may increase until the hog reaches a weight of 260 pounds, and then it declines. Hogs weighing 350 to 400 pounds have only about 40 per cent of their weight in the primal cuts, and there are correspondingly higher yields of fat cuts and lard.

The average lard production for hogs slaughtered under federal inspection is about 35 pounds per hog slaughtered or about 14 pounds per 100 pounds live weight.[7]

Trimming the bacon belly

The cutting floor pork cut "rough belly" is trimmed into a bacon side suitable for the trade. After the side has been put through a roller, it is trimmed even on the edges into a square-cut belly. The side is then cut through the mammary gland; this is called the teat trim. If the mammary gland or seed shows pigmentation, a further trim or seed trim is necessary. The final bacon slab is known as the "clear belly," which is seedless and trimmed square. The pigmented seed or "seedy cut" may be black, red, or white. An investigation of the occurrence of the seedy cut at Wisconsin Agricultural Experiment Station [8] led to the following findings. The black is present in the black breeds to the extent of 50 per cent of the gilts and 9 per cent of the barrows. The black-and-white breeds have 23 per cent of black seed in the gilts and 6.5 per cent in the barrows. The common red breed had 20 per cent black seed in the gilts and none in the barrows. The barrows and gilts of white breed are free from black seed. Sows and stags of all the breeds are free from black seed. There is also a red, pink, or vascular seed which appears in immature gilts. It is related to the estrous cycle.

As bacon is a high-priced common wholesale cut, the presence of the seedy cut is of economic importance. Trimmings from bacon sides are used for lard or, if comparatively lean, in sausage.

---

[7] *Livestock Market News Statistics,* U.S.D.A., 1956.

[8] L. J. Cole, J. S. Park, and Alan Deakin, " 'Seedy Cut' as Affecting Bacon Production," *Res. Bull. 118,* Wis. Agr. Exp. Sta., September, 1933.

Fig. 159. The pork cutting room in a packing plant. In this plant 350 people take part in cutting up each hog carcass. (The Rath Packing Co.)

Wholesale prices of pork

Data are available on average prices of common wholesale pork cuts on the New York market for a period of time. These prices reveal the relative demand, for the processors price the cuts so as to move them into consumptive channels.

Cured pork products, with the exception of fat back, dry salt cured, and picnics, sell for more than the usual fresh pork cuts.

Listed on page 421 are the pork cuts for which data are available on the New York market for an 8-year period.[9]

[9] *Livestock Market News Statistics*, Agricultural Marketing Service, U.S.D.A., 1956.

Fat backs are the lowest priced of the quotable cuts. The fat back demand is mainly in the South. However, when the purchasing power of persons who commonly use fat backs is higher than usual, they switch to more desirable cuts.

PORK CUTS	AVERAGE PRICE PER HUNDRED POUNDS, NEW YORK
Backs, dry salt, 16–20 pounds average	$20.13
Spareribs, half sheets, 3 pounds down	40.76
Picnics, smoked, 4–8 pounds average	38.65
Butts, Boston style, 4–8 pounds average	41.73
Loins, 8–12 pounds average	48.45
Smoked skinned hams No. 1, 12–16 pounds average	54.92
Smoked skinned hams No. 1, 16–18 pounds average	53.52
Bacon, smoked, No. 1 dry cure, 8–10 pounds average	49.47
Lard, refined prime steam, 1-pound cartons	20.25

Fig. 160. Hams slide down stainless steel chute for sorting into weight and grade classifications. (Armour & Company.)

Ham is the highest priced wholesale cut on the basis of the quality listed, that is, No. 1 smoked and skinned, weight 12 to 16 pounds. It has replaced bacon as a high-priced cut on a wholesale basis. Deviation from this weight is accompanied by decrease in price.

Retail prices of pork

Sliced ham (center cuts) is the highest priced common pork cut on the retail market, followed by bacon and pork chops. Ham sells for more than bacon when the center cuts are sliced for the trade. Of the common retail meat cuts on which retail prices are available for a period of time in New York,[10] sliced ham is outsold by one meat cut, porterhouse steak. It is obvious from the above that the lean cuts are the higher priced.

Hog types and yield of wholesale cuts

A certain amount of fatness is essential in a hog carcass to give acceptable pork cuts. Carcasses too lean will lack thickness to the cuts such as the bacon, and the cuts will usually lack firmness and attractiveness. Fat carcasses need to be heavily trimmed and have relatively heavier fat cuts.

A comparison of the cuts from the lard or fat-type hog and the meat-type hog of comparable weight and quality illustrates the difference in yields.

It will be noted that the meat type has a lower carcass and lard yield but excels in leaner cuts. When the lean cuts are in a stronger demand than fat cuts and lard, which is usually the case, the meat type will have the higher cutout value. Tests which stop at carcass yield or dressing percentage may therefore give an incorrect idea of the meat returns from a hog.

APPROXIMATE PERCENTAGES OF CARCASS WHOLESALE CUTS
AND PRODUCTS IN 100 POUNDS OF LIVE HOG [11]

	LIVE WEIGHT RANGE, POUNDS, 180–250	
	CARCASS WEIGHT RANGE, POUNDS	
ITEM	*128–180* *Choice Lard Type*	*124–178* *Choice Meat Type*
Belly—sweet pickle	11.20	10.65
Belly—dry salt	. .	. . .
Loins	8.90	9.95
Hams	13.30	13.80
New York shoulder 1½ rib	10.75	11.25
Jowl	1.85	1.50
Spareribs	1.55	1.70
Neck bones	.85	1.00
Feet	1.85	2.00
Tail	.20	.20
Lean trimmings	2.50	3.00
Fat trimmings	7.35	6.30
Rough fat backs *	9.75	7.50
Cutting shrinkage	1.25	1.15
Total carcass †	71.30	70.00
Liver	1.40	1.40
Heart	.25	.25
Kidney	.20	.20
Head	4.60	4.65
Leaf fat	2.15	2.05
Scrap leaf fat	.15	.15

[10] Quoted in *Livestock, Meats, and Wool Market Statistics and Related Data,* U.S.D.A., August, 1949.

[11] Arthur T. Edinger, *Meat Cutting and Pricing Methods,* U.S.D.A., November, 1940.

| | LIVE WEIGHT RANGE, POUNDS, 180–250 | |
| | CARCASS WEIGHT RANGE, POUNDS | |
ITEM	128–180 *Choice Lard Type*	124–178 *Choice Meat Type*
Caul fat	.50	.55
Ham facing	.30	.35
Killing shrinkage and other products	19.15	20.40
Total live hog	100.00	100.00
Lard yield ‡	15.50	12.75

* Commercial fat backs should weigh 6 pounds or over after trimming, otherwise they are used as lard. Trimmings amount to about 2 pounds of lightweight fat backs and 3 pounds on heavier ones.

† Leaf fat, ham facings, kidney, and head removed.

‡ Lard yield: choice grade—leaf fat 94 per cent, fat backs 80 per cent, caul 65 per cent, trimmings 70 per cent, ham facing 75 per cent; good and medium grade—leaf fat 90 per cent, fat backs 75 per cent, caul 60 per cent, trimmings 65 per cent, ham facings 70 per cent.

There is also a difference in the yields of small, intermediate, and large-type hog carcasses of comparable weight and grade. As the smaller type hog is higher in finish at a given weight than the large type, it has higher yield of high-fat-yielding cuts. Given the same degree of fatness, the yields are fairly comparable.

The data tabulation on page 424 indicates the yield differences of these different types at uniform weights and uniform fatness.[12]

This study leads to the conclusion that, of the types studied, the intermediate most nearly meets current requirements. Also, this type embodies the greatest possibilities for modification.

BUYING HOGS ON CARCASS YIELDS

In many countries slaughter animals are purchased on the basis of carcass grade and weight rather than on-foot grade and weight. Nearly all of the slaughter hogs in Denmark, Sweden, and Canada and some in Great Britain are sold on that basis.

The selling of hogs on the basis of a guaranteed dressing percentage flourished for a time in this country. This practice started in the eastern corn belt, where it was initiated by cooperative shipping associations in 1923; it expanded until about 1930 and then declined. More recently, some packing plants have made the buying of hogs on carcass grades available to their patrons. In this plan the sales were made on the basis of the on-foot grade and the carcass weight.

In Canada selling on the basis of carcass grade and weight has been

[12] O. G. Hankins, *A Study of Carcass Characteristics in Relation to Type of Hogs,* American Society of Animal Production, 1940.

CARCASS YIELDS OF LARGE-, INTERMEDIATE-, AND SMALL-TYPE HOGS

	AT UNIFORM WEIGHT			AT UNIFORM FATNESS		
	Large Type	Intermediate Type	Small Type	Large Type	Intermediate Type	Small Type
Number of hogs	96	137	42	26	67	59
Final feed-lot weight, pounds	224.0	223.1	223.2	261.9	223.2	149.6
Market grade of slaughter hog *	Good	Low choice	High choice	Low choice	Choice	Choice
Market grade of chilled carcass *	Good	Low choice	High choice	Low choice	Choice	Choice
Chilled carcass weight, pounds	166.7	164.6	174.1	202.5	168.4	110.8
Dressing percentage	74.3	73.6	78.2	77.2	75.3	74.0
Carcass yield of certain cuts, per cent						
Ham	19.7	18.8	17.7	18.0	18.1	18.2
Bacon	12.4	12.8	13.6	12.3	11.9	12.6
Loin	14.7	14.1	13.3	14.4	14.2	13.1
Total of ham, bacon, and loin	46.8	45.7	44.6	44.7	44.2	43.9
Shoulder	9.9	9.3	8.8	8.1	8.0	8.0
Butt	5.1	4.9	4.2	4.8	4.9	4.5
Back fat (skinned), leaf fat, and fat trimmings	14.4	16.6	20.7	18.8	18.7	18.7

* Market grade on a relative basis in order of rank or order of merit from High choice down to Good.

highly successful and is mandatory in plants killing over 3,000 head per year. Government graders are responsible for the grading and the weighing in automatic scales. Canadian export demand calls for a specific type, weight, and grade of hog. Their market objective is an exportable Wiltshire side. Our market is much more diverse than the Canadian.

The system of selling hogs on the basis of dressing percentage and carcass grade has the following decided advantages, according to W. O. Fraser.[13]

1. It provides for paying each farmer for the exact amount and grade of pork he produces—which, after all, is the objective of the feeder in raising hogs.

2. It makes possible the positive identification of hogs that are soft and oily and the purchase of such hogs on the basis of their correct value.

3. It makes it possible to trace the origin of bruises and correct their source.

4. It provides for determining the origin of diseased hogs and for correcting the cause that may have been responsible for the diseased condition.

The arguments seem to favor buying by carcass grade and weight, but there are many difficulties to overcome in this country in initiating such a plan. Our present system tends to level off prices, and often individual producers fail to receive the value they should for their hogs, although the packer pays what the entire kill is worth.

It has been found that 45 per cent of the total variation of individual values was removed by the live-weight method of marketing alone. An additional 38 per cent could be removed through the carcass weight and grade system.[14] The balance, or 11 per cent, occurs because all carcasses within a grade are not the same value per pound.

CURED PORK

Much of the pork carcass may be cured. Some of the more commonly cured pork cuts are hams, bacon bellies, picnics, skinned shoulders, boneless butts, Boston butts, fat backs, jowls, bacon squares, and boneless loins. The boneless loin or loin strip is known in the trade as Canadian bacon, or Canadian Style bacon.

There are two common types of cured pork cuts cured in two different ways.

[13] *Report,* American Society of Animal Production, 1938.
[14] Gerald Engelman, *et al.,* "Marketing Slaughter Hogs by Carcass Weight and Grade," *Tech. Bull. 187,* Minn. Agr. Exp. Sta., April, 1950.

Sweet pickled cured cuts are prepared pork cuts cured by soaking, with or without injection, in a solution of common salt with sugar, sirup, and/or honey, together with one or more of the following, each in its proper proportion: sodium nitrite, sodium nitrate, potassium nitrate, with or without the use of spice. Tenderized hams of several types are on the market. After curing and washing, such hams are smoked at high temperatures.

Fig. 161. Hams in stockinettes and hung on racks are guided into the smoke ovens where hardwood smoke is used to provide proper flavor. A cured smoked ham is one of highest priced pork cuts. (Swift & Company.)

Dry salt pork is the prepared pork cut cured by the application of dry common salt, with or without the use of one or more of the following: sodium nitrite, sodium nitrate, potassium nitrate, sugar, a sirup, honey, spice; with or without the injection of a solution of common salt to which may have been added one or more of the following: sodium nitrite, sodium nitrate, potassium nitrate, sugar, a sirup, honey.

Often the cured cuts are smoked by subjecting them to the direct action of the smoke of burning wood or similar burning material.

LARD AND PORK FAT

Lard is rendered from the fat of hogs. In the rendering process fat is melted out from the fatty tissues and the moisture is driven off.

Because of the different materials used in rendering there is a differentiation in the products from the hog carcass. That difference is indicated by the definitions.

Fig. 162.   Lard is an important by-product from hogs. Many modified lards are available on our markets. (Swift & Company.)

Lard.   Lard is the fat rendered from fresh, clean, sound, fatty tissues from hogs in good health at the time of slaughter, with or without lard stearin or a hardened lard. The tissues do not include bones, detached skin, head fat, ears, tails, organs, windpipes, large blood vessels, scrap fat, skimmings, settlings, pressings, and the like, and are reasonably free from muscle tissue and blood.

Rendered pork fat.   Rendered pork fat is the fat other than lard, rendered from clean, sound carcasses, parts of carcasses, or edible organs from hogs in good health at the time of slaughter, except that stomachs, tails, bones from the head, and bones from cured or cooked pork are not included. The tissues rendered are usually fresh, but may be cured, cooked, or otherwise prepared and may contain some meat food products. Rendered pork fat may be hardened by the use of lard stearin and/or hardened lard and/or rendered pork fat stearin and/or hardened rendered pork fat.

That which is designated as rendered pork fat comes mainly from the trimmings of cured meats. In usual packing-plant operation it will amount to about 15 per cent of lard in volume of production.

Types of lard

Lard may be classified on the basis of the part of the carcass from which it is derived and the method of rendering. Some lards have antioxidants added which improve the keeping qualities. Many packing plants make specially prepared lards which are sold under brand names.

Lard substitutes. Lard substitutes are manufactured products containing vegetable fat and oil, which are used in place of lard. Cottonseed oil is the main material used in such products. These substitutes have increased greatly in usage, and in general they sell for a higher price than lard.

Lard prices and hog prices

The prices of hogs and lard tend to move together; however, the margin between the two has narrowed considerably and in recent years lard has sold for less per pound than hogs. Export demand has lessened and domestic demand has not been sufficient to keep the lard price as high as that of live hogs. Heavy hogs, or those with high lard yields, have therefore been heavily discounted in market price. A comparison of prices of pork cuts and lard is shown in Figure 163.

SOFT PORK

There are two main causes of softness in hog carcasses: first, oily feed and, second, immaturity and lack of finish. The second type of softness can be recognized on foot since it occurs in underfinished hogs. Softness resulting from oily feeds cannot be identified on foot. Wider use of soybeans in swine rations results in more soft hogs. Peanuts are an old offender in the soft-pork problem. Oily feeds such as these must be fed in limited quantities if firm, acceptable carcasses are to be produced. Pigs starting on soybeans at 100 pounds will usually yield good-quality, firm carcasses if the ration contains 10 per cent or less of the beans.

Soft pork is of no lower nutritive value than firm pork, and it is of acceptable taste and flavor. Since soft carcasses do not firm in the cooler, the cuts are soft, flabby, and oily. As a consequence, the appearance of soft-pork cuts makes them less acceptable to the trade. Also, the lard is inferior because of its low melting point. Pork cuts like bacon that are soft are difficult to slice. The fat of soft and oily pork has more than the usual amount of unsaturated fatty acids which have relatively low melting points. Such fat and oils are less resistant to rancidity.

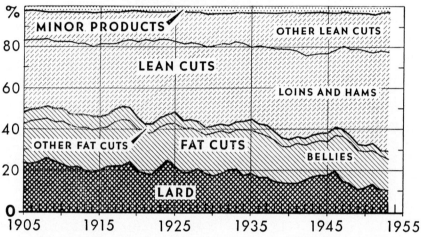

PORK CUTS
Value as Percentage of Carcass Value*

WHOLESALE PORK PRICES (FRESH BASIS), CHICAGO; CONSTANT YIELDS OF VARIOUS CUTS AND LARD

Fig. 163. Value of pork cuts as per cent of carcass value. Lard and fat cuts have decreased relatively in value; fat for lard often sells for less than the live hog price. (U.S.D.A., Agricultural Marketing Service.)

PORK AND LARD CONSUMPTION

For a period (about 1899–1933) the total production and consumption of pork increased at about the same rate as human population. Per capita consumption since then has fluctuated around a comparatively stable level, but it appears to show a slight downward trend. Production was low following the drought years of 1934 and 1936. In fact, some pork was imported in the years of short supplies. (See Figure 164.)

Exports have varied markedly from time to time, and this causes changes in our supply available for home consumption. However, the production is a greater factor in the amount for domestic consumption. In recent years our exports have been very small. Most of our meat production has been used for domestic consumption. Our meat production is shown in Figure 164.

The total and per capita production and consumption of lard have varied in about the same way as pork. In spite of the competition from lard substitutes, lard consumption has remained at a fairly high level.

The yearly per capita consumption of pork, excluding lard, from 1929 to 1955, inclusive, ranged from a high of 79.2 pounds in 1944 to a low of 48.1 pounds in 1935; the average yearly consumption for a late 10-year period was 67.6 pounds. (See Figure 55.)

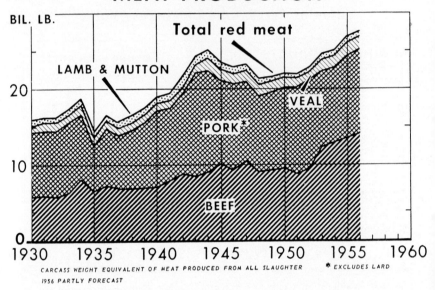

MEAT PRODUCTION

CARCASS WEIGHT EQUIVALENT OF MEAT PRODUCED FROM ALL SLAUGHTER * EXCLUDES LARD
1956 PARTLY FORECAST

Fig. 164. Meat production in the United States. The increase in total meat production and in per capita consumption has been mainly in beef. (U.S.D.A., Agricultural Marketing Service.)

Lard consumption has also fluctuated markedly for the same period, the high being 14.5 pounds per capita in 1940 and the low 9.6 pounds in 1935. The average yearly production has been 12.69 pounds per person; consumption as food has been somewhat less.

There is some variation in the consumption of pork and lard by sections. The per capita consumption is the greatest in the southern states, somewhat above average in the north central states, and considerably below average in the western and northeastern states. The consumption in rural sections is more than in urban sections.

There are several peoples of the world who do not consume pork, namely the Jews, Egyptians, Hindus, and Mohammedans.

PORK AND LARD EXPORTS AND IMPORTS

Exports of pork and lard tend to be high when we have heavy production and low when there is a shortage of slaughter hogs. Production in other countries and trade barriers also affect our exports.

During World War II there was a sizable quantity of pork exported. In fact, in some years it was more than the export of lard. Since then pork exports have dwindled, but a considerable quantity of lard is still exported. For the past decade it averaged over 500 million pounds yearly. Cuba, the United Kingdom, West Germany and Austria have been our largest recent outlets for lard and rendered pork fat. This is somewhat less than it was formerly except in the late 1930's. Lard production has been slow to adjust to current needs. (See Figure 165.)

LARD: U.S. PRODUCTION AND EXPORTS

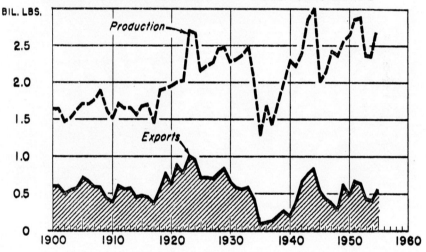

Fig. 165. Lard, United States production and export. The United States accounts for nearly one-third of the world production of lard and is the leading country in lard exports. (U.S.D.A., Foreign Agricultural Service.)

Our imports of live hogs, pork or lard have always been comparatively small and not much of a factor in the trade. There has been a small increase in pork imports the past few years.

BY-PRODUCTS FROM HOG SLAUGHTER

The by-products, other than lard, from hog slaughter are of small value as compared with the returns from pork and lard, also as compared with by-products of other slaughter animals. On the basis of the average dollar the meat packer receives from sale of pork, lard, and by-products, the income is divided approximately as indicated on page 138.

The principal by-products from the slaughter of hogs, those finished by the packing plant and those manufactured after leaving the packing company, are listed below.

Fig. 166. Making pork sausage. (Swift & Company.)

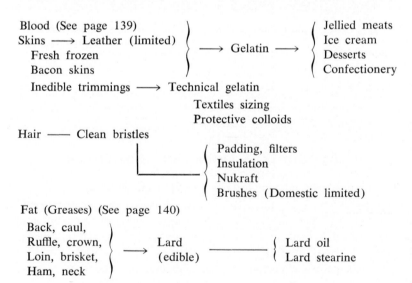

Blood (See page 139)   ⎫   ⎧ Jellied meats
Skins ⟶ Leather (limited)   ⎬ ⟶ Gelatin ⟶ ⎨ Ice cream
  Fresh frozen   ⎪   ⎪ Desserts
  Bacon skins   ⎭   ⎩ Confectionery
    Inedible trimmings ⟶ Technical gelatin
                                 Textiles sizing
                                 Protective colloids
Hair ——— Clean bristles
                                 ⎧ Padding, filters
                                 ⎪ Insulation
                                 ⎨ Nukraft
                                 ⎩ Brushes (Domestic limited)
Fat (Greases) (See page 140)
  Back, caul,   ⎫
  Ruffle, crown,   ⎬ ⟶ Lard —————— ⎧ Lard oil
  Loin, brisket,   ⎪   (edible)   ⎩ Lard stearine
  Ham, neck   ⎭

Gallstones (rarely found in young pigs)
Bile
Bones (See page 139)

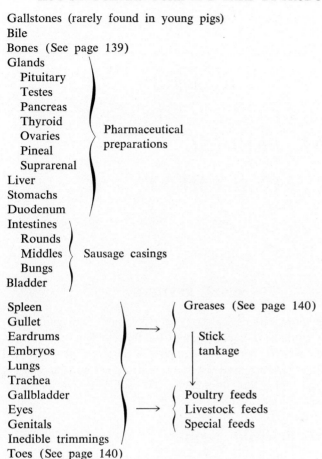

Glands
   Pituitary
   Testes
   Pancreas
   Thyroid
   Ovaries
   Pineal
   Suprarenal
Liver
Stomachs
Duodenum
           Pharmaceutical preparations

Intestines
   Rounds
   Middles
   Bungs
Bladder
           Sausage casings

Spleen
Gullet
Eardrums
Embryos
Lungs
Trachea
Gallbladder
Eyes
Genitals
Inedible trimmings
Toes (See page 140)

→ Greases (See page 140)
   Stick tankage

→ Poultry feeds
   Livestock feeds
   Special feeds

Chapter 26

SWINE FEEDING
AND MANAGEMENT

SWINE FEEDING

Swine are more economical converters of feeds into gains than the other slaughter animals. The explanation for this efficiency lies in the fact that hogs grow faster in proportion to their size. A larger proportion of the feed consumed is therefore used for body tissue (meat and fat). A pig has a simple stomach and a limited capacity for feed; but, size considered, it consumes a large amount of feed.

PECULIARITIES OF SWINE FEEDING

The hog is likewise distinctive in that the feeds used are largely concentrates. Roughage, or pasture, usually represents but a small portion of the nutrient intake. As the ration may be without roughage or forage, nutritional deficiencies are not uncommon, since these classes of feeds are often the safety factors in protein, mineral, and vitamin needs. For example, the nutritional properties of good forage will overcome many of the shortcomings of a straight grain ration. It is evident that, with pigs or sows which are confined to small areas without vegetation, care must be used in formulating the ration. In the absence of self-gathered feed, the ration fed is of necessity more complex.

Swine feeding is unique in another respect, and that is that corn is so widely used. This is not because other feed grains are unsatisfactory, but rather because corn so often has the advantage in economy of production. The common custom of restricting feed consumption to one grain, especially corn, is responsible for the rather widespread inadequacy of swine rations.

434

Deficiencies are far more prevalent in rations for swine than for other live-stock. Proper supplementation of the basal feed is often overlooked. Cost of feed is a very important factor in the economy of hog raising, for feed costs constitute 75 to 85 per cent of the total cost of producing a marketable pig. More specifically, the chief factor is the relationship between feed prices and hog prices, or the hog-feed price ratio.

Swine feeders in the main have not paid much attention to feed require-ments and feeding standards. This is due to the rapidly changing require-ments of swine, in growth and fattening, and the widespread use of group feeding rather than feeding individuals separately. Self-feeding has also detracted from interest in the use of feeding standards. The actual feed re-quirements of swine for protein and energy have not been studied with the completeness that marked such investigations with cattle and sheep. There are several feeding standards for swine, including the Recommended Nutrient Allowances of the National Research Council.

COMPOSITION OF SWINE AT DIFFERENT WEIGHTS

The rapid change in actual needs is indicated by the marked change which takes place in the composition of the pig as it grows and fattens. In the tabulation that follows there are included data on average composition of swine based upon analysis at the Agricultural Research Center, U.S. Department of Agriculture, Beltsville, Maryland.[1]

BODY COMPOSITION OF SWINE

CONDITION OF FATNESS	WEIGHT AT SLAUGHTER, POUNDS	BODY SUB-STANCE, POUNDS	COMPONENTS OF BODY SUBSTANCE, PER CENT			
			Water	Protein	Fat	Ash
Thin	106	100	56.3	14.9	25.8	3.1
Moderately fat	162	154	49.2	13.7	34.2	2.9
Fat	219	210	44.3	12.6	40.6	2.5
Very fat	230	219	41.4	10.5	45.9	2.3
Extremely fat	343	327	37.7	10.8	49.5	2.1

It should be pointed out that wide ranges in composition would be preva-lent at the weights given, and that such factors as age, type, and method of feeding would be related to composition as well as to weight and fatness. Relatively, that is, in comparison with other slaughter animals, the mineral or ash content is low and the fat content is high. It will be observed from inspection of the tabulated data that heavier pigs are fatter and have less water, protein, and ash than lighter pigs. It is therefore apparent that the

[1] *1939 Yearbook of Agriculture,* U.S.D.A., p. 708.

ration for the older pig is used more for formation of fat. Since much of the fat is made from the feed carbohydrates in the pig and 2.25 pounds of the latter equal 1 pound of fat in energy value, it is evident that fat gains require more feed than protein gains.

Since it is difficult to divide maintenance from production, most of the feeding standards for swine combine the economic maintenance with production. For example, a 250-pound bred gilt makes a substantial storage in the fetal growth which is not easily separated from maintenance needs. In general, recommendations in feeding standards are sufficiently great to meet all the usual nutrient needs. In maintenance studies it has been found that needs are not directly proportional to weight. For example, 1 pound per day of such feed as yellow corn, middlings, and tankage per 100 pounds will maintain 225-pound pigs; but for 60-pound pigs the requirement is 1.5 pounds per 100 pounds live weight. It has also been found that values for a feed in protein or energy vary with the type of body function, that is, growth, fattening, pregnancy, and lactation. In other words, a feed of a given energy value usually has a higher energy value for maintenance than for fattening.

The protein requirement under usual swine feeding methods is of far greater concern than the energy needs. Most farm feeds are inadequate in protein for swine, and supplements are needed for best results; of the proteins in grains about 75 per cent are digestible and of this only about one half is of the kind needed for tissue building in the body. Rations are often deficient in amount of protein and also in protein-building capacity or biological value.

NUTRIENT REQUIREMENTS OF SWINE

In the Morrison Feeding Standard, the following is suggested as an adequate allowance for the various classes of swine. These are selected only as representative of the needs not a complete statement of requirements for all weights and conditions.

A comparison of the requirements given in the standard will bring out the difference in needs for various classes of swine. The requirements for sows at 300 and 400 pounds are given. The requirements for a 200-pound growing and fattening pig are also given.

It will be noted that the class for brood sows nursing pigs is more heavily fed than the other classes listed; also, the nutritive ratio is somewhat narrower.

Growth and fattening needs

The young pig, for optimum growth, needs a ration with a high percentage of protein. Likewise, to be adequate, all the nutritive essentials must

DAILY REQUIREMENT PER HEAD, MORRISON FEEDING STANDARD [2]

CLASS	WEIGHT, POUNDS	DRY MATTER, POUNDS	DIGESTIBLE PROTEIN, POUNDS	TOTAL DIGESTIBLE NUTRIENTS, POUNDS	CALCIUM, POUNDS	PHOS-PHORUS, POUNDS	CARO-TENE, MILLIGRAMS	NET ENERGY, THERMS
Growing and fattening pigs	200	6.1– 7.4	0.65–0.79	5.0–6.2	0.034	0.025	4.0	4.8–5.9
Wintering pregnant gilts	300	4.9– 5.9	0.65–0.79	4.0–5.0	0.030	0.024	15.0	3.8–4.7
Wintering pregnant older sows	300	4.0– 4.8	0.49–0.60	3.2–3.9	0.025	0.020	12.0	3.0–3.7
Older sows nursing pigs	400	9.7–11.8	1.22–1.50	8.0–9.8	0.06	0.048	28.0	7.6–9.3

[2] F. B. Morrison, *Feeds and Feeding*, 22nd ed., The Morrison Publishing Co., Ithaca, N. Y., 1956.

be provided. It is obvious that ample energy is needed for growth and maintenance.

As the pig becomes older and fatter, the protein intake may be lessened in proportion to the energy. For example, for a 50-pound pig the level of protein in the ration would be about 14 to 16 per cent, while for the 150- to 200-pound pig about 12 per cent is satisfactory. When pigs are being fed on good pasture, a lower level of protein in the ration fed will prove satisfactory. The pig, if permitted the free choice of feeds, will shift in proportions of feeds consumed to meet this changing requirement, provided palatable feeds are fed.

Feeding standards have been of some help to swine feeders, especially in checking feeding operations; however, their use has been less extensive than in other livestock.

Fig. 167. Purebred Hampshire sow and her litter. Suckling sows require liberal rations.

In general, swine feeding has been resolved into evaluation of various feed combinations and measurement of results in terms of rate of gain and feed required per unit of gain.

Reproductive and lactation requirements

As swine reproduce at a comparatively early age, reproduction and lactation often overlap with growth. The needs are much the same; that is, the ration should be relatively narrow in the nutritive ratio, ample in all of the essentials, and sufficient in amount. The pregnancy ration needs to be ample in amount, for during this period sows build up for subsequent lactation. Even though sows are self-fed during lactation, if lactation is heavy, weight is not maintained. Under good conditions early weaning, that is, less than eight weeks suckling, may be successful, if a complete weaning ration is fed the pigs and careful management is practiced.

Mineral, vitamin, antibiotic, and other needs

Corn and other grains lack some of the essentials for growth, that is, some of the indispensable amino acids, minerals, and vitamins. Only by the use of satisfactory supplements can the deficiencies be overcome.

The mineral needs are extensive in quality but in quantity quite small, as is the case with vitamins and similar essentials. This is an expanding field and beyond the province of this text. It is quite evident that these essentials must be supplied in the ration—either fed or picked up from the lot, pasture, or range. Since only small amounts of these newly discovered essentials, like some of the B-complex vitamins, for example, are needed, most rations otherwise well balanced and with some variety are fairly complete nutritionally without them. Under adverse feeding conditions, with young pigs or pregnant or suckling sows, inadequate feeding often occurs if these are neglected. Antibiotics and perhaps arsonic acids may be growth promoting under certain conditions.

PRACTICES IN THE FEEDING OF SWINE

The breeding herd

The sow breeding herd that is producing two litters per year is fed for production almost all the year. The period of economic maintenance is quite short, since a prebreeding period of feeding or flushing is customary. The effectiveness of flushing has been questioned, especially if the sows are not permitted to reach a low plane of nutrition. Feeding during pregnancy overshadows flushing because proper feeding then reduces prenatal deaths, which is more important than ova shed.

In summer the breeding herd is kept on pasture, which lowers costs and has many other beneficial effects. Enough concentrated feed is needed to permit the maintaining of fairly good condition. Concentrate feeding is stepped up as the time for breeding nears. Following breeding, the ration effect may be quite marked on the litter size and vitality of the pigs. Good feeding of an adequate ration is to be stressed, especially during the latter part of the gestation period. If this period is in the winter, as it is with spring-farrowed pigs, good legume hay should be a part of the ration. In the summer good pasture is advised.

At farrowing, feeding with caution is indicated; when the sow has returned to normal, heavy feeding is needed to induce milk flow and maintain condition. After weaning there is a short recovery period when the sows should be on pasture or in the fields.

In practice, the boar pigs are castrated when 1 to 2 weeks old and weaning takes place when the pigs are about 8 weeks old.

Fig. 168. Market pigs of the right type. Grand champion carload at the International Livestock Exposition. Shown by Howard Charlot, Blair, Neb.

The feeding of pig crops

There are two general methods used in feeding of pig crops: (1) the full feeding method in which pigs are heavily fed from weaning time until they are marketed, and (2) the limited feeding plan in which a limited amount of feed is used. The latter plan is often modified by finally finishing the pigs by the full feeding plan.

In general, the limited feeding method is used on late-farrowed spring pigs in order to get the maximum use of forage crop and to finish them on the new corn crop.

The full feeding plan is used for early-farrowed spring pigs, and generally for fall pigs. Where the two-litter-a-year plan is carried out, such full feeding is desirable to prevent overlapping of crops of pigs.

In choosing a feeding plan suitable to a situation, one must consider the equipment, feed, labor, and pasture available. Production should be timed to the market; that is, the crop should be fed out so as to sell when hog prices are not seasonally low.

Effect of feeding on carcass composition

Within limits it is possible to affect the composition of the carcass of the pig. Inherited characteristics set the pattern, but an important factor in the fulfillment of the pattern is nutrition.

Pigs fed liberal rations will have carcasses with more fat and less lean than pigs fed scanty rations. The relation between carcass composition and method of feeding is illustrated by the data given below.

The pigs were fed to weigh 200 pounds. The weight of the pigs fed high for the first 16 weeks was 100 pounds. Pigs fed low weighed but 50 pounds at 16 weeks of age.

For the leanest carcasses pigs should be fed slowly throughout; this may not, however, be practical or economical. The fattest carcasses were produced on the plan of feeding slowly at first and then rapidly. This appears to be the least practical of the methods used from the viewpoints of both raiser and processor. Liberal feeding throughout produces more fat than limited feeding for the latter part of the feeding period. Self-feeding is a very practical method, and also an economical one. It may be worth while to deviate from this practice, but this would depend upon the prices paid for lean hogs and fat hogs and their production costs.

RESULTS OF DIFFERENCES IN RATE OF FEEDING ON CARCASS COMPOSITION [3]

METHOD OF FEEDING OR PLANE OF NUTRITION	PER CENT OF CARCASS WEIGHT				
	Fat	Muscle	Bone	Skin	Tendon Glands
High-high	38.3	40.3	11.0	5.3	5.1
High-low	33.4	44.9	11.2	5.4	5.1
Low-high	44.1	36.3	9.7	4.8	5.1
Low-low	27.5	49.1	12.4	5.8	5.2

Trials such as the above have been conducted more extensively on hogs for Wiltshires or the bacon type. It has also been found with such hogs that additional protein above the minimum requirement will not increase the lean.

WEIGHT AT WHICH TO MARKET PIGS

The feed to produce gain and the differential between the prices of various weights are to be considered in deciding at which weight to market pigs. In years when the feeding ratio is favorable, farmers feed their hogs to heavier weights. The relation of weight to carcass yields has been previously discussed. In general, heavy or fat hogs are graded and priced lower than lighter or leaner hogs.

The feed required for an additional 50-pound gain and the rate of gain is given in the table on page 442. The pigs in the U.S. Department of Agriculture investigation were of intermediate type and were self-fed.

It will be noted that, as the weight is increased, more feed is required for a unit of gain. Gain in weight decreases markedly after the pig reaches

[3] *1939 Yearbook of Agriculture,* U.S.D.A., p. 474.

275 pounds. In fact, that weight appeared to be the limit of profitable feed under normal conditions and that would be only when feed prices are comparatively low. Under most conditions the most profit is made from the hog enterprise when pigs are sold at the weight of 200 to 225 pounds.

DAILY GAINS AND FEED FOR GAIN FOR PIGS OF VARIOUS WEIGHTS [4]

WEIGHT, POUNDS	AVERAGE DAILY GAIN, POUNDS	FEED FOR 50 POUNDS OF LIVE-WEIGHT GAIN, POUNDS
75 to 124	1.62	167
125 to 174	1.75	190
175 to 224	1.71	206
225 to 274	1.65	223
275 to 324	1.46	253
325 to 374	1.31	276

SWINE MANAGEMENT

Proper management is essential for success in swine raising. There are critical periods in the handling of the breeding herd, and careful attention during breeding, farrowing, and raising the pigs to weaning is necessary for a productive herd. The mortality of the young is much higher with swine than with other kinds of livestock; normally not more than 60 per cent of the pigs farrowed are raised to marketable weights.

Sanitation is also a troublesome problem in swine raising. Since hogs live close to the ground, they are subject to many filth-borne parasites and diseases. The statement that "hog health makes wealth" is literally true; since unhealthy hogs are generally unprofitable. Only by avoiding disease and parasitic losses by skillful handling and treatment is it possible to have a highly profitable swine herd. The efficient management of the breeding herd plus good feeding is imperative for low production costs. Up until weaning time there is little difference in the cost of raising a large litter and one of average size. Therefore, we want sows that farrow and raise large litters, but in order to be productive the sow herd must be well fed and cared for.

Hogs are kept on a farm or ranch to convert some of the home-raised feeds into profitable gains. The manager must see to it that all needs are provided so that the hogs will serve this purpose and also so that a profit will be realized from the enterprise.

Essential factors which the manager must keep in mind are:

1. Usable supply of feed. Since hogs use mainly concentrated feeds, an ample supply should be available. The supply of basal feed, like corn, usually is sufficient, but for efficiency there is need for protein-rich feeds, mineral supplements, suitable forage and roughage, and perhaps vitamin

[4] *Science in Farming, Yearbook of Agriculture 1943–47, U.S.D.A.,* 1947.

supplements. If the home supply of a feed like corn is not properly supplemented, the results will not be satisfactory.

In keeping down production costs the swine man first examines the feed costs, since these comprise over three quarters of total costs.

2. Equipment needs. The equipment needed depends upon the weather conditions and the general plan of hog raising. Ample farrowing quarters are needed for early farrowing, such as is practiced in the two-litter-a-year plan. Also, fall pigs require some protection in the wintertime. Movable houses can be used quite satisfactorily for some situations, but a central hog house has many advantages. Suitable shelter for young pigs reduces pig losses.

Other than housing equipment, there is necessity for many other equipment items which are time savers. Self-feeders, feeding floors, hog waterers, fencing, troughs, hurdles, and sunshades are but a few of the many pieces of equipment that may be found on a well-managed hog farm. The size of the hog-raising enterprise on the farm will determine the need for the various items.

Many hog-raising farms have a combination of housing that is both a central house and a movable house. Farrowing is carried out in the central house, and then movable houses permit decentralization for the utilization of clean ground pastures. It has been found that dividing the hogs and pigs into small groups is advantageous. This is more easily accomplished with movable houses and many lots. Also, the movable housing permits greater range and exercising. However, other equipment is required when the hogs are spread out, for feeding and watering are not centralized.

3. Labor involved. At certain times during the year the swine herd requires a considerable amount of labor. With a crop of pigs well started, the labor needed may be quite low if the equipment is satisfactory. Hog raising should be arranged so that the work is integrated with the other farm work. Spring farrowing, then, should not conflict with the time of planting the crops. Actually, the labor cost is one of the smaller items, usually running about 5 per cent of the total cost.

4. The market outlook. The hog enterprise is very flexible, and producers attempt to take advantage of the relative profitableness of swine raising by altering the size of the pig crops. The limiting factor is usually the equipment for handling the hogs. The capacity of the equipment is to be considered at breeding time, yet it is impossible to foretell the size of the litters and the number that will be raised. To some extent production may be adjusted in accordance with the hog price outlook and the outlook for other salable products, production of which may be expanded or contracted. In laying plans for hog raising, the seasonal variation in hog prices and the cost of production are also to be considered. When a time of marketing is decided upon, the time of breeding is set so that with the method of feeding used the pigs are finished properly at the time of marketing. A good manager plans to have the market pigs ready to sell when the hog price is high, or, if he sells on a low market, his cost of production should be low.

5. Keeping records. Carefully kept records assist the manager in making an analytical study of the various phases of swine production. For the usual swine herd kept for market hog production, a breeding record, a farrowing record, a litter identification, and a financial record will serve most of the needs. With a purebred herd more extensive records are essential.

6. Disease and parasites. There are several rather common diseases which may cause very heavy losses in swine herds unless proper preventive measures are followed. We can immunize against some diseases, for example, hog cholera. Strict sanitary measures are essential for control of others. There are also several parasites of swine which may cause heavy losses if not controlled. The common intestinal worm can be controlled by the McLean County or clean-ground system. Until this method was developed, unthrifty herds were far more prevalent. Skillful management of the herd involves the avoiding of diseases and parasitic losses by the time-tried control methods.

There are many other services which the manager must perform or have performed to maintain a productive herd. Attention to proper feeding, selection, and breeding are just a part of the job. For good results an ample water supply and comfortable surroundings are imperative.

Many other tasks, such as castrating and weaning, must be performed. Although hog raising may be, under some circumstances, quite automatic, on the usual farm close attention and supervision are necessary.

MANAGEMENT RECOMMENDATIONS OF AMERICAN FEED MANUFACTURERS ASSOCIATION

The American Feed Manufacturers Association has made a study of all research data on swine management recommendations. The purpose was to bring more uniformity in the recommendations for all phases of swine management. The recommendations follow:

A. Growing and fattening phase

FEEDING MANAGEMENT

1. The number of pigs per linear foot of self-feeder space or pigs per self-feeder hole should be:

	ON DRY LOT	ON PASTURE
Weaning to 75 lbs	4	4–5
76 lbs to market	3	3–4

(A 10-foot self-feeder open to pigs on both sides provides 20 linear feet of feeding space.)

2. The percentage of self-feeder space given to protein supplement should be:

	ON DRY LOT	ON PASTURE
Weaning to 75 lbs	25%	20–25%
76 lbs to 125 lbs	20%	15–20%
126 lbs to Market	15%	10–15%

3. Three self-feeder holes, or 3 linear feet of mineral box space, should be allotted for 100 pigs when salt or a mineral mixture is fed free-choice.
4. For hand feeding in troughs or for hand watering, the length of the trough per pig should be:

Weaning to 75 lbs	0.75 ft
76 lbs to 125 lbs	1.00 ft
126 lbs to Market	1.25 ft

(A 10-foot trough is considered to provide 10 feet of feeder space whether pigs eat from one or both sides.)

5. When pigs are confined from weaning to market, 15 square feet of feeding floor space should be provided per pig if the pigs are fed from troughs and 10 square feet of feeding floor space if fed from self-feeders. This is in addition to sleeping space.
6. One automatic watering cup should be provided each 20 pigs. (An automatic waterer with 2 openings should be considered 2 cups.)
7. The minimum capacity waterer for 10 pigs per day should be 25 gallons in the summer time and 15 gallons in the winter time.
8. The drinking water should not fall below a temperature of 35° to 40° Fahrenheit during the winter.

GENERAL MANAGEMENT

9. The area of shelter provided should be:

	SUMMER TIME (SHADE OR HOUSING)	WINTER TIME (HOUSING)
Weaning to 75 lbs	7 sq ft	6 sq ft
76 lbs to 125 lbs	9 sq ft	8 sq ft
126 lbs to Market	12 sq ft	10 sq ft

10. The use of sanitary hog wallows during hot weather is recommended. Up to 50 pigs can be accommodated per 100 square feet of wallow providing shade or shelter is nearby.
11. Ringing of pigs is recommended where rooting becomes a problem.
12. A program of strict sanitation to prevent infestation is recommended for control of round worms in swine. Where such a

program is not effectively carried out, worming of pigs soon after weaning and repeated later if needed, is recommended.

13. Effective mange and lice treatment is recommended at weaning and whenever needed thereafter.

14. On good legume or legume-grass pasture allow 20 growing-fattening pigs per acre on a full feeding program and 10 to 15 per acre on a limited-feeding program.

15. Pigs of widely varying weights should not be run together. It is recommended that the range in weight should not exceed 20% above or below the average.

B. Breeding and gestation phase

GENERAL MANAGEMENT

1. Gilts to be retained for the breeding herd should be separated from the market herd at 4 to 5 months of age or at 150 to 175 pounds. They should have at least 12 well developed teats.

2. Gilts should be at least 8 months old and weigh near 250 pounds before they are bred.

3. Worming of sows and gilts before they are bred is recommended, and sanitary measures should be followed to prevent reinfection.

4. "Flushing" (increasing feed intake) during the breeding season is recommended. The feed intake should be increased 7 to 10 days before breeding starts and maintained until all sows or gilts are bred.

5. Under conditions of hand, or individual mating, two services per sow or gilt are recommended. The first mating on gilts should be on the first day of estrus and the first mating on sows on the second day of estrus. The second service should follow the first by 24 hours.

   (Note: When only one mating can be made during the estrus period, it is recommended that gilts and sows be served on the second day of estrus.)

6. When weaning under 2 weeks of age, it is recommended that sows be bred on the second heat period after weaning. It is generally satisfactory to breed sows on the first heat period following weaning at three or more weeks.

7. It is recommended that gilts and sows be kept separate during the gestation period, unless they are self-fed a bulky ration.

8. Effective mange and lice treatment is recommended during gestation.

9. Boars should be 8 months old before being used in the breeding herd.

10. Whenever practical, it is recommended that boars be used to serve several sows or gilts outside the breeding herd prior to serving those in the breeding herd.

11. Boars of the same age or size can be run together during the off-breeding season. Boars of different ages, junior and mature, should not be run together.

12. The recommended size of exercise lot for holding a boar is ¼ acre.

13. The maximum number of services per boar should be:

	PER DAY	PER WEEK	PER MONTH
Mature Boar [5]	3	12	40
Junior Boar [5]	2	8	25

14. The use of a breeding crate is recommended when breeding gilts to old boars. It is often desirable to use a breeding crate when mating old sows to young boars.

15. Hand or individual mating of boars to sows or gilts is recommended over field mating. However, if field mating is practiced, two methods are recommended. One method is to split the sow or gilt herd so as to have one boar per group. Another method that is recommended is to alternate boars in the sow or gilt herd; that is, use one boar or set of boars one day and another boar or set of boars the next day.

16. On good legume or legume-grass pasture, allow 10 to 12 gilts or 8 to 10 sows per acre.

17. The square feet of housing or shade per animal should be as follows:

	WINTER (HOUSING)	SUMMER (SHADE OR HOUSING)
Gilt or Junior Boar	15 sq ft	17 sq ft
Sow or Mature Boar	18 sq ft	20 sq ft

FEEDING MANAGEMENT

18. Hand feeding of sows or gilts during gestation is generally recommended, for greater utilization of pasture and other desirable roughages can be attained and the condition of the sows and gilts can be more closely watched, but specially adapted bulky rations can be successfully self-fed.

19. When sows and gilts are self-fed during gestation, the number per linear [6] foot of feeder space, or per self-feeder hole, should be as follows: pasture, 3 to 4; drylot, 2 to 3.

---

[5] Mature boar considered to be 15 months or older, junior boar under 15 months.
[6] Linear Foot—one foot of feeder or watering space. For example, a 6-foot feeder open on both sides has 12 linear feet of feeding space.

20. For hand-feeding in troughs of gilts and sows during gestation or for hand watering, the linear feet of space required per gilt or sow is 1½ to 2 feet.

21. When alfalfa hay is fed in a rack, 4 sows may be fed per linear foot of rack space.

22. Bred sows and gilts may be used to glean corn left in fields, providing an excessive amount of corn is not on the ground and supplement is available.

23. One automatic watering cup should be provided for each 12 gilts or for each 10 sows. (An automatic waterer with 2 openings should be considered 2 cups.) Additional watering space may be required during warm weather.

C. Sow and litter phase

HOUSING AND SHELTER

1. A farrowing house temperature of 55° to 65° Fahrenheit is recommended provided adequate ventilation is obtained.

2. Heat lamps placed in a corner, accessible only to pigs, are recommended especially when the farrowing house temperature falls below 65°F. If a heat lamp of 250 watt size is used, it should be suspended approximately 24 inches above the bedding. Condition pigs to doing without the lamp by turning it off during warmer periods or by raising it.

3. Farrowing pens in a central farrowing house or individual farrowing houses should have a minimum size of 6 feet by 8 feet for gilts, and 8 feet by 8 feet for sows.

4. Farrowing stalls or crates should have widths of 20 inches for gilts and 24 inches for sows, and minimum lengths of 6 feet for gilts and 7 feet for sows. The space beneath the bottom board should be ½ the stall width. The recommended minimum width on each side of the stall or crate for pigs up to 2 weeks is 18 inches.

5. Guard rails 8 inches above the bedding and 8 inches from the wall are recommended in central farrowing house pens and individual farrowing houses.

6. The farrowing pen or individual farrowing house should be lightly bedded with chopped or short straw or hay, shavings, ground corn cobs, bagasse, peanut hulls, cottonseed hulls, oat hulls, or other suitable bedding material. More liberal bedding may be used in unheated houses during cold weather provided it is short or fine material that will not interfere with the movements of the pigs.

7. Recommended shade area is 50 square feet per gilt and litter and 60 square feet per sow and litter.

FEEDING AND WATERING SPACE

8. For self-feeding either in dry lot or on pasture, a minimum of one linear foot of self-feeder space or one self-feeder hole per sow or gilt and litter is recommended, provided the young pigs have additional feeding space in a creep.
9. For hand-feeding in troughs either in dry lot or on pasture, a minimum of 1½ linear feet of feeding space is recommended per sow or gilt and litter, provided the young pigs have additional feeding space in a creep.
10. For watering by automatic cup, provide at least 1 cup, not less than 6 inches in diameter or the equivalent, for each 4 sows or gilts and their litters. (An automatic waterer with 2 openings should be considered 2 cups.) For hand watering in troughs, provide at least 2 linear feet of trough space per sow or gilt and litter. Additional watering space may be required during warm weather.
11. Creep feeding beginning the first week is recommended. The maximum number of pigs per linear foot of feeder space should be 5. The edge of the feeder trough should not be more than 4 inches above the ground or floor. A maximum of 40 pigs per creep may be allowed.

    Creep feeders should be placed close to a water supply and near the area where the sow is most of the time. They should be inside, in a well-lighted place in cool weather and, when placed outside in warm weather, should be covered to provide shade and protection from rain.

GENERAL MANAGEMENT

12. When possible, the size of litters should be adjusted to the number of functioning teats or nursing ability of the sow. Transferring pigs from sow to sow should be done as early as possible. 3 to 4 days after farrowing is usually the maximum length of time that this can be done, unless the odor of the pigs is masked, when it may be possible to transfer at a later time.
13. For large litters, for pigs that are to be transferred, or when injuries to pigs or sows' teats are a problem, clipping needle teeth of pigs at birth or the first day is recommended. Only the tips of these teeth should be clipped.
14. Anemia in pigs farrowed in houses should be prevented, beginning the first week, by making clean soil or sod available, cop-

peras solution on the sow's udder, individual iron pills, or other methods. This may also be necessary for pigs farrowed on pasture when weather is unfavorable.

15. The age at which litters and sows may be run together should usually be 2 weeks, although small groups may be put together as early as 1 week. The age difference between such litters should not be more than 1 week in central farrowing house or 2 weeks on pasture. The recommended number of sows with litters put together in a group is not more than 4 in a central farrowing house or 6 on pasture.

16. On good legume or legume-grass pasture, allow 6 to 8 sows or gilts and their litters per acre.

17. Castration of the pigs should be done during the first 4 weeks. It should not be done during the 3 weeks following cholera vaccination. Also, pigs weaned at 4 weeks or earlier should not be castrated within 1 week of the time of weaning.

18. Pigs should be protected from infection by worms, as well as other diseases, by good sanitation. Worming before weaning is not recommended and it should not be done within the 3 weeks after vaccination with living (virulent or modified) hog cholera virus.

19. Cholera, erysipelas, and certain other diseases are prone to affect swine in various parts of the country. These diseases, where they do arise, can limit other efforts toward efficient pork production. Therefore, veterinary medical advice should be sought with regard to proper methods of vaccination and other disease control measures.

WEANING

20. Pigs may be successfully weaned at 5 to 6 weeks without the use of a sow's milk substitute when proper nutrition and management are practiced.

21. If pigs are to be weaned at 5 weeks or earlier, the following conditions are recommended:

For early weaned pigs, housing that is warm, dry, and draft free is required. Supplemental heat such as a heat lamp and special feeders and waterers are recommended.

	AGE IN WEEKS				
	5	4	3	2	1
Minimum pig wt, lbs	21	15	12	9	5
Farrowing house temperature, °F	60	65	70	75	75
Minimum floor space per pig, sq ft	6	5	4	4	4
Maximum number of pigs per linear ft [7] of feeder space	4	4	4	5	5
Maximum number of pigs per linear ft [7] of water space	10	10	12	12	12
Maximum number of pigs per group	25	20	10	10	10

[7] Linear Foot: one foot of feeding or watering space. For example, a 6-foot self-feeder open on both sides has 12 linear feet of feeder space. The same principle applies to trough space.

Chapter 27

SWINE BREEDS AND BREEDING

The breeding of swine has been investigated somewhat more completely than that of other farm animals. The rapid reproductive rate permits the use of larger numbers in a short period of time. The effect of inbreeding, for example, has been studied extensively in swine, whereas there is little information available on the effect of this practice in cattle, sheep, or horses.

The subject of swine breeding is discussed under the following headings: the reproductive process, the breeds, breeding systems, and breeding stock selection.

THE REPRODUCTIVE PROCESS

REPRODUCTION

Gilts become sexually mature when they are from 6 to 8 months of age if they have been liberally fed. Well-grown gilts may come in heat at 4 months of age. There is some seasonality of breeding, but litters are produced in all months. There appears to be an intensification of the heat periods in the fall, yet sows come in heat quite regularly except when they are suckling pigs. The number of farrowings reaches its peak in the spring and in the fall. The normal length of time from one heat period to the next is about 21 days. The period of estrus will range from 40 to 65 hours, and is shorter in gilts than in older sows. Usually sows come in heat a few days after weaning a litter, but some come in heat while suckling litters.

Ovulation occurs in the latter half of the heat period. It appears from investigations that sows can be bred too early or too late in the heat period to have the maximum litter size. A sow will shed about 18 ova. Some of these are not fertilized, and many of the fetuses degenerate during the gestation period.

State of nutrition will affect the estrous cycle, and if the plane of nutrition has been low the number of ova shed may be below normal. Flushing is practiced, with beneficial results in some cases. It is questionable whether increased feeding at breeding would affect litter size if nearly adequate nutrition were provided. Certainly the feeding during gestation overshadows flushing, for it can very definitely affect the litter size and strength of the newborn pigs.

The average length of the gestation period in swine is 114.5 days with a standard deviation of 2.2 days. The birth weight for pigs is about 2.5 pounds, and the males slightly outweigh the females. There is quite a range in the birth weights of pigs. The larger pigs are the strongest and most likely to survive. Feeding during pregnancy affects the birth weight of the pigs. Also, the number of pigs in the litter, the age of the sow, breed, crossbreeding, and inbreeding are factors affecting birth weight.

Gilts commonly have their first litter when they are 1 year of age.

The boar matures sexually at 6 to 7 months of age. Many boar pigs are used for breeding; consequently his first crop of pigs is farrowed when the boar is about 1 year old. Farmers prefer to use younger boars because of the ease in handling and the smaller amount of feed needed. It is quite common to castrate the boar after the sows have been settled and sell him as a stag. Since the average size herd of hogs is smaller than that of cattle or sheep, the ratio of boars to sows is lower than the ratio between breeding males and females in cattle or sheep.

LITTER SIZE

Under normal conditions there is a great range in litter size. Most herds average about nine pigs per litter, but within a herd there may be a great range. Some of the factors related to litter size are age of the sow, the service boar, nutrition, type, and individuality of the sow, and time of mating.

Older sows have larger litters than gilts. The litter size increases with the age of the sow up to about 2 years of age then it appears to remain constant until the 8th or 9th litter; then it declines. If the sire of the litter is bordering on infertility, this condition may affect litter size. Ample feeding on an adequate ration will produce larger litters than rations inadequate in quality or amounts. Breed and type are also related to prolificacy.

The number of pigs raised per sow farrowing has shown a slight upward tendency in the last two decades, during which time reports from pig crop surveys have been available. The number of pigs raised per sow per litter is about 7.0. Slightly larger litters are raised in the corn belt than elsewhere. Fall litters are a little larger than spring litters.

TIME OF FARROWING

April and March are the months of heaviest farrowing; in fact, nearly one half of the pigs raised are farrowed in March, April, and May. Heavy farrowing also takes place in August and September, but less than one fifth of the entire year's crop is farrowed in those months. There seems to be an increase in the fall farrowings coincidental with the greater use of the two-litter-a-year plan and the multi-farrowing plan.

ARTIFICIAL INSEMINATION WITH SWINE

In general, artificial insemination has been only mildly successful in swine. Usually only small litters are produced when this method is used. Although the boar produces a greater volume of semen than do other farm animals, the ejaculate from a single service can inseminate very few sows. Also, the sperm cannot be kept fertile as long as sperm from other common farm animals.

SWINE BREEDS

There is much variation in all of our swine breeds; even the Danish Landrace, which in that country went through many generations of production testing, is still quite variable in conformation and performance. Among most of our breeds can be found individuals which, bred either straight or crossed, could provide the stock for a successful enterprise. There is no one breed that is the best, all things considered, because of variations in the breeds.

A brief discussion of the swine breeds, their origins, native homes, early improvement, characteristics, and adaptability follows. The old breeds are included first and in alphabetical order, followed by the breeds of rather recent origin, the European breeds recently imported, and other breeds.

OLDER BREEDS

Berkshire

The Berkshire originated in the south-central part of England mainly in the counties of Berkshire and Wiltshire and adjoining counties. Berkshire are one of the oldest swine breeds. They were used in the improvement of several other breeds. The Old English hog formed the basis for this breed. It is thought that the Chinese, Siamese and Neapolitan breeds were crossed on the native stock in the breed's formation. Berkshires were the most numerous breed in England in 1789, but it was not until 1830 that the

Fig. 169. A junior champion Berkshire boar at the Wisconsin State Fair. Bred and exhibited by Milo Wolrab, Mt. Vernon, Iowa.

Fig. 170. Champion Berkshire gilt at the 1956 National Barrow Show. Shown by Rex Whitmore, Burltington, Wis. (American Berkshire Association.)

breed took definite form and, reportedly, crosses with Oriental breeds were made as late as 1842.

The Berkshire was first brought to the United States in 1823 and soon thereafter numerous importations were made. In this country there was much modification of the breed by several constructive breeders.

The present day Berkshire is medium in size and, as compared with other breeds, markedly different about the head. The face is slightly dished and broad between the eyes; the ear is erect, and the snout is short and broad. The color is black, with white feet, face, and tip of the tail. Occasionally the hair coat shows a tinge of bronze or copper. White markings previously indicated may be missing and there may be other white markings.

The Berkshire commonly produce excellent carcasses. The breed is active and the sows are good mothers. Berkshires have been criticized for being slow in maturing, lacking in prolificacy and too short and dished in the face. These defects are being eliminated in the present-day Berkshire.

Chester Whites

The native home of this breed was in southeastern Pennsylvania in the counties of Chester and Delaware. Much of the initial improvement took place in the Eastern States, particularly Pennsylvania, early in the 1800's and somewhat later in Ohio. The breed came from several stocks. The English Yorkshire, Lincolnshire, and Cheshire hog were used and also the Chinese and the Bedfordshire. From these breeds and strains came the Chester County White; the "county" was dropped from the name in 1848.

The breed is quite large. A clear white hair coat and skin is desired. Freckles or small blue spots on the skin are objectionable; large spots and off-color hair are disqualifications. The color of the hair and skin add to the attractiveness of the carcass, but white hogs may sunburn and show up unfavorably in dirty conditions.

Chester White sows are very prolific, good mothers and excellent milkers. Because of their inherent size, Chester White make relatively fast gain and can be ready for marketing at a young age. In addition to the objections which might be raised to the color, the breed has been faulted for excessive fatness in some individuals.

Duroc

This breed had its origin in the northeastern part of the United States from strains of reddish hogs, particularly the Jersey Red, Duroc, and the Red Rocks. The name Duroc Jersey was adopted in 1877 but later the "Jersey" was dropped.

This breed is of large size and, consequently, is fast gaining. Durocs are a medium cherry red in color without other admixture. There is a range in color from light to dark reddish brown. Black or white spots or flecks or white markings on the legs are objectionable.

Fig. 171. An outstanding Chester White boar pig, a champion at the National Barrow Show. Shown by Bud Roger, Assumption, Ill.

Fig. 172. A prize-winning Chester White gilt, a champion at the National Barrow Show. Shown by Ruben Schreyer, New Ulm, Minn.

Fig. 173.   A champion Duroc boar at the Duroc Congress, Rocket Crown. Shown by Willard Klein, Iowa Falls, Iowa.

Fig. 174.   A winning Duroc gilt at the Duroc Congress, Majesty Lady. Shown by the 4-Star Farm, Mayfield, Ky.

Durocs are a very popular breed because the adaptability of their color and their size, hardiness and prolificacy. The sows are excellent mothers. Because of the productivity of the sows and the fast economical gains of the market pigs, the Duroc has been widely accepted for commercial pork production. In some individuals there is excessive fatness resulting in higher than average yields of fat cuts and low yields of lean cuts. Selection pressure is toward leanness in Durocs as it is in the several of the other so-called lard breeds. Since there is variation within the breed progress toward the meatier kind is possible, for heritability of carcass quality is fairly high.

Hampshire

The Hampshire is the American belted breed of hogs and had its origin in Boone County, Kentucky. There are several breeds with a belted color pattern in various parts of the world. The Essex, a belted breed of England, is thought by some to be the progenitor of the Hampshire. A different breed that was completely black but also from Essex County, England, and bearing the same name was not uncommon in this country in the early 1900's. Wessex Saddleback, another belted breed, have been brought to the United States.

The Hampshire is somewhat smaller than some breeds and therefore ranks in the middle in growth rate. The basic color is black with a white belt that should entirely circle the body, including both front legs. White on head, other than on the front of snout, or higher on hind legs than the bottom of the ham is a disqualification. Some pigs are ineligible for registration because of the color requirements. The striking color pattern of the typical Hampshire is one of the attractive features of the breed.

Hampshire sows are active, quite prolific. The sows are very good mothers and raise a large proportion of their pigs. They perform well in crosses and are very popular with commercial hog producers and on hog markets. The breed ranks high in quality and in carcass merit. Consequently Hampshires have shown up well in interbreed carcass competition.

Hereford

The Hereford breed was started in Missouri in the early 1900's from the Durocs, OIC, and perhaps other breeds. Since its formation there have been some modifications by introduction of other breeding. The ideal color is cherry red, with white markings confined to the face, ears, jowl, neck, legs, and tassel of tail. There is considerable variation in the color markings. Also, there is room for improvement in the meatiness of the breed.

The breed appears to do quite well under corn belt conditions but it has not become very numerous.

Fig. 175. A Hampshire boar pig of the correct type, junior champion boar at the Illinois State Fair. Shown by Ralph Wilson, Burlington, Wis.

Fig. 176. An excellent Hampshire sow pig, a junior and grand champion sow at the Wisconsin State Fair. Shown by Walsh Bros., Beloit, Wis.

OIC

This is an offshoot from the Chester White breed; in its first stages it was the Ohio Improved Chester White. For a time difference of opinion existed as to whether it constituted a separate and distinct breed. As there was sharp and irreconcilable conflict on this point, OIC breeders were given the right to designate their stock as a breed.

The OIC was not hit by the big type craze early in this century, but more recently it has changed from the small, chuffy type to the intermediate meat-type hog. The present-day OIC is not unlike the Chester White. This breed is not numerous, but it is quite widespread through the United States.

Poland China

The native home of this breed was in southwestern Ohio in the Miami Valley, mainly in the counties of Butler, Warren, and Hamilton. The breed came from the Big China, Byfield, Russian, and other crosses on the common native stock. The Warren County hog was first formed from the crosses; they were white or spotted and of large size. The Berkshire and the Irish Grazier breeds were brought in to Warren County hogs. They had a great influence upon the swine breeding stock. From this combination arose the "Magie hog," the forerunner of the Poland China. The year 1850 has been taken as the starting time of the breed, but it was not given the current name until 1872.

The Poland China is one of the largest of our swine breeds and, consequently, it ranks high in gaining ability. The color is mainly black, with a blazed or white marked face, four white feet, a white brush on the tail and occasional other white markings. Some of the white markings may be missing without objection but there can be too much white on the body and legs.

Poland China have been extremely popular in all areas where hogs are produced in this country. They are fast growing, early maturing and of excellent carcass quality. This breed has an excellent record in interbreed competition, both on foot and in the carcass. It has fluctuated more in size type than the other breeds, but currently the ideal to which most breeders adhere is the intermediate-size meat type. The breed has shown improvement in litter size and mothering ability.

Spotted Poland China

The Spotted Poland China is like the Poland China in many respects. They were developed mainly in Indiana and neighboring states. The foundation was from the basic stocks from which the Poland China descended; in fact, the early breeders sought to retain the spotted color typical of the Poland China in the formative period. The Poland Chinas were

Fig. 177. A Poland China boar pig of the present-day type, a junior champion at the Wisconsin State Fair.

Fig. 178. A winning Poland China sow pig of the approved type, a junior champion at the Wisconsin State Fair.

Fig. 179. An excellent Spotted Poland China boar pig, a junior champion at the Iowa State Fair.

Fig. 180. A prize-winning Spotted Poland China gilt. Shown by A. J. Anderson, Kellogg, Iowa.

used later in the breed's development, and also some of the Gloucestershire Old Spot from England.

With the exception of the difference in color the present-day Spotted Poland China is quite comparable to its basic source, the Poland China. It is required that the white be not less than 20 per cent and not more than 80 per cent of the body surface. This breed is quite popular with breeders and market hog raisers because of its general adaptability as a "farmer's hog."

Tamworth

This very old breed came to us from central England. The breed name came from the town of Tamworth, Staffordshire, England. The foundation was the Old English hog, which came from the wild stock. Some believe that it was modified by the Irish Grazier breed. Tamworths were first brought to this country in 1882, and have become widely distributed but not numerous.

This breed is medium in size and of the so-called bacon type. The color is red with shades from light to dark. The head is distinctive in that it is long, rather narrow, with a long snout and the ears carried erect. In conformation it tends toward leanness, which is typical of bacon hogs.

Tamworths are very active, good grazers, extremely prolific, and good pig raisers. With their somewhat small size the growth rate is a little slow.

Yorkshire

This breed was developed in northern England in the Yorkshire area from the Old English hog. It is thought by some that the Berkshire and the Leicester breeds were used in forming the Yorkshire. There are three size types in England, small, medium, and large. The latter is known as the Large White in that country and was first imported in 1893. Only the Large White or Yorkshire became popular in this country. We now recognize two kinds, the Canadian and the English; the former is somewhat more refined.

The Yorkshire is noted for its large frame, long body, and bacon-type conformation. The color is white, but occasionally there are black spots or flecks in the skin. Breeders object to the black spots and off-colored hair is a disqualification. Yorkshires are extremely good in litter size and mothering ability. There is much variation within the breed; some have a slow growth rate and are late maturing. The crosses with other breeds are highly acceptable to the feeder and packer. In rail grade tests and carcass competition this breed, both straight and crossed, ranks high.

Fig. 181. A champion Tamworth mature boar.

Fig. 182. A champion Yorkshire mature boar.

NEWER BREEDS

Several new breeds have been developed at Agricultural Experiment Stations and by the U.S. Department of Agriculture from crossbred foundations. Crossing of inbred lines and production testing were used in formation. Starting with a crossbred foundation, the herd would be closed to outside blood and development with subsequent improvement would come from within. The various methods used were cross-breeding, inbreeding, testing, and selection. These breeds are often crosses of inbred lines, such as are used in producing hybrid boars. Several such breeds are now in existence, and they have a registration organization, the Inbred Livestock Registry Association.

Beltsville No. 1

This is a United States Department of Agriculture breed developed from crosses started in 1934. At the present time it is 75 per cent Danish Landrace, 25 per cent Poland China and 35 per cent inbred. The breed is mostly black in color with 10 to 40 per cent white. In conformation it is not unlike the predominate breed in its ancestry, the Danish Landrace.

Beltsville No. 2

This is the second of the United States Department of Agriculture developments. It was started in 1940. The breed carries 58 per cent of the Yorkshire from Denmark, 32 per cent of Duroc, 5 per cent of Landrace and 5 per cent of Hampshire. The color is red with some black spotting and a white underline. In general conformation it is typical of the present meat type.

Hamprace or Montana No. 1

Hamprace is another United States Department of Agriculture breed developed at the U.S. Range Livestock Experiment Station, Miles City, Montana. They are also known as the Montana No. 1 and Miles City Blacks. This breed came from the crossing of non-belted Hampshires with the Landrace. In percentage of blood the breed is about 55 per cent Landrace and 45 per cent Hampshire; inbreeding is about 32 per cent. The color is black and the swine are somewhat like the Landrace in appearance.

Maryland No. 1

This breed was the product of the cooperating agencies, the Maryland Agricultural Experiment Station, United States Department of Agriculture, and a private organization. The breed now has 62 per cent Danish Landrace and 38 per cent Berkshire breeding. The breed is black with white spots. In conformation it resembles the two foundation breeds.

Minnesota No. 1

This is one of the best known and most widespread of the breeds in this category. It was started in 1936 by the Minnesota Agricultural Experiment Station. The breed is made up of approximately 52 per cent Tamworth and 48 per cent Landrace. The color is red with occasional small black spots. The breed is somewhat like the Landrace ancestor in general conformation but shows some of the distinctive Tamworth characteristics. It was the breeders of Minnesota No. 1 that formed the Inbred Livestock Registry Association in 1946.

Minnesota No. 2

This is another breed developed by the same methods at the Minnesota Agricultural Experiment Station. The No. 2 breed had its origin in 1942 from crossing the Canadian Yorkshire with Poland Chinas. Finally the proportion of blood was 60 per cent Poland China and 40 per cent Yorkshire. Black with white marks or spots is the color of this breed.

Minnesota No. 3

The most recent of the Minnesota developments is the No. 3, which is being derived from Poland China and San Pierre crossed sows and from boars of the following breeds: Welch, Gloucester Old Spot, English Large White, and Beltsville No. 2.

San Pierre

This breed was started by an individual, A. Sahuela, on the Johnson Farms at San Pierre, Indiana, from Canadian Berkshire and Chester White crosses.

Washington No. 1 or Palouse

The Danish Landrace and the Chester White were inbred and crossed to form this breed at the Washington State College.

EUROPEAN BREEDS RECENTLY INTRODUCED OR IMPORTED

Several breeds new to this country have come to us from England and the Landrace has come from the Scandinavian countries.

Landrace

The first Landrace hog brought to this country came to us in 1934 from Denmark, where Landrace swine had been through many years of improvement by production testing. Some of the stock tracing to the original importation carries a trace of Poland China outcross. In recent years importations have been made from Norway, Denmark, and Sweden.

The breed is now known as the American Landrace, and they have their own registry association. Landrace have made a definite contribution in the forming of the new breeds previously described. Further, recently they have become popular and widely distributed in their own right.

Fig. 183. A grand champion Landrace boar at the Indiana State Fair. Bred and exhibited by Kekionga Farm, Decatur, Ind.

The Landrace is a medium-size, long-bodied, long-eared, white-colored breed, quite lean and meaty in conformation. A few freckles are tolerated in the skin, but not black hairs. The breed is fast growing and the crosses with domestic breeds are among the best in rate of gain. The sows are extremely prolific and are excellent mothers. The Landrace may lack some of the ruggedness desired for adverse conditions and the feet and legs are often faulty by our standards, but in carcass quality they rank very high.

Other breeds

Large Whites, Large Blacks, Wessex Saddlebacks, Welch, and others have been imported to this country recently.

OTHER SWINE BREEDS

There were two white breeds that at one time were fairly well known in the United States. They are the Cheshire and the Victoria. A small black breed, the Essex, also developed in the United States, is nearly extinct.

The Suffolk, an English white breed, was imported but never became numerous. The same might be said for the black-colored breed, the Large Black. Recently some of one of the belted breeds from England, the Wessex Saddleback, have been imported.

We at one time had quite a few Red Berkshires in this country. The Mulefoot breed of hogs is prevalent in some areas.

The student should consult the various breed associations regarding the current requirements for registration, breed improvement plans, and other pertinent matters subject to change. The more prominent breeds have score cards describing their ideal and in many instances hold breed type conferences.

GENERAL CONSIDERATIONS

Types within a breed

As previously indicated, we have types within a breed. For example, we recognize by form or general conformation small type and large type and also those in between. The intermediate is common and popular today. The small types were popular in the early part of the century. This type proved uneconomical on the farms because of the slow gains and low prolificacy. They were also unsuited for farm feed-lot and forage-crop utilization. They produced pork cuts that were small and yielded large quantities of lard.

The extreme rangy kind which followed the small type was also not the best for the packer or the producer. These were slow maturing, lacked finish at desirable marketable weights, and had an excess of bone and too large pork cuts. Generally, they were too large for the usual farm farrowing-house equipment.

Since neither the large nor the small suited the producer or the packer, the tendency of late has been to stay with the intermediate type. This kind has the greatest adaptability, is unexcelled in economy of production, and is highly acceptable to the consumer. Some changes in type will occur, but with closer cooperation between packers and producers they will perhaps be less violent than previously.

Some breeds have switched more in type than others, and breeders within a breed are not wholly in agreement as to the ideal type.

Choosing a breed

There is no superior breed for all conditions. One breed may be suited to certain situations because of its peculiar characteristics. Yet, for the most part these distinctive external characteristics are such features as color or shape of head and ears, which are not highly related to economy of production. The response of the various breeds may be much the same under similar circumstances. Some breeds are larger or more prolific or better grazers than others, and these are features that affect production. There is considerable difference in the carcasses of various breeds. Local market demand and suitability to local conditions, along with economy of production, should form the basis for breed selection.

Breeds change in their popularity, yet some breeds have less fluctuation in popularity than others.

Differences in the size of breeds

Based on the weights of prize-winning animals, breeding swine at the National Swine Show can be classified as to size. The Poland China and the Duroc appear to be the largest of the swine breeds. The Yorkshire, Hampshire, and Tamworth are in the lighter-weight group. The Chester White, Spotted Poland China, and Berkshire are much the same in weight and in between the two other groups. The breeds heavier as pigs usually retain that advantage in all the age classes. Boars generally outweigh sows.

Interbreed competition

At the International Live Stock Exposition, for the past decade Berkshires and Poland Chinas, ranked high in interbreed competition. These breeds have had most of the champions in the carload, carcass, and individual classes.

BREEDING SYSTEMS

Since swine reproduce rapidly, considerable experimental evidence is available on the different breeding systems. Likewise, breeders have gone further in trying out different breeding systems.

GRADING UP

This method has long been used by hog raisers for the improvement of native or scrub stock. A purebred boar is used on the scrub and grades, and in three or four generations the high grades are practically equal to purebreds in market value. Since this process has been going on for years, very low-grade or scrub sows are now rarely used for breeding. Swine retrogress if they escape from domestication and forage for their living; this is the history of the razorback hog. The amount of improvement possible from the use of a purebred boar on low-grade and scrub hogs of nondescript breeding is shown by some Alabama experiments.[1]

---

[1] J. C. Grimes, W. E. Sewell, and W. C. Taylor, "Grading Up Hogs," *Bull. 234,* Alabama Polytechnic Institute, November, 1930.

	SCRUBS	50 PER CENT GRADES	75 PER CENT GRADES	87.5 PER CENT GRADES
Days to reach 200 pounds	244	201	201	187
Daily gain, pounds	0.95	1.18	1.19	1.26
Feed for 100 pounds gain, pounds	465	403	388	382
Feed cost for 100 pounds gain	$9.31	$8.07	$7.75	$7.63

These data clearly indicate that the pure breeding causes an improvement in the rate of gain and feed for gain when used with scrubs. It will also be noted that the improvement is less marked as the breeding of the females approaches that of the purebreds.

CROSSBREEDING

This practice has proved its worth in experimental trials and in the hands of swine raisers. We do not know how all crosses will respond, and we have found that some crosses give better results than others.

What might be expected in crossbreeding of swine is summarized in an Iowa bulletin.[2]

The following statements concern the average results. There was much individual variability from litter to litter and from pig to pig even in the same litter, both among crossbreds and among purebreds.

The results obtained at the Iowa Agricultural Experiment Station involve 1,015 pigs farrowed in 108 litters. These data include the Landrace-Poland China crosses as well as those made with the Duroc, Poland China, and Yorkshire breeds.

The percentage of stillborn pigs was smaller among the crossbreds than among the purebreds.

Crossbred pigs were somewhat more vigorous at birth than purebreds, as shown by their ability to survive until weaning age.

Crossbred pigs averaged about 3 or 4 pounds heavier at weaning time than purebreds. The weaning weight of crossbred litters averaged more than that of comparable purebred litters, partly because of the larger size of the crossbreds and partly because the crossbred litters on the average contained slightly more pigs at weaning time.

Crossbred pigs gained about 0.09 to 0.12 pounds per day more while in the feed lot than did the purebreds, which means a saving of about 10 days to 2 weeks time in getting them to a weight of 225 pounds.

Crossbreds reached a weight of 225 pounds on 25 to 30 pounds less feed than was required by purebreds.

The crossbred sows observed in this study proved to be efficient pig

[2] J. L. Lush et al., "Crossbreeding Hogs for Pork Production," Bull. 380, Iowa Agr. Exp. Sta., June, 1939.

producers, whether mated back to a boar of one of the parent breeds or to a boar of a third breed. When sired by a purebred boar, the pigs from the crossbred sows, either backcross or three-breed cross, compared favorably with the first-cross pigs.

There is some reason to suppose that breeds differ in their response to crossing, and also that families or strains within breeds differ.

Crossbreeding can be continued as a steady policy only by going to purebred herds for the boars needed for replacement. Crossbred animals have a lower value than purebreds as transmitters of inheritance. Crossbred sows may be used successfully for breeding if the boar is a purebred. In this way the hybrid vigor of the crossbred dam in nursing and rearing pigs may express itself enough to more than compensate for her lower value as a transmitter of inheritance. No such offset for his lowered transmitting value could exist in the case of a crossbred boar. Planless and unsystematic crossing may quickly result in a mongrel herd from which the owner will get neither profit nor pride of ownership.

USING CROSSBRED SOWS

Crossbred sows are generally efficient pig producers. They may be mated back to a boar of the parent breeds, which is backcrossing. If mated to a boar of another breed, the practice is called three-way crossing. "Crisscrossing" is the term applied to backcrossing carried past the first generation, in which boars of the parent breeds are alternated on the crossbred sows.

Crisscrossing

The plan for crossing of two breeds, crisscrossing, for successive generations is as follows, with the approximate per cent of the two breeds in each generation.

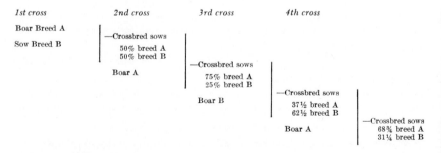

1st cross	2nd cross	3rd cross	4th cross
Boar Breed A	—Crossbred sows		
Sow Breed B	50% breed A		
	50% breed B		
	Boar A	—Crossbred sows	
		75% breed A	
		25% breed B	
		Boar B	—Crossbred sows
			37½ breed A
			62½ breed B
			Boar A —Crossbred sows
			68¾ breed A
			31¼ breed B

Rotation breeding

When a third breed is used in the crossing scheme, or there is rotation breeding, the plan and the per cent of the various breeds is as follows in the different generations.

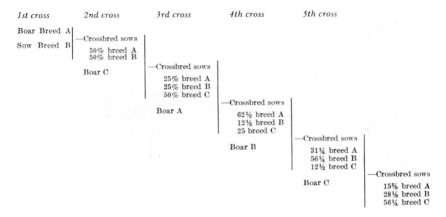

1st cross	2nd cross	3rd cross	4th cross	5th cross

Boar Breed A
Sow Breed B
—Crossbred sows
50% breed A
50% breed B

Boar C
—Crossbred sows
25% breed A
25% breed B
50% breed C

Boar A
—Crossbred sows
62½ breed A
12½ breed B
25 breed C

Boar B
—Crossbred sows
31¼ breed A
56¼ breed B
12½ breed C

Boar C
—Crossbred sows
15⅝ breed A
28⅛ breed B
56¼ breed C

INBREEDING IN SWINE

Inbreeding in swine results in reduction of vigor and productivity. When practiced with rigid selection, the loss of vigor may be very slight. This system was used rather widely in the formation of our swine breeds. By means of inbreeding, recessive characters can be eliminated, and the inbreds may be pure for their characters.

Inbred lines of swine within some of the breeds have been established by the U.S. Department of Agriculture, by some experiment stations, and by some breeders. Crosses of such lines in some cases give favorable results. Such crosses are referred to as "hybrids." The terms incross or linecross are also used for such crosses. Some hybrids are crossbred as well as being crosses of inbred lines. When breeds and lines are in crosses they may be designated as linecrossbreds.

BREEDING STOCK SELECTION

As but a small percentage of any crop of pigs is necessary to produce the next crop, swine breeders have an opportunity to practice rather heavy selection in choosing the replacements for the breeding herd. The average interval between generations in swine is 2 to 3 years; that is, the parents have an average age of about 2½ years when their offspring are born. Of course, it is possible in swine for the sow producing the litter and the sire of the litter to be not more than 12 months of age when their first litter is born. The average interval is greater because many of the sows are kept for more than one litter and because herd boars are often kept for more than one pig crop. Cases are on record where swine have produced offspring when over 10 years of age. It has been estimated that 10 to 15 per cent of the sows and 1 to 2 per cent of the boars produced are needed for replacement if the hog population is not increasing. Compared to other classes of livestock, the number of swine needed for replacements is much lower, because the brood sow has a much higher productive rate than the mare, cow, or ewe.

BASIS FOR SELECTION

We can select individuals for the breeding herd on the basis of conformation or individuality, pedigree, or performance. Performance is the best single basis, but this is only available when an individual has produced. Consequently, our breeding herd selection often is based on appearance, pedigree, and performance of the individual's close relatives.

Hog raisers range from the purebred breeder to the market hog raiser, and selection is a far different matter for the one than for the other. The producer of purebreds, because of the sale of breeding stock from his herd, retains for breeding a high percentage of hogs raised. The market hog raiser, on the other hand, may sell all of his pig crop for slaughter. The farmer who raises market hogs depends upon the swine breeder for his replacements and selects, therefore, what he thinks will be economical converters of feeds into gains. He also has some idea what the meat packer wants and tries to satisfy him. Briefly, the man who raises market hogs wants a hog that will make rapid gains on a low feed requirement and that will be in demand when finished for market. His selections are, therefore, based on these two main objectives. Fortunately, there is no conflict between the characteristics necessary to accomplish these objectives. It is possible to have in the same individual efficient and rapid conversion of feed into gains and high desirability of carcass.

TYPE FOR THE COMMERCIAL PRODUCER

The breeder who sells breeding stock to the market hog raiser must have what the commercial producer needs in order to continue in the swine breeding business. Such breeders must practice selection to hold high merit in the herd. They, likewise, cannot afford to sell for breeding anything that they think might prove inferior. Actually, even in supposedly well-selected individuals, the response in the breeding pen is not always satisfactory.

Perhaps some features of selection should be pointed out before a plan of selection is suggested. In the first place, selection is usually most effective when first practiced, and then diminishes in effectiveness. If, for example, we are selecting heavily for litter size, the first steps in that direction are likely to be the more effective. After the size of the litter has been increased, further improvement is less rapid. In fact, heavy selection may be necessary to hold the gain. This property of selection is a factor in buying a herd boar. A boar may show marked improvement in the offspring when used in a herd of average merit, but in a herd of superior sows its progeny may be below the herd average.

Seldom in selection do we gain as much as we expect to. We get but a portion of what we select for. There is a big difference in the heriditability of various characteristics. Litter size is but slightly hereditable—about 10 per cent—and fat back is at least 50 per cent hereditable. Selection may be a very effective means of altering a characteristic in a breed. However, in deciding what to keep in the breeding herd we are always confronted with the fact that we are selecting for many characters at once. The individual selected is a composite and represents a series of concessions in regard to many characters. Selection effects are difficult to separate from changes caused by influences that are nongenetic. For example, at a Swedish agricultural experiment station the feed to produce 1 pound of gain on growing and fattening pigs was reduced from 4.15 to 3.35 pounds in a 15-year period. This increase in efficiency was due, no doubt, to improvement of feeding methods as well as to better breeding.

Desirable characteristics

It might be well to review briefly what we desire in our breeding hogs, i.e., the points we should consider in judging or selecting breeding hogs. For the brood sow, these considerations might be broken up into the following general headings.

1. Size. Rather large size is demanded in breeding hogs because it is potential size that imparts the quality of rapid growth. Rapid growth and economical gains are positively correlated. We can have too much size in breeding hogs, as was evident in the extreme or rangy type. If pigs have been full fed and do not have sufficient finish at 200-pounds, their parents are probably too large.

2. Form. The form desirable in a market hog is highly acceptable in a breeding sow. Less width and a little more length of body and legs are typical of the breeding gilt at 200 pounds, as compared with a market barrow. Extremes in either direction are to be avoided. The tall, rangy kind lacks fleshing qualities; the short, compact kind finishes at too young an age and lacks growing qualities. All things considered, the intermediate type is the most desirable. A strong, evenly arched top, smooth sides and shoulders, uniform width, and heavy hams suit the most critical in form.

3. Quality. In the breeding sow, quality is usually a matter of smoothness and trimness. It should not be carried to the point of sacrifice in size, ruggedness, or ample bone. A good growth of hair is desirable, but curly, bristly, or wavy coats are objectionable. Swirls or rosettes in the hair along the top line are objectionable on most purebred swine.

4. Feeding qualities. The qualities associated with feeding capacity are highly desired in breeding hogs. Length, width, and depth of body are the principal indicators of capacity to convert feed into gains.

5. Maturity. As early market maturity is essential in a good market hog, it is also requisite in the brood sow. To be finished for market at a young age and at desired market weight is the objective in the market hog, and for the brood sow we want evidence that she will produce that kind.

6. Fleshing. High condition or fatness is neither advantageous nor desirable in a brood sow. Yet heavy fleshing, as indicated by wide, plump hams and ample width of back and loin, is highly desirable. In selecting gilts or boars at weights about 200 pounds, a measure of their meatiness as opposed to fatness can be made by the fat back probe of the live animals. It is most meaningful when a full feeding program has been followed, for potential fatness would not be expressed with limited feeding.

7. Vigor. As hogs are often troubled with parasites and disease, we should select only those with strong constitutions, as shown by a deep, wide chest, strong heart girth, and a body of good depth. An active, animated appearance indicates vigor.

8. Feet and legs. Strong underpinning is of great importance in breeding sows. The ideal set of legs is such as is preferred in the draft horse, that is, straight and under the four corners. Hog men, however, desire straight rather than sloping pasterns. With reference to breeding hogs, hog men often use the word "soundness," referring to freedom from any noticeable defects.

9. Breeding qualities or sex characteristics. A good brood sow is one that can successfully suckle a large litter. She should have at least 10 teats of uniform size and evenly placed. Inverted or blind teats, those that fail to emerge, should be discriminated against. Some breeds are requiring at least 12 good well-placed teats and some attention is given to the rudimentaries in the boars. The udder, together with general refinement throughout, is regarded as an index of the maternal qualities of the sow.

10. Disposition. A sow that is quiet and has a tractable disposition will be more likely to prove herself as a good pig raiser. In the usual herd sows must be handled a great deal; so a good disposition is essential.

11. Constitution and health. Great caution should be exercised with respect to vigor and health, for disease control is a very important consideration. The absence of unusual symptoms, such as cough, rough hair coat, poor appetite, or thin condition, assures one that the individual is probably in good health. Yet there are numerous diseases of swine not readily recognized by external symptoms. It is also well to guard against such things as common intestinal worms, lungworms, hog mange, and other parasitic conditions.

12. Breed type. The difference between breeds in physical characteristics is referred to as "breed type." These differences in swine are largely in size, color, form, shape of the head, carriage of the ears, and other features distinctive of the breed. These characters are not highly related to utility.

All the above points have bearing on selecting the individual brood sow. The various points are not evaluated, because a notable deficiency in any one would constitute a disqualification. These items are considered always with respect to age and the changes incident to age.

For the breeding boar, we would use much the same pattern, altering only such things as apply to sex. More ruggedness is wanted in the herd boar. Masculinity is stressed.

OTHER GENERAL FEATURES TO BE CONSIDERED IN SELECTION

In addition to the features determined by inspection of the individual, or individuality, there are other items to survey in making a selection. Following are listed some of the more important features.

1. Ancestry, parentage, or pedigree. By knowing something about the ancestry of an individual we can make some estimate of its breeding ability. Of course, immediate ancestors are a better basis for judging an animal's worth than remote individuals in its pedigree. An individual receives a sample inheritance from each of its parents. The sample received is a matter of chance and, as individuals are not homozygous or pure for all their characters, it is impossible to estimate from pedigree alone what an offspring will be. On the other hand, consideration of the pedigree may help to eliminate some errors that might be made if selection were on individuality alone.

2. Performance. Future performance cannot be forecast without error. There are many different measures of performance, or progeny tests, which may be helpful in making an estimate of production. We have in swine husbandry applied some measures of production. This has been more difficult for swine than for some other classes of livestock. In dairy cattle, for example, the production of cows has been measured by the milk scale and the Babcock test; standards have been set up and selective registration based on performance is practiced. What have hogmen to use in measuring production? Following, a few measures are listed: (1) records on litter size at birth and at weaning time, (2) measuring weight at various ages for pigs and litters, (3) feed efficiency tests, (4) records of performance tests, (5) carcass evaluation. Interbreed competition in production trials and show-ring on-foot carcass classes are helpful, but with these there may be big environmental differences.

Testing

Testing merely uncovers the facts concerning the individual or litter and does not show up environmental differences, which are minimized when the tested pigs are treated in the same manner. Testing may fall short of its effectiveness unless applied to all individuals in the herd.

Performance testing may be on the individual or upon the progeny. A boar or gilt may be tested for rate of gain and efficiency of feed conversion and then the same tests may be applied to the offspring. Sow testing is on a litter basis. Often, results of such tests are included in the pedigree of purebreds in the production registry or certified meat hog programs. Testing, as applied to swine, has included litter size, weights at a given age, feed efficiency, on-foot fat back measurements, and carcass evaluation. The latter is determined from litter mates or other relatives.

Farm testing, commonly known as "sow testing," has long been practiced. It involves ear notching the pigs shortly after birth to identify the litters and then weighing at some definite age, usually weaning time, and again when at marketable weights, usually around 180 days of age. Individuals and organizations have successfully carried out such programs and, in some instances, feeding tests for determining feed efficiency have been included.

Organizations

Several of the swine purebred associations have production registry programs. Also, there is an all-breed production registry plan. It is applied to litters, dams, and sires. To qualify, a mature sow's litter must number 8 and weigh 320 pounds at 56 days; for a gilt or sow farrowing under 15 months of age, the minimum weight is 275 pounds. Production-registered sows must have farrowed 2 qualifying litters. Boars are qualified when they have sired 15 qualified litters, 5 qualified daughters, or 10 sows with 1 production-registered litter each, or various combinations. There have been modifications of the requirements made by the different associations or made generally to recognize variation in weaning ages.

There is also a certified meat hog program adopted by the National Association of Swine Records. It is based upon minimum standards for rate of gain to 200 pounds, or equivalent at 180 days of age, and carcass quality, in addition to production-registry requirements. Carcass quality is determined from the loin area at the 10th rib; carcass length and fat back thickness standards have been set up for three weight groups. The fat back is measured in three places, at the first rib, the last rib and the last lumbar vertebra from the outside of the skin and at right angle to the back. Loin area is determined from tracing of loin eye with a planimeter. The carcass length is measured from the junction of the front of the first rib and the vertebra to the aitch bone.

Swine testing has recently gone one step further with the establishment of testing stations, where more complete and accurate measures and tests can be made. Boars so tested are available to producers. Buyers are provided with information as to the boar's rate of gain, feed conversion efficiency and back fat thickness. Also, carcass information is given on full and half brother barrows.

By means of these tests, we hope to acquire in our brood sows high prolificacy and production of heavy litters of pigs, pigs with high efficiency in making gains, and pigs of high carcass value. Further, with production-tested boars used as sires, we can foretell better what the results of mating might be; however, there is still one intangible, "nicking."

Limitations of selection

Selection has a definite field of usefulness in the swine herd and breed improvement. It does also have limitations. In the first place, it is difficult to separate the effects of environment from the effects of heredity. Then too, the ideal hog is a composite of many features and, therefore, progress toward improvement in any one character by selection may be slow. Our ideal for many characters (like type) is not toward either extreme but toward the intermediate; consequently, we cannot put selection pressure on any one character to the exclusion of others.

Part III–SHEEP

Chapter 28

SHEEP—GENERAL VIEW

Sheep, like others of our domesticated farm animals, were used by man prior to our historic time. In the days of pastoral agriculture sheep raising flourished, for sheep were raised entirely upon herbage. Sheep were easily domesticated, and one person could care for a large flock. They were a source of meat, wool, pelts, and milk; early in man's culture they became the object of husbandry. Shepherding is one of man's oldest professions.

ORIGINS

TIME OF DOMESTICATION

Domestication of sheep, in all probability, was in the early Neolithic Age. Sheep are referred to in the first writings of man and they were among the first animals to be domesticated. In the earlier passages of the Bible sheep are mentioned. The word "sheep" is of ancient origin. The word "avi," in Sanskrit, was applied to sheep; its meaning is to keep or to guard. Early man tamed, confined, and protected or guarded sheep which yielded meat, milk, and skin for his use. Sheep are pictured on the earliest Egyptian monuments, which date some time between 5000 and 4000 B.C. Sheep were also used by the early people of Europe, for bones have been found in the inhabited caves and the lake dwellings.

It is quite probable that sheep were domesticated in different regions or at different times, and do not descend from a single wild species. Central and western Asia, probably Turkestan, were the first places of domestication.

With the spread of civilization, sheep moved to the countries where they could be grown. Today, sheep husbandry is practised in practically all agricultural regions.

ZOOLOGICAL CLASSIFICATIONS

Domesticated sheep, as well as goats, belong to the subfamily *Ovinae* *(Caprinae)*. This in turn is a part of the *Bovidae* family, which includes cattle, antelopes, chamois, musk ox, and others, all of which are hollow-horned ruminants. The subfamily *Ovinae* are principally highland or mountain dwellers, and there are many divisions of the group. The genus *Ovis* includes all sheep and the domesticated sheep are of the *aries* species.

Differences of opinion exist as to which of the several wild species is the progenitor of domestic sheep; it seems quite probable that they may stem from several sources. The wool-specialized breeds are supposed to have spread from Asia Minor through Greece and Italy to Spain. The wild sheep of northern Europe domesticated by the Nordic tribes are the assumed foundation for the mutton type.

CLASSES OF SHEEP

Within the range of animals classed as sheep there is a wide variety of races and breeds. The tail characteristic is extremely variable in sheep, as is the nature of the hair or wool. The following classes of sheep are recognizable.

1. Long-tailed sheep. This includes the sheep common to the United States, which for the most part came from Europe. The hairy sheep of Africa, such as the Persian, belong to this group.

2. Fat-tailed sheep. The Karakuls are typical of this group. They have long tails which are broad, flat, and tapering rapidly toward the end.

3. Short-tailed sheep. Marsh or moorland sheep of northern Europe are of this kind.

4. Fat-rumped sheep.[1] There are several local breeds of this kind throughout central Asia. The distinctive feature is the fat on the rump which is in the form of two great cushions, divided by a median cleft on the buttocks; these sheep have no tails.

INTRODUCTION TO THE UNITED STATES

The bighorn or Rocky Mountain sheep, which are confined to the Rocky Mountain region from Alaska to California, were native to this con-

---

[1] An attempt is being made to develop a breed of sheep without tails at the South Dakota Agricultural Experiment Station. Fat-rumped sheep from Siberia were used with domestic breeds, the object being to develop a breed that had desirable mutton and wool qualities and would not have to be docked. This project was started in 1914, but progress is slow, for the tailless character is not dominant in crossing. James W. Wilson, "Development of the No-Tail Sheep," *Circ. 28,* S. D. Agr. Exp. Sta., 1940.

tinent. However, domesticated sheep were first brought by the Spanish explorers. Columbus brought sheep and goats in 1493. Cortez brought Merino sheep into Mexico in 1530. The Spaniards who founded Santa Fe in New Mexico were thought to have brought in multicolored sheep from which the Navajo Indian sheep descended. English breeds of sheep were brought over to the colonists along the eastern seaboard, and were moved westward with colonization. The first sheep brought to this country direct were imported to Jamestown in 1609. Merino breeds from Spain were first introduced to the United States in 1793, and by 1810 there developed a strong demand for such sheep. Heavy importations of Merinos were then made for a few years from Spain, but that import demand ended in 1816.

GROWTH OF SHEEP PRODUCTION IN THE UNITED STATES

The sheep population of the United States was estimated at 7 million head in 1810. As sheep production moved westward with pioneering farming, numbers increased. By 1830 farming had crossed the Allegheny Mountains, and in 1840 there were 19 million head reported in the census. The Civil War affected sheep production, first by causing an increase in the price of wool because of the demand for woolen goods and, second, by limiting the supply of cotton. Following the war, wool prices fell because of lessened demand and increased competition from cotton and imported wool. Following the expansion and contraction caused by the Civil War, numbers of sheep increased, and in 1883 and 1884 our estimated number on farms exceeded 50 million head of stock sheep, which has not been equaled since.

Sheep were raised in our pioneer agriculture mainly for wool. In the farming states the mutton-type sheep are more suitable for most systems of farming; consequently, the fine-wooled sheep are localized in certain of the farming areas and are extensive in the range country.

STOCK SHEEP AND LAMBS IN THE UNITED STATES

Stock sheep and lambs are those sheep maintained upon ranches and farms and not being fed out for market. This other group is designated as sheep and lambs on feed. Yearly estimates are made of the sheep and lamb population as of January 1, and this estimate is then broken up into stock sheep and lambs, and sheep and lambs on feed. For the decade 1946–1955 the total number of stock sheep and lambs was about 28.6 million head, and there were about 4.4 million sheep and lambs on feed or a total sheep population of 33 million head. Stock sheep and lambs declined in numbers until recently, and there has been a downward trend in the number of sheep on feed for market. There have been reductions in number in both the western and the native sheep states. (See Figure 184.)

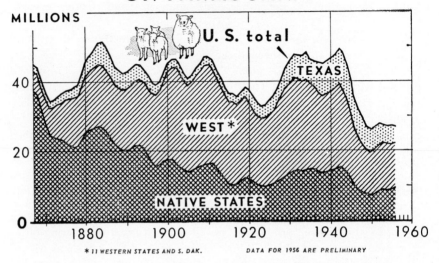

STOCK SHEEP AND LAMBS ON FARMS JAN. I

MILLIONS

U. S. total

TEXAS

40

WEST *

20

NATIVE STATES

0

1880   1900   1920   1940   1960

*11 WESTERN STATES AND S. DAK.   DATA FOR 1956 ARE PRELIMINARY

Fig. 184. For a long time the trend in sheep numbers was neither upward nor downward. Numbers declined markedly from 1944 to 1949. Recently there has been some shifting from range to farm flocks and from west to east. (U.S.D.A., Agricultural Marketing Service.)

SHEEP AND LAMBS: METHODS OF MANAGEMENT

Lamb.feeding areas in the range country

EASTERN BORDER OF RANGE COUNTRY
West of this line sheep are produced under range conditions and east of this line sheep production is carried on with small farm flocks

Fattening lambs in cornfields of western corn belt

Western lambs fattened in barns for winter market

Early lambing areas (Jan. and Feb.)

Lambing in barns and sheds

Fine wool-producing section of southeastern Ohio and southwestern Pennsylvania

Early lambing areas. Lambs dropped Nov.-Jan. Sheep run on range in summer and on farms and ranches in winter

Early lambs produced on blue grass pastures

Piney woods range sheep

Range sheep in fenced pastures. Wool principal product. Some wethers carried.

Fig. 185. Distribution of sheep and lambs in the United States. (U.S.D.A., Bur. of Agri. Economics.)

486

AREAS OF SHEEP RAISING

The distribution of sheep in this country is shown in Figure 185, and the changes in sheep production, as indicated by the number of stock sheep, are shown in Figure 184. About 70 per cent of our breeding or stock sheep are in the 17 western states, where there is also considerable winter lamb feeding. The breeding flocks in this area are grazed on the native vegetation of the range and use much of the forage grown in this great pasture area. Sheep can be ranged on the more arid lands more easily than other domestic animals. The sheep industry first developed in California and New Mexico and later spread to the other range states. Montana and Wyoming were the last of the range states to be reached by sheep production. Sheep are widely spread through the western states, but heavy concentrations are in the Edwards Plateau of Texas, the Sacramento Valley of California, and the irrigated valleys in the range area.

Sheep raising has not always centered on the western range. About a century ago Vermont was a leading sheep state. Sheep have persisted in the hilly sections of the East and Midwest. It will be noted that heavy concentrations of sheep exist in east central Ohio, southwestern Pennsylvania, West Virginia, Virginia, southern Michigan, north central Kentucky, Indiana, central Tennessee, northern Missouri, and southern Iowa.

The center of sheep population for this country has moved westward with each census and now is in the region of southwestern Nebraska. There has been some slight veering from a straight westward movement. Lately there has been more of an increase in the native sheep states than the western states. Productive conditions cause the sheep population to shift, but in general the feed supply is the greatest factor in such changes.

Farms and ranches raising sheep

The recent agricultural censuses show that sheep are reported on 8.1 per cent of the farms and ranches. The states in the east north central geographical division (Ohio, Indiana, Illinois, Michigan, and Wisconsin) have the largest proportion of farms and ranches with sheep. Other divisions that have a large proportion of farms and ranches with sheep are the mountain and west north central. The east south central and the south Atlantic sections have but few farms with sheep.

About one fourth of the farms and ranches of Wyoming, Ohio, and Nevada have sheep, while in South Carolina, Florida, and Georgia about 1 in 200 farms reported sheep.

Leading states in sheep production

Sheep production of the various states may be compared. Following is a listing of some of the states leading in sheep numbers. These numbers are the average of yearly estimates made as of January 1 of each year and they include stock sheep and those on feed. In other words, they present a complete sheep inventory.

STOCK SHEEP AND LAMBS—NUMBERS IN LEADING STATES

10-Year, Yearly Average [2]

STATE	THOUSAND HEAD
Texas	7,551
Wyoming	2,316
Montana	2,056
California	1,908
New Mexico	1,499
Utah	1,477
Colorado	1,365
Ohio	1,152
Idaho	1,130
South Dakota	1,067
Missouri	1,011
Iowa	849
Oregon	794
Minnesota	761
Kentucky	730
North Dakota	517
United States	31,682

SHEEP POPULATION IN LEADING SHEEP COUNTRIES

Australia, South Africa, Argentina, and New Zealand are large sheep-producing countries. The ratio of sheep to human population is wide in those countries; therefore, a considerable portion of their production, especially wool, enters the world trade. In this country we have less than one sheep for five inhabitants; we produce about all the mutton and lamb we use and import much of the wool we use. Since our population has been increasing and sheep numbers have not shown any decided trend, the ratio of sheep to people has widened. In the decade ending in 1870 the ratio was even. In Australia there are over 16 sheep to each human inhabitant.

The sheep population of the entire world is over 800 million head. Therefore, we have less than 4 per cent of the world sheep population.

On page 489 is a list of the leading sheep-raising countries and their sheep population for a recent 5-year period.

ORIGIN OF BREEDS

Most of our domestic breeds of sheep originated in Great Britain. There are more than 200 breeds of sheep. In our census enumeration of registered

[2] *Agricultural Statistics,* U.S.D.A., 1955.

purebred sheep 18 different breeds are listed separately; a large number are included with other and unspecified breeds. Breeds of sheep were developed to meet specialized conditions; it is quite common to name the breeds for the county in which they originate.

In general, the breeds of sheep vary in their type, character, and fineness of wool, size, and presence or absence of horns. Color markings, or color of the hair on the face, ears, and legs, wool covering, form, and shape of head and ears are also features in which breeds differ. Sheep breeds are discussed in some detail in Chapter 34.

SHEEP: NUMBER IN LEADING SHEEP COUNTRIES

1952–1956 Average [3]

COUNTRY	THOUSANDS
Australia	127,102
U.S.S.R.	104,260
Argentina	51,537
India	40,000
New Zealand	37,741
Union of South Africa	35,859
United States	31,586
Uruguay	26,130
Turkey	25,565
United Kingdom	22,708
Brazil	16,952
Iran	16,724
Yugoslavia	11,261
Italy	9,886
French Morocco	9,491
Greece	8,358
Iraq	8,341
France	7,854
Algeria	5,372
Mexico	5,100
Estimated World Total	867,540

CLASSIFICATION OF BREEDS ACCORDING TO TYPE

On the basis of principal use, sheep breeds are divided into two types —mutton and wool. Mutton sheep are often divided further on the basis of the character of the wool into medium-wool and long-wool breeds.

In some classifications a carpet-wool type is recognized, including the Blackfaced Highland breed. The breeds which have resulted from a long-wool–fine-wool cross, such as the Corriedale, Columbia, Panama, Romeldaie and Targhee are sometimes termed the "crossbred wool type."

[3] *For. Agr. Circ.,* U.S.D.A., 1956. Average of 5-year period if available, otherwise for any year or years within the period.

Medium-wool sheep

Medium-wool sheep are kept primarily for mutton and lamb production. The wool on this class is medium in length, fineness, and weight. A 12-month growth will range from 2 to 5 inches in length. The fleece is usually quite compact and light colored on the exterior. This class is medium to large in size.

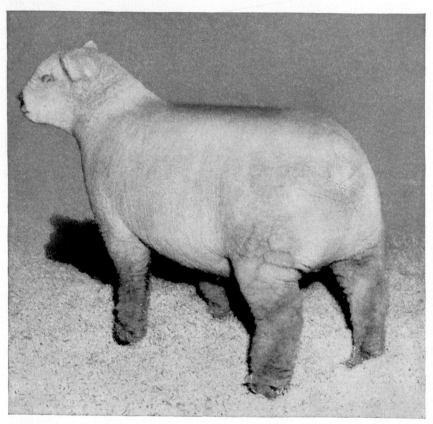

Fig. 186. A medium-wool sheep. Southdown wether lamb, grand champion wether at the International Livestock Exposition. Bred and exhibited by the University of Kentucky, Lexington, Ky.

Long-wool sheep

Long-wool sheep are also primarily mutton sheep. The fleece is light colored, high in luster, and hangs in definite curls or locks. The wool is distinctive and it is long, lashy, and hairlike in appearance. A length of from 5 to 12 inches is acquired in a year's growth. Long-wool sheep are of large size and very rugged.

Fine-wool sheep

Fine-wool sheep are mainly of the conformation of typical wool-type sheep, and the main goal in their development has been wool production. A fleece from 1 to 4 inches in length results from a year's growth, and the fiber is very fine with numerous crimps (16 to 22 per inch). The fleece is high in yolk, very compact, and usually dark on the outside because of the dirt which adheres to it. The fine-wool sheep are small or medium in size, and a white color is typical of the face and legs. Rambouillets are quite large in size, and with this breed about equal emphasis goes to wool and mutton.

TYPE	SUBTYPE	BREED
Mutton	Medium wool	Shropshire Hampshire Dorset Southdown Cheviot Oxford Suffolk Tunis Ryeland Corriedale Columbia Panama Romeldale Southdale Targhee Montadale
Mutton	Long wool	Lincoln Cotswold Leicester English Border Leicester Romney Blackfaced Highland
Wool	Fine wool	Merino (American and Delaine) Class A Class B Class C Rambouillet Class B Class C Australian Merino
Fur		Karakul

Fur-type sheep

The Karakul sheep originated in Bokhara in west central Asia.[4] Im-

[4] C. G. Potts, "Karakul Sheep," *Farmers' Bull. 1632*, U.S.D.A., 1931. Karl Jahn. *Karakul Fur Sheep Breeding.* Breeder's Publications, Chicago, Ill., 1937.

portations were made to this country as early as 1909. Quarantine laws have prevented importations since 1914. This breed is valuable because it produces lamb skins suitable for fur. These fur skins are classified in the trade into Broadtail, Persian, and Karakul or Caracul. (See page 618.)

Fig. 187. A long-wool sheep. A cotswold ram, grand champion at the International Livestock Exposition. Owned by Ralph Shaffer, West Milton, Ohio.

NUMBERS OF DIFFERENT BREEDS

The number of sheep that are registered purebred is quite low. In the 15th Census the leading breeds in registered purebreds were ranked as follows: Rambouillet, Hampshire, Shropshire, Merino, Oxford Down, and Southdown.

Recently reported registrations by the record associations indicated the following order in number of registrations for 1 year: Hampshire, Corriedale, Shropshire, Suffolk, Columbia, Rambouillet and Southdown.

SHEEP AND CATTLE COMPARED

Sheep and cattle are both ruminants, consequently they have many characteristics in common. There are, however, some distinctive features of sheep which make them more adaptable to some situations than cattle. Sheep are less well adapted for consumption of coarse roughage, yet they can utilize short herbage effectively because of the flexibility of the external

Fig. 188. A fine-wool sheep. Rambouillet ewe lamb, first-prize winner at the International Livestock Exposition. Bred and exhibited by King Bros., Laramie, Wyo.

mouth parts which permits close grazing. Poor quality, scanty, arid, rough pasture, cut-over and wooded areas, and crop aftermaths are usable with a flock of sheep. Short grasses and herbage and small bushes are grazed more extensively by sheep than by other domestic grazing animals, except goats. Sheep can be handled in comparatively large flocks. It is not unusual for one herder to take care of a flock of over 2,000 head on the range. Farm flocks are usually kept under 40 head of breeding ewes.

SHOW-RING CLASSIFICATION OF SHEEP

At the livestock shows and expositions sheep are in two main divisions, breeding and market or fat sheep. There may also be classes for feeder sheep. The breeding classes are for purebreds; in the market and feeder classes purebreds, grades, and crossbreds compete. The show classification for sheep is somewhat more uniform than that for cattle. The base date for computing age is commonly January 1, although some breeds have September 1 for their date. In market or fat classes the showing is generally limited to wether lambs, and there are group classes which include pens of three and carloads. In some instances there is a top limit in weight. In the showing of breeding sheep three classes are common for rams. These are 2 years or over, 1 to 2 years, and lambs under 1 year. Often the older class is deleted from the classification for breeding ewes, and only yearling ewes and ewe lamb classes are shown. There are classes for groups such as get of sire, flock, lamb flock, three ram lambs, three ewe lambs or pen of lambs, and championship awards for individuals.

Chapter 29

MUTTON-TYPE SHEEP

Sheep are classified, on the basis of the main objective in their production, into mutton type and wool type.[1] Mutton sheep have been raised mainly for the economy and quality of their meat. Breeding and feeding in this type were pointed mainly toward meat production, and the fleece was a secondary consideration. More emphasis has been placed on fleece in some breeds of the mutton type than in others. It will be recalled that the breeds classified as mutton type were divided into two classes—the medium-wool and the long-wool. Although there are many breeds of the mutton type, there is a considerable range in size and ruggedness, body and head shape, color, markings, wool covering, and character of the fleece. The wool is not to be minimized; even in mutton-sheep flocks, ewes efficient in both lamb and wool production are needed for profit.

Sheep have a fleece which is variable in length and which can be modified by trimming. Consequently, handling of sheep is imperative in judging. Even on the market, sheep are handled to determine fleshing. In sheep judging a systematic, thorough examination is essential for an understanding of the various features of form which affect a sheep's value for a given purpose.

DETAILED DESCRIPTION OF THE IDEAL MUTTON TYPE

THE MUTTON-SHEEP SCORE CARD

The score card is a description of the standard of perfection or ideal. It is of value in making a detailed study of an individual, for the various parts are enumerated. Also, the relative value or importance of the different parts is given. The common score card is for fat or mutton market sheep or those

---

[1] Wool type sheep are discussed in Chapter 34.

that are finished for marketing. Standards of perfection for breeding ewes or bucks and also feeder sheep are similar to those for market sheep, for breeding flocks of good mutton type should produce the desired kind for market and good feeders finish into the kind in demand on the livestock markets. The mutton-sheep standard is patterned after, and is similar in many features to, the standard used for the beef steer. The common anatomical parts of the sheep are shown in Figure 189.

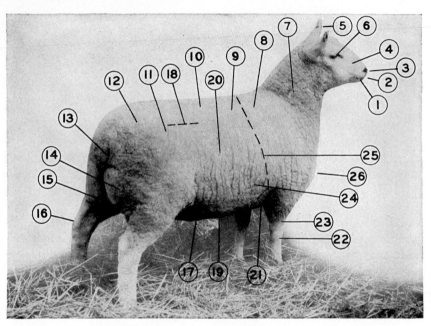

Fig. 189.   Parts of a market lamb.

1—Mouth	8—Top of Shoulder	15—Twist	22—Knee
2—Muzzle	9—Back	16—Hock	23—Forearm
3—Nostril	10—Loin	17—Rear Flank	24—Chest
4—Face	11—Hip	18—Loin Edge	25—Heart Girth
5—Ear	12—Rump	19—Underline Belly	26—Brisket
6—Eye	13—Dock	20—Ribs	
7—Neck	14—Leg or Thigh	21—Fore Flank	

Suggested student score card for a market sheep

Following is a market sheep score card suitable for instructional use.

MARKET SHEEP

Scale of Points

GENERAL APPEARANCE—41 points:

    1. WEIGHT—according to age and market requirement

    2. FORM—wide, deep, compact, low set, straight top line and under line, trim middle, stylish, symmetrical

3. QUALITY—free from coarseness; smooth in form and fleshing
4. CONDITION—degree of fatness indicated by thick, firm covering over shoulder, back, loin, and ribs, thick dock, and plump breast; no soft, loose fat
5. DRESSING PERCENTAGE—high condition, trim middle, light pelt

HEAD AND NECK—4 points:

6. MUZZLE—wide, strong
7. EYES—large, open, quiet
8. FACE—short, forehead wide
9. EARS—fine, well carried
10. NECK—short, thick, throat clean

FOREQUARTERS—7 points:

11. SHOULDERS—smoothly joined with neck, wide and smooth on top, well covered
12. BRISKET—wide, full, trim
13. LEGS—straight, short, strong, wide apart, forearm thick

BODY—26 points:

14. CHEST—wide, deep, full back of shoulders
15. BACK—wide, straight, thickly and firmly fleshed
16. RIBS—well sprung, deep, thickly and firmly fleshed
17. LOIN—wide, thick, firm, smoothly covered

HINDQUARTERS—13 points:

18. RUMP—long, level, wide to the dock, covered with thick, firm flesh
19. LEG OF MUTTON—deep, wide, plump, heavy
20. TWIST—deep, full, firm
21. LEGS—straight, short, wide apart

FLEECE—9 points

22. QUANTITY—dense, long, body completely covered
23. QUALITY—fiber fine, crimp close and even, uniform, free from dark fibers
24. CONDITION—sound, bright, clean, soft, lustrous; sufficient yolk, evenly distributed

Score-card points

There follows a discussion of the different parts of the mutton sheep.

1. General appearance. Most of the features are appraised at some distance away from the sheep.

A. WEIGHT. Weight for age is important because fast gains are usually economical gains. In sheep we have a market which prefers lambs, and generally lambs that are 90 pounds or under. Heavier lambs may at times top the market, but the general preference is for the lighter weights. Size depends upon breed. In the Southdown breed, which is the smallest of the mutton breeds, ewes at maturity weigh from 135 to 155 pounds. Ewes of the Lincoln breed, which is the largest size, weigh 250 pounds. Lambs from very large parents may not have sufficient fatness to top the market at the desirable weight.

B. CONFORMATION. The form desired in market sheep is similar to that of the beef steer. A typical mutton form is one in which there is ample width, depth, compactness, and low-setness. Straight lines, both top and sides, are desirable, as is a trim middle. Symmetry and style are features of form which affect market value. A blocky, muttony form is desired.

C. QUALITY. As this term relates to form and fleshing, it is far less important in sheep than in the beef steer. Some range of quality is observed, and high quality is indicated by freedom from coarseness, combined with smoothness and neatness of form and fleshing and fineness of bone. The head, which is refined, clean cut, and covered with fine hair or wool, shows quality. Quality is also denoted by the fineness of the fleece.

D. CONDITION, FINISH, OR FLESHING. Of the individual items on the score card condition carries the greatest weight. Lambs of acceptable weight are seldom overfat. Usually underfinish prevails in market lambs. The covering over the shoulder, back, loin, and ribs, the thickness of the dock, and the plumpness of the breast indicate fatness or condition. A thick, firm, uniform covering is desired. Fatness is estimated by the spinal covering; a fat lamb has a large amount of covering on his backbone; a thin one has a prominent backbone with little covering. Fat lambs or wethers are pretty largely placed by the covering on their shoulders, back, ribs, loin, and rump, and the fleshing of the leg of mutton.

Sheep, especially those older than lambs, can be too fat and wasty. Heavy accumulations of fat in the foreflank are not uncommon in older sheep. This is commonly referred to as "slipped," but actually there is no slipping of fat from the upper part.

E. DRESSING PERCENTAGE. Finished sheep trim in the middle and light in the pelt dress high. A lower dressing percentage, because of a heavy fleece, is not objectionable, for the fleece sells for more than the carcass.

2. Head and neck. Although this is listed as a major division, the weight value on the score card is low. A broad, short head, with a wide, strong muzzle, large, open, quite clear eyes, a short face, wide forehead, and fine well-carried ears is desired. The neck should be short, thick, and trim at the throat. In breeding sheep more emphasis is given to the head and neck, for each breed is somewhat distinctive about the head. The shape, carriage, color, and ears are features characteristic and quite uniform within a breed. There is much difference among breeds in the size, shape, and wool covering of the head.

3. Forequarters.

A. SHOULDERS. If the shoulders are smoothly joined with the neck, well covered with flesh, wide and smooth on top, they are considered ideal.

B. BREAST. The breast should be wide, full, and trim. A good, well-finished market sheep has a plump breast, and this is of great importance in a breeding sheep, for it is an indication of constitution.

C. LEGS. Straight, short, strong front legs, well set from both front and sides, are desired. Usefulness on the range and in the feed lot depends upon ample underpinning. A thick, well-developed forearm is in keeping with ideal mutton conformation.

4. Body. This section includes several parts which yield valuable mutton and lamb cuts. Therefore, it is second only to general appearance in weight of score.

A. CHEST. Width and depth of chest are stressed, and fullness back of the shoulders. A strong constitutional vigor is indicated by a chest or breast of ample development.

B. BACK, LOIN, AND RIBS. As a straight top line is wanted, the back and loin should be straight; these parts are wide, thick, smooth, and firmly fleshed in the ideal mutton sheep. The ribs should also carry heavy, smooth flesh and should be well sprung to give a wide back. As these parts yield the high-priced cuts, mutton sheep are carefully handled over the back and loin to ascertain flesh covering.

5. Hindquarters. The hindquarters are given considerable weight because the leg of mutton is a high-priced cut of meat.

A. RUMP. In the carcass the rump becomes a part of the leg of mutton. On foot the desired conformation is one in which the rump is long, level, wide to the dock, and heavily fleshed.

B. LEG OF MUTTON.[2] Next to the back and loin this part carries the most score card weight. Light legs of mutton are too common. A heavy, plump, deep, wide leg of mutton is wanted in a good slaughter sheep.

C. TWIST. As this is the inner thigh and forms a part of the commercial cut leg, it should be deep, full, and firm.

D. LEGS. Well-set hind legs with straight hocks are desired.

6. Fleece. In mutton sheep fleece is of secondary importance. Yet on the score card for a mutton sheep it is given about 10 per cent of the total value. Although breeders of mutton sheep have recognized that wool sells for more than mutton, they have also found that too much emphasis on wool will result in inferior mutton conformation. In judging mutton sheep it is common to consider the quantity, quality, and condition of the fleece. For a more complete discussion of the factors affecting market value of wool the student is referred to the chapters on Wool and Wool Sheep.

[2] On a lamb this part is referred to as "leg of lamb."

A. QUANTITY. A long, dense fleece covering the body fairly completely is desired. There is a marked difference among breeds in the covering and also the amount of wool.

Fig. 190. A Southdown wether lamb, reserve grand champion wether, International Livestock Exposition. Shown by Pennsylvania State College.

B. QUALITY. This refers to the fineness of the wool fiber. A fine fiber usually has a close, even crimp. The finer wools are usually the highest priced. Quality varies within a fleece, but a fleece quite uniform in quality is desired. Wool usually is clear white, and deviation from this, such as black fibers, is objectionable.

C. CONDITION. Many circumstances influence the condition of the fleece. A sound, bright, clean, soft, lustrous wool is wanted. Also a sufficient amount of evenly distributed yolk (oil or grease) is wanted as it protects and preserves the wool fibers and also helps to prevent cotting or matting of the fleece.

ADDITIONAL CHARACTERS STRESSED IN BREEDING SHEEP

In breeding sheep, less emphasis is given to fatness or condition. However, heavy natural fleshing is stressed, and the rams and ewes of the mutton type should be thick, wide, and well fleshed, even though actual fatness or condition is not high. The feet and legs are also given more attention in breeding sheep than in market sheep. The selection of sheep for the breeding flock is discussed in Chapter 34.

CATCHING AND HOLDING SHEEP

As handling is essential to estimate their various properties, sheep are held for examination. Sheep in a small pen can be caught around the neck or by grasping the right hind leg high up near the flank. Larger sheep are generally caught by the head and neck; smaller sheep are caught by the flank. The left hand is used to hold the sheep by grasping the skin and wool under the lower jaw. The right hand is then placed on the rump and dock to move the sheep about and, when the sheep is held in position, the right hand is placed on the top of the head or the back of the neck. Care should be taken not to catch or hold a sheep by its wool.

Fig. 191. Grand champion Shropshire wether at the International Livestock Exposition. Bred and exhibited by Oklahoma A. & M. College, Stillwater, Okla.

SHEEP JUDGING

OBSERVATION

Before handling, the sheep should be viewed from the side and both ends from some distance away. This observation will give some appreciation of size, straightness of lines, compactness, length of legs, symmetry, width, depth, and the general appearance of the head. Likewise, the set and strength of the feet and legs are to be observed. An experienced sheepman makes a careful observation of the sheep from a little distance before closer examination and handling. A common error of the beginner is to omit or slight observation of the sheep before handling. Observations may be more helpful than handling in placing breeding sheep.

HANDLING

A systematic method of handling is desirable. It is quite common to begin the close inspection at the rear end and work toward the front, but some begin at the front end and work toward the rear. The starting place is of no importance, but complete examination is essential. The hand should confirm or reject impressions acquired from observation and also uncover defects not observed by vision. For best inspection and least damage to the fleece, the fingers are kept together and laid nearly flat on the sheep. The ability to estimate fleshing and condition is acquired by experience.

Steps in handling

A rather common method of procedure in the handling of sheep is as follows. A right-handed person will usually stand at the left rear of the sheep and use his right hand for the detailed examination. The top line is handled beginning at the dock and going forward to the top of the shoulder. By a slight movement of the fingers over the backbone the fleshing is noted. The neck and shoulder are handled with both hands. This inspection includes length of the neck and smoothness with which it is joined to the shoulder, also smoothness with which the shoulder blades are laid and flesh covering. The depth is noted by placing the right hand on the sheep's top back of the shoulder and the other hand on the floor of the chest just back of the forelegs.

By handling with both hands just back of the shoulders the heart girth is inspected. The hands are moved backward to note the width of the body and the flesh covering. Width and thickness of the loin are appraised by holding the hands vertically, with one on either side of the loin. The rump is examined for its width and squareness with one hand on either side. The leg of mutton is grasped with both hands to estimate its size, thickness, plumpness, and depth. The twist is examined for fullness and depth by placing one hand on the top of the rump and the other palm up between the rear legs.

Examination of the head

The teeth are usually examined, since they are a fairly good indication of age. The bite should also be examined while the lips are parted with the fingers, for set of incisor teeth of the lower jaw and the dental pad should close on each other. In polled breeds the presence or absence of horns should be noted.

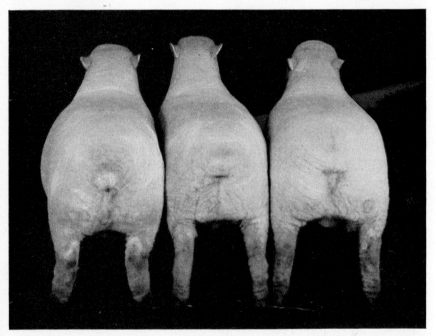

Fig. 192. Champion pen of three Southdown wethers, International Livestock Exposition. Note the difference in thickness. Because of differences in wool length, handling is necessary to determine actual body width. Shown by Pennsylvania State College.

Examination of the fleece and skin

The wool is usually parted at the natural divisions in three places along the side of the sheep (shoulder, mid-side, and thighs) for examination. The length, density, quality, condition, and other attributes of the fleece which affect its value are determined by inspection.

Further examination

In breeding classes rams are examined to ascertain whether the testicles have descended into the scrotum and whether they have developed normally. Ewes are examined for normal development of the udder.

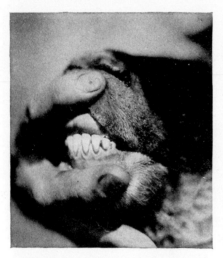

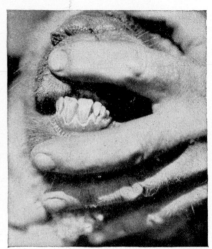

Fig. 193. A lamb's mouth, four pairs of temporary incisors or milk teeth.

Fig. 194. A yearling mouth, one pair of permanent and three pairs of temporary incisors.

ESTIMATING AGE FROM THE TEETH OF SHEEP

Estimates of age can be made from the teeth of sheep. Examination of the teeth or "mouthing" is common to determine approximate age. As a breeding ewe has a relatively short productive life, age is an important consideration in the value of a sheep.

A mature sheep has 32 functional teeth, of which 24 are molars and 8 are incisors. The incisors are on the lower jaw, and on the upper jaw there is a dental pad. Temporary deciduous or milk teeth are typical of the lamb. These are replaced at quite regular intervals by the permanent incisors. The latter are larger in that they are broader and longer than the milk teeth. A yearling has the middle pair of temporary incisors replaced by a pair of permanent incisors. A two-year-old has two pairs, a three-year-old three pairs, and a four-year-old four pairs, or all permanent incisors. After 4 years of age the incisors spread apart, become worn down, and break out. The regular dentition table may be altered by conditions of nutrition. Lambs usually make the first tooth change at 14 months, but it may be hastened or delayed by factors affecting the development of the sheep.

The variation of the above general rule has been studied at the Montana Agricultural Experiment Station.[3] Rambouillet ewes of good quality and of known age were examined in November. They were lambed in April and May, during the summer they were run on mountain pasture, and in the winter they were on foothill range.

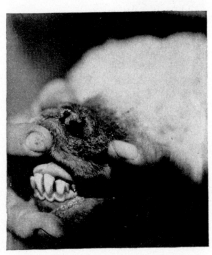

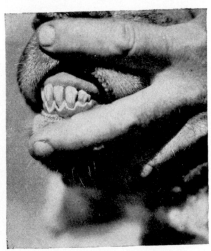

Fig. 195. A 2-year-old mouth, two pairs of permanent incisors.

Fig. 196. A 3-year-old mouth, three pairs of permanent incisors.

In the examination, if a permanent pair of teeth had erupted but were not up in wear, it was called ½ year. It will be noted that 6 per cent of the sheep at about 18 months had not lost any of their lamb incisor teeth, 84 per cent had the one pair of permanent incisors up in wear, and 10 per cent had made the change but the permanent incisors were not in wear. But 37 per cent of the two-year-olds and 28 per cent of the three-year-olds showed the usually expected dentition.

A tabulation of the age estimates made follows.

ACTUAL AGE	NUMBER	PER CENT NORMAL	FRONT TEETH AGE COMPARED TO ACTUAL AGE			
			½ Year Under	1 Year Under	½ Year Over	1 Year Over
Yearlings at 18 months	850	84	10%	6%		
Two-year-olds at 30 months	490	37			6%	57%
Three-year-olds at 42 months	640	28			22%	50%
Four-year-olds at 54 months	370	88	7%	5%		

It would appear from this investigation that yearlings and four-year-olds are older than would be estimated from the teeth; and two- and three-

[3] "Judging the Age of Sheep by their Teeth," *Circ. 149*, Mont. Agr. Exp. Sta., June, 1936.

year-olds are younger. Real age does not follow closely the usual order, especially in the two- and three-year-olds. For example, 63 per cent of the two-year-olds and 72 per cent of the three-year-olds are younger than would be estimated from their teeth.

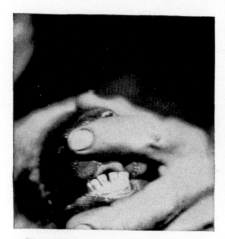

Fig. 197. A 4-year-old mouth, all permanent incisors in proper place.

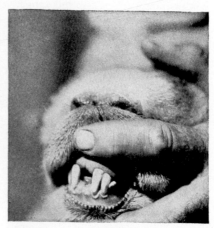

Fig. 198. A broken mouth, over 6 years old.

Smoothmouthed sheep, or "gummers," and broken-mouthed sheep are discarded because of their limited usefulness.

Abnormalities appear in the fit of the incisor teeth with the dental pad. In the normal mouth the teeth close on or immediately in front of the dental pad, according to Nordby.[4] When the lower jaw is shorter than the upper jaw and the incisor teeth strike back or inside of the dental pad, this is termed "overshot mouth" or "parrot mouth." When the lower jaw is longer, the mouth is "undershot." In other words, the teeth on the lower jaw extend too far beyond the dental pad. Either of these defects impairs the grazing ability of sheep and is to be avoided in selecting breeding sheep. Of 1,500 ewes examined at the U.S. Department of Agriculture Experiment Station, Dubois, Idaho, 24 had definitely overshot jaws. Lambs with the same defect weighed about 7.5 pounds less at weaning time than lambs with normal mouths.

[4] Julius E. Nordby, "Overshot and Undershot Jaws in Sheep," *National Wool Grower,* Vol. 21, No. 2, February, 1931.

Chapter 30

SHEEP MARKETS

MARKETING SHEEP

In marketing their product, sheep raisers in general have available the same methods of disposal as cattlemen, and sheep are handled much the same way as cattle. As sheep raising has a different pattern than cattle raising (compare Figures 6 and 184), the market movement is not entirely the same. The western states have the largest numbers of sheep, which in marketing pass eastward toward the centers of human population. Also, lamb and mutton per capita consumption is heaviest in the eastern states. Over 80 per cent of the lambs raised are raised west of the Mississippi River, and 78 per cent of the lamb is consumed east of the Mississippi. Lamb and mutton travels farther from the surplus-producing regions of the west to the deficient areas in the east than beef, and pork is produced nearer the consumer than beef. The distance from the center of sheep raising to the center of human population is 850 miles.

METHODS OF MARKETING

It is common to designate the marketing method as direct or indirect. A sale from a grower to a feeder or a packer is direct, because the transfer of ownership is made without making use of a public stock commission agency. Sales made on public stockyard markets are indirect transactions, since the owner is represented by an agency.

The percentage of slaughter sheep sold directly to the slaughterers has shown an upward tendency. For the period 1923–1928 it amounted to about 15 per cent of the total. Following 1928 there was a gradual increase in directs until 1932 and, since that time, the increase has been irregularly upward. For the past 10 years over 40 per cent of the sheep and lambs slaughtered by packers under federal inspection were purchased direct. (See Figure 144.) There has also been an increase in the direct movement of feeder sheep, as indicated by the decrease in shipments of feeder sheep from the public markets.

For the last 5 years [1] 45 per cent of the feeder sheep and lambs moving into the 9 north central states were purchased at the public stockyards. The balance, 55 per cent, were purchased direct but may have moved through a public market and inspected, while stopping for feed, water, and rest, en route to the feeder. However, they were not purchased on a public stockyards market.

LEADING SHEEP MARKETS

Denver, Ogden, Fort Worth, and Omaha are the leading sheep markets on the basis of total and salable receipts. Chicago led in aggregate number of sheep receipts for a long period. In recent years Chicago receipts have declined and those at Denver have shown an upward trend. A smaller number of feeder and stocker sheep and lambs have been passing through

Fig. 199. Sheep at the stockyards. A band of lambs being moved in an alley of the Union Stockyards, Chicago, Ill.

[1] *Agricultural Statistics,* U.S.D.A., 1955.

the Chicago market, and an increased proportion have been sold direct. The rank of markets on the basis of receipts, which of course fluctuate materially from year to year, is continually changing. The shifting of production areas, and also the feed conditions in the areas served by a market, affect its receipts. Reshipments for slaughter and feeding are discussed later.

The leading sheep markets and their yearly receipts based on a 5-year period are as follows.

SHEEP AND LAMBS, YEARLY TOTAL AND SALABLE RECEIPTS
AT PUBLIC MARKETS

Average of 5 Years—1951 to 1955 [2]

MARKET	TOTAL AVERAGE	SALABLE AVERAGE
1. Denver, Colo.	1,684,372	1,078,390
2. Ogden, Utah	1,341,039	611,427
3. Fort Worth, Tex.	986,658	770,619
4. Omaha, Nebr.	977,758	781,559
5. Jersey City, N. J.	704,117	6,245
6. Pittsburgh, Pa.	875,204	32,913
7. St. Joseph, Mo.	632,766	270,777
8. Kansas City, Mo.	702,962	370,397
9. St. Louis (Ill. and Mo.)	614,829	309,948
10. Chicago, Ill.	672,277	500,945
11. S. St. Paul, Minn.	714,675	574,956
12. Sioux City, Iowa	557,089	395,535
13. N. Salt Lake, Utah	381,463	39,838
14. Buffalo, N. Y.	454,530	25,022
15. S. San Francisco, Cal.	370,568	227,112
Total	15,270,920	8,411,241

The division between eastward- and westward-moving market sheep and lambs is farther west than for other kinds of livestock. There has been a marked shift in the division line. (See Figure 23, page 55.) Western markets and western slaughter have increased accordingly.

SEASONAL VARIATION IN SHEEP RECEIPTS

There is a marked seasonal variation in the marketing of sheep and lambs. The usual pattern is lambing in the spring and marketing in the fall. Heavy receipts occur in September and October, with fairly heavy receipts for the months following through February. The receipts are low in the spring and July has the lightest receipts of the year.

Origin of market receipts of sheep by months

There is considerable variation in the marketing season for sheep and lambs from various states, as is shown in Figure 200. The California lambs

[2] From reports of Livestock Division, Agricultural Marketing Service, U.S.D.A., and based on reports submitted by stockyards companies.

are the first to appear on the markets; they are nearly all marketed in April and May. With improved methods of parasite control in the native sheep states it has been possible to extend the marketing of lambs over a much longer period than formerly. The southern lambs from the corn and wheat belts closely follow or overlap the California lambs. Then the range lambs start moving to the markets. This is climaxed in October, which is the end of the mountain pasture feeding. From May to November grass lambs comprise the bulk of the marketing. Fed lambs make up the major portion of receipts from January to April; these come from the lamb-feeding areas of Colorado, Nebraska, Kansas, and the corn-belt states.

FEEDER SHEEP ON THE MARKET

Many of the lambs coming to the market are insufficiently finished to be highly acceptable to meat packers. These lambs and also a few sheep older than lambs are classed as stockers and feeders and are reshipped to the feed lots for feeding. More than one half of the feeders are shipped to the corn-belt states. Heavy winter lamb feeding is also practiced in Colorado, Nebraska, and Kansas. On January 1 of each year these are listed as lambs and sheep on feed to distinguish them from stock sheep.

The movement to the country from the public markets and direct to feeders is very heavily peaked in the fall. Over 65 per cent of the feeder lambs bought by corn-belt farmers are purchased in the months August to November, inclusive. This movement coincides with the marketing of the lambs from the range country before inclement weather begins.

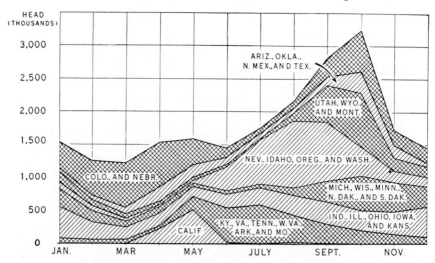

Fig. 200. The marketing of sheep and lambs is seasonal. The marketing season varies for the different states. (U.S.D.A., Bur. of Agri. Economics.)

Leading markets for feeder and stocker sheep

The leading public markets for feeder and stocker sheep are much the same as the markets of the maximum or total receipts, for the total receipts include those reshipped for feeders. The larger proportion of feeders in the receipts will be found on western markets or those nearest the western range.

Following is a listing of the larger public stockyards feeder sheep markets and their average receipts per year for the 10-year period 1946–1955. Not included are the feeder sheep handled as "directs."

LARGE PUBLIC STOCKYARD MARKETS FOR FEEDER SHEEP

Average Yearly Inspected Receipts for a 10-year period, 1946–1955 [2]

MARKET ORIGIN	THOUSAND HEAD
Denver, Colo.	659
Ogden, Utah	440
Fort Worth, Tex.	209
Omaha, Neb.	189
South St. Paul, Minn.	166
Salt Lake City, Utah	159
Sioux City, Iowa	133
South St. Joseph, Mo.	124
Kansas City, Mo.	98
Sioux Falls, S. D.	56
St. Louis area	37
Chicago, Ill.	25
All other inspected	344
Total	2,672

SHIPPING

Shrinkage in shipping

The weight loss between home weights and sale weights at the market, or shrinkage, is a factor in marketing costs. Sheep shrink more heavily in transit than cattle or hogs. Actually, as sheep are fed and watered at the yards before selling and weighing, some of the shipping loss is regained. This is called "fill."

Shrink varies with length of time and other conditions in shipping. Shrinks are greater in the spring and summer than in the fall and winter. A tabulation of the usual range of shrinkage for sheep follows:

SHRINKAGE OF SHEEP IN SHIPMENT [3]

	TRUCK		RAILROAD		
	50 Miles	*100 Miles*	*400 Miles*	*1,000 Miles*	*2,000 Miles*
Fat lambs	2–3%	2½–3½%	4–6%	6–8%	7–10%
Feeder lambs	3–4%	3½–4½%	5–7%	6–9%	7–10%
Ewes	4–5%	4½–5½%	6–8%	7–9%	8–10%

[2] *Livestock Market News Statistics,* U.S.D.A., 1956.

[3] Information from Edward N. Wentworth, Armour and Co., August, 1950.

A 90-pound lamb at home selling for $20.00 per hundredweight would bring $18.00. With a 10 per cent shrink in weight, the lamb would have to sell for $22.22 per hundredweight to bring $18.00.

Transportation to the market

Sheep are shipped to the market less by truck than hogs or cattle. At public stockyard markets 53 per cent of the sheep and lambs arrived by truck in 1953–1955, whereas a larger per cent of other livestock were delivered to the markets by motor trucks. Sheep and lambs are generally shipped farther than hogs and cattle, consequently rail shipments still predominate. The receipts are divided into rail and truck receipts.

Shipping by truck

Following is the number of sheep per truck for safe loading.

SHEEP PER TRUCK

Recommended Load per Deck

FLOOR LENGTH, FEET	AVERAGE LIVE WEIGHT, POUNDS			
	60	80	100	120
8	28	23	20	18
10	35	29	26	23
12	43	35	31	28
15	54	45	40	36
18	65	54	48	43
20	73	60	54	48
24	88	73	65	58
28	103	85	76	68
30	110	92	81	73
32	118	98	87	78
36	133	110	98	88
42	145	128	115	103

Number of sheep and lambs per railroad car

To prevent losses from death and bruising, it is essential that sheep like other livestock be not too crowded in the car. Underloading is also objectionable, and if the sheep have too much space in the car a partition to shut off the excess space will reduce bumping around en route to market. Double decking is practiced with sheep, and usually the upper deck is less heavily loaded than the lower deck. The number of sheep or lambs of various weights to load in a car is given in the tabulation which follows.

SHEEP AND LAMBS PER RAILROAD CAR PER DECK [4]

CAR SIZE, FEET	AVERAGE LIVE WEIGHT													
	50	60	70	80	90	100	110	120	130	140	150	160	170	180
36	155	143	131	120	112	105	101	97	93	89	85	81	78	75
40	170	156	143	133	124	116	111	106	102	98	94	90	86	83

[4] *Bull. 20*, Swift & Company, May, 1941.

Shipping losses

A study of the dead and crippled sheep and lambs arriving by railroad and truck at Kansas City, St. Joseph, Omaha, Sioux City, and St. Paul public stockyards by the National Livestock Loss Prevention Board shows, in a 2-year summary, the following percentages of dead and crippled.

ANIMALS SHIPPED	PER CENT DEAD		PER CENT CRIPPLED	
	Rail	*Truck*	*Rail*	*Truck*
Sheep and lambs	0.083	0.324	0.034	0.093

The higher rate of dead and crippled in truck shipments was due in part to poor loading conditions and improper handling. Trucking of livestock is comparatively new and not so well supervised as rail shipment; consequently the damage in loading and en route is higher than in railroad shipments.

MARKET DIVISIONS OF SHEEP

On the sheep markets there is a considerable amount of sorting into market classes and grades. Standardization of such divisions makes possible more accurate reporting of the market and gives the producer a more accurate picture of demand. Likewise, market standards make possible a more accurate determination of value and permit trading without personal inspection.

Cattle are more completely sorted than sheep on the livestock market, yet the latter are divided into lots for sale more than hogs. Mixed loads of lambs and sheep on the public market are quite generally sorted into salable packages or lots, and often a buyer sorts the lot further before final acceptance.

PRINCIPAL USES FOR MARKET SHEEP

Sheep received on any public livestock market or sold direct are either sold to packers or bought by feeders or farmers for further feeding or for breeding purposes. These divisions are based upon the suitability of the individuals for the purpose specified and the demand for each class. Thin or unfinished lambs and sheep usually are reshipped from the market for further feeding and those finished sufficiently are purchased by slaughterers. However, borderline individuals or two-way sheep go to satisfy the greatest demand.

PLACE OF ORIGIN

Quite generally on sheep markets, receipts are designated by the region or state of their origin. Thus we hear of western sheep which come from the range and "native sheep" which originate from farm flocks of the Midwest, East, or South. We also hear of "Montanas," "Idahos," "Wyomings," "Colorados," etc. Although these terms at one time may have been meaningful, at present the sheep from one section or state are not uniform. Western sheep, for example, used to be mostly "white faced" of fine wool breeding, and range reared. The sheep of that area have changed as new breeds were introduced and feeding practices changed. Consequently, descriptive terms based upon the place of origin have lost much of their former significance.

CLASSIFYING AND GRADING SHEEP AND LAMBS

The object of the classing and grading is to form groups of animals that are similar.

Classifying then is divided into the major subdivisions known as "classes, subclasses, age, and weight." The classes and subclasses are based upon sex or sex condition and use, and age and weight are used for further division.

Grading, or the final separation, results in smaller, more uniform lots than classifying. Commonly on the market, grading is used to designate both classing and grading. The grade is dependent upon form, quality, and finish. The higher grades, for example prime lambs, are nearly ideal in form, quality, and finish.

MARKET CLASSES AND GRADES OF SHEEP

Following is a tabulation of the market classes and grades which may be on the market.

	BASIS FOR GROUPING				
	Sex	*Age*	*Use*	*Weight*	*Grades*
Divisions in each group	Ewe Wether Ram	Hothouse lambs Spring lambs Lambs Yearling 2 and 3 years 4 years and older	Slaughter Feeding Breeding	Light Medium Heavy Handy Mixed	Prime or fancy Choice Good Utility Cull

When wooled and shorn sheep or lambs are on the market, this is a further basis for division. Wool length of 1½ inches is required for the unshorn class.

Definitions and descriptions of market groups [5]

The term "sheep" includes ovine animals of all ages. In practice, however, this species is divided on the basis of age into two groups, sheep and

[5] From "Market Classes and Grades of Lambs and Sheep," *Circ. 383*, U.S.D.A., March, 1936; revised July, 1940.

lambs. Lambs include those approximately 1 year of age and younger, and sheep include all those about 1 year of age and older.

Ewes. A ewe is a female sheep.

Wethers. A wether is a male sheep which was castrated before it had reached sufficient maturity to make reproduction possible and which has not developed male characteristics. As a rule, castration is done before the animal is 6 weeks old.

Rams. A ram is an uncastrated male sheep.

Slaughter animals. Slaughter animals are those possessing sufficient fat or finish to meet the requirements of the consuming trade. This designation covers all animals which will produce meat wholesome and fit for human food. Any such animal may be slaughtered and consumed.

Feeders. Feeders are animals which lack sufficient finish to produce the highest grades of meat but which show evidences, as a rule, of ability to take on additional flesh and fat economically, most of the gain resulting from additional fat or finish rather than growth.

Shearers. Shearers are a subclass of lambs; they are animals in full fleece purchased primarily for their wool. Such lambs, as a rule, are either fat or in higher flesh condition than most feeders and they usually have longer wool. They are taken to feed lots and shorn; then, after a brief feeding period, they are returned to the market for resale.

Breeders. Breeders are sheep or lambs sold for breeding purposes. As a rule transactions in breeding sheep at the public markets are confined to females of the species, and ordinarily not many ewe lambs are sold for this purpose. Most of the breeding ewes sold at the market are relatively young ewes from range bands. They possess good conformation and quality and show evidence of improved breeding.

Lambs. A lamb is a young ovine animal which has not yet acquired its first pair of permanent incisor teeth. The age at which this occurs varies in individuals from around 10 to 15 months. As the animal approaches the yearling stage, therefore, it is sometimes necessary to inspect the mouth to determine whether it is still a lamb. If it has not yet acquired its first pair of permanent teeth, it is considered a lamb. Ewe and wether lambs, as a rule, produce similar carcasses; therefore buyers do not differentiate between them. At many of the leading markets, however, ram lambs are discriminated against because they show the influence of sex development, especially if they are more than 4 or 5 months of age. They tend to develop thicker necks and slightly broader and heavier shoulders than do ewe and wether lambs. The differences in this respect are seldom sufficient to justify separate descriptions.

Hothouse lambs. A hothouse lamb is a very young animal that has been raised, as a rule, in confined quarters and has received an abundance of its mother's milk during the short period of its life. Both the lamb and its mother receive special care so that maximum growth and finish may be attained, since most hothouse lambs are marketed at 6 to 10 weeks of age. Such lambs are usually marketed during the period from Christmas to the Easter holidays through wholesale houses or direct on order at weights ranging from 30 to 60 pounds.

Spring lambs.   "Spring lamb" is a term generally applied to new-crop lambs that come to market in the spring of the year. It is used to distinguish them from old-crop or fed lambs that were born the previous year. In market practice the term "spring" is dropped on the first Monday in October and the more common term "lamb" is used. On account of varying climatic conditions in different sections of the country, young lambs arrive at some markets throughout the summer and early fall. Old-crop lambs are classified as yearlings beginning the first Monday in July.[6]

Spring lambs are those generally ranging from 3 to 7 months in age which have run with their dams from birth and derived a large part of their food therefrom. Since the spring lamb is older than a hothouse lamb, the wool is longer. The body is slightly deeper and wider in proportion to its length and is less cylindrical than that of the hothouse lamb. The face is somewhat longer and the eyes, nostrils, mouth, and ears are relatively larger. As compared with older lambs, however, the spring lamb is relatively small, and its wool is shorter than that of one approaching the yearling stage. This gives it a decidedly youthful appearance. Spring lambs weighing from 70 to 90 pounds are in most demand.

Lambs.   During the latter part of the summer and early fall the lambs coming to market show less and less the effect of subsisting largely on milk and more and more that of subsisting on feed other than milk. This group includes those older and more fully developed than spring lambs. They range in age from approximately 7 to 15 months, but the bulk are from 8 to 12 months old. Those that approach the yearling stage show greater maturity in all respects than do spring lambs. As a rule, they are relatively wide and deep in body and heavily fleshed. The wool is longer and slightly darker in color, owing to greater exposure to weather and dirt. The head and face are longer and show greater maturity around the mouth, eyes, and ears. Included in this group are the so-called "fed lambs" marketed during the winter and early spring.

Grade factors [7]

The three major grade factors—conformation, finish, and quality—on which this system of grading is based, comprise most of the essential characteristics of the sheep or lamb and its carcass. Each of these factors exists to some degree in every animal, and the outstanding differences between animals in each grade consist chiefly in the different degrees of the three factors

---

[6] On some markets this change is made June 1.
[7] *Circ. 383*, U.S.D.A., July, 1940.

possessed by the individuals. Definitions and descriptions of the grade factors follow.

Conformation. Conformation is build, shape, outline, or contour of the animal. It is a matter of symmetry or relative proportions among parts. The degree of conformation is determined by the proportionate relationships of width, depth, and length of the body. In live animals, standards of conformation vary according to the immediate use to be made of the animals. Grade for grade, thicker flesh and more rounded conformation are usually demanded in slaughter animals than in those that are to be used as feeders.

Finish. Finish is fat. It involves not only the quantity of fat that covers the body but also its character and distribution. A thick, firm covering over the ribs, spinal column, loin, and rump is an indication of a well-finished animal. Standards for degree of finish vary with the use of the animal. In the carcass it includes the fat on the walls of the abdominal and thoracic cavities, the seams of fat between the muscles, and the intramuscular and intercellular fats.

Quality. Quality in an animal is that inherent property which, in combination with other characteristics such as refinement and breeding, influences its relative degree of excellence as a meat animal. The degrees of firmness and thickness of flesh over the back, ribs, and loin are indications of degree of quality. Refinement includes smooth, even features of the face and head, smooth shoulders and rump, fine hair on face and legs, and smooth, medium-sized knee and hock joints. Breeding refers to indications of the degree of improved blood lines as compared with nondescript breeding.

Other factors that affect market value

Three factors other than the grade factors—conformation, finish, and quality—affect the market prices of sheep and lambs. These factors are weight, excessive finish, and yield.

Weight. Weight is an important price factor in both sheep and lambs, but it is especially important in lambs. As a rule, heavy sheep and lambs are in less demand at the markets than animals of lighter weight.

Slaughter lambs that weigh 70 to 90 pounds usually are preferred, and they bring a higher price per pound, grade for grade, than do those weighing more than 90 pounds. This difference in price is based on demand and is largely the result of consumer preference for small or medium-sized cuts. Slaughter ewes that weigh 90 to 120 pounds are in greater demand than those weighing over 120 pounds. Because of the rather limited demand for the heavier ewes, most of which are considered by the trade to be too fat, heavy ewes usually sell considerably lower than lighter ewes.

Excessive finish. "Overfat," "wasty," and "excessive" finish are terms frequently used in the wholesale meat trade, referring to carcasses that have a very large amount of fat in proportion to lean. This condition is more frequent with heavyweight ewes and wethers, but it sometimes occurs with lambs, especially those that have been fitted for show purposes.

Carcass yield.   Carcass yield, or the carcass weight in relation to live animal weight, is another element that affects the price of slaughter sheep and slaughter lambs.

Since the meat of the animal is its principal commercial product, the number of pounds of carcass the slaughterer obtains from each 100 pounds of live weight is a matter of real consequence and determines to a considerable extent the price of slaughter lambs. For that reason, yield often is considered by some as a grade factor. Under certain conditions yield is closely related to grade, because, as a rule, higher yields are obtained from the better grades and low yields are associated with low grades. Other factors affecting yield are weight of pelt and amount of fill.

Weight of pelt varies greatly among animals of the same grade, depending on type of breeding, length of staple, and quantity of foreign material it contains. All these factors influence the total weight of pelts, which greatly affects the carcass yield. As a rule, weight is of much greater importance than the quantity or grade of the wool. At times when wool prices are high the price of slaughter lambs is influenced by both the wool and the carcass yield. The pelts from fine-wool-type sheep usually weigh more than those from mutton-type sheep, because of the heavier fleece and thicker skin characterized by folds or wrinkles.

Carcass yield also is influenced by the fill, or quantity of feed and water an animal consumes after it arrives at the market. This varies somewhat with the method of transportation, time in transit, and distance trucked or shipped to market. Lambs that have been hauled relatively short distances by truck show evidences of greater fill than those which have been shipped long distances by rail.

DIFFERENT MARKET CLASSIFICATIONS

There is some variation of classifications used at different sheep markets; in fact, on a given market there may be variation in the classing and grading. The official grade standard is used as a basis for the Market News Service of the U.S. Department of Agriculture. Most market reports by private livestock marketing agencies conform fairly well with the official standard.

The following schedule shows how slaughter lambs and sheep are divided in market groups according to the official standard, as to classes, subclasses, age, weight, and grades.

A detailed description of the grades in all the individual classes is deemed unnecessary. The successive grades are merely less acceptable in the grade factors: conformation or form, quality, and condition or fleshing. Some of the better grades will be described.

OFFICIAL SCHEDULE FOR LAMBS AND SHEEP

SCHEDULE: MARKET CLASSIFICATION FOR SLAUGHTER LAMBS [8]

CLASS	AGE GROUP	WEIGHT	GRADE
Ewes, wethers and rams	Hothouse	60 pounds down	Prime
	Spring	Medium weight, 70 to 90 pounds Heavyweight, 90 pounds up	Choice Good Utility Cull
	Lambs	Lightweight, 75 pounds down Medium weight, 75 to 95 pounds Heavyweight, 95 pounds up	

SCHEDULE: MARKET CLASSIFICATION FOR SLAUGHTER SHEEP [8]

CLASS	AGE GROUP	WEIGHT	GRADE
Ewes	Yearling	Lightweight and handyweight, 90 pounds down Medium weight, 90 to 100 pounds Heavyweight, 100 pounds up	Prime Choice Good Utility Cull
	Mature (2 years old and older)	Lightweight and handyweight, 120 pounds down Medium weight, 120 to 140 pounds Heavyweight, 140 pounds up	Choice Good Utility Cull
Wethers	Yearling	Lightweight and handyweight, 100 pounds down Medium weight, 100 to 110 pounds Heavyweight, 110 pounds up	Prime Choice Good Utility Cull
	Mature (2 years old and older)	Lightweight and handyweight, 115 pounds down Medium weight, 115 to 130 pounds Heavyweight, 130 pounds up	Choice Good Utility Cull
Rams	Yearling	All weights	Choice Good Utility Cull
	Mature (2 years old and older)	All weights	Good Utility Cull

Prime grade of slaughter lambs

A prime grade slaughter lamb (see Figure 201) has excellent conformation, finish, and quality, and is comparable to a top mutton lamb as described in Chapter 29. Following is a brief description of such lambs.

[8] "Market Classes and Grades of Livestock," *Bull. 1360,* U.S.D.A., 1926; slightly revised December, 1948.

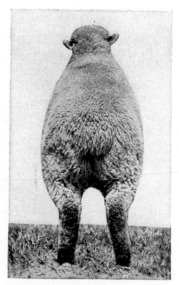

PRIME

CHOICE

Fig. 201. United States Grades of Slaughter Lambs, Prime to Utility. (U.S.D.A., Agricultural Marketing Service.)

520

GOOD

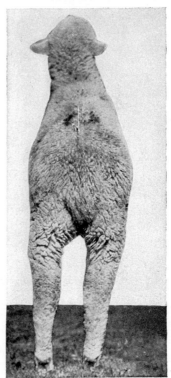

UTILITY

521

Conformation. The body is very compact and symmetrical. It is very deep and wide in proportion to its length. All parts are fully developed, producing a very smooth and even body outline. The flesh over all parts of the body is very thick, giving it a plump and well-rounded appearance. The back, loin, and rump are very wide. The leg of lamb is large and plump, and is full and low in the twist. A prime lamb has a uniform, straight-lined middle. The crops are very full and the shoulders are very thick, blending smoothly into the body. The neck is thick and very short.

Finish. The fat covering is thick but not excessive, and it extends well over all parts of the body. It is very firm and smooth and evenly distributed. The fat covering over the back, ribs, and loin almost entirely conceals the bones from the touch.

Quality. A prime-grade lamb has excellent quality. It is very smooth and firm in all parts of the body. It has a refined, medium-sized head and rather small leg or cannon bone. The shoulders are smooth and are even in width with the rest of the body. The proportion of flesh to bone is very high. Such a lamb is usually of mutton type. The thick, evenly distributed finish over the body indicates a generous supply of fat throughout all parts of the carcass. These characteristics generally indicate a very high degree of quality in the flesh.

FEEDER SHEEP AND LAMB SCHEDULE

There follows the schedule for the classing and grading of feeder sheep and lambs.

SCHEDULE: MARKET CLASSIFICATION FOR FEEDER SHEEP
AND LAMBS [9]

CLASS		AGE GROUP	GRADE
Lambs: ewes and wethers		All ages	Fancy
			Choice
			Good
			Medium
			Common
			Inferior
Sheep	ewes and wethers	Yearlings	Fancy
			Choice
			Good
			Medium
			Common
			Inferior
	ewes	Mature (2 years old and older)	Choice
			Good
			Medium
			Common
			Inferior

[9] "Market Classes and Grades of Livestock," *Bull. 1360,* U.S.D.A., December, 1948.

Fancy-grade feeder lamb

A fancy-grade feeder lamb has superior conformation, finish, and quality.

Conformation. The body is compact and very symmetrical. It is wide and deep in proportion to its length. The flesh over all parts of the body is thick. The back, loin, and rump are wide. The leg is large and is full in the twist. The middle is uniform in width and depth with the shoulders and hips. The crops are full, and the shoulders are smooth and about the same width as the rest of the body. The neck is very short, and the head is medium in size.

Finish. The fat covering is moderately thick and smooth and is evenly distributed over the body.

Fig. 202. Receiving sheep at the stockyards. Sheep delivered by truck are classed as "drive in." This category includes all sheep received by other means than rail. (Swift & Company.)

Quality. The fancy-grade lamb has excellent quality. The skin is thin and smooth. It has refined, medium-sized head and bone, and the shoulders are smooth. Such a lamb is usually of mutton type and has either purebred or crossbred markings.

BREEDING SHEEP

It will be noted in the sheep and lamb schedule that breeding sheep are not included. Some sheep on the markets go out into the country to form breeding flocks. There has been an increased direct trade in western ewes, for they have proved to be good lamb producers in the native sheep states when bred to mutton rams. Although ewes acceptable for the breeding flock may be found on the central sheep markets, rams on the large markets are scarce and usually of inferior conformation. The ewes culled from range flocks, if not broken-mouthed or "gummies," may be purchased by farmers in the Middle West and used for one or two crops of lambs.

Ewe lambs are sometimes taken out as breeding sheep but those in demand for this purpose are ewes that can immediately go into the breeding flock. The trade is quite seasonal, for the heaviest supply and demand occur just before the breeding season which is in the fall of the year. Ewe lambs would for the most part have to be kept over until the second fall for breeding. Slaughterers compete strongly for the younger ewes which could go into breeding flocks.

Fancy breeding ewes are the top grade, and there are relatively few available. In form such ewes must meet the requirements for a top breeding ewe. (See page 625.) Well-bred ewes are preferred. They must be good-sized, uniform, stylish, of good quality, and have good fleeces.

The lower grades fall short of the top grade in some of the essential qualities, and the lowest grade (common) is quite inferior.

Fig. 203. Improper handling in loading sheep. Lifting sheep by the wool pulls the skin away from the flesh, causing damage to the carcass. (Harry J. Boyts, National Livestock Loss Prevention Board.)

TRIMMING LAMBS FOR MARKET

DOCKING LAMBS

It is usually advocated that all lambs should be docked when 1 to 2 weeks of age. Docked lambs are cleaner and are generally more easily kept free from maggots. Also, docked lambs are more attractive in appearance.

CASTRATION OF LAMBS

Early castration of the male lamb is also advocated. In fact, it is usually done at the same time as docking. In a very young lamb the presence of the testicles would not detract from the quality of the meat. Usually the discount on the markets in the native sheep states on ram lambs as compared with ewes and wethers becomes effective between May 1 and June 1 and becomes greater as the season advances. A ram lamb under 75 pounds in weight is not very "bucky" in appearance, and the secondary sexual characters up to that size have not shown any appreciable development.

An investigation at Cornell University [10] on whether it pays or not, under farm conditions, to go to the extra labor and risk of docking and castrating male lambs indicated the following conclusions:

1. Wether lambs did not gain faster than ram lambs.
2. Differences in the carcass early in the season are very slight. As the lamb becomes older the wether carcasses are more desirable.
3. Wethers have a higher percentage of rack and loin and a more plump leg than rams. Rams have a higher percentage of head, shoulder, breast, and leg than wethers. The market grade on the wethers was higher.
4. A buyer could afford to pay over 5 per cent more for live weight from wethers than from rams in this test in which the rams were 96 pounds when slaughtered and the wethers (same age) 88 pounds.
5. In the flocks observed one ram died as a result of injuries received while fighting.

A trial at Maryland Agricultural Experiment Station [11] showed no significant advantage from castration in rate of gain or quality and palatability of meat. The advantage in carcass grade, the great plumpness, and the higher dressing yield of wethers over rams, especially at ages of 20 to 52 weeks, would seem to indicate the desirability of castration as a regular flock management practice.

SHEEP PRICES

Although the value of the by-products from the slaughter of sheep is relatively high, the carcass lamb or mutton is the main source of income from sheep. Mutton and lamb are highly perishable and, as a consequence,

[10] R. B. Hinman, *The Results of Five Years' Work on Castrating Market Lambs.* American Society of Animal Production, 1931.

[11] Wells E. Hunt, DeVoe Meade, and B. E. Carmichael, "Effect of Castration of Lambs on their Development and Quality of Meat," *Bull. 417,* Md. Agr. Exp. Sta., June, 1938.

must move into consumptive channels soon after slaughter. Prices of competitive meats, industrial activity, and the general price level are also factors in sheep prices.

SHEEP PRICES AND SHEEP NUMBERS

The prices of sheep are related to sheep production. This cyclical movement in sheep numbers is due to the sheepman's response to sheep prices. When sheep and lamb prices are relatively high, sheep raising is expanded by increasing the size of flocks and establishing new flocks. The production of lamb and mutton increases, and finally prices must be reduced to move the supply of meat into consumption. This process continues to the point where production becomes unprofitable and retraction of sheep raising begins. When production has been reduced, the level of prices begins to rise, and expansion occurs. Usually, these cycles are completed in 7 to 10 years, 3 to 5 years of increasing production being followed by a period of the same length of decreasing production.

A comparison of the price of lambs at Chicago and the inspected slaughter of sheep and lambs will illustrate the relation between receipts and prices, both seasonal and year to year. Demand for lamb, mutton, and wool is affected by consumer incomes; when the demand is good and supplies are not excessive, prices are fairly high.

SEASONAL VARIATION IN SHEEP AND LAMB PRICES

In a study of the seasonal variation of sheep prices, it should be recalled that, as most lambs are dropped in the spring, there is a difference in lambs marketed at various seasons. In the late spring and early summer spring lambs predominate; grass lambs are marketed in the fall; and feeder lambs in the fall and early winter. Fed lambs are marketed during the winter and into the spring.

Lamb prices usually are highest in May and June, and producers of native lambs try to have their lambs ready for that market. Prices decline during the summer and fall and then rise in January. This is shown in the tabulation of sheep and lamb prices by months. These averages also illustrate the seasonal change in sheep prices. Low prices prevail in the spring; prices are higher in the winter and early spring.

The early spring drop in prices of lambs and sheep is due to shearing, for the wool is worth more than lamb or mutton. Also it is customary to change the market terms about June 1, and lambs of the previous year, or the old-crop lambs, are classed as yearlings.

Sheep are mostly old ewes from farm flocks; some are range ewes and a few are yearlings. On the Chicago market native spring lambs are on the market only during April and May. In June the Chicago market changes to a new-crop basis.

SHEEP AND LAMB PRICES

Average Price per 100 Pounds at Chicago, 1946–1955 [12]

MONTH	SHEEP	LAMBS
January	$10.12	$23.93
February	10.98	24.33
March	11.62	25.54
April	10.90	25.52
May	9.76	26.15
June	8.16	26.13
July	7.78	25.13
August	8.01	24.22
September	8.30	23.13
October	8.30	23.25
November	8.46	23.42
December	9.11	23.53
Average	9.30	24.52

It will be noted that the prices of sheep and lambs do not move in the same fashion. May and June are the high months in lamb prices. Lambs are at their best and unshorn then, and the supply is relatively short in comparison with the demand. The changes in lamb receipts to the shorn basis and then to the new-crop basis cause the market changes in the prices of good and choice grades, usually resulting in a May drop and a June high. In the summer months ewes are at the lowest price because they have been shorn and thin ewes predominate because they have not recovered the flesh lost from suckling lambs.

Fig. 204. A grand champion carload of market lambs at the International Livestock Exposition. Purebred Southdowns shown by H. C. Besuden, Winchester, Ky.

[12] *Livestock and Market News Statistics—1955*, U.S.D.A., 1956.

CASH INCOME FROM LAMBS, SHEEP, AND WOOL

Of the income from the sheep-raising enterprise the greatest proportion comes from the sale of lambs: usually, from 60 to 70 per cent. The sale of wool constitutes a larger source of cash income than the sale of old sheep.

Chapter 31

SHEEP SLAUGHTER—MUTTON
AND LAMB—BY-PRODUCTS

SHEEP SLAUGHTER

Sheep slaughter is somewhat more restricted than the slaughter of other farm animals. Actually, establishments operating under federal inspection which slaughter sheep and lambs are less numerous than those slaughtering cattle, calves, or hogs. The average number of head slaughtered per plant is lower with sheep and lambs than with hogs. There is less farm or home slaughter, and less retail slaughter, in sheep than other slaughter animals. The four national packing concerns (Swift, Armour, Wilson, Cudahy) handle a larger proportion of the slaughter of sheep and lambs than of other kinds of livestock. Home slaughter of sheep and lambs is low because sheep slaughter is somewhat more difficult than that of cattle and hogs, and the consumption per person is less.

Practically all mutton and lamb is consumed fresh, and rapid movement of the meat to consumers is highly desirable. Aging the carcass is not practiced, and curing is comparatively rare. Mutton did not become a factor in the meat trade until artificial refrigeration was established. Lamb has become generally available to consumers in the last 40 years, with improved mutton-type breeding in sheep and the development of efficient meat distribution.

CENTERS OF SHEEP SLAUGHTER

Many public or central markets are places of heavy slaughter of sheep and lambs. In some markets of the West a larger proportion of the receipts are reshipped, either for feeding or for slaughter elsewhere. Denver, for example, is about the largest sheep market, receipts considered, but it ranks eighth in numbers of sheep slaughtered in a recent 10-year period. Following is a list of the centers of sheep slaughter.

SHEEP AND LAMBS—YEARLY SLAUGHTER UNDER FEDERAL INSPECTION, BY STATIONS

10-Year Average, 1945–1954 [1]

MARKET	THOUSAND HEAD
New York, N. Y.	2,102
Omaha, Neb.	956
Chicago, Ill.	904
Kansas City, Mo.	782
St. Louis NSY, Ill.	623
Denver, Colo.	538
South St. Paul, Minn.	440
Sioux City, Iowa	414
All other stations	806
Total	14,817

DISTRIBUTION OF SHEEP SLAUGHTER BY MONTHS

Although there is a very uneven marketing of sheep through the year, the outlet for feeders leaves a fairly uniform supply for slaughter. February, a short month, has the lowest total receipts, yet its slaughter is over 7 per cent of the year's total. Slaughter in April and May is the lowest in an average year. October, the month of heavy receipts, has less than 10 per cent of the entire year's slaughter.

PROPORTION OF SHEEP AND LAMBS SLAUGHTERED

The proportion of lambs in the sheep slaughter has been increasing. In fact, as late as 1890 the *Chicago Daily Drovers Journal* gave no quotations of fat lambs on the Chicago market. Market reports do not generally segregate sheep and lambs; rather, sheep are classified into (1) lambs, (2) yearlings, and (3) sheep or ewes. This separation was made in the reports of slaughters as early as 1923, when lambs and yearlings made up 87 per cent of the slaughter. In 1932 it was about 96 per cent, where it remained until 1942. With the reduction in sheep numbers beginning in 1942, there was an increase in the proportion of sheep in the total slaughter. For the past decade about 12.4 per cent of the sheep and lambs slaughtered under federal inspection were classified as sheep; lambs and yearlings made up the balance. Definitely, the market demand is for lamb rather than mutton. With the expansion and contraction of sheep numbers, proportions vary. Also,

[1] *Agricultural Statistics,* U.S.D.A., 1955.

the favorableness of the current market and the market outlook cause the proportion to change.

THE SLAUGHTERING PROCESS

The endless-chain method is used in sheep slaughter in the modern packing plant. The sheep are shackled and put on a wheel hoist which delivers them to an overhead rail. Sticking is done as the sheep hang by the hind legs; a double-edged knife is inserted into the neck just below the ear so that it severs the large blood vessel in the neck. After bleeding, the first process is breaking the forelegs at the pastern joint just above the foot. A

Fig. 205. Lambs like these are preferred on the market. Lambs make up the largest proportion of the receipts.

lamb will break a "lamb joint"; in sheep the foot is removed at the round joint. The pelt is then removed; in this process the fell [2] on the carcass should not be damaged. This is followed by removal of the hind feet, head, internal organs, windpipe, and gullet. The kidney remains in the carcass.

As with cattle, sheep and lamb are slaughtered separately for the kosher trade. The cutting of the throat is done by the "Shochet" and the dressing process is supervised by the rabbi or a representative of the Rabbinical Board. (See page 130.)

[2] Fell is the thin, tough membrane covering the carcass immediately under the pelt. It prevents the meat from drying out on refrigeration or while being roasted. It does not affect the flavor in properly dressed carcasses.

The carcass is opened down the median line and the breastbone is split. The forelegs are folded back at the knee joint and held there by a skewer or a rubber band. A small wooden stick about 8 inches long is inserted in the belly to allow for proper chilling and to give shape to the carcass. The carcass is then washed and moved promptly to the cooler. The pelt, which is the skin plus the wool, is sent to the wool pullery, if it has sufficient wool, or to the tannery, if it has short wool.

The pluck consists of the heart, lungs, liver, and trachea or windpipe.

The carcasses are hung on a rack, 10 to a rack, and taken to the cooler after they have been completely washed, wiped, and weighed. The cooling period is from 24 to 72 hours. Some of the better grades are wrapped in special coverings for marketing.

THE DRESSING PERCENTAGE

One of the largest factors in the dressing percentage of sheep is the weight of the pelt. Since wool is worth more than the carcass per pound, the wool yield may be an important item in the slaughter return, and dressing percentage lowered by heavy wool yields would represent high total return. A heavy paunch, or light fleshing, detracts from the value of a slaughter sheep because the carcass is worth more than the by-products other than wool. Certain small parts in the by-product sell for more per pound than the carcass, but the carcass has a higher value per pound than the offal, other than the wool.

High-dressing sheep are therefore in demand on the market, irrespective of the pelt. Mutton-type sheep usually have light pelts, trim middles, and heavy fleshing and, as a consequence, they dress high.

The dressing percentages for the various classes of slaughter sheep are as follows: [3]

CLASS AND GRADE	DRESSING PERCENTAGE	
	Average	*Range*
Slaughter lambs		
Prime	50	47–53
Good	47	45–50
Choice	45	43–47
Utility	43	41–45
Cull	40	38–43
Slaughter sheep, mutton ewes		
Choice	50	47–53
Good	47	45–50
Utility	44	42–46
Cull	41	38–44

[3] Information from C. L. Strong, Agricultural Marketing Service, U.S.D.A., Jan., 1957.

The average dressing percentage based upon a monthly survey of whole-sale slaughters under federal inspection for an 8-year period was 47.2 per cent, with an average live weight of 95.98 pounds and a carcass weight of 45.28 pounds. Sheep dress high following shearing. The average live weight is the lowest in June, because of light pelts on the slaughter sheep and the young age of the market lambs.

FEDERAL MEAT INSPECTION OF SHEEP AND LAMBS

Lamb or mutton which enters interstate or foreign trade is subject to federal inspection, both prior to and after slaughtering. In sheep there are relatively few condemnations by the meat inspection service. In one fiscal year the ante-mortem inspection resulted in passing 99.95 per cent. In the post-mortem inspection, which included all those inspected on foot except those condemned, 99.47 per cent were passed. Pleurisy or pneumonia and emaciation are the largest causes for condemnations after slaughter.

MUTTON AND LAMB

MEAT FROM SHEEP

Meat has been previously defined. Mutton is meat derived from sheep nearly 1 year of age or older, and lamb is meat from younger sheep. Immaturity of lambs is rarely encountered in market lambs or as a cause for condemnation on slaughtering.

Mutton is distinguished from other meats by its firm, dense, fine fibers and its dark-red color. The fat is hard, firm, brittle, and pure white.

GOAT MEAT

Some goats are slaughtered for food, but the number slaughtered under federal inspection is quite small.[4] The goat carcass is quite different from the sheep carcass in that it has less fat and longer shanks. The meat is generally paler than sheep meat. The fat is chiefly in the kidney capsules, and there is very little fat on the outside of the carcass or within the muscles. In appearance goat carcasses are somewhat like those of thin wool-type sheep, and occasionally goat meat is substituted for mutton or lamb. Meat from an older goat is dark in color and has practically no marbling. "Chevon" is the term applied to the meat of the goat. The meat of young goats, "kids," is tender and quite acceptable. The odor and flavor of the meat and fat of older goats usually are strong, resembling that of the live goat.

[4] For the fiscal year 1953, 30,000 head of goats were slaughtered under federal inspection.

DISPOSITION OF THE CARCASS LAMB AND MUTTON

For the most part lamb and mutton go to the retailers fresh and as whole carcasses and are distributed much the same as beef. Usually the carcasses are broken down into retail cuts directly by the retailer. However, some wholesale cuts are recognized and are available on wholesale markets of some size.

A small amount of mutton and lamb is frozen and held for a future market. Also there is a very small quantity cured. Carcasses of the kind that are not acceptable to the trade are processed at the packing plants. This gives an outlet for canner sheep, mainly old thin ewes. These are processed and sold as prepared meats and meat food products.

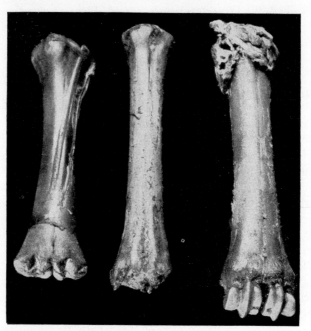

Fig. 206. Joints at which the front foot is removed in dressing sheep and lambs. A smooth joint from a mature sheep (right), a crushed break joint from a yearling (center), and a break joint from a lamb (left).

LAMB, YEARLING, AND MUTTON [5]

We recognize on the market carcasses of lambs, yearlings, and mutton. The exact age at which these changes take place is a little indefinite. There

[5] From *Food and Nutrition News,* Vol. VII, No. 5, National Livestock and Meat Board.

are certain features characteristic of the different groups; these differences result from changes which occur at different stages of maturity in the animal. Age produces changes in the character, color, and consistency of the flesh and bones, and, to a lesser extent, in the consistency and character of the fat. In conformation it is commonly noted that lambs have a narrow, compact front quarter, while yearling and mutton carcasses are wider or "spready" appearing through the front quarter.

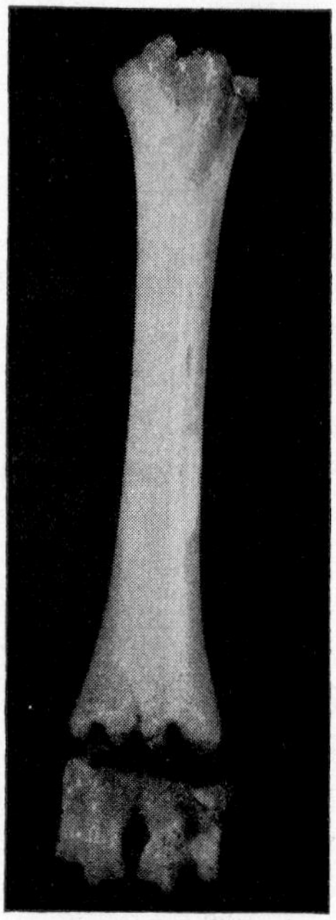

Bones

The hardness and color of the bones are a good indication of age, in every case. Hardness of bones can be determined by observing the color of the ribs in the chest cavity and the bones in the shank and break joint. Redness in bones indicates a young animal and whiteness indicates age.

The "break joint" is the most reliable indication of age. In young lambs, the forefeet are taken off at the break joint or, as it is sometimes called, "the lamb joint." The break joint has four well-defined ridges which are smooth, moist, and red.

As lambs approach the yearling stage, the bones become harder and white. The break joint retains some of the sawtooth effect but is harder and more porous. Ewes tend to ossify the break joint earlier than do wethers.

When the mutton stage is reached, the break joint cannot be made and the forefeet must be taken off at the round or "spool" joint, just below the true break joint. (See Figs. 206 and 207.)

Fig. 207. The bones of the foreleg of a lamb, from the knee to the pastern joint, showing both the break joint and the smooth joint. The smooth or mutton joint is nearer the foot than the break or lamb joint.

Color of flesh

Another means of distinguishing between lamb and mutton is the color of the lean. In lamb, the color of the flesh varies from light to dark pink. As the animal grows older, the color deepens. In yearlings, it is medium pink to light red; in mutton it ranges from light to dark red.

Fat

Lamb fat is softer than that of yearling or mutton. It is creamy white or slightly pink in color. The fat in yearlings is whiter and slightly more brittle than lamb fat. Mutton fat is white and possesses still more hardness and brittleness than yearling fat.

MARKET CLASSES AND GRADES OF DRESSED LAMB AND MUTTON

The carcasses of lambs, yearlings, and mutton are graded largely on the basis of two general factors—conformation, and quality. The grade and the classification are much the same as those used for beef. Following are the definitions of these terms and their application to carcasses.[6, 7]

Conformation

Conformation is the form, shape, outline, or contour of the carcass. It ranges from the smooth, plump, well-rounded, well-proportioned conformation of the most highly developed carcass produced, to the rough, rugged, irregular, disproportioned conformation of the thinnest, boniest, most poorly shaped carcass produced.

Finish or fat is now considered under conformation and quality. It includes the fat which appears on the outer surface of the carcass, on the inner walls of the chest and abdomen, around the kidneys, the seams of fat which sometimes lie between the larger muscles, and the distribution of fat through the muscle tissues. Finish involves not only the quantity of fat but its quality and distribution. Finish ranges from that of the carcass which is almost completely covered both inside and outside with a smooth layer of firm fat, to that of the carcass totally lacking in discernible fat. Conformation is influenced by the quantity and distribution of external fat.

Quality

Quality is largely a characteristic of the flesh. It includes texture, tenderness, juiciness, flavor, and color. Quality also involves ratios or proportions of flesh to bone and of fat to lean meat. Quality, therefore, ranges from that of the small-boned, heavily fleshed, highly finished, well-proportioned carcass possessing a very high degree of tenderness, juiciness, and flavor, and very fine fiber or texture, to that of the very large-boned, thinly fleshed, ill-proportioned carcass with an extremely low degree of tenderness, juiciness, and flavor, and extreme coarseness in texture. The interior fat deposits are considered in the indirect evaluation of quality. The evidence of ample carcass finish in order of importance are as follows: (1) The fat intermingled within the lean between the ribs called "feathering," (2) The

---

[6] From *Regulatory Announcement 123,* U.S.D.A., March, 1931; reprinted December, 1939.

[7] Changes were proposed in 1956 and made effective in 1957, to make the standards more precise and definite, also to reduce the emphasis placed on maturity as a grade factor; particularly in the prime and choice grades for lamb carcasses. The range of quality included in the choice grade was reduced. Federal Register, Agricultural Marketing Service, U.S.D.A., Oct. 31, 1956.

LAMB CHART

Numerals in circles ○ refer to wholesale cuts. Letters refer to retail cuts.

WHOLESALE CUTS

①② and ⑥ HIND SADDLE

  ① Leg
  ② Loin
  ⑥ Flank

③④ and ⑤ FORE SADDLE

  ③ Hotel Rack
  ④ Chuck
  ⑤ Breast

RETAIL CUTS

① LEG

  a. Roast
  b. Chops or roast

② LOIN

  Loin and kidney chops

③ HOTEL RACK

  Rib chops or roast

④ CHUCK

  a. Roast or chops
  b. Neck slices or stew

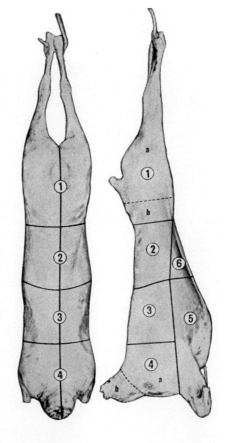

⑤ BREAST
Stew

⑥ FLANK
Stew

YIELDS OF WHOLESALE CUTS

Percentage of Carcass Weight

①② and ⑥ Hind saddle	50.0%	③④ and ⑤ Fore saddle	50.0%
① Leg	33.0%	③ Hotel rack	11.0%
② Loin and ⑥ Flank	17.0%	④ Chuck	25.0%
		⑤ Breast, inc. shank	14.0%

Fig. 208. Lamb carcass, indicating the wholesale and retail cuts. (U.S.D.A., Agricultural Marketing Service.)

streaking of fat within and upon the inside flank muscles, and (3) The fat deposited over the inside of the ribs adjacent to the backbone called "overflow fat."

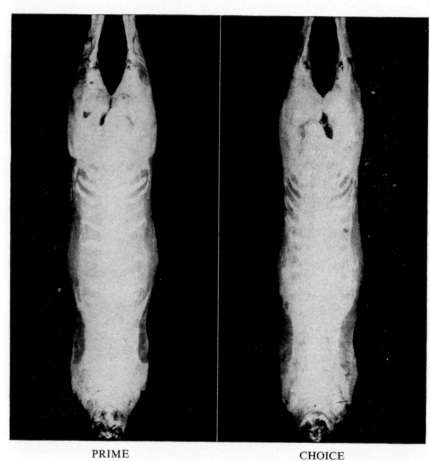

PRIME   CHOICE

Fig. 209. Lamb carcasses representative of the grades Prime and Choice. A ribbon grade is placed by a Government grader on all of the principal wholesale cuts. (U.S.D.A., Agricultural Marketing Service.)

Following is the schedule used for sheep carcasses:

CARCASSES	GRADES
Lamb	Prime
Yearling	Choice
Mutton *	Good
	Utility
	Cull

* Prime grade not used for mutton.

WEIGHT OF SHEEP CARCASSES

A weight separation of carcasses is common in market quotations. A market report shows the common weight divisions, grades, and prices.

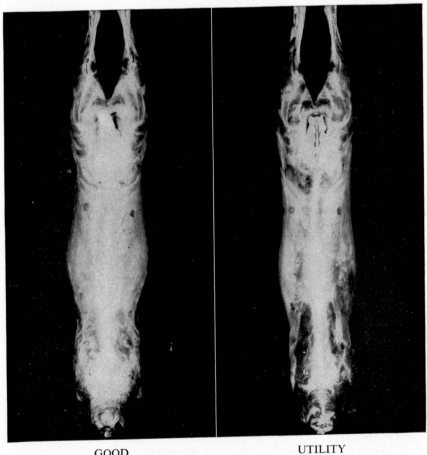

GOOD   UTILITY

Fig. 210. Lamb carcasses representative of the Grades Good and Utility. A ribbon grade is placed by a Government grader on all of the principal wholesale cuts. (U.S.D.A., Agricultural Marketing Service.)

It will be noted from market reports that both grade and weight are factors in the market price. The heavier carcasses are discounted in price because of the consumer preference for small cuts. Lamb carcasses in the weight range of 35 to 45 pounds are usually quoted at the highest prices, but there may be times when more or less weight is accepted without a price discount. Heavy lamb carcasses up to 60 pounds compete with light yearling and mutton carcasses. In some cases very heavy lamb carcasses are sold as yearlings even though they may show a break joint.

CARCASS GRADES AND FATNESS

The higher grade lamb carcasses are those which carry the most finish or fat. Such carcasses may have a lower proportion of lean, but they contain a larger edible portion and a smaller percentage of bone and ligament. The relationship of grade to physical composition is shown in the data tabulated below. This U.S. Department of Agriculture study included the carcasses of 51 lambs.

AVERAGE PHYSICAL COMPOSITION OF LAMB CARCASSES OF THE DIFFERENT MARKET GRADES

| | GRADES OF CARCASS | | | | | |
	Prime	Choice	Good	Commer-cial or Medium	Utility or Common	Cull
Average chilled, dressed carcass weight, pounds	50.6	43.2	34.5	31.9	21.3	16.6
Dressed carcass as analyzed						
Separable fat, per cent	32.5	29.6	22.5	18.6	16.2	7.1
Separable lean, per cent	50.1	50.4	53.8	58.2	55.1	57.8
Edible portion, per cent	82.6	80.0	76.3	76.8	71.3	64.9
Bone and ligament, per cent	17.4	20.0	23.7	23.2	28.7	35.1

It will be noted that, in the physical separation, as the fatness increased so did the carcass weight and also the percentage of edible portion, while the percentage of separable lean and bone and ligament decreased. Lamb graded prime is too fat for wide acceptance in the retail trade.

WHOLESALE CUTS OF LAMB AND MUTTON [8]

The major wholesale cuts of lamb and mutton (see Figure 208) generally recognized in all markets are hindsaddle and foresaddle, each comprising about 50 per cent of the carcass weight. The division is made between the twelfth and thirteenth ribs, one pair of ribs remaining on the hindsaddle. Saddles are subdivided into legs, which represent 33 per cent, and loins, including flank, which comprise 17 per cent of the total weight of the carcass. These cuts are divided as shown in the figure. Loins include the flanks and kidneys.

[8] W. S. Davis, "Commercial Cuts of Meat," *Circ. 300,* U.S.D.A., April, 1940.

Foresaddles are subdivided into hotel racks, which include parts of nine pairs of ribs, or 11 per cent; chucks, including neck, or 25 per cent; and breasts, including shanks, or 14 per cent of the carcass weight. Slight variation in percentage weights of the various cuts at different markets is not unusual; there is also slight variation in yields of cuts from different grades. Neither of these, however, is very marked.

Other terms fairly common in certain markets are "rattles," "stews" and "slugs." These terms refer to the same cut, which consists of the chucks, breasts, neck, and shanks. It comprises all of the forequarter except the rack. A "wing" consists of the two shoulders, shanks, neck, and breasts. A "bracelet" comprises the rack plus the portions of the breast which correspond with the plates in a beef carcass.

PRICES OF MUTTON AND LAMB CARCASSES

Mutton is much lower priced than lamb. On the wholesale market in Chicago the average price for good-grade 40- to 50-pound lamb carcasses was $51.11 for a 5-year period. During that same period mutton carcasses (ewes) of good grade weighing 70 pounds and down were a little more than half as much as lamb.

Prices of different lamb cuts

Low prices for some lamb cuts are necessary in order to sell the entire carcass. The most desirable cuts are priced high to balance the cuts that must be priced low to move them. On the retail market loin chops are the

Fig. 211. A champion lamb carcass at the International Livestock Exposition. University of Illinois, Champaign, Ill.

highest priced, followed in order by rib chops, leg of lamb, lamb chuck, shank, neck, and breast.

LAMB AND MUTTON CONSUMPTION

Our imports and exports of lamb and mutton have been negligible and, as a consequence, production is practically the same as the amount consumed. Cycles in consumption occur which are the same as the cycles of production, for the meat is domestically consumed and there is little storage of lamb and mutton.

Per capita consumption of lamb and mutton was quite low from 1917 to 1929. Since 1929 consumption has been at about the same level as the 1900–1915 period. From 1929 to 1955, inclusive, the yearly per capita consumption has ranged from a high of 7.3 pounds in 1951 to a low of 3.4 pounds in 1951, with an average of 4.59 pounds for the past 10 years. Recently consumption has decreased markedly. (See Figure 55.)

Lamb consumption is the heaviest in the middle Atlantic, New England, and Pacific states, where the per capita consumption is over 12 pounds per year. About 70 per cent of our lamb production is consumed in those sections.

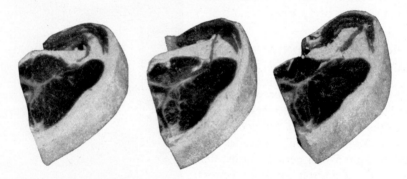

Fig. 212. Loin chops of lamb, the highest priced common cut of lamb. (National Livestock and Meat Board.)

The per capita mutton and lamb consumption is quite high in Australia and New Zealand.

BY-PRODUCTS FROM SHEEP SLAUGHTER

The value of the by-products from sheep slaughter is higher proportionately than that from other slaughter animals. This is due to the value of the pelt which accounts for about 14.5 per cent of the slaughter income. The by-products other than the pelt commonly return an income about comparable to that of cattle, exclusive of the hide, and somewhat less than calves and more than hogs. Stated in another manner, the by-product return from slaughter exclusive of the hide or pelt is most for calves and least for hogs, while sheep and cattle are intermediate. For sheep the income from the by-products other than the pelt is about 4.1 per cent of the slaughter income. It should be pointed out that the value of the pelt depends primarily upon the quality and quantity of wool which it carries. The entire by-product return equals 18.6 per cent; therefore, 81.4 per cent of the slaughter income is from the carcass meat. Income from meat and by-products changes from time to time. In the early days of the packing industry the by-products were a liability rather than an asset.

Fig. 213. Applying depilatory to the flesh side of a pelt preparatory to "pulling" the wool. (Armour & Company.)

YIELD OF VARIOUS PRODUCTS

In the following tabulation the main products and the quantity yielded from the slaughter of sheep are given. This is based upon approximate yields for an average lamb.

WEIGHT (BY PERCENTAGE) OF VARIOUS LAMB PRODUCTS [9]

SUMMARY	POUNDS OF PRODUCT IN AVERAGE LAMB	PER CENT OF FINISHED PRODUCT TO LIVE LAMB
Dressed lamb (carcass)	39.5	47.0
Edible by-products		
Tongue, liver, heart, sweetbreads, brains	1.7	2.0
Oleo oil and stearine	2.0	2.4
Inedible by-products		
Pelt { Wool	4.0	4.7
Pelt { Skin	5.5	6.6
Fats: rendered tallow, oil, and grease	.6	.7
Soft bones	.5	.6
Trotters	1.3	1.5
Blood (dried)	.7	.8
Casings (finished)	.5	.6
Tankage	2.4	2.8
Valueless material and shrinkage	25.3	30.3
Total	84.0	100.0

In the case given, the 84-pound lamb dressed 47 per cent and yielded a 39.5-pound carcass. About 30 per cent of the live lamb is valueless material and shrinkage. The latter is mainly moisture loss, and the valueless material is paunch contents and such.

DISPOSITION OF SHEEP BY-PRODUCTS BY A LARGE PACKING COMPANY

The principal by-products from sheep slaughter in addition to those listed in the general section on packing house by-products in Chapter 8, are as follows:

Blood
Gall bag
Bones
Fat   } (See page 139)
Glands
Pelt

Wool $\longrightarrow$ Textile fibres and fabrics
Degras $\longrightarrow$ Lanolin $\longrightarrow$ Cosmetics
Skin $\longrightarrow$ Sheepskin leathers
Small intestines $\longrightarrow$ Special sausage casing
Sutures, racquet strings

[9] *Agr. Res. Bull. 10,* Swift & Company, November, 1937.

Gullet
Weasand
Paunch
Peck
Rennet
Lungs
Inedible trimmings   (See page 139)
Gall bladder
Genitals
Eyes
Large intestines
Bladder

PULLED WOOL

After slaughtering the pelt is sent to the wool house or "pullery." If the packing plant does not have such facilities available, the pelts are treated with salt and so preserved for storage until the accumulation is delivered to the "pullery." Pelts with short wool—less than ¾ inch—are sold in pelt form rather than separated into the pulled wool and skin.

A lamb pelt suitable for pulling will yield about 4 pound of pulled wool and have a skin with a weight of 5.5 pounds. The season of slaughter is a big factor in pulled-wool yields. Pulled-wool yields are lower than shorn yields because the pelts are washed before the wool is pulled, wringing to remove excess water following washing. A depilatory solution made of sodium sulphide, slaked lime, and water is applied to the skin side of the pelt and after hanging on a rack for a time the wool is removed by hand pulling. As the wool is pulled it is put into containers by grades.

The amount, quality, and condition of the fleece, therefore, affect the value of the pelt, as do the length, shrink, and color of the wool. The value of the skin is also a factor in the return from the pelt.

SHEEPSKINS

After the wool is pulled, the skin or "slat" is washed and soaked in salt pickle solution which contains salt and some sulphuric acid. After this treatment, the pelts are graded for quality and size. Leather from sheepskins varies a great deal. Leather from the long-wool breeds is quite durable, but leather from Merino pelts is thin and generally poor in quality. The skin is then manufactured into leather and is used for coats, jackets, gloves, cheap shoes, slippers, linings for shoes, ladies' shoes, hat sweatbands, chamois skin, diplomas, and many other items.

Sheepskins with short wool are tanned with the wool on and used for coats, robes, rugs, felts, slippers, and other articles.

Fig. 214. Pulling wool. As the wool is pulled it is sorted into grades. (Armour & Company.)

SHEEP FATS

Most of the fat from the sheep is left with the carcass. Sheep fat has a high melting point owing to a large proportion of highly saturated fatty acids in the fat. The caul and ruffle fat are used as edible fats. The inedible fats and greases are used in soaps, glycerin, and other commercial products.

OTHER BY-PRODUCTS OF SHEEP SLAUGHTER

A wide range of pharmaceutical or medicinal substances are recovered in the dressing of sheep. The glands of the pituitary, thyroid, ovary, pancreas, suprarenals, and other parts are the source of such materials. For example, suprarenalin, which is obtained from the adrenal gland just above the kidneys, is a powerful astringent and heart stimulant. The glands from 135,000 sheep are necessary to yield 1 pound of the extract. Glue, tankage, bone meal, fertilizer, fancy meat casings, ligatures, and a host of other useful materials are by-products in sheep slaughter.

Chapter 32

WOOL

Wool is the most important of the animal fibers. The fleece may return from 20 to 40 per cent of the total income from the farm flock and even a greater proportion with a range or ranch flock. Apparently, sheep were among the first of the animals domesticated, for the arts of weaving and felting are among the first recorded.

CLASSES OF TEXTILE FIBERS

Roughly there are three classes of fibers.

Animal fibers

These include wool, mohair, alpaca, vicuña, cashmere, camel's hair, horsehair, and cattle hair. Silk is likewise an animal product.

Vegetable fibers

This group includes cotton, flax, hemp, jute, and many other fibers and grasses of less importance.

Artificial fibers

These man-made fibers make up a sizable percentage of textile materials. Included in this group are nylon, orlon, dacron, acrilan, dynel, vicara, vicose, acetate, and similar fibers.

There are four important textile materials—cotton, wool, rayon, and silk. The annual per capita consumption of cotton is about 34 pounds, but there are wide fluctuations in the amount used. The annual consumption of scoured wool is about 2.0 pounds of apparel wool and 0.86 pound of carpet wool per person. During the war period the wool consumption per person was doubled. Nearly 90 per cent of the apparel wool used in this country is used in fabrics for wear. The use of rayon yarn has increased. The annual consumption per person of rayon is about 5.5 pounds and somewhat less, about 0.8 pound, for silk. Consumer habits are continually changing, and improved manufactured textiles have caused changes in the materials consumed. Wool for clothing is in less demand than formerly because of our more sheltered living.

WOOL PRODUCTION

WORLD WOOL PRODUCTION

The largest proportion of the world wool supply is raised in the southern hemisphere. A considerable part of this production enters into the world trade, since the wool-deficient countries are in the northern hemisphere. For a 10-year period the annual world wool clip (grease basis) has averaged 3,850 million pounds. The production in the United States is less than 10 per cent of the world production.

Wool is a large item in international trade. Following is a list of some countries with surplus stocks, which, consequently, are exporting countries. Reports on recent imports and exports are rather incomplete for several countries.

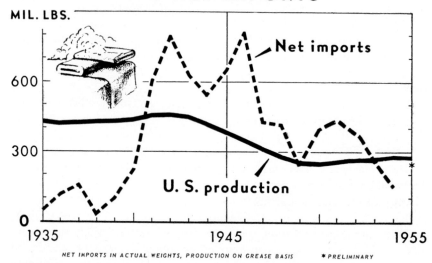

APPAREL WOOL PRODUCTION AND NET IMPORTS

MIL. LBS.

600

300

0

Net imports

U. S. production

1935   1945   1955

NET IMPORTS IN ACTUAL WEIGHTS, PRODUCTION ON GREASE BASIS   *PRELIMINARY

Fig. 215. Production and imports of apparel wool. Net imports as well as production have declined. (U.S.D.A., Agricultural Marketing Service.)

PRINCIPAL EXPORTING COUNTRIES [1]

AVERAGE EXPORTS, 1946–1950
MILLION POUNDS

Australia	1,060
Argentina	450
New Zealand	372
Union of South Africa	273
Uruguay	163

Some of the countries which produce an insufficient amount of wool for their own needs and are therefore heavy wool importing countries are listed below.

PRINCIPAL IMPORTING COUNTRIES

AVERAGE IMPORTS, 1946–1950
MILLION POUNDS

United States	776
United Kingdom	557
France	435
Belgium	219
Italy	178

WOOL PRODUCTION IN THE UNITED STATES

The yearly production (grease basis) in this country for a recent 8-year period was 228 million pounds of shorn wool and 38 million pounds of pulled wool. Converted on the basis of 44 per cent yield for shorn wool and 75 per cent yield for pulled wool, the approximate clean equivalent would be 128.6 million pounds. During the same period we imported for consumption 194 million pounds of apparel wool. This does not include the wool stored in this country by the British government and later re-exported. Therefore, there was annually 322 million pounds of apparel wool (clean basis), available for consumption. In the 8-year period a large part of the apparel wool used in mill consumption was imported, but in recent years the net imports have declined. This is shown on the scoured basis in Figure 215.

We produce but little carpet wool, which is wool too coarse to be classed as apparel wool. Carpet wool is usually not finer than 40's and is duty free. About 143 million pounds of such wool has been imported recently.

Leading wool-producing states

Most of the wool raised in this country is grown in the range states. Following is a list of the states ranking high in total amount of wool shorn for a recent period.[2]

---

[1] *Agricultural Statistics*, U.S.D.A., 1955.
[2] *The Wool Situation*, 1957 Outlook Issue, Agricultural Marketing Service, U.S.D.A., Nov., 1956.

STATE	WOOL SHORN, THOUSAND POUNDS
Texas	61,992
Wyoming	22,476
Montana	19,276
California	17,154
Utah	13,068
New Mexico	12,573
Colorado	11,986
Idaho	11,057
Ohio	10,181
South Dakota	8,949
Missouri	7,738
Iowa	7,124
Oregon	6,931
Minnesota	5,841
North Dakota	4,830
Kentucky	4,291

The yield of wool per sheep per year is high in the range states. For the period, the average annual yield per sheep in this country was 8.07 pounds. The western states averaged 8.76 pounds per sheep, and Wyoming and Idaho topped the other states with a 9.8-pound average yield. The annual yield of wool per sheep for the south Atlantic states was 5.3 pounds, and Florida was low with a 3.7-pound average. The difference in fleece yield is due to breeds, nutrition, extraneous material, and other conditions.

WOOL CHARACTERISTICS AND MARKET GRADING

WOOL AND HAIR COMPARED

Wool is a modified hair structure. The slight differences from typical hair are responsible for the economic value of wool. Wool is elastic and has a scaly exterior. Hair is less elastic, quite smooth, and larger in diameter.

Fig. 216. Typical wool fiber magnified 160 diameters. (From *Structure of the Wool Fiber,* by F. H. Bowman.)

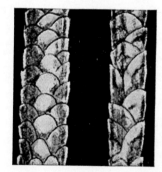

Fig. 217. Human hair magnified 120 diameters. (From *Structure of the Wool Fiber,* by F. H. Bowman.)

These differences give wool fiber its "felting" qualities, for the serrated fibers cling together. This peculiar property, together with elasticity, makes it possible to spin a strand of yarn as the fibers interlock in the sawlike edges of their scales. Wool also differs from hair in appearance, for the wool fibers are crimped but hair is always straight, wavy, or curled.

Fine wool usually is more crimped than coarse wool, although this is not always the case. The crimps per inch range from 10 to 36.

WOOL SHRINKAGE

The fleece as it is shorn from the sheep is known as "grease wool," "greasy wool," or "wool in the grease." The foreign material in the fleece, the "shrinkage," is removed by scouring the greasy wool in a soap and soda solution. The clean scoured wool is termed "yield of clean content" of the fleece. The wool impurities which constitute the shrink have been grouped by Burns [3] as follows:

Wool impurities

1. Indigenous, i.e., native or from within
    a. Accretions, such as kemps, gray fibers, and gray hair
    b. Excretions, such as dung, manure dust, and urine
    c. Secretions, such as yolk or grease, and sweat or suint
2. Extraneous, i.e., foreign or from without
    a. Of animal origin, such as ticks and bugs
    b. Of vegetable origin, such as burrs, straw, sagebrush, greasewood, and cactus
    c. Of mineral origin, such as sand and dirt
    d. As applied by man, such as paint, tar, and dips

Moisture is also present in the fleece, the amount being dependent upon moisture in the air. Prior to shearing, sheep are often held in an enclosed place to cause them to sweat, which moistens the fibers, softens the yolk, and facilitates shearing. Shearing in rainy weather or making the sheep sweat too heavily should be avoided, for it causes the moisture content to be high. The moisture content of wool normally ranges from 12 to 17 per cent and may be as high as 30 per cent.

Amount of shrinkage in wool

The amount of shrinkage is an important factor in determining the value of a fleece. In wool grading shrinkage may be considered and the wool of a grade may be divided further on the basis of its shrink. That is, we may

[3] Robert H. Burns, *Bull. 225,* Wyo. Agr. Exp. Sta., February, 1938.

have fine-staple wool with (1) heavy shrink, (2) medium shrink, (3) light shrink. Many quotations of wool prices are on the basis of clean or scoured wool. If, for example, wool is quoted at 45 cents per pound as grease wool, and if the loss in weight from removal of foreign matter is 50 per cent, then the wool would be worth 90 cents per pound as scoured wool, neglecting the cost of scouring.

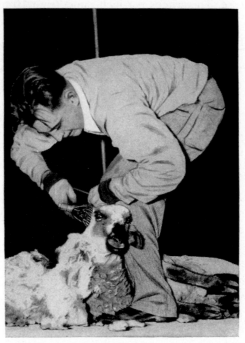

Fig. 218. Shearing by machine. Most sheep are shorn by machine rather than by hand clippers. (Chicago Flexible Shaft Co.)

The shrink in wool may range from 30 to 80 per cent. Most wools shrink from 50 to 65 per cent. Fine wool shrinks more heavily than coarse wool. Buck fleeces commonly shrink more than ewe fleeces of the same type, especially in the fine-wool breeds.

Shrinkage may be determined by scouring a sample of the wool. The sample may be taken by the core sampling method. Estimates of shrinkage are made by an appraisal committee of three wool experts.

The refined wool fat is lanolin, which has various commercial uses, for example, as a base of salves and ointments.

Variation in scoured wool

There is much real variation among breeds in the physical characteristics of the wool. In fact, no two fleeces are identical and, even within a single

Fig. 219. Sheepshearing in competition. Note the stages in the removal of the fleece shown by the different contestants. (Chicago Flexible Shaft Co.)

Fig. 220. A fleece tied up with paper twine. Wool as it comes from the sheep is known as "grease wool" or "greasy wool." (U.S.D.A., Agricultural Marketing Service.)

fleece, there may be much variation. The wool on the breech is coarser, for example, than the wool on the shoulder. Even within a sample, fiber size varies. Apparently there is no relation of clipping to wool growth; frequent shearing does not increase the wool growth rate and lack of shearing, even annually, does not affect it.

Scouring is the washing of the grease wool with soap, hot water, and alkali, usually sodium carbonate. Scouring is generally done by the emulsion process, in which the wool fat combines with the wash water, instead of dissolving in it as in the solvent process.

WOOL GRADING

The grade of wool is determined mainly by the diameter or fineness of the fiber. Other factors which affect value, such as condition of the fleece, length of the staple, and strength and character of the fibers, are considered in grading, but fiber thickness is the dominant factor. Grading is a term used for the entire separation process both into classes and into grades.

Fig. 221. The wool grader at work. A lock is examined to determine the fineness and strength of the staple. (Ohio Wool Growers Cooperative Association.)

The purpose of grading is to make available to the trade wool of fairly uniform characteristics. The grading is done by experienced graders who can identify grade by appearance and touch. In the process of grading the grader examines each fleece individually, noting the fineness of the fiber. He removes a lock of wool from the fleece by holding the tip or outside end of the lock. The length is measured by pulling the lock back along the thumb. This is called "stapling," and the length is referred to as "staple." A combing wool will extend down to the second joint of the thumb, about 2½ inches. After an examination of two or three representative locks, the grader throws the fleece into a pile or bin for the class and grade.

Wool is seldom graded on the farm. This function is performed by an agency, dealer, or cooperative organization which usually has facilities for storing. Wool processors make their purchases from such agencies because they buy by grade and because their purchases are not so seasonal as the movement of wool.

Fig. 222. Wool being graded. The wool sack is opened and each fleece is graded separately by an experienced grader. (Wool Growers Association of South Dakota, Minnesota and Iowa.)

Grading of wool a necessity

Manufacturers of woolen goods require specific grades. Most manufacturers produce only a few kinds of yarns or fabrics and, as a consequence, the grades which one mill may use are very few. In fact, in mills the individual fleeces are divided up into parts (which is called "sorting") to form groups of more uniform characteristics. Wool textile mills are very highly specialized and are generally limited in the fabrics they make; so they purchase graded wools.

The various qualities that affect the value of wool to a manufacturer are fineness, length, strength, elasticity, crimp, softness, pliability, uniformity, color, luster; also felting, spinning, and working properties. The manufacturer uses the term "character," referring to the spinning quality of wool when scoured. Wool that is soft and springy to the touch, even in crimp, good in color, and not frowzy or wasty has good character.

WOOL GRADES

There are two systems of wool grades: (1) The English or spinning count system, and (2) the United States system. In this country we are changing from the latter to the former system of grade nomenclature. The official U.S. Standard Wool Grades adopted in 1926 are based on the count system. The English or spinning count system is based on the number of hanks of yarn that can be made from 1 pound of scoured, combed wool or top. The finer the wool fiber the greater the length of yarn from a given weight. A hank is 560 yards. A grade of 50's would therefore indicate that 50 hanks could be made from 1 pound. In practice, however, less than 50 hanks are usually made from 50's wool. A 60's wool is finer than a 50's wool.

The American system is based on certain grade terms which developed with our wool trade. This grading system is commonly called the "blood system." It was supposed to have originated when Merino wool was termed "fine" and other wools were graded on diameter of fiber based on fineness compared to Merino wool. Supposedly the term indicated proportions of Merino blood or breeding. So the grades were (1) fine, (2) half blood, (3) three-eighths blood, (4) quarter blood, (5) low quarter blood, (6) common, and (7) braid. In wool statistics and market reports the last two grades are pooled together.

Following is a list of equivalent grades of the English and American systems, in order. For example, 56's is equivalent to three-eighths blood.

ENGLISH	AMERICAN
80's, 70's, 64's	Fine
62's, 60's	Half blood
58's, 56's	Three-eighths blood
54's, 50's, 48's	Quarter blood
46's	Low quarter blood
44's	Common
40's, 36's	Braid

Most of the wool produced in this country is of the first four grades. For a 10-year period 96.5 per cent of our shorn wool was quarter blood or finer, 2 per cent was low quarter blood, 1 per cent common, and 0.5 per cent braid.

Size of wool fibers

In a fleece graded as a 40 there will be a range in the diameter of the wool fiber from 10 to 70 microns.[4] Even with a Merino fleece a range in the diameter of the fibers from 10 to 30 microns is common. In medium wool on the fine side the average diameter of the wool fiber is about 24 microns; in medium wool on the coarse side about 32 microns. The fine fibers are on the shoulders; the coarse fibers are on the thighs.

[4] A micron equals 1/1000 millimeter, or 1/2500 inch.

Fig. 223. Wool in storage at a warehouse of a wool growers cooperative. After grading, the wool is stored by grade until it is sold. (Wool Growers Association of South Dakota, Minnesota and Iowa.)

Official standard grades

The first system of grades established by the U.S. Department of Agriculture, in 1923, was based upon United States grades. In 1926 new standards were devised based upon the British system of spinning counts. Both systems are in use optionally in the trade, except that in United States licensed warehouses the newer standard is used.

Samples of wool representing the official grades and mounted upon cardboard can be secured from the U.S. Department of Agriculture. (See Figure 225.)

Classification of wool by length

Sheep, it will be recalled, were grouped into the classes fine wool, medium wool, and long wool. Wool staples range in length from ½ inch up to 12 to 15 inches. As length of wool is one of the characteristics which affects the value of wool to the manufacturer, wool graders also classify wool on length.

There are three length classes of wool—strictly combing, French or baby combing, and clothing. Wool classified as strictly combing must be 2½ inches long to be combed by the English system. The coarser the wool the longer it must be to class as combing. The grades common and braid (36's to 44's) are not divided according to length of staple for they are usually of strictly combing length. The finer grades are classified by staple length. The term French or baby combing is applied because the French system of combing permits the use of somewhat shorter wool than the English system for the manufacture of worsteds. The shorter wools are classed as clothing, for it is not profitable to use them for combing and worsted goods production. (See page 563.)

Classification of wool by regions [5]

In market practice the trade freely identifies wool with the state or region in which it was grown, because the character and appearance of the wool often are affected by conditions in those areas. At least four major regions of the United States so affect the character of wools grown therein as to distinguish them from wools grown in other regions. Grease wools grown in these regions differ in condition, shrinkage properties, and color because of differences in soil, in grazing and climatic conditions, and in husbandry practices.

A.   B.   C.

Fig. 224. Typical wool fibers of different grades: A, fine wool; B, quarter blood wool; C, braid wool (magnified). (U.S.D.A., Agricultural Marketing Service.)

These variations often affect materially the market value of the grease wools, even of the same grade. In recognition of this fact, the wool trade has broadly classified domestic wools into four general groups based on areas of production, as follows: territory wool, semibright wool, bright wool, and southern wool.

Territory wool. That part of the domestic clip produced west of the one hundredth meridian is known in the trade as "territory wool." It comes from the states of Washington, Montana, Idaho, Wyoming, Nevada, Utah, and Colorado, the western halves of North Dakota and South Dakota, and occasionally from western Kansas and Nebraska. Sheep in the "territory" states graze over wide areas, are subject to widely varying soil, climatic, and grazing conditions, and usually are without protection from the weather. All this affects the quality and shrinkage of the wools.

Wools grown in Texas, California, and Oregon are generally known by

[5] From James W. Christie, "Grading Wool," *Farmers' Bull. 1805*, U.S.D.A., 1945.

the name of the state in which they are produced. Arizona and New Mexico wools also are classed separately because wools from these states have certain distinguishing characteristics. About two thirds of our wool production is territory wool.

Semibright wool. Wools produced in Oklahoma, in the eastern parts of Kansas, Nebraska, South Dakota, and North Dakota, and in parts of Missouri, Iowa, Minnesota, and Wisconsin have a dark or stained color caused by deposits in the fleeces of bits of soil. The fleeces thus affected appear dirty and unattractive, but they scour out white.

Semibright wools often are grouped and graded with territory or with bright wools, according to their predominating characteristics.

Bright wool. Nearly all wools grown in the northern states east of the Mississippi River are of this type. Bright wools are also grown in parts of

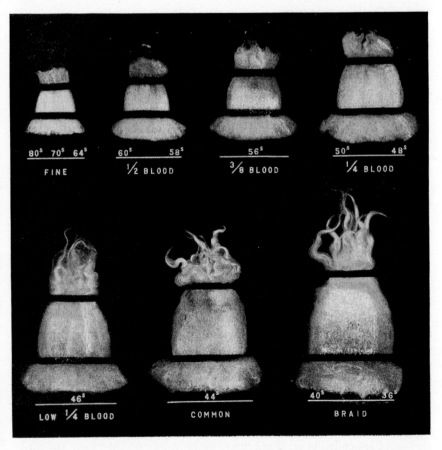

Fig. 225. Grades of wool representative of the official standards of grades of wool and the corresponding numerical terms. (U.S.D.A., Agricultural Marketing Service.)

Minnesota, Iowa, and Missouri.[6] These wools are less exposed to colored soils and other foreign matter than wools in various western areas; so the fleeces are much cleaner and brighter. Such wools have fairly uniform shrinkage, whereas wools from the semibright and territory regions have widely varying shrinkage.

Southern wool. Wools grown in the southeastern states are of bright color and in this respect they are similar to bright wools produced in the states east of the territory and semibright regions, but they are designated by the trade as southern wools. Many so-called southern wools are inclined to be brashy, run out, and uneven, for they are shorn from sheep belonging to no particular breed or class.

In some of the southern states, however, especially in Kentucky, Virginia, and Tennessee, where better strains of sheep are raised, some choice wools are produced that grade three-eights and quarter blood. Very little wool of the fine grade is produced in the southeastern states.

Texas wools. In wool quotations, Fine Texas Wools are listed separately. These wools from the range areas of Texas are sold in the original bags. Such wools are mostly bright in color and moderate in shrinkage, except in the Panhandle district, where they are considerably darker in color and heavier in shrinkage.

Occasionally, wools grown east of the range country are called "fleece" or "domestic wools," but this should refer to wool grown in this country as compared with imported wool. "Fleece wool" or "native wool" is used to designate wools from the farm states east of the range region.

Miscellaneous factors in the classification of wool

Beside fineness of fiber (grade), length of fiber, and origin, several other factors may influence the use or value of a fleece. These factors determine certain further classes of wools, designated by special terms.

1. Pulled wool. Wool removed from the pelts of sheep after they have been slaughtered is classed as "pulled wool." The wool is sorted according to color, length, and grade. Shears are used to remove the wool which is not readily pulled, such as that on the head. After pulling, the wool is dried and sacked. Since pulled wool has been partially cleansed of foreign material, it sells for a higher price than similar grease wool. For a recent period, 17.5 per cent of our wool production was pulled.

2. Black and gray wool. These terms are used on the market to describe colored wool. Black is usually applied to wool that is nearly all black; colored fleeces containing relatively large quantities of white, brown, or gray wool are called gray. Black fibers in the wool prevent its use for white

[6] *Agricultural Statistics,* U.S.D.A., 1948.

materials. Colored wools are desired for certain uses and may even command a premium at times.

3. Carpet wool. Wool of this class is long and coarse and resembles hair; very little is produced in this country.

4. Off wools.[7] These are fleeces that are otherwise known as "discounts," "rejections," or "unmerchantable" wools. Among the wools classified by the trade as off wools are fleeces in the following conditions: burry, seedy, chaffy, cotted, black and gray, dead and murrain or murin, and tags.

Burry, seedy, and chaffy are descriptions applied to wool which has excessive quantities of burrs, seeds, chaff, or other vegetable matter entangled in the fibers. When this condition exists additional chemical or mechanical treatment is necessary.

Cotted fleeces are those in which the fibers have become badly tangled or matted. Hard cots or soft cots are terms denoting the degree of tangle or mat in the fibers. (The English spelling is cotts.) Special mechanical treatment is usually necessary to open these fleeces when preparing them for manufacture.

Dead wool is wool that has been clipped from sheep shortly after their death. When wool is recovered from decomposed remains found on the ranges, it is designated by the term "murrain" or "murin."

Tags are parts of the fleece heavily matted with dung and other animal or vegetable impurities. The term "tag locks" is sometimes applied to such discount wool.

Off wools are of inferior quality, and the quality of many is further impaired by the severe cleaning process necessary to put them in usable condition.

WOOL STRENGTH AND NUTRITION

Wool growth is like growth of other body parts. The quantity and also the quality may be affected by feeding at a low plane of nutrition. A sufficient amount of feed to maintain good health will permit normal growth of the fleece in amount and quality. Periods of underfeeding or sickness give rise to weak or tender spots in the fiber which detract from the commercial value of the wool. Good feeding will give heavier fleece weights, also wool that is longer, stronger, loftier, and more distinctly crimped. Accelerated growth of wool fiber often takes place in the early summer because of luxuriant and highly nutritious pasture. Lambing and suckling may retard the rate of growth of wool fiber. "Tender wool" and "hunger fine" result from poor nutrition or sickness. Such wools are always classed as "clothing wool."

[7] *Farmers' Bull. 1805*, U.S.D.A., 1939.

PRICES OF VARIOUS CLASSES AND GRADES OF WOOL

Fine wools when scoured sell higher than coarse wool and long wools outsell short wools, but not always. Fine wool may be substituted for coarser samples, but coarse wool cannot be made into fine-wool fabrics. There is a demand for both, so the price of a kind depends upon the amount available for the demand. (See Figure 226.)

WOOL PRICES AT BOSTON AND RECEIVED BY GROWERS

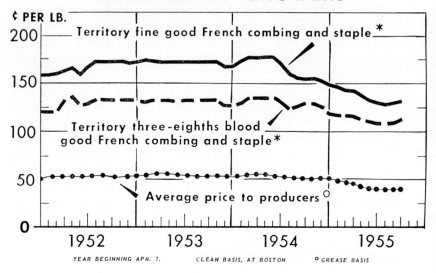

Fig. 226. Wool prices at Boston and average prices received by farmers. Prices at Boston are for scoured wool. The price received by the farmer is for grease wool. (U.S.D.A., Agri. Marketing Service.)

For a recent 10-year period [8] the average price per pound received by farmers was 57.85 cents for shorn wool. Prices of wool over a period of years have moved in approximately 9-year cycles.

WOOL CLOTH MANUFACTURE

For wool cloth manufacture the longer wools or "combing wools" are in greater demand than the shorter wools known as "clothing wools."

[8] *The Wool Situation*, Agricultural Marketing Service, U.S.D.A., Nov., 1956.

WORSTED AND WOOLENS

In the wool manufacturing industry the longer wools are used for "worsted" which is a close woven cloth. There are two systems of worsted manufacture, the "Bradford" and the "French." In the Bradford, long staple is required; in the French wool as short as 1 inch may be used; consequently, there is a separate class for French combing wools. The short wools are used in the manufacture of "woolens."

COMBING WOOL

One of the first processes in the manufacture of materials from wool is combing. In this process the fibers are arranged to lie all in the same direction and are combed together into a ropelike strand of yarn known as "wool top." The longer fibers are the "top," which is used for worsted, which requires smooth, twisted yarns. The part combed out is called "noils," and this is used in making woolens. In making woolens the fibers are interlaced or laid in as many directions as possible. Such wools are carded and spun into soft, fuzzy yarns for soft woven materials.

CLOTH YIELDS

Since more of the short fibers are usable in woolens than in worsteds, it takes more wool to make a pound of worsted cloth than woolen cloth. It requires about 3.7 pounds of grease wool to make 1 pound of the usual wool cloth. An average-sized three-piece man's suit requires about 3.5 yards of cloth. If the cloth weighs 16 ounces per yard it would require about 13 pounds of grease wool to make a suit of clothes.

PREPARATION OF WOOL FOR CLOTH [9]

There are seven main steps in the preparation of wool for cloth.

1. The first is the growing of good wool. This is achieved by proper feeding, handling, and breeding. Good wool should have uniformity of fiber size, strength, color, luster, and reasonable cleanliness.

2. The second step is the shearing of the wool from the sheep. This is usually done by machine and should be done on a clean floor. The shorn fleece should be tied flesh side out with paper twine.

3. The third step is "sorting" the wool, that is, dividing it into lots according to fineness, length, character, color, and spinning qualities.

[9] Adapted from Mary Brandon Potts, *Classification, Grades and Uses of Wool,* U.S.D.A., A.H.D. No. 13, 1935.

4. The fourth step is "scouring," which removes the grease and dirt from the wool.

5. The fifth step is the removal of burrs and other foreign matter. Carbonization is resorted to, if necessary, to remove vegetable matter not removed by combing. In this process the burrs, etc., are charred by acid, such as sulphuric, and then removed by crushing and dusting.

6. The sixth step is "carding," that is, passing the wool through a carding machine, a large iron frame on which are a series of iron rollers covered with leather in which slightly bent wire teeth are set. The wool is passed from roller to roller and is finally reduced to the size of untwisted yarn.

7. The seventh step is the spinning operation which twists the fibers together, giving them strength and making them into yarn.

In the case of worsteds, there is a combing operation which passes the wool through circular combs. In this process the fibers are laid parallel. The combs separate and draw off the long fibers called "tops" in a continuous length. The remaining short fibers are called "noils."

SHODDY

"Shoddy" is the term used for reworked wool.[10] There are many different kinds of shoddy, reflecting the range of materials used in its manufacture. It is made of cloth trimmings and rags which are sorted, torn up, and finally put through a garnetting machine, which is similar to a carding machine. As garnetting is a more severe process than carding, fibers are broken to some extent. The shoddy is blended with longer staple wool when it is spun into yarn.

WOOL PRODUCTS LABELING [11]

In 1941 a federal "Wool Products Labeling Act" became effective. One purpose of this act is to protect producers, manufacturers, distributors, and consumers from the unrevealed presence of substitutes and mixtures in spun, woven, knitted, felted or otherwise manufactured wool products.

Wool products, with certain exceptions, must be labeled to comply with the law. The label must have the information listed below in nontechnical terms and in type big enough to be easily read.

1. The amount of new wool in the fabric.
2. The amount of reprocessed wool.
3. The amount of reused wool.
4. The amount of each nonwoolen fiber in more than 5 per cent of the

[10] Some restrict the term to reused wool.
[11] *Consumers' Guide*, Vol. 7, No. 15, U.S.D.A., May, 1941, p. 5.

fabric; such nonwoolen fabrics as rayon, cotton, silk, etc., may be used with the wool, and they are referred to as other fibers.

5. The percentage of weighting, filling, or other adulterating matter.

6. The name of the manufacturer and/or the distributor or seller.

New wool is virgin wool that has not been previously used or worn. Reprocessed and reused wool have been previously described. The terms "reprocessed" and "reused" do not necessarily indicate poor serviceability, for such wools may actually outwear poor new wool. Wool woven twice loses in strength and resiliency; consequently, reworked wool is inferior to new wool of comparable grades.

WOOL CLASSIFICATION AND USE

The following is a list, grouped according to fineness of wool, of the more common breeds of sheep, together with a description of the kind of wool each produces and the uses to which it can be put in the manufacture of cloth.

CLASSIFICATION OF THE POPULAR BREEDS OF SHEEP AND THE GRADE
OR GRADES OF WOOL PRODUCED BY EACH BREED [12]

CLASSIFICATION	NAME OF BREED		GRADE	
			Spinning-count System	*United States System* *
Fine-wool breeds	American Merino		64's–80's	Fine
	Delaine Merino		64's–80's	Fine
	Rambouillet		60's–80's	Fine and fine medium
Middle- or medium wool breeds	Blackface or "Down" breeds	Southdown	56's, 58's, 60's	½ blood, ⅜ blood
		Hampshire	50's, 56's	⅜ blood, ¼ blood
		Shropshire	50's, 56's	⅜ blood, ¼ blood
		Suffolk	50's, 56's	⅜ blood, ¼ blood
		Oxford	46's, 48's, 50's	¼ blood, low ¼ blood
	Dorset		50's, 56's	¼ blood, ⅜ blood
	Romeldale		56's, 58/60's	½ blood, ⅜ blood
	Corriedale		48's, 50's, 56's, 58's	⅜ blood, ½ blood, ¼ blood
	Cheviot		50's, 56's	¼ blood, ⅜ blood
	Tunis		50's, 56's	¼ blood, ⅜ blood
Long-wool breeds	Lincoln		32's, 36's	Braid
	English Leicester		36's, 40's	Braid, common
	Border Leicester		40's, 46's	Common, low ¼ blood
	Cotswold		36's, 40's	Braid, common
	Romney		40's, 44's, 46's, 48's	Low ¼ blood, ¼ blood, common

* The grade listed first for each breed is that most likely to be found among typical representatives of that breed.

[12] J. E. Wilson, "Wool Production and Improvement of the Clip in California," *Circ. 106,* University of California, November, 1937.

The fibers relatively large in diameter, such as those of the Oxford, are also longer, have fewer crimps per inch, greater stretch, and greater strength. Fibers smaller in diameter are shorter and have more crimps per inch, less stretch, and less strength. Even from a sample that is from one breed the larger fibers in diameter are longer, more elastic, and stronger.

WOOL MARKETING

WOOL SHEARING AND PACKING

Shearing begins in February in the southwest, gradually moves northward, and is generally completed in May. Weather conditions affect the time of shearing. In the South shearing may precede lambing, but for the most part it follows lambing. In the sheep states shearing is done by machine shears and by professional shearers, who may average from 160 to 170 sheep in a 10-hour day.

Shearing is usually done only once a year, except in parts of Texas, California, New Mexico, and Arizona. Wool sheared twice a year ranges from 15 to 25 per cent of the wool production of Texas. The main factors which influence the fall shearing are (1) range conditions, (2) demand for short wool, (3) financial position of the growers. Fall shearing increases slightly the yield of wool and lessens slightly the death loss, but it does not affect the body weight or the size of the lamb crop. Twice-a-year shearing may be necessary in rough hilly country or when the range is heavily infested with such weeds as catclaw.

Shearing close to the hide to get a long staple is desirable, and second clips are to be avoided, for they affect the fiber length and also give some very short fibers.

After shearing, the individual fleece is tied up with twine. Paper twine is the most desirable tying material because it can be removed intact and fragments remaining in the fleeces are removed in scouring. Loose fiber twines are undesirable, since the sisal or jute from which they are made may persist in processing and show up in the woven material.

In this country wool is usually packed for shipping in large sacks up to 7 feet long which may hold 200 to 350 pounds of wool or up to 40 fleeces. Wool in the world trade, such as from Australia, is made into bales weighing 325 to 350 pounds which may contain 40 fleeces each. The Australian and New Zealand wools are generally scoured before they are sold by the producer. Most of our wool is scoured at or near the place of manufacture into cloth. Freight rates favor this practice, and our wools are sorted before scouring.

METHODS OF SELLING WOOL

The wool grower may have one or more of the following avenues of marketing at his disposal:

1. The local buyer. Many small clips are sold to local buyers who may buy on their own account or as local representatives for a wool agency.

2. The wool merchant. Most of the wool in this country is handled by wool merchants. Such merchants store and grade the wool and then sell it to the manufacturer.

3. Order buying. Wool merchants make purchases for manufacturers on order. The merchant purchases the wool from the grower for delivery at a future date to the manufacturer at an agreed price.

4. The mill buyer. Some mills buy direct from the growers, although the volume handled in this manner is small.

5. Selling on commission. In this method the wool is consigned to a wool merchant who acts as agent for the grower and who sells the wool to mills on a commission basis.

6. Cooperatives. These function as sale agencies for wool growers and, through wool pooling, perform the services usually performed by a wool merchant.

7. Auctions. Selling wool by auction is common in some countries, but rare in the United States.

Cooperative wool marketing agencies [13]

Since wool producers have not always been satisfied with returns from wool sales, many cooperative agencies for wool marketing have been formed. Wool growers are not, in general, well acquainted with wool marketing practices and the factors that influence wool price. Some have secured help in solving problems by joining cooperatives. Through the united efforts of a group, large quantities of wool are pooled at a warehouse, graded, and then sold. Cooperatives are grower-owned and controlled, and the trained employees manage the enterprise. All cooperatives do not perform the same functions. Some merely assemble a clip and sell to the highest bidder; others assemble, grade, and market the wool in an orderly manner.

The important activities of a state cooperative wool marketing association are: [14]

1. Making preshearing loans to its members
2. Assembling carloads of wool at various shipping points for grading or shipment to a central concentration point in the state or to Boston

[13] L. B. Mann, "Western Cattle and Sheep Areas," *Bull. 3,* U.S. Farm Credit Administration, September, 1936.
[14] Alva H. Benton, "Wool Marketing," *Bull. 252,* N.D. Agr. Exp. Sta., November, 1931.

3. Grading the clips and submitting a statement to each member on the grades of his wool

4. Making advances on graded wool to members

5. Supplying wool twine and wool sacks to members

6. Shipping the graded wools to the national wool marketing corporation at Boston

7. Securing cash advances from the national wool marketing corporation on the security of wool graded and shipped

8. Distributing the final returns to the members after the wool of the various grades in the seasonal pool has been sold

Cooperative marketing associations pool the wool of their constituents. The wool then loses its identity of ownership on grading, and a member is given credit for the grade and weight of the wool he pools. As each member's wool is graded, the producers having higher grading wool will receive higher prices. The main objectives of the pooling are to keep the cost of marketing low and to secure the full market price for the wool. When wool prices are falling, a grower may receive more for his wool by an outright sale at shearing time, but when prices are rising price appreciation is secured by pooling. The seasonal low price for wool is from April to June when wool is being marketed. Cooperatives provide an alternative marketing method. A cooperative may, through pooling and storing, avoid the usual low time of wool prices.[15]

The national wool marketing corporation

This corporation is a "pool of pools" which was organized November 19, 1929, by a group of wool and mohair growers at San Angelo, Tex. Cooperative groups of wool growers, local, state, or regional, may have membership in this National Wool Exchange. This organization, through the control of a large volume of marketed wool, tends to increase the bargaining power of the growers and to stabilize the marketing of wool.

Principal wool markets in United States

The principal market for wool, both domestic and imported, is Boston, where nearly three quarters of our wool clip and over one half of the imported wool is marketed. Since Revolutionary days Boston has been our leading wool market. This is because most of the manufacturers of woolens and worsted in this country are located within a few hundred miles of Boston. Other important wool markets are St. Louis, Philadelphia, Chicago, and New York.

[15] The Ohio Wool Growers Cooperative Association reported in 1950 that in 28 of the past 32 years, consignors have made money by pooling their wool. Net returns have averaged 3.3 cents per pound yearly above the country price.

Wool tariff

There has been an import duty on wool since 1816, with the exception of two periods which aggregated 10½ years in length. The schedule of wool tariffs was modified in 1948. There is also a tariff on manufactured goods or compensatory duties comparable to the duty on wool. The tariff is higher on some grades, particularly the fine wools, as noted from the following:

WOOL TARIFF ON THE CLEAN CONTENT BASIS [16]

Cents per pound

	IN THE GREASE OR WASHED	SCOURED
1. Not finer than 40's	13	16
2. Not finer than 44's	17	20
3. Finer than 44's	25.5	27.75
4. Wools not finer than 40's for use in carpets	Free	Free

It was previously noted that comparatively little carpet wool is raised in the United States and that the bulk of our home-grown wool is 48's or finer. The duty appears to be fully effective on medium wool most of the time and quite effective on fine wool. The difference between import parity price and prices realized, for a 12-year period, was about one fifth of the wool duty. In other words, about four fifths of the duty was reflected in price increase and the remainder was due to other factors affecting wool prices. Annual imports of wool have been nearly 400 million pounds for the past decade, but appear to be declining, see Figure 215.

National wool act of 1954

Wool is recognized as an essential and strategic commodity. Therefore, in order to encourage sufficient production to meet our domestic needs, an "incentive payment" plan was instigated. A wool grower is paid under the National Wool Act of 1954 the percentage difference between the incentive level and the average United States price on the wool he sells. If the incentive level is 62 cents per pound and the average United States price is 44 cents there would be a difference of 18 cents per pound or 41 per cent. The grower then would get a government payment of 41 per cent of the net dollars he received in payment for his wool.

The Act also includes a "self help" clause provision for promotion work for wool and lamb. It is believed that this plan will encourage production, improve quality and also eliminate the stockpiling of wool.

[16] *Summaries of Tariff Information,* Vol. 2, "Wool and Manufacturers." Part 1, "Raw Wool and Related Hair," United States Tariff Commission, 1948.

MOHAIR

The long, curly, lustrous fiber from the Angora goat is known as "mohair." It is distinguished from wool by its absence of serrations and natural crimp. The mohair fiber is comparatively smooth and wavy. The epidermal scales, upon magnification, are but faintly visible and hardly overlapping. In size the fiber is about the diameter of that from long-wooled sheep. It is more lustrous in appearance than wool and, though mohair has less felting qualities, it is the second most used animal fiber for materials.

The Angora goat is a native of Asia, and goat raising is centered in the district of Angora. The Turks domesticated Angora goats more than 2,000 years ago, and they are used as a source of milk, meat, and material for cloth. Our flocks were established from importations made from Turkey.

Mohair production in the United States expanded rapidly until 1931. During the 1940's production declined; recently production has increased. In 1954 2,492 thousand goats were clipped and the average clip per goat was 5.5 pounds. Practically all of the mohair grown in the United States is produced in the Edward Plateau area of Texas. Mohair is usually shorn twice a year in Texas, Arizona, New Mexico, and California. In arriving at the number of goats clipped in those states, the number of goats and kids clipped in the spring is added to the kids clipped in the fall. The total production in the 7 leading states (in addition to those previously mentioned, Oregon, Utah, and Missouri) for a recent 8-year period has been nearly 14 million pounds yearly, grease basis. The average price on the Boston market for 26's (medium) grade has been about 86 cents per pound, grease basis. Farmers have received about 78 cents per pound, grease basis, for mohair the past few years. The countries of Turkey and the Union of South Africa follow the United States as leading countries in Mohair growing.

Goats tend to browse more than cattle and sheep; consequently, they are often used to clean up brush.

USES OF MOHAIR

Mohair is used extensively in the manufacture of materials (plushes and braid) for chairs, seats for furniture, automobiles, and railway cars. Tropical suitings, dress linings, knitted outerwear, and novelty fabrics are made from mohair. Its outstanding features as material are its brilliancy and durability. Cotton is generally used as base with mohair for the pile.

THE MARKET GRADES OF MOHAIR

The finest quality of mohair is from young goats and is usually called kid. Following are the grades of mohair designated separately in the U. S. Department of Agriculture Reports on the wool situation:

1. 40's
2. 36's
3. 32's
4. 30's
5. 26's
6. 22's
7. 18's

It will be noted that the grades are on the spinning count basis. There may also be a division as regards time of shearing—that is, into spring shorn and fall shorn. In the trade the word kempy is used to designate mohair containing medulated fibers and the word stain to designate mohair that is discolored, due primarily to the absorption of urine.

OTHER ANIMAL FIBERS USED IN MATERIALS

Wool and mohair are not the only animal fibers used in material manufacture. Other similar fibers are:

1. Alpaca. This is shorn every 2 years from alpacas, raised principally in Peru.

2. Vicuña. This is shorn from animals of the same name in Peru and Bolivia.

3. Cashmere or Kashmir. This is the product of the Kashmir goat, raised in the Himalayan Mountains in Asia. It comes from the fine downy wool at the roots of the hair.

4. Camel's hair. This is obtained commercially from China and Russia.

Chapter 33

SHEEP FEEDING
AND MANAGEMENT

Although sheep grazing is common both in the range country and in farm areas, feeding and management on the range are vastly different from feeding and management on the farm. Large-sized bands of sheep predominate on the range, where it is not unusual to handle flocks of from 1,000 to 3,000 head. In the farming sections from 25 to 50 ewes are common, and sheep raising is combined with other farming enterprises. On many farms the farm flock fills a place in the diversification of farming; it provides a use for considerable feed which otherwise would not be utilized.

NUTRITIONAL REQUIREMENT OF SHEEP

Sheep, like cattle, are ruminants and as a consequence are fitted to utilize roughage. Many sheep are never fed concentrated feeds like grains but are raised on pasture and hay from weaning time until they are marketed. Ewes in the breeding flocks are fed mostly, and in some cases entirely, upon pasture and hay.

A 120-pound pregnant ewe, a suckling ewe, and a 60-pound fattening lamb require nutrient material as tabulated on the following page, according to the Morrison Feeding Standard.

It will be noted that the suggested amounts of nutrient are increased as the ewe approaches parturition, and at the same time the nutritive ratio is narrowed. The suckling period calls for additional nutritive material to supply the needs for milk production. It will be noted that the 60-pound lamb being fattened is allowed much more than half of what is recom-
572

mended for the 120-pound ewe. This indicates the need for more concentrated feed for the lamb.

It should be pointed out that a ration balanced according to a feeding standard is not always complete nutritionally or entirely adequate. Such standards merely give the amount of dry matter, protein, and energy materials needed. Quality of protein and quantity and quality of minerals and vitamins are also dietary essentials. The mineral elements: calcium, phosphorus, and iodine, and also vitamins may possibly be inadequate in the feeds. These probable deficiencies should be anticipated in making feed selections, and the feeding standard should be used as an approximate guide. Generally, however, a ration balanced according to the feeding standard is quite complete and satisfactory if it contains a variety of feeds.

DAILY REQUIREMENT, MORRISON FEEDING STANDARD [1]

CLASS	WEIGHT, POUNDS	DRY MATTER, POUNDS	DIGESTIBLE PROTEIN, POUNDS	TOTAL DIGESTIBLE NUTRIENTS, POUNDS	CAL- CIUM, GMS.	PHOS- PHO- RUS, GMS.	CARO- TENE, MILLI- GRAMS	NET ENERGY, THERMS
Pregnant ewe— Up to 4 to 6 weeks before lambing	120	3.2–3.9	0.18–0.22	1.8–2.2	4.3	3.4	7.2	1.4–1.7
Last 4 to 6 weeks of pregnancy	120	3.5–4.2	0.23–0.26	2.2–2.6	4.6	3.7	7.2	1.8–2.1
Ewe nursing lambs	120	3.8–4.5	0.30–0.33	2.5–2.9	6.4	4.7	7.8	2.1–2.4
Growing ewe lambs	60	1.9–2.4	0.14–0.18	1.2–1.5	2.9	2.6	3.3	1.0–1.3
Growing ram lambs	60	2.2–2.7	0.18–0.21	1.4–1.7	3.9	3.2	3.3	1.2–1.5
Fattening lambs	60	2.0–2.5	0.18–0.21	1.5–1.8	2.6	2.2	3.6	1.3–1.6

KINDS OF SHEEP ENTERPRISES

There are three kinds of sheep enterprises, farm or range flock production and commercial lamb feeding. There is some slight overlapping of these divisions, yet each is quite distinct and has distinctive managerial problems. Breeding is involved in the maintenance of flocks; so the operator of a farm or range flock is classed as a breeder, and some of them are breeders of purebreds. To some extent they are feeders, as well, especially the farmer with a flock who finishes lambs for the market. However, this term is usually reserved for those finishing livestock for market.

Sheep, if they are a part of general farming plans, make possible a more

[1] F. B. Morrison, *Feeds and Feeding,* The Morrison Publishing Co., Ithaca, N. Y., 1956.

complete utilization of the feeds raised on the farm. On the range, because of their grazing habits, sheep utilize efficiently herbage which would otherwise not be used. Cattle on the range are competitive for the pasture, but sheep have definite advantages under certain conditions. Sheep can range on high mountain pastures and on much other land unsuited for other domestic animals.

DIVISIONS OF FEEDING AND MANAGEMENT

Inasmuch as feeding and management in the range country is so different from farming, this discussion is divided on the basis of the farm flock and the range flock. It is not our purpose to cover completely all matters pertaining to feeding and management. That is beyond the scope of this text, and for such information the student is referred to the specialized works on sheep and feeding listed at the end of this book.

A brief discussion of the general principles involved in the various divisions of feeding and management follows.

THE FARM FLOCK

The place of sheep on the farm is to supplement the other farm enterprises and to provide a market for labor and feed, including weeds and unharvested crops. A flock of 30 to 40 ewes is of sufficient size so that its production of lamb and wool can be marketed advantageously. With the development of wool pools and local auction sales, the small producer has been greatly helped in his marketing problems. A flock of 30 to 40 can be handled on an average-sized farm and, if the equipment is ample, the care of the flock can be integrated well with other farm work. A flock large enough to utilize economically the feed, equipment, building, and labor available on the particular farm should be the goal. If the flock is too small, there is a tendency to neglect it in favor of the larger farm enterprises; also its ram cost would be relatively high. Although the labor requirement for sheep raising is low, neglect is costly and attention is necessary at critical periods.

THE FARM FLOCK IN SUMMER

The farm flock in the summer consists of the ewes, their lambs, and the rams. Ewe flocks that have had lambs are generally quite heavily fed until the lambs are weaned. Early finishing and marketing of lambs is highly desirable. The ewes, after weaning the lambs, are fed mainly upon pasturage. During this dry period they are not in need of any special care or feeding. A pasture program which involves cultivated pastures, as well as permanent pastures, is highly desirable. By switching to different pastures of various kinds, succulent, palatable forage of ample quantities can be made available throughout the grazing season. In many sections bluegrass is the main pasture used. Although this may be good early and late in season, it has a semidormant period when it is not very productive. If it is supplemented with such pastures as rye, wheat, rape, and alfalfa, it is possible to work out an all-season grazing schedule. Pasture rotation is essential in parasite control; therefore, old bluegrass pastures are to be avoided, especially with lambs.

Flushing or increased feeding prior to breeding is quite commonly practiced on the ewe flock. Liberal feeding prior to breeding is advantageous, especially with thin ewes that have been suckled heavily. It is quite generally believed that flushing will cause the ewes to come in heat earlier, conceive more readily, and have more multiple births of stronger lambs. Experiments have not wholly substantiated this claim.

Fig. 227.   A farm flock on the farm of Adolph Anderson, Davis, Ill.

THE WINTER PERIOD

Ewes are commonly bred in the fall. The winter season, then, coincides with the pregnancy period, which causes extra demands for nutrient material. Feed requirements can be met with roughages, especially during the early part of pregnancy. Care should be taken to have leguminous roughages of good quality for the breeding ewes and also to provide some variety, for if sheep are limited to a single roughage feed, the ration may be inadequate. Field feeds, such as crop aftermaths, corn fodder, stubble fields, etc., when available, prove economical and usually quite satisfactory.

As lambing time approaches, the ration allowance should be increased; supplemental grain feeding is generally advisable. A feed allowance ample to permit a gain of 15 to 30 pounds per ewe during pregnancy is sufficient. The kind of roughage used determines the kind and amount of concentrates. If alfalfa hay or other leguminous hay has been fed liberally during the winter, home-grown grains are sufficient. If, on the other hand, a non-leguminous roughage has been fed, concentrate feeding should start earlier in the pregnancy period and protein concentrates may be needed. Concentrate feeding adds to cost; therefore the amount should be adequate but not excessive. For an average-sized ewe about 20 pounds of concentrates and 400 to 600 pounds of dry roughage are needed for the winter period of 5 to 6 months.

Exercise is to be stressed in wintering pregnant ewes. Close confinement is to be avoided and regular exercise made the rule.

LAMBING TIME WITH THE FARM FLOCK

The lamb crop of a farm flock is usually born in the late winter and early spring. Early lambing is preferred, for the lambing then does not conflict with the spring work on the farm and if the lambs come early enough they can be marketed as genuine spring lambs. Early lambs require more attention and equipment than late lambs and more feed other than pasture. Early lambs tend to avoid stomach-worm infestation and can be finished before the summer decline in prices if they are properly fed and handled. Late lambs may cost less to raise, but they usually sell on a lower market than early lambs. At lambing time the feed allowance is restricted, and during the suckling period the ration is increased so as to stimulate milk production.

Protection is needed for ewes with early lambs. This need not be pretentious; a dry, well-bedded barn free from drafts is about all that is required. Sheep, even young, can stand considerable cold but are quite susceptible to harm from cold rains or wet snow.

THE BREEDING RAM

In small flocks the ram is to be handled like the ewes during a considerable part of the year. Rations and management successful for ewes will also be satisfactory for rams. Special feeding prior to breeding time, as suggested for the ewe flock, is advisable for the ram. The ram should be in good condition during the breeding season; this requires good nutrition.

Fig. 228. Mutton ewes and lambs on pasture. Hampshires on the Buck and Doe Run Valley Farms, Coatesville, Pa.

GROWING AND FATTENING THE NATIVE SPRING LAMB

The early days of a lamb's life are critical and require the close attention of the shepherd.

Docking and castrating may be done simultaneously when the lambs are 10 to 14 days old.

Lambs start to eat supplementary feeds when they are about 2 weeks old. A lamb creep arrangement will permit feeding special feeds to the lambs without interference from the ewes. Grain feeding is essential to finish the lamb for an early market. Good pasture has a high value for young lambs. Even though an excellent ration is fed the suckling ewe and the lambs are creep-fed also, the addition of good forage will promote faster gains and give higher finish. Pasture feeding, if clean and comparatively free from parasites, gives more economical gains than dry-lot feeding.

SHEEP ON THE FARM

Compared with other livestock enterprises in farming areas, sheep rank high in pasture and roughage utilization and in fertility maintenance. On most farms sheep raising is a minor enterprise; so it does not provide a market for great amounts of feeds, especially concentrates. Properly handled, the farm flock will contribute substantially to the farm income.

THE RANGE FLOCK

The following, concerning feeding and management of sheep on the range, is adapted from "Range Sheep Production," *Farmers' Bulletin 1710* of the U.S. Department of Agriculture.

The range sheep unit, or band as it is called, may vary considerably in size but is usually composed of from 2,000 to 2,500 sheep. From lambing time until weaning approximately 1,200 ewes with their lambs are kept together in a band. After the lambs are weaned, two bands of ewes are combined for the breeding and winter feeding period.

With slight variations and one notable exception, the sheep producers of the western ranges use the same general system in handling their sheep. They give a band into the care of one herder who, with his dogs, stays with the sheep day and night throughout the season. He is quartered in a wagon equipped for his needs, except during short periods when he is near headquarters or in the summer when he takes his sheep to high mountains where his wagon cannot follow; then he uses a tent. A camp tender, with his wagon and team or pack animals, attends to the herder's needs by supplying him with food and moving his camp as the sheep exhaust the

Fig. 229. A band of sheep on the western range. The sheepherder and his dog care for a large number of sheep in one band.

grazing in the immediate vicinity. One camp tender takes care of two or more herders, depending on the distance he must haul supplies and the roughness of the country. In large organizations a range foreman usually is in charge of several bands on his allotment of range; in smaller outfits of one or two bands the owner may take the place of both camp tender and range foreman. Additional help is required seasonally, especially during lambing and shearing.

The exception to this general method is found in some parts of the Southwest, particularly Texas, where sheep are kept in paddocks or pastures. Here the operators own or have long leases on nearly all their grazing land, an arrangement which enables them to build fences and let the sheep graze undisturbed in these large pastures. They employ fence riders at all times and additional help during lambing, but on a year-round basis one man can attend to a much larger number of sheep than he can under the herder system.

BREEDING

The time of breeding in different localities varies, depending largely on range and weather conditions during lambing, but the general principles involved are similar throughout the range country. The sheepman desires that all ewes be bred to lamb in a short space of time, thereby ensuring a lamb crop of reasonably uniform age. He also desires a good percentage of lambs. The progressive sheepman is coming to realize that, to obtain these results it is essential to have a uniform band of thrifty ewes, good vigorous rams, and a breeding range with plenty of feed.

The number of ewes allotted to one ram on the range varies greatly, but ordinarily best results are obtained when 3 rams are allotted to each 100 ewes. The length of the breeding season also may vary, but the rams should be left in at least from 35 to 40 days.

WINTER HANDLING

The range sheepman may choose between wintering on the range and wintering in the feed lot. Most range sheep are brought into the feed lot at some time during the winter. The time varies considerably, depending on the condition of the sheep at the beginning of the winter, the condition of the range, the quantity of feed available, and the severity of the winter. In some particularly favored locations and during mild winters the sheepman may allow his flock to graze for the entire winter.

SPRING HANDLING

The largest problem confronting the range sheepman in the spring is lambing. His success at lambing time always has a very definite bearing on the income derived from his business.

Shed lambing

Early shed lambs are raised in many parts of the West for the purpose of getting the lambs on the market at a date somewhat ahead of the large run of range lambs. These lambs, shipped late in the spring and early in the summer, arrive at the markets at a time when demand is brisk, supply small, and prices relatively high. For successful lambing late in the winter or early in the spring it is necessary to have, in addition to sheds and other equipment, an abundant supply of feed and sufficient early range forage to finish the lambs after turning them out on the range. During lambing time an abundant supply of good hay and grain is necessary and some form of succulent feed is highly desirable.

The main advantages of the shed system of lambing are:

1. The band can be lambed early before grass comes and the lambs marketed correspondingly early.

2. More care can be given to the band during lambing, resulting in a greater percentage of lambs raised.

The number of lambs marketed is commonly well over 100 per cent of the number of ewes nursing lambs in the band.

Sheds may be constructed of lumber, galvanized iron, canvas, or straw, or large tents may be used. The interior arrangement of lambing sheds varies with almost every outfit, but the principle is the same in all. Small individual claiming pens, or "jugs," are provided where the ewe and newborn lamb can be placed. Then a system of pens is arranged so that as the lamb grows older the ewe and lamb gradually mix with larger numbers of ewes and lambs. It is desirable, if not absolutely essential, that all the pens in which lambs are placed after they are a few days old be provided with a shelter and an outside run.

It is not always possible, although highly desirable, that space be provided in the shed for the lambing band. In cold stormy weather many lambs may be saved by having the lambing band under shelter. By some crowding a band can be accommodated in approximately 6 square feet per ewe, but more space is preferable. Ample ventilation is essential, from doors, windows, or overhead ventilators.

Range lambing

In range lambing the sheepman plans to have his ewes begin to lamb as soon as grass is available in the spring. A part of the range containing suitable feed, shelter, and water is set aside for lambing and the ewe band is moved in shortly before the lambs are due to be born. When the first lambs are born the day's drop, with the ewes, is gradually brought together before night, and the rest of the ewe band is moved away under charge of the herder. Flags or scarecrows are set up near the group of lambs and ewes, or fires are built to protect it from coyotes during the night. Similarly, the lambs born on the bed ground at night are left by the main band in the morning. These small groups of ewes and lambs are given the best possible care, weak lambs are helped to suck; as the lambs become a little older and gain in strength they are combined until small bands of ewes and lambs are made up and given into the care of herders. Because these young lambs are not able to travel long distances, it is necessary that feed and water be close by.

Small tents are frequently used to protect ewes with newborn lambs during storms. Because of lack of shelter and less individual attention, losses on the range are a great deal heavier than in shed lambing. It is not unusual to lose practically all the lambs born during a severe stormy period.

Fig. 230. Feeder sheep in stockyards, en route to corn-belt feed lot. About 50 to 60 per cent of the lambs are fed in the corn belt.

SHEEP AND LAMB FEEDING

In the fall of the year a great many sheep and lambs from the range country can be profitably used for further feeding. Lambs predominate for this purpose because of the greater margin which usually exists between feeders and finished individuals. The consumer prefers lamb to mutton and will pay more for finish in lamb than in mutton. Lambs make as large or nearly as large gains as older sheep and consume considerably less feed; so the feed cost of their gains is relatively cheap. Lambs need from one third to one half less feed per unit gain than yearlings. On the market, feeder lambs are higher priced than yearlings. Although the number of stock sheep in the country has not shown any pronounced long-time trend, sheep and lambs on feed have varied markedly and have recently declined.

A demand for feeders arises in the fall because of the accumulation of a season's crop. The corn-belt farmer uses the feeder as a means to dispose of his roughage and concentrate feeds. The western feeder in the inter-mountain region feeds beet by-products and similar feeds which become available in the fall. In the estimates of sheep on January 1 each year the number on feed has been about 4 million head.

It has been noted that the greatest movement of feeders and stock sheep and lambs is in the fall. Lambs from California may be available as feeders in May, and those from Texas may be on the market as late as February. Conditions on the range affect the movement of the feeders. With a shortage of range pasture the marketing is early. Geographical distribution of feeder receipts is based on the termination of the range or pasture season.

WHERE FEEDER SHEEP ARE PURCHASED

It has been noted previously that the large markets for feeders are near the range. The feeder may buy at the public market or direct. Since 1930 direct marketing of sheep and lambs for feeding has increased sharply. For the past ten years direct shipments to the corn belt states have outnumbered the purchases from public stockyards markets. Contract feeding, which has also increased in the same time, is a form of direct marketing. In feeder lambs it is quite common for a dealer to contract with a sheep rancher for his entire band of lambs. The dealer then sorts and sells to individual buyers.

In the farming states feeder sheep may be available locally and in relatively small lots. When feeder lambs are purchased at public stockyards markets, many are shipped to the place of feeding by railroad. The feeder lambs are generally purchased in lots of 150 head, the usual capacity of one deck in a car. Truck shipments are made in smaller numbers.

As would be expected, the number of lambs fed in an area is quite variable and largely dependent upon the supply of feed available.

LAMB FEEDING AREAS

Sheep and lambs from the producing and grazing areas are sold for slaughter or, if they are to be fed, they go to winter pasturing and feeding sections or to feeding areas. In the latter, roughage and concentrate feeding is practiced. The northeastern Colorado area is typical; up to 1 million lambs are fed there annually, the principal feeds being alfalfa, beet pulp, and corn. An example of a winter pasture and feeding section is southern Kansas; winter grazing on the winter wheat there is practiced and supplemental feeding is varied according to the condition of the wheat. The western sheep areas are described in *Circular C—103* of the Farm Credit Administration.

Large lamb feeding states

The state destination of inspected feeder sheep shipped from the public stockyards may indicate the extent of sheep feeding within a state. This includes only shipments from public markets and does not cover direct shipments. Below is a list of some of the leading feeding states for a recent 10-year period, with the average number shipped yearly to each state from the public markets.[2]

	THOUSAND HEAD
1. Nebraska	426
2. Iowa	387
3. Colorado	298
4. California	231
5. Missouri	225
6. Kansas	213
7. Illinois	182
8. Minnesota	145
Total United States	2,699

The distribution and marketing of sheep and lambs on feed in the western states and the corn belt has been previously noted. (See Figure 200.) Nebraska- and Colorado-fed lambs are marketed from February to April; the feeding there is largely on a large-scale basis. Corn-belt lamb feeding is done by farmers, usually on a moderate scale, and by some commercial feeders who handle large numbers. The latter group commonly operates through the year. Farm-fed lambs are marketed mainly in December, January, and February.

Lambs kept until shearing time are often shorn and sold as sheared lambs. Experimental tests have shown conflicting findings about the value of this practice. There seems to be no great difference in the feed-lot response of lambs before and after shearing. A comparison of the market prices of wooled lambs, sheared lambs, and wool will indicate the probable profitability of the practice in a given year. The feeder should consider the shearing cost as well as the estimated return for the fleece. Lambs fed until late spring or early summer are kept more comfortable if they are shorn, and warm weather may improve the response from feeding.

[2] *Livestock Market News Statistics,* Agricultural Marketing Service, U.S.D.A., 1956.

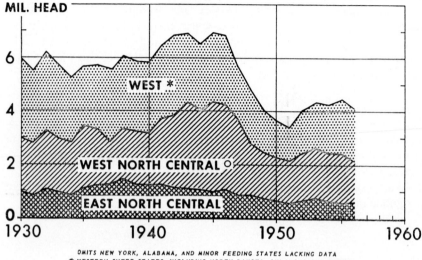

SHEEP AND LAMBS ON FEED JAN. 1

MIL. HEAD

WEST *

WEST NORTH CENTRAL ○

EAST NORTH CENTRAL

6   4   2   0

1930   1940   1950   1960

OMITS NEW YORK, ALABAMA, AND MINOR FEEDING STATES LACKING DATA
* WESTERN SHEEP STATES, INCLUDING NORTH DAKOTA, OKLAHOMA AND TEXAS
○ EXCLUDES NORTH DAKOTA

Fig. 231. Sheep and lambs on feed, by areas. (U.S.D.A., Agricultural Marketing Service.)

FEEDING PLANS WITH FEEDER LAMBS

The feeders offered on the market vary widely in type, breeding, and weight. These differences influence the system of feeding to be used. McDonald[3] has described various groups of feeder lambs available on the markets and suggested appropriate feeding methods as follows:

Black-faced lambs vary in weight from 60 to 75 pounds. The lighter, thinner lambs finish rapidly in the feed lot and can put on a lot of gain on pasture before they are placed in the dry lot. Those weighing over 70 pounds must be finished quickly so that they will not be penalized on the market because of excess weight. Black-faced lambs running under 60 pounds are likely to be unthrifty.

White-faced crossbred lambs range in weight from 55 to 75 pounds. Like the black faces, the heavier lambs need to be crowded so that they will not be too large, rough, and course when finished for market. They feed well but do not finish so rapidly as the black-faced lambs.

A class of lambs called quarter bloods (one quarter black face) ranges in weight from 50 to 75 pounds. These lambs often show a mottled-colored face. They are strong and vigorous open-faced feeding lambs with a com-

[3] C. W. McDonald, "Buying and Feeding Lambs," *Ext. Cir. 230,* Iowa Agr. Exp. Sta., Dec., 1940.

paratively tight fleece. The lighter weight lambs of this breeding are more suitable for a long feed.

Rambouillets, often called "white faces," "tight-wooled lambs," or "fine wools," vary greatly in weight and in type and conformation. They range in weight from 50 to 80 pounds and vary in type from a comparatively smooth meaty type approaching the quarter bloods in conformation to the heavy, wrinkled kind with wrinkles on the neck and body.

Where the wrinkles predominate, the wool must often be sheared from around the eyes to prevent wool blindness. This is perhaps the least desirable type of feeding lambs. They fatten slowly and are discriminated against on the market because of the heavy pelt and low dressing percentage. Contracts for purchasing lambs usually stipulate that there shall be

no wrinkled lambs, and no bucks, long tails, or light lambs under 40 or 50 pounds.

There are two kinds of smooth-type, open-faced Rambouillets: the tight-wooled kind, and the more open, fluffy-fleeced lambs. Both kinds are hardy and thrifty but feed somewhat more slowly than the black-faced or crossbred lambs. Their gains, however, are about as economical.

Many feeders prefer the tight-wooled white-faced lambs because they are thrifty and lighter in weight, since they have been raised on scanty ranges where the black-faced and crossbreds do not thrive.

Most of the feeder lambs available in Texas, Arizona, and New Mexico are of Rambouillet breeding. Here, too, the smooth-bodied lamb, free

Fig. 232. Sorting western lambs. Those lacking sufficient finish for slaughter will be fed out on corn-belt farms.

from wrinkles and skin folds, is much preferred over the heavier pelted lamb. Smooth-bodied lambs of straight Delaine breeding are not so desirable for feeding as Rambouillets since they are smaller framed and do not have the capacity to make rapid gains.

Native mutton-type lambs may sometimes be picked up locally or may be purchased on central markets. Naturally, lambs assembled in this manner would be less uniform in quality, weight, and thrift than western lambs. To be successful in the feed lot, they must be treated for stomach worms; when so treated and fed in small bunches they make acceptable feeding lambs. Their gains have ranged from 20 per cent below to equal with choice western lambs. To be profitable they must be purchased considerably lower than western lambs.

Native fine-wooled lambs of Delaine breeding consume less feed daily than either native mutton lambs or western lambs. They gain more slowly and require more feed per 100 pounds of gain. Because of the heavier pelt they yield less, and the finished lot will probably run 10 to 15 per cent more culls than either native mutton or choice western lambs. If they can be bought at wide enough price differential, drenched for stomach worms, and given long feed, they make acceptable feeding lambs.

Fig. 233. Finished range lambs. First-prize range lambs, International Livestock Exposition. Bred and raised by T. J. Drumheller, Patrick, Wyo.; fed by Ralph Fulton, Ashton, Ill.

FEEDS USED FOR FATTENING LAMBS

Farm-fed lambs in the corn belt are fed mainly on corn and oats; satisfactory rations are supplemented with such feeds as legume hay, a protein supplement like linseed meal, and frequently corn silage. A 60-pound lamb fed a 100-day period gains from 30 to 35 pounds in the feed lot. For this gain 2 to 2½ bushels of corn and 130 to 170 pounds of legume hay are needed and, if a protein concentrate is used, 15 to 20 pounds of concentrate. Farmer feeders either fatten lambs in the dry lot or allow them to clean up the fields—corn fields or stubble fields, or fall pasture.

Commercial feeders of lambs use a greater variety of feeds than farmers; they use many by-products or special feeds. Commercial feeding of sheep first started with the use of screenings from flour mills for feeding. Now many lambs are fed in part on the by-products from beet sugar manufacture, such as beet pulp and beet molasses.

Hand feeding or limiting the feed allowance is the usual method with lambs. Self-feeding is practiced only when the roughage and concentrate can be mixed and fed together. When lambs are given free access to concentrated feeds, they overeat and the death loss may be quite high.

Fattening western lambs is not so different from finishing native lambs. The same general principles apply and in the corn belt the same feeds are used. With the native lamb it is usually a case of growing and fattening. Western lambs grow on the range and while suckling; fattening is delayed until the lambs are put into the feed lot.

PROBLEMS IN LAMB FEEDING

Death losses

Extreme care must be taken in the feeding and management of feeder lambs. The grain allowance, if excessive—that is, over 2 pounds per lamb daily—will cause disturbances which result in death losses; so also will unusual conditions, such as abrupt changes in feed. A death loss up to 3 per cent is not unusual in feeder lambs during a 90-day feeding period.

To avoid death losses, pasture and roughage are used in starting the lambs and concentrated feeds are introduced slowly into the ration, only after the lambs are well started. Vaccination for overeating disease is usually effective in reducing the death loss. An inexpensive open shed will do for shelter, but dryness overhead and underfoot is essential. Clean fresh water must be constantly available.

Risks in lamb feeding

Feeding of commercial lambs is attended with some risk because of death losses and other problems. The margin between feeders and finished lambs cannot be predicted accurately; this is one element of uncertainty. Feed prices, too, are uncertain, and, except for the cost of the feeders, feed cost is the largest single item in the enterprise. Weather also affects the way in which lambs feed out. All items considered, lamb feeding is a speculative venture. To a large extent success depends upon buying feeders worth the money and selling on a good market.

LAMB FEEDING OR FARM FLOCK

In farming areas the farm operator may either have a farm flock or do lamb feeding or both. With sheep production shifting to the range areas, more unfinished lightweight lambs are available for feeding and farm feeding has been on the increase. On the other hand, the summer grazing of a farm flock makes use of pasture and assists in weed control. Farm flocks consume principally pasture and roughage, and there is the twofold income—lambs and wool. Labor, too, is utilized throughout the year with the farm flocks.

Lamb feeding is preferred by some over farm flock maintenance because it is more flexible. In fact, if the feed supply is short, or the ratio of feed prices to finished lamb prices unfavorable, the lamb feeding can be omitted. Usually less trouble is encountered from internal parasites with lambs on feed than with the farm flock. Experience is a valuable asset to the lamb feeder, but it is risky to gain it with a large lot of feeder lambs. To attain experience a small farm flock has a distinct advantage.

MANAGING THE SHEEP FLOCK

Skillful management is essential for success in the sheep enterprise. Attention especially at the critical periods of breeding, lambing, and weaning pays good returns with sheep. Careful attention is necessary to disease and parasite control and to proper feeding and management of the breeding flock and the lambs. The ability of the operator is more of a factor in sheep raising than in raising other kinds of livestock.

Whether the enterprise is range or farm flock or feeding, certain considerations influence its outcome. The capable manager manages the sheep so that the objects for which they are kept are attained. A plan of production, to be successful, must take into account the following.

THE USABLE FEED SUPPLY

As sheep are kept mainly to provide a market for home-produced feed, a careful estimate of the probable feed supply will indicate the reasonable limit of sheep breeding and feeding. Purchased feeds at times may be necessary, especially supplements, but in general the home supply of feed may be regarded as the factor limiting expansion. Costs of marketable feeds and their returns sold as sheep or lamb gains must also be estimated from time to time to determine the most profitable outlet for the feed supply.

THE EQUIPMENT REQUIRED

Great losses may occur when housing is inadequate. Sheep can normally withstand cold weather but they need protection against rain and sleet. Inexpensive buildings that are dry, well-ventilated, and convenient are desired. Lambing time needs must also be anticipated by the good manager. Equipment, other than housing, aids in handling the sheep more effectively and with less labor.

THE LABOR INVOLVED

One man can care for a relatively large number of sheep with good equipment and proper aids. On the farm labor needs may be dovetailed with the labor needs of other farm enterprises. On the range the flocks are divided into units which can be handled by one sheepherder.

THE MARKET OUTLOOK

The outlook for sheep, lamb, and wool is continually changing. The sheep raiser has two markets to watch—sheep and wool. A good manager anticipates demands and seasonal variations in prices and markets accordingly. The feed situation, livestock on feed, and outlook for lamb and wool are given in U.S. Department of Agriculture reports, which are of inestimable value in planning.

KEEPING RECORDS

Careful records are helpful in studying results and in determining which phases or practices are profitable or unprofitable. A breeding record, production record, and financial record are valuable in making plans for the enterprise. Careful records are imperative with the purebred flock.

PARASITE AND DISEASE CONTROL

One of the greatest stumbling blocks in successful sheep raising is the loss which comes from parasites. Although sheep appear susceptible to disease and lacking in resistance, loss from disease is not generally excessive and, as noted previously, slaughter condemnations of sheep from disease are low. Parasites, such as stomach worms, tapeworms, etc., are widespread, and successful sheep management must include parasite control. Phenothiazine is very effective in removal of several species of nematodes from the digestive tract of sheep, such as the common stomach worm, the lesser stomach worm, the bankrupt worm, the hookworm, the large-mouthed worm, and the nodular worm, and is also slightly effective for some other parasites. Copper sulphate and nicotine sulphate have long been used for removal of gastrointestinal worms of sheep; they are effective against the common stomach worm but less effective against several other intestinal parasites than phenothiazine. Proper feeding and management are very important in enabling an animal to resist the invasion and ill effects of internal parasites. Lambs are usually more susceptible to parasitic damage than older sheep.

CONTROL OF LOSSES FROM DOGS AND PREDATORY ANIMALS

Many precautions can be taken to safeguard the flock against losses from dogs and wolves. Corrals with "dogproof" fencing are helpful in eliminating such losses.

OTHER DUTIES OF MANAGER

There are also other duties of the manager of a sheep flock. He must know sheep, sheep selection, and sheep feeding. He also looks after such details as shearing, dipping, weaning, docking, and castrating.

Chapter 34

SHEEP BREEDS AND BREEDING

Robert Bakewell, previously mentioned as the pioneer animal breeder, improved the Leicester breed of sheep. This breed was used later in the modification and improvement of other sheep breeds. Outstanding because of its ideal mutton conformation, the Southdown, too, has been useful in improving other breeds. John Ellman, Sussex County, England, is credited with being the leader in early Southdown improvement. This work was started in the latter part of the eighteenth century and his methods, "inbreeding and rigorous culling," were similar to those of Bakewell. Leicester sheep supposedly were used in the Southdowns at an early date.

Since the time of Bakewell and Ellman many other sheep breeders have attempted to develop superior sheep through better understanding of reproduction in sheep and sheep-improvement methods.

For convenience, the subject matter on sheep breeding is divided into the reproductive process, breeds, breeding systems, and breeding stock selection.

THE REPRODUCTIVE PROCESS

With most breeds of sheep there is a limited time of the year in which the estrus cycle occurs. Of the British breeds, the Dorset Horn has a very long breeding season. The Merinos, Rambouillets, and Tunis also may have a much longer breeding period than the other breeds.[1] With the other breeds the breeding season extends from August to January. Lambs have a shorter breeding period than older sheep. It is thought that the cool of

[1] The ewes of these breeds with long breeding periods are used for producing winter or "hothouse" lambs, special off-season lambs, a market for which exists in sections of the eastern states from December to Easter time.

the autumn nights causes the ewes to come in heat. Another theory is that coming in heat is controlled by the shortness of the hours of daylight and that when the hours of daylight fall below 13 to 14 the ewes come in heat.

Ovulation takes place toward the end of the estrus or heat period. However, there is some range in time of ovulation as compared with estrus; it may occur after estrus has ended. The period of estrus is about 29 hours in duration and the estrus cycle is about 17 days. Most of the variations are within the range of the fourteenth and nineteenth day. A ewe, then, will normally be in heat for about a day's time every 17 days. Much variation has been observed in apparently normal individuals.

Nutrition has been found to affect reproduction in sheep. Ewes on a low plane of nutrition have a short breeding period, longer estrus cycles, and a lower rate of ovulation. Shepherds who flush their ewes will increase the heat periods and the number of ova shed if the ewes being "flushed" are raised from a low to a high nutritional plane. It is considered good practice to have the ewe flock gaining in weight just prior to and during the breeding season.

The gestation period in sheep is about 148.9 days and the standard deviation of individual gestation lengths is 2.3 days. Single lambs are heavier at birth than twins, and triplets are outweighed by twins. There is also considerable breed difference in birth weight, but lambs generally average from 8 to 10 pounds.

Ewe lambs are not generally used in the breeding flock; they are usually kept open until they are yearlings. About 75 to 85 per cent of the ewe lambs come in heat and can be bred. With mutton-type ewes under favorable conditions, the practice may be followed without injury to the flock.

Rams mature sexually before they are 1 year of age, and many ram lambs are used in the breeding flock. During the nonbreeding season the ram continues to produce sperm, but they are less numerous and active than those of the normal breeding season. Rams overly fat or heavily wooled may be impotent. It appears that spermatogenesis is affected by temperature. A temperature lower than that of the body cavity is necessary for normal sperm formation. An active, vigorous ram, well fleshed but not fat, is most serviceable in the breeding season. Such rams from 1 to 4 years old will settle from 35 to 50 ewes if they are permitted to run with the flock.

MULTIPLE BIRTHS

The number of lambs raised, or lamb crop, may be expressed as the per cent lamb crop, which is the number of lambs raised per 100 ewes. Fertility in ewes is largely determined by the number of ova shed, for prenatal deaths are comparatively infrequent. Breeds vary in fertility, and nutrition may influence the lamb crop. Fine-wooled ewes are less prolific than mutton ewes. The larger ewes within a breed are more prolific than the smaller ewes, and prolificacy increases with age until the ewes are 5 years old. Twins are more common in some breeds than single births; however, identical twins rarely occur in sheep.

With farm flocks of mutton breeding, it is not unusual for 100 ewes to have 150 lambs or more; in range flocks the prolificacy is much lower. In the number of lambs saved as a percentage of ewes over 1 year of age in the year 1955, Minnesota led with 118 and New Hampshire and Washington were next with 117. The northwestern states had larger lamb crops than the southern states on the percentage basis—for example, Washington had 117 and Oregon 100 per cent, while Arizona had 84 and New Mexico 79. For that year the percentage of lambs saved in the entire country was 95. This difference between farm flocks in the native sheep states and range flocks in the western states, approximately 15 lambs per 100 ewes, is due mainly to breeding and in part to nutrition.

Occasionally, a ewe will have three or four lambs, but usually there are but two teats on the ewe's udder; so a ewe is not capable of suckling more than two lambs. Rarely, the ewe's udder has four sections and four teats. Selection for the multinipple character, with probable increase in prolificacy, has not increased the lamb crop beyond what might be experienced in a prolific mutton-type flock.

There are slightly fewer rams than ewes in the lambs at birth, the percentage of males being 49.5.

TIME OF LAMBING

As the breeding is seasonal and confined in most breeds to the fall, lambing is in the spring.

Off-season or hothouse lambs are the product of ewes from breeds with longer breeding seasons.

ARTIFICIAL INSEMINATION

There has been a considerable amount of artificial insemination practiced with sheep. The semen of the ram is very concentrated and, even though the ejaculate is quite small (about 1 cubic centimeter), a large number of ewes (30 to 40) can be inseminated from one ejaculation. Also, the sperm can be kept fertile for a longer period of time (about 5 days) under good conditions than can the sperm of other common farm animals. It has been reported from Russia that 2,600 ewes were impregnated from 1 ram in one season. Another Russian report credited the semen of 9 rams with use on 45,000 ewes, which by normal service would require 900 rams. Ram sperm can be readily transported. Many cases of long-range paternity are on record in sheep. In 1937 shipments of rams' semen were made from the U.S. Department of Agriculture Station at Beltsville, Maryland, to Moscow, Idaho, a distance of approximately 2,600 miles, which required on the average 45 hours in transit. The semen was used successfully in impregnating ewes.

A summary by the Bureau of Animal Industry in 1939 reported a total of 309 inseminations made with ram semen that was shipped by airplane for distances from 700 to 2,600 miles. The semen, which had been kept for periods of 22 to 200 hours, resulted in 31 pregnancies or about 10 per cent of the inseminations.

Although artificial insemination is quite successful with sheep, it is not used very much in practice.

SHEEP BREEDS

Sheep breeds are still in the making. We are developing breeds suited to our conditions, such as the Columbia, Panama, Romeldale, and Targhee. We have also imported the Corriedale from New Zealand, which is a comparatively new breed.

Most of our mutton breeds are of English origin; the single exception is the Tunis from Africa. The breeds from Great Britain are roughly of two general types. The large-type sheep from England is a long-wool sheep. In this group we have such breeds as the Lincoln, Cotswold, Romney Marsh, and Leicester, developed in the low fertile sections. The smaller type of sheep from England is in the medium wool class and includes the so-called "down breeds." The common breeds of this group are the Southdown, Shropshire, Hampshire, Suffolk, Oxford Down, and Dorset Horn. These breeds were developed in the upland regions for herding on the commons and downs. The upland regions were joint pastures that were used before the advent of fencing, and the downs are the chalk hills of England such as the Southdowns and Midale downs. The wool-type breeds came originally from the Spanish Merino. However, we have formed two wool-type or fine-wool breeds, the American Merino and the Delaine.

ADAPTABILITY OF VARIOUS SHEEP BREEDS

Sheep breeds were developed under various conditions which affect their general adaptability. Very significant differences are evident between sheep breeds; for example, breeds are significantly different in length of gestation period and parasite infestation. Some of the subtypes have general adaptability. The long-wool sheep were raised in a low-altitude, ample-forage area where heavy feeding prevails. Such sheep are heavy feeders and do well under conditions like those in their native home. Fine-wool breeds like the

Merinos and Rambouillets do well under more adverse conditions. They are suited to range conditions and are not so adversely affected by inadequate rations as the long-wools. In an attempt to secure a more meaty conformation, the Rambouillet and the Delaine Merinos were developed from the Spanish Merino, which was strictly of the wool type. Medium-wool sheep like the long-wools were developed mainly for meat production in Great Britain. As contrasted with the long-wool sheep, the medium-wool sheep were generally raised at higher elevations and under less liberal feeding conditions. In both cases, wool was a secondary product. On lands where grazing is poor to fair, fine wool is produced, but the lamb or mutton is poor to fair. On more productive lands better mutton and lamb are produced, but the fleece is classed as medium wool.

The climatic conditions, soil, altitude, and natural feed are factors in determining adaptability as well as the production demanded. Constitution, hardiness, and prolificacy to a large extent determine the usefulness of a sheep. In general, the breed to choose is that which is suitable to local conditions and meets the requirements of the available market.

There follows a brief discussion of the rather common breeds of sheep. This includes their native home, early improvement, characteristics, and adaptability.

THE MEDIUM WOOL BREEDS

Most of these breeds had their origin in England. Most breeds with dark faces are known as "down breeds," having come from the hilly areas of England.

Black-faced Highland or Scottish Blackface

A few of this breed have been brought to the United States. They are from the upland country of Scotland. They are very hardy mountain sheep that require the minimum expenditures for their upkeep. Both sexes are horned, and the color of the head and legs is black, which may be mottled. The fleece, which is of carpet grade, has a hair-like outer coat and a finer wool-like under coat. This breed, which is small in size and adapted to adverse conditions of feeding and protection, has met but little acceptance in this country.

Cheviot

The border country between England and Scotland, the Cheviot Hills, is the native home of this breed. It is a hilly grazing area with a rigorous, moist climate. The sheep in this area graze the upland pastures during the summers and are taken to the valley lowlands in winter. Little is known about the origin of this very old breed, but it is reported that Leicesters,

Southdowns, Merino and Blackfaced Highland stock were brought into the Cheviot Hills to improve the native stock. Importations of Cheviots were made to Canada in 1825 and to New York in 1838; subsequently several other importations were made. This breed is smaller than many

Fig. 234. A champion Cheviot ewe and ram, Michigan State Fair. Shown by Ben D. Kelly, Marshall, Mich.

of the medium-wool breeds; a well conditioned ram weighs 175 pounds and a ewe 35 pounds less. The head is woolless, hornless, and carried erect. There is white hair on the head and on the legs below the knees and hocks. The fleece, which usually grades quarter blood combing, is quite compact. In 12 months the fleece is 3 to 5 inches long and weighs 5 to 7 pounds.

The Cheviot is a very hardy and attractive breed with good mutton form. For range conditions larger, heavier-shearing, tighter-wooled sheep with greater flocking instinct are desired. The breed is quite well adapted to several farming situations, particularly where rough pasture grazing prevails and where hardiness is required.

Dorset

This breed originated in Southern England in Dorset and adjoining counties. The area, with low, rolling hills, has a good, substantial agriculture. The origin of the breed is obscure, but it is thought by some that Spanish Merino rams were used on the indigenous feral sheep. Selection is credited with being the effective means of developing the Dorset. Comparatively, the Dorset is not one of the older breeds in the United States; the first recorded importation was made in 1885.

Fig. 235. A champion Dorset ewe. Dorset ewes, because of their long breeding season, are often used for hothouse lamb production. Owned by W. E. Huff, Lexington, Ky.

The Dorset is a medium to fairly large breed; mature rams in good condition weigh 175 to 250 pounds and ewes 150 to 175 pounds. Dorsets have white hair on most of the head and the legs. Horns are present on both sexes; in fact, the breed was formerly known as the Dorset Horn. In 12 months the fleece is 3 to 4 inches long and weighs 6 to 8 pounds. The grade is quarter to three-eights blood.

In form the Dorset is typical of the mutton type and may be criticized for lacking in wool production. The breed does well under conditions of liberal feeding. Since the ewes breed early, are prolific, and good milkers, they fit in well in early and off-season lamb production.

Hampshire

The native home of this breed was south central England, more particularly Hampshire and adjoining counties. This is rolling country that produces fair crops. Two strains of native sheep were crossed for the foundation and then Southdowns and Cotswold were introduced for im-

Fig. 236. A typical Hampshire ram. The Hampshire breed is noted for its fast-growing lamb. Owned by the University of Wyoming, Laramie, Wyo.

Fig. 237. A medium-wool, mutton-type ewe. A champion Hampshire ewe shown by H. H. Cherry, Cedarville, Ohio.

provement. The Hampshire was one of the first of the medium wool breeds introduced to this country; some were imported prior to 1840. However, it was not until after 1910 that the breed was recognized to any great extent in the United States.

The Hampshire is one of our larger breeds of sheep; mature rams, well conditioned, weigh 225 to 300 pounds and ewes 150 to 200 pounds. The color of the face, ears, and legs is black or a very deep brown. The breed is polled. The head is rather large and quite impressive. Dark wool or wool on the head extended beyond a line with the eyes is not desired. In 12 months the fleece is 2 to 2½ inches long and weighs 6 to 8 pounds. The wool is commonly graded quarter to three-eights blood combing and may contain black fibers. Hampshires may not shear as heavy fleeces as some other breeds widely used in farm flocks.

This breed is fast gaining because of its size and it is suitable for heavy feeding. In form it is typical of the mutton type. The lambs have shapely, well-muscled carcasses. The ewes are prolific and very good milkers. The breed is very, very popular for farm flocks and also in range flocks where it is used mostly for crossing. The Hampshire has been our most popular breed for cross-bred market lamb production.

Fig. 238. An excellent Oxford Down ram. This breed is the largest of any of the medium-wool breeds. Champion Oxford ram shown by W. Duncan, Wilson, Ill.

Oxford

This breed is another product of south central England, having had its origin in Oxford County. The breed came from crosses of Hampshire rams with Cotswold ewes with the use of some Southdown breeding.

Oxfords were first brought to this country in 1846, and subsequently many importations have been made. The breed is not numerous; the distribution in the United States is limited mainly to the north central states and where conditions such as liberal feeding favor a large sheep.

The Oxford is the largest of the medium wool breeds. Mature rams weigh from 250 to 350 pounds and ewes from 175 to 250 pounds. The face, ears, and legs are a dark gray or brown and there is quite a range in color. The head, which is polled, is carried high; in fact, the breed is somewhat upstanding and rectangular in form. There is considerable variation in the fleece; the 12 months weight is commonly from 10 to 12 pounds and 3 to 5 inches in length. The fleece grade is usually quarter or low quarter combing.

This strong, rugged breed has proved its worth in the farming states in situations where large size and heavy fleeces are desired. Lack of uniformity and inability to develop sufficient finish at desirable weights for market lambs are the chief breed faults. Oxfords are less active than most of the medium wool breeds and less well adapted to sparse vegetation.

Ryeland

This very old breed is sometimes called the white-faced Shropshire. A few have been brought to this country from their native home, Herefordshire, England, but they have not become very numerous, although they are popular in several other countries.

Shropshire

The original home of this breed was in Shropshire and Stafford counties in west central England. This area of England is noted for a mild climate, rolling pasture lands and good crops of cereals and root crops. The breed came about from the blending of several native strains and improvement by use of Southdown, Leicester and Cotswold. In 1855 the first importation of Shropshire sheep was made to the United States. Many importations were made in subsequent years and many noted flocks were established in the farming states.

In size the Shropshire is intermediate among the medium wool breeds. Well-conditioned mature rams weigh 200 to 250 pounds and ewes 135 to 175 pounds. The color of the face, ears, and legs is commonly a dark brown, ranging from dark gray to a soft black. Some individuals have excessive wool covering on the polled head, which predisposes to wool blindness. The fleece is one of the Shropshire's outstanding qualities. A 12-

Fig. 239. A typical Shropshire ram. This breed is noted for its heavy fleece of excellent quality and for its good mutton form. It is a popular breed for the farm flock. Champion ram at the International Livestock Exposition, shown by F. M. Shultz, DeGraff, Ohio.

Fig. 240. An excellent Shropshire Ewe, grand champion at the International Livestock Exposition. Owned by F. M. Shultz, DeGraff, Ohio.

month growth is from 2½ to 4 inches in length and weighs 8 to 10 pounds. Most fleeces grade three-eighths blood but some grade one-half blood. The extreme wool covering of the face and legs, once desired, is now being de-emphasized.

This breed has excellent mutton form and is early maturing. The meatiness and the heavy fleeces make it highly desired for farm flocks, for it is intermediate in meat and wool production. The breed has never been popular for crossing on the range because of its insufficient size. The ewes are very prolific and excellent mothers; consequently for good farm flock conditions this breed has been very popular.

Southdown

This is one of our oldest breeds of sheep. The chalk hills known as the South Downs along the English Channel, southeastern England, are the breed's native home. This area has long been noted for its sheep husbandry. The abundant feeds, fine herbage, moderate elevation, and mild climate provide an excellent environment for sheep raising. The Southdowns' early origin, marked uniformity, and superior mutton form account for its wide use in the formation of other English breeds. Native sheep

Fig. 241. A typical Southdown ram. This breed is unexcelled in mutton-type form. Owned by W. B. Belknap, Goshen, Ky.

formed the basis for the breed and improvement was made by selection and inbreeding. The first importation to the United States was made in 1803. Numerous importations have been made, and in some specialized areas they became quite numerous.

This is the smallest of our common sheep breeds. Mature rams in good condition weigh 175 to 215 pounds and ewes from 125 to 150 pounds. The head is polled and the color of the face, ears, and legs is a steel gray with considerable variation, ranging from light gray to mouse brown. The fleece has a length of 2 to 2½ inches in 12 months and a weight of 5 to 7 pounds. The grade will range from three-eights to one-half blood—combing or clothing.

As this breed is unexcelled in mutton form and early maturity, it has been used extensively for early spring lamb production in Kentucky and has also been used for siring hot-house lambs.

Southdowns have not been popular in the range country. This is due to their small size and light fleece. Even in crosses, several other breeds outperform the Southdown in gains because of their capacity for size and their ability to move about and use large quantities of feed. Southdown are superb in finishing at young age under good feeding conditions, when good-quality, superior-conformation carcasses are desired.

Suffolk

The origin of this breed was in southeastern England in the counties of Suffolk, Norfolk, Essex and Kent, in an area extending from the low, flat productive area of Suffolk to the good farming and livestock region of Norfolk. The breed came from wild, hardy, active, blackfaced, horned, poorly wooled but well fleshed native sheep called Norfolk; this was modified through use of large dark-faced Southdown rams to form the new breed. Suffolks are an old breed in England but in the United States their popularity is of recent origin.

In many respects the breed is like the Hampshire. The weight of mature, well fleshed rams ranges from 225 to 300 pounds, that of ewes from 160 to 225 pounds. The hornless, woolless head is black; so also is the hair on the ears and legs. The fleece is relatively short and light. A fleece with a year's growth is from 2 to 2½ inches long, weighs 4 to 5 pounds, and usually grades three-eights blood clothing.

The Suffolk, being a fairly large sheep, may appear upstanding because of the lack of underline wool. Muttony conformation, which comes mainly from the Southdown, is typical; Suffolk are wide, deep and muscular. Since Suffolks grow fast, they are popular for lamb production on the range and in feed lots. The carcasses are thick fleshed, particularly in the loin and leg. The ewes are extremely prolific and are good milkers. On the range this breed has demonstrated its adaptability, especially as crossbreds.

Fig. 242. A champion Southdown ewe at the International Livestock Exposition. Owned by Earl Jenkins, Ashley, Ohio.

Fig. 243. A champion Suffolk ram, International Livestock Exposition. Shown by the University of Wyoming, Laramie, Wyo.

Tunis

Tunis sheep are also in the medium-wool mutton-type classification. It is a breed of fat-tail sheep that was developed in Tunis, North Africa. The Tunis is a small breed of sheep that are polled and have a wide range

Fig. 244. A grand champion Suffolk ewe at the International Livestock Exposition. Shown by Elmcroft Farms, Oshawa, Ontario, Canada.

of face and leg coloring, including white, yellowish, and brown. The fleece may have black fiber and some fleeces have a grayish-brownish or reddish cast. The tail is rather broad, flat, and tapering. The ewes are prolific, good milkers, and can be bred almost any season of the year. They are adapted to warm climates, but they have failed to meet with any sustained popularity in the United States.

CROSSBRED MUTTON AND WOOL BREEDS

These breeds are of the medium-wool group and have resulted from the crossing of long-wool and fine-wool breeds.

Crossbreeding has long been practiced for range sheep production in an effort to secure better mutton qualities in the lamb. The basic foundation commonly was fine-wool breeding, mainly Rambouillet; through the use of long-wool rams, like Lincoln, the lamb crop was improved in size and mutton conformation. The cross ewes were generally quite satisfactory as lamb producers. Use of black-faced medium-wool rams on fine-wool ewes has also been practiced rather extensively. The plan in most instances was to use both black-faced and fine-wool rams on the fine-wool ewes and to keep the straight breds for flock replacements. The crossbred ewes by the black-faced rams were inferior to fine-wools for replacements, for they lacked herding instinct and were light shearing. Crossbreeding systems, aimed at maintaining a balance of desired characteristics and using ewes of one breed and rams of another may be expensive and rather complicated to follow.

In order to take advantage of crossing qualities secured, several cross-breed or compromise breeds from a long-wool fine-wool cross have been established. Some of these breeds are:

Columbia

This breed was developed in the United States for the purpose of pro-ducing a sheep suitable for the western range country. The U.S. Depart-ment of Agriculture workers, after trying several long-wool breeds in crosses with Rambouillets, found that the best results, all things considered, were from the use of Lincoln rams on Rambouillet ewes. Currently the association has an inspection for merit for purebred registration.

The Columbia is one of the larger medium-wool breeds. Rams weigh

Fig. 245. A champion Columbia Ewe, International Livestock Exposition. Shown by James Court, Albion, Mich.

225 to 275 pounds and ewes 130 to 200 pounds. The fleece attains an average length of 3½ inches in a year and weighs 11 to 13 pounds. The breed is polled and has a white face. And, being open-faced, it is not disposed to wool blindness. Also, the breed is smooth or free from body wrinkles.

Columbias are fast growing and fairly good in mutton form. They are vigorous; the lambs, like the ewes, are suited to range conditions. The ewes are prolific, good milkers, and flock well.

Corriedale

This is the first developed of breeds in this category. It is a product of New Zealand and Australia. Australian Merinos, Lincolns, and perhaps Leicesters formed the basic foundation for the breed. This was followed by inbreeding and careful selection. In 1914 the U.S. Department of Agriculture brought the first Corriedales to this country. They were well received.

In size the mature ram in good condition weighs from 185 to 250

Fig. 246. A champion Corriedale ewe. Bred and exhibited by Malcolm Moncrieff, Big Horn, Wyo.

pounds and the ewes 125 to 185 pounds. White hair covers the face, ears, and legs, but occasionally black or brown spots occur. The head is hornless and the face is free from wool. Most Corriedales in this country are quite acceptable in mutton form but some individuals reflect their Merino breeding and lack general meatiness.

The wool of the Corriedale is medium in fineness, usually graded three-eights blood combing. In 12 months a fleece has a length of 4 or more inches and weighs 10 to 12 pounds. Wool production is one of the breed's strongest assets.

Many range producers prefer more size and ruggedness than is possessed by the Corriedale. The ewes are regarded as just fair in prolificacy and milk production.

Montadale

The Montadale was created in the midwest from a cross of Cheviot rams on Columbia ewes. The herd book is still open. Emphasis is being placed by the breeder on milking ability and fast growing, rapidly developed market lambs.

Panama

This breed, another one of the newer United States breeds of crossbred foundation, is very much like the Columbia. In fact, they came from the same breeds of foundation stock, used in reverse, Rambouillet rams on Lincoln ewes.

The development was accomplished by selection under range conditions. The Panama is a little smaller and less meaty in conformation than the Columbia.

Romeldale

This is another breed developed in our country, somewhat like the Columbia in general appearance. Romney rams were crossed on Rambouillet ewes for the foundation. The breed is intermediate between Columbia and Corriedale in size, ruggedness and many other features.

Southdale

The U.S. Department of Agriculture, to secure a crossbred with the good mutton form of the Southdown and fleece comparable to the Corriedale, has crossed these breeds in a systematic way. Success of the project has not been established to date.

Targhee

The U.S. Department of Agriculture developed this breed at the Sheep Experiment Station, Dubois, Idaho, beginning in 1926. The foundation was made by crossing Rambouillet rams on Lincoln-Rambouillet and Lincoln-Rambouillet-Corriedale ewes and by following a range performance testing plan. In size the breed is intermediate; the rams weigh about 200 pounds and the ewes some 40 pounds less.

The breed is white-faced and polled. The fleece grows 3 inches and weighs 11 pounds in a year's time, and grades half-blood combing. The open face and freedom from folds possessed by the breed are highly desirable in range sheep production.

LONG-WOOL BREEDS

The long-wool breeds came to this country from England and they have met with some success in the United States, especially when used in crossing. There are many features which these breeds have in common. They are the largest of the sheep breeds. The form is inclined to be rectangular. The backs are wide and commonly thickly fleshed. The fleece is characterized by length, coarseness, and openness. The common grade is braid and the shrinkage moderate. These breeds have white hair on the face and legs and in appearance they are very much the same. Because of their size and other characters, these breeds are best suited for lowland farm-flock conditions when bred straight. For the most part they have been used for crossing in commercial production.

Cotswold

This breed originated in the Cotswold Hills in the county of Gloucestershire, England. The foundation stock was native plus some outside blood which included some Leicester. The breed was brought to this country in 1832; many other importations were made but the breed never became numerous. The typical Cotswold is large, tall and very stylish in appearance. In size it is exceeded only by the Lincoln. The long wool is distinctive, for it hangs in long, wavy ringlets. In spite of the excellent activity, hardiness and productiveness of the ewes and consequent wide adaptability, the breed has not had extensive continued use in the United States.

Leicester

There are two divisions of this breed, the more common or English Leicester, which came from Leicester county in central England, and the Border Leicester from England-Scotland border country. Robert Bakewell worked with the English Leicester and by inbreeding and selection greatly improved them. The breed was brought to this country at an early date but never became very numerous. It is large, rather rectangular in form and has typical long wool. The face and legs are white. The Border

Leicester is somewhat smaller and has a head not unlike the Cheviot, that is, devoid of wool.

Lincoln

This breed originated from Lincolnshire county on the eastern coast of England. Lincolns came from the native sheep, which were improved by the introduction of Leicester breeding and by selection. It is reported that old-time Lincolns were brought to the United States at an early date,

Fig. 247. A grand champion Lincoln ram at the International Livestock Exposition. Owned by H. M. Lee, Highgate, Canada.

but the modern form was imported in 1825. They are the largest of our sheep breeds and have a very long, heavy fleece with large broad locks with a distinctive curl on the end. The form is typical of long wool, with a wide, strong back and a rectangular body. The fleece, which is graded braid, is at least 8 inches long in 12 months and weighs from 14 to 20 pounds.

The breed has been most popular in crossing and in the formation of new breeds. Bred straight, their size is against them, for the lambs may not have sufficient fatness at desirable weight. They are lacking in activity and are most suitable to abundant feeding. The open fleece, too, is objectionable on the range and detracts from the breed's hardiness. Most of our Lincolns are in the northern or northwestern states.

Romney—Romney Marsh or Kent

This breed is also classified as a long-wool, but it is quite different from the previously described long-wool breeds. Romneys came from southern England, a damp, cold, low-land area of heavy vegetation. The native sheep from the Romney Marsh area were the foundation stock and it is probable that Leicester breeding plus selection accounts for their present form. They are somewhat smaller than the other long-wool and also finer and more compact in the fleece. The Romney is low set, rugged, and quite muttony in conformation. Fleece weights average from 10 to 12 pounds of braid to quarter blood grease wool.

This breed has a rather restricted popularity in the Pacific northwest, mainly Oregon.

WOOL-TYPE SHEEP

All the breeds of wool-type sheep have come from the Merino, a native of Spain. From Spain fine-wooled sheep have spread to all the major agricultural countries of the world, and many breeds have been founded from the original Spanish stock. In this country there have been developed the American Merino and the Delaine, and we have used extensively the Rambouillet, a French-developed Merino.

The sheep of Spain had certain characteristics which made them valuable in their native land and also in other sheep-growing areas. First, a very fine wool was produced, and second, the Spanish sheep were very hardy and could travel great distances. Some of the flocks traveled from the south of Spain to the northern mountain pastures and back in a year's time. This permitted taking advantage of favorable forage and climate. The banding instinct or flocking quality became highly developed in these sheep. Shepherds could handle fairly large flocks, even while traveling, for the sheep stayed close together.

The fine wool in America

Merino sheep that were taken to Saxony, Germany, in 1765 were as successful there as in their native home. Soon thereafter a demand arose in the United States for a wool sheep. This demand was caused in part by the Embargo Act of 1807. Between 1808 and 1816 fine-wool sheep expanded greatly in numbers, and a boom for such sheep caused large importations to be made. During the War of 1812 wool sold as high as $2.50 per pound and sheep were sold up to $1,000 per head.

Although the Merinos from Spain were first imported in 1793, it was not until 1840 that Rambouillets from France were brought to this country. For the foundation of this breed Merinos were taken to France from Spain in 1786 and 1801.

In this country fine-wool sheep are most numerous in the western range states and certain midwestern states, notably Ohio. Rambouillets predominate in the western states; in fact, about 70 per cent of the breeding of range sheep is estimated to be of that breed. Because the range states have heavy sheep populations, Rambouillets are one of the most numerous breeds in this country. Ohio, Texas, and Iowa rank high in numbers of American and Delaine Merinos. A section comprised of southeastern and east central Ohio and adjacent areas in Pennsylvania and West Virginia has a dense Merino population and is known as the tri-state fine-wool territory. Because of the rough land in that section the major portion of farm acreage is kept in grass.[2]

Comparison of the wool type and mutton type

Irrespective of the fleece, there is much difference between the wool- and mutton-type sheep. The width, depth, compactness, low-setness, and straightness of lines which typify the mutton sheep are usually quite lacking in the wool type. The fine-wool sheep are narrower, more leggy, and more rangy than the mutton type. Low backs and drooping rumps are also more common in the wool type. More angularity of conformation is likewise typical. Thick, fleshy conformation is usually lacking in the fine-wool sheep; flat ribs, light loins, and light thighs are quite common. The mutton conformation, as seen in the mutton-type breeds, is seldom duplicated in the wool-type breeds, yet within this type are many which yield highly acceptable carcasses.

The fleece of the fine-wool sheep is very compact as well as fine. The exterior of the fleece is very dark in color because of the accumulation of dirt which forms a dark, gummy material with the yolk on the tips of the wool locks. A heavy secretion of yolk is typical of the wool sheep, as are the folds or wrinkles in the skin.

FINE-WOOL BREEDS

The wool-type breeds differ in size, body conformation, and the folds and wrinkles in the skin, as well as in the character of the fleece. Some of the fine-wool sheep are heavily wrinkled; others are comparatively free

[2] In 1954 an importation of Australian Sheep of the Polwarth breed was made to South Carolina.

from wrinkles. Mutton qualities have been of secondary consideration, the fleece being the main aim in the development. Yet there is within fine-wool sheep much range in mutton properties.

There is so much difference in the breeds and their characteristics and also in the ideals of the breeders that it is advisable to consider the fine-wool breeds separately. Smooth Merinos are now the popular kind; consequently Delaine and Merino are practically the same.

The American and Delaine Merino

The sheep first imported from Spain had a fleece fine in quality but light in weight. A ewe would shear from 2 to 4 pounds and a ram double that amount. Great progress was made by the early American breeders, for size was greatly improved and also the yield and quality of the fleece. Vermont was a center of American Merino improvement. In a period of 40 years fleece yield was increased fourfold. Emphasis was placed upon the wool, and in some flocks the number of wrinkles on the body was increased. The mutton qualities were practically ignored.

The *Delaine* was developed in Ohio and Pennsylvania from the American Merino. In this type of Merino the ideal was a smooth body with good mutton form, combined with a heavy fleece of good quality. These sheep yielded a fleece long enough for combing; so it could be made into cloth known as "Delaine." The sheep were named Delaine Merinos.

Characteristics of the Merino

The Merino includes sheep quite diverse in general appearance. Wrinkles or folds in the skin are qualities of the type. A single description will not fit the entire group. However, certain essentials that prevail in all Merinos are covered in the following discussion.

General appearance. The Merino is rather small in size, upstanding, rangy, narrow, and angular, rather than rectangular in form. Often the backbone projects far above the shoulder blades. The back may be low, the hips high, and the rump drooping. Straight top lines are less common than in the mutton type or the Rambouillet, and there may be a lack of fullness and plumpness of such parts as the back, loin, and leg of mutton.

The head of the Merino is rather short, medium wide, and clean cut. The ewes are polled; the rams have rather large, heavy, spirally turned horns. The hair on the face, ears, and legs is white and very fine. Occasionally, reddish-brown spots appear. The skin and also the lips and nostrils are a deep pink. The masculinity of the ram head is quite pronounced, and for the ewe a feminine appearance is desirable. The neck is somewhat longer than in the mutton type and less smoothly joined with the shoulder.

The front quarter of the Merino typifies angular conformation, for the top of the shoulder is usually high, and chest and body capacity comes more from depth than width. The chest and body may be wide in the lower part, but the body is generally narrow on top. The body is inclined to be relatively long and deep. The back, loin, and leg of mutton have not been the object of extreme emphasis, as they are in the meat-type sheep; so lack of width, thickness, and plumpness of these parts prevail.

The legs are often faulty in conformation. They are usually too long, and often the front legs are close at the knees. The hind legs often are too close, especially at the hocks, and crooked or sickled hocks are quite common. Straight, strong, well-set legs with ample bone, strong pasterns, and well-developed, uniform feet are the ideal and are found in the more desirable individuals.

The wool completely covers the body and extends down upon the legs and over the head. There is some variation in wool covering. Under range conditions the wool covering on the head can be too heavy. Wool blindness from wool growing over the eyes is a distinct detriment in range sheep. There is a wide range in the length, density, grade, and yolk in Merino sheep. The wool in general is the finest of all sheep. There may be from 10,000 to more than 50,000 fibers per square inch, and the diameter will range from 10 to 30 microns. The crimp is very distinct, uniform, and fine. In grade fleeces will range from 60 to 80 or fine in the United States system.

A, B, and C types of Merinos. At the livestock shows Merinos formerly were placed in three classes, A, B, and C. This classification is based upon number of folds and wrinkles, character of the fleece, and size and form. The A type is now nearly extinct and the popularity of the B type has waned.

The smoother type or C approaches the mutton type in form, but of the three types it has the coarsest fleece. The types of wool sheep are described by Nordby and Beeson [4] as follows.

C type or Delaine type is free from folds on the body with only two or three on the neck. It is the largest of the three types and has more mutton qualities, being shorter legged, wider ribbed, and heavier fleshed, with more balance and stronger constitution. The wool is not dense on the legs and head as it is in types A and B. The best individuals have very desirable mutton qualities and make creditable meat producers. Although the wool has less crimp and density than the A and B type, it is a fleece that measures from 3 to 4 inches in length. Rams should yield 18 pounds and ewes 11 pounds of wool. Rams in full fleece should weigh from 150 to 225 pounds and ewes from 90 to 150 pounds.

Adaptability of the Merino. Merinos of the larger size are adaptable to many conditions and they have demonstrated their ability to withstand hardships on the range. They are active and good grazers and thrive well

[4] Julius E. Nordby, W. Malcolm Beeson, and David L. Fourt, *Livestock Judging Handbook,* The Interstate Printers & Publishers, Danville, Ill., 1947.

on scant pastures. In the feed lot they make economical gains, and the rate of gain is fair. They have been widely used in the southern range country and are popular in many farming areas. Ohio tests [5] have indicated that wrinkly, excessively greasy-fleeced American Merinos may have fewer wool fibers per unit of skin area than smooth-bodied individuals, also that improved length of staple and great density of fiber are not incompatible.

Fig. 248. The wool-type sheep. Rambouillet rams.

The Rambouillet

As previously stated, the Rambouillet was developed in France and descended from the Spanish Merino. Although it was brought to this country as early as 1840 and enjoyed some popularity for a time, the interest in the breed began to wane after 1860. A revival of interest in the breed occurred following the exhibit at the Chicago World's Fair in 1893 of Rambouillets from the Baron von Homeyer flock of Germany. Many large importations followed, mostly from Germany, and present-day Rambouillets trace to the von Homeyer breeding about as frequently as to the sheep direct from Rambouillet, France.

The Rambouillet is now the most numerous sheep breed in this country.

The Rambouillet is a general-purpose breed, and, as will be noted in the score card, equal emphasis is given to mutton form and fleece. This breed thrives under farm and range conditions and, as a consequence, there is no widely accepted universal standard for the breed.

The Rambouillets are large, rugged, vigorous sheep. The mature rams weigh 250 pounds and upward when unshorn, and comparable ewes weigh

[5] D. S. Bell, D. A. Spencer, and J. I. Hardy, "The Influence of Various Factors Upon the Growth and Quality of Fine Wool as Obtained from Merino Sheep," *Bull. 571,* Ohio Agr. Exp. Sta., Wooster, Ohio, July, 1936.

150 pounds and over.[6] In form they are fairly blocky and low set, and they usually carry sufficient width, thickness, and fleshing to simulate mutton type. The rams are horned and the ewes are polled. Some polled or horn-less rams are being produced. A white hair covering exists on parts not covered by the fleece.

Fig. 249. A champion Merino ram (A type) at the Ohio State Fair. Owned by J. Krautz and Son, Dover, Ohio.

The fleece is 2¼ to 3 inches long at 12 months, and the wool covers the entire body except around the eyes and on the nose. Open-faced sheep are preferred on the range to those with heavily wooled heads. Desirable length is associated with medium fineness. A dense fleece with a distinct crimp is desired. Ewes shear from 10 to 18 pounds and rams from 15 to 25 pounds of grease wool. A large flock [7] over a period of years under range conditions had fleeces that averaged 10.60 pounds in the grease,

---

[6] In a study of size and production of fine-wool ewes, W. E. Joseph of Montana found that size was the best single measure of the ability of ewes of the fine-wool type to raise heavy lamb crops. None of the ewes weighing 100 pounds or less in their mature form produced lamb crops that weighed above the average for the entire group, and most were distinctly below the average. *Bull. 242,* Mont. Agr. Exp. Sta., March, 1931.

[7] D. A. Spencer, J. I. Hardy, and Mary J. Brandon, "Factors That Influence Wool Production with Range Rambouillet Sheep," *Tech. Bull. 85,* U.S.D.A., 1928.

2.33 inches in length, and 61.05 in spinning count. A desirable fleece has a fiber diameter of from 5.5 to 6.5 ten-thousandths of an inch (about 14 to 16.5 microns) and a density of 34,000 fibers per square inch.

Fig. 250. A Merino ram (B type). Owned by W. M. Staley, Marysville, Ohio.

Adaptability of the Rambouillet.   In the range sheep sections today the term "fine wool" has come to mean only one breed, the Rambouillet, according to Hultz and Hill.[8] The foundation of most range flocks is fine-wool breeding. Rambouillets have been increasing in Texas, once a Merino stronghold. As the market advantage swings from wool to lamb and back, some of the western sheep raisers switch to rams of the mutton breeds like the Hampshire, Corriedale, Lincoln, Cotswold, or Romney Marsh and then to the Rambouillet, in compliance with the demand. The Rambouillet is preferred in the breeding of the range ewes because of its tight fleece,

[8] Fred S. Hultz and John A. Hill, *Range Sheep and Wool,* John Wiley & Sons, Inc., New York, N. Y., 1931.

banding instinct, grazing qualities, hardiness, and general adaptability. In farm flocks and as feeders in the corn belt and elsewhere the Rambouillet has proved its worth.

Fig. 251. A yearling Rambouillet ram, grand champion at the International Livestock Exposition. Bred and exhibited by King Bros., Laramie, Wyo.

FUR TYPE

There is only one breed of fur-type sheep in this country, the Karakul.* Pelts of other breeds can be converted into fur-type material, such as mouton fur. The fiber of fur is different from that of typical wool. Although both are hair fibers wool is more elastic and has a scaly exterior, which gives it the felting qualities.

Karakul

As indicated previously, the native home of this breed is Bokhara, U.S.S.R., in Central Asia. The elevation is high, the rainfall scant, and the vegetation sparse in that area. The origin of this very hardy breed is obscure, but they are of the fat-tail group. Very few Karakuls have been

* "Karakul Sheep," *Farmers Bulletin 1632,* U.S.D.A., Oct., 1938.

Fig. 252. Rambouillet ewe. University of Wyoming.

Fig. 253. A Rambouillet wether, champion at the International Livestock Exposition. Owned and shown by Purdue University, Lafayette, Ind.

imported to this country, the first being in 1909, but probably some Persian sheep were brought here earlier.

Fig. 254. The fur type. A Karakul ewe and lamb. Pelts from the lambs are used for Persian lamb fur.

The breed is medium in size and has a form inferior to the meat-type sheep breeds. The fleece has two types of fiber, the long outer coat, which is course and grayish brown, and the undercoat, which is finer and dark brown or black. It is of carpet-wool grade, like that of many Asian sheep.

The principal value of this breed is for pelt or fur production; the fur comes from the very young or prematurely born lamb. There is considerable quality variation in the pelts and there is difficulty in marketing small quantities. These problems have been stumbling blocks in commercial expansion. There are but few fur pelts produced, for most of the stock is sold for breeding stock. Most of our Persian lamb fur is imported, mainly from Bokhara or Central Western Asia, East Africa and South America.

BREEDING SYSTEMS

Sheep raisers may use a breeding system based upon the relationship of the individuals in the flock, such as grading up, crossbreeding, or inbreeding. Or breeders may control the matings and, on the basis of resemblance, follow assortative mating, such as breeding like to like.

The use of various breeding systems is of long standing in sheep husbandry. Bakewell practiced inbreeding with his Leicester sheep, and also crossbreeding.

GRADING UP

Purebred rams have been extensively used in the improvement of lamb crops from common or scrub stock. If the flock is comparatively poor, the best way to bring about improvement is through use of a good sire. By the retention of graded-up ewes, the merit of the flock is increased. Each successive step increases the value of the offspring roughly by one half over that of the poorer parent. As the flock is bred up the improvement made in the offspring by each newly introduced purebred sire is lessened, and if an inferior sire is used the herd merit declines. After two or three purebred crosses, there seems to be little difference between the purebred and the high grade. Within any pure breed great differences are noted. For example, in such kinds of production as can be measured objectively, such as fleece weights, lamb crop, and daily gains, all flocks of a breed are not the same.

USE OF PUREBRED MUTTON RAMS ON NATIVE EWES

In many sections of the southern states, a very inferior type of sheep is found and these are referred to as "natives." This term is also used to designate farm-raised sheep on midwestern livestock markets.

The changes in meat and wool characteristics resulting from the use of purebred mutton rams on native ewes have been studied at the North Carolina Agricultural Experiment Station.[9] The ewes used in this experiment were described as follows. They were unusually small, with narrow, poorly shaped bodies and long legs, and their legs, bellies, and faces were bare of wool. The wool on the body was short and coarse, lacked uniformity in color, and contained considerable hair. In fact, the only desirable features possessed by these native sheep were their hardiness and early breeding

[9] J. E. Foster and Earl H. Hostetter, "The Changes in Meat and Wool Characteristics Resulting from the Use of Purebred Mutton Rams on Native Ewes," *Tech. Bull. 60*, N.C. Agr. Exp. Sta., April, 1939.

habits. These ewes were mated to Shropshire and Hampshire rams representative of the better type that have been used to sire market lambs. Shropshire rams were used the first three years, Hampshire the next two, and native eastern North Carolina rams the next four breeding seasons. The half-blood Shropshire and Hampshire ewes from the first cross were bred to other rams of the same breed. The findings of this investigation are summarized as follows:

A vast improvement in meat and wool characteristics resulted from the use of both Shropshire and Hampshire rams on native ewes. (See Figure 255.) Greater size and more rapid gains were obtained in the Hampshire crosses than in the Shropshire crosses, but the latter excelled the former in compactness and quality of form and in weight and quality of fleece. The second and subsequent crosses did not show so great an improvement over the preceding crosses as did the first cross over the natives, but noticeable improvement continued, especially in conformation, quality, breed characteristics, and quality of fleece, until it was difficult to distinguish them from purebreds. The grades never equalled the purebred Hampshires either in size or in rate of gain, but they did in grade of market lambs.

Satisfactory and useful farm ewes were developed from rams of both the Hampshire and Shropshire breeds, and the methods used proved practical for the development of a grade farm flock.

The ability of the purebred to improve the merit of the flock is clearly demonstrated by this and other experiments. Purebreds are being improved; breed improvement rather than expansion is being stressed so that the purebred breeders may have still further improved breeding stock to offer the commercial grower.

USE OF WESTERN EWES IN NATIVE SHEEP STATES

There has been an increase in the use of western range ewes for the production of lambs in the native sheep states. The western ewes have more size and are freer from parasites than many that are raised in the native sheep states. Western ewes are bred to mutton-type rams and, because they are larger size, healthier and more vigorous, often produce more superior lambs than the native ewes.

CROSSBREEDING

Sheep raisers have in many instances resorted to crossbreeding to form new breeds. The Oxford breed, for example, was formed from a Hampshire Cotswold cross. This same method has given us the Corriedale breed, and we have several breeds recently formed in this country by this method. During the formative period the breeds from crossbreds are not uniform, but before long they breed true, and the offspring conform quite consistently to the accepted breed type. Forming a breed by crossbreeding requires large numbers and several generations to arrive at the desirable combination of genes. When the new ideal is intermediate between two breeds in desired characteristics, crossing can give the desired characters and then, by inbreeding, uniformity or homozygosity can be established.

Crossbreeding is extensively used in producing market lambs. This is an old practice in England and quite widely used in this country. The crossbreds have hybrid vigor. It is possible to get qualities in the crossbred lambs which may be advantageous for market lambs. In range flocks, for example, Rambouillet breeding has many advantages, and ewes of such breeding will produce highly acceptable market lambs when bred to mutton-type rams. Miller [10] crossed Rambouillet ewes with rams of several breeds. He found that the lambs sired by the Hampshire and Suffolk rams were the largest, those of the Shropshires next, and those of the Southdown, Romney, and Rambouillet about equal and smallest.

Breeds of the mutton type are less suited to range conditions than fine-wool sheep. Consequently, on the range the ewe flock of fine-wool breeding is preferred. The common ewe breeds on the range are the Rambouillet, Merino, Corriedale and the rather new breeds Columbia, Panama, Targhee and Romeldale. Such ewes are gregarious, hardy,

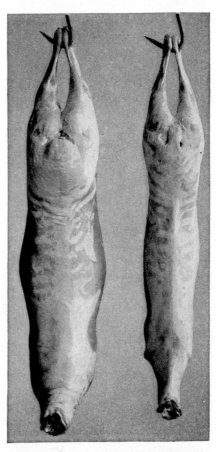

Fig. 255. Two ewe carcasses. The larger carcass is from a second cross yearling mutton ewe, while the other is from a 3-year-old native ewe. Two top crosses of purebred mutton lamb on the native ewe made a decided change in mutton form. (Earl H. Hostetter, University of North Carolina.)

long lived, good grazers, can subsist on short pasture, breed early and produce a good dense tight fleece. The lambs from mutton rams of early-matur-

10 Robert F. Miller, "Crossbreeding Investigations in the Production of California Spring Lambs," *Bull. 598,* Calif. Agr. Exp. Sta., 1935.

ing breeds on wool-type ewes bring a better price on the market than pure-bred, fine-wool lambs. Crossing is therefore practiced when market lambs are selling well. The crosses of the medium-wool rams on range ewes are not retained in the breeding flock because they may lack the herding instinct and hardiness essential in the range flock. Sheep ranchers who cross, there-fore, breed enough of the ewes straight to supply ewe flock replacements. Of the medium-wool breeds, the Hampshire and the Suffolk have met with favor for crossing, especially under good pasturing conditions. The long-wool breeds, especially the Lincoln, Cotswold, and Romney, have likewise been used for crossing on the range flocks. In some areas the crossbred ewes have proved quite satisfactory on the range, which explains the development of new breeds from such crosses.

Although sheepmen can accomplish certain objectives by crossbreeding, the practice may be overdone. It should be used to attain certain ends, and a well-thought-out system should be followed. Indiscriminate crossing is not to be encouraged.

SPECIES CROSSES WITH SHEEP

Within the group known as sheep, which includes long-tailed sheep, fat-tailed sheep, short-tailed sheep, and fat-rump sheep, crosses are made with no apparent loss of fertility. Goats have been crossed with sheep. The chromosome complex of the sheep differs from that of the goat so that a hybrid would probably have a dissimilar genetic constitution. Sheep have a chromosome number of 54, goats a number of 60. Female goats mated to rams may become pregnant but early fetal death results. The reverse mating or the egg-transfer method apparently does not result in pregnancies.

BREEDING STOCK SELECTION

The foundation of success in sheep raising is the breeding flock. The perpetuation of a good breeding flock is attained only by careful selection. Selection has been a very effective means of improvement, and it no doubt will continue to be of great value. However, its maximum efficiency is se-cured only in combination with other means of improvement. In other words, selection, to be effective, should be used with a breeding plan such as grading-up, crossbreeding, or inbreeding. About 2 to 4 per cent of the rams and 45 to 55 per cent of the ewes in a normal lamb crop are needed for flock replacement. With farm flocks a smaller proportion of the ewe lambs are needed for replacements because of the larger lamb crop. It is therefore possible normally to cull one half of the ewe lambs and over 95 per cent of the ram lambs.

BASIS FOR SELECTION

We can use, in deciding upon an individual for the breeding flock, the pedigree, the production record, and the individuality. The breeding performance of the individual and its relatives as well as the individual's appearance should form the basis for selection.

The most reliable basis of selection is on actual performance, but the measurement of performance in sheep is difficult, and such performance tests as we have require much time. Choices for the breeding flock must be made before performance-test results are available. The pedigree is likewise a valuable aid. Early in the nineteenth century, in fine-wool sheep, excessive emphasis was given to pedigree breeding which resulted in excessive speculation.

Selection of breeding mutton sheep on performance

Records are a necessity in selecting for performance. Date of lambing, number of lambs at birth, and number of lambs and their weights at weaning are helpful records. The flock replacements should be selected from the first lambed and fastest gaining individuals. It has been observed that ewe lambs dropped early in the year tend to lamb early.

Culling of the ewe flock should be on an objective basis. For a well fed and well managed farm flock a productive requirement of 85 to 100 pounds of lamb and 10 to 12 pounds of wool per ewe yearly is suggested.

Selection of breeding mutton sheep on appearance

In form, quality, fleshing, and fleece the mutton-type breeding ram and ewe should be comparable to the ideal mutton sheep for market as described in Chapter 29. Briefly reviewed, the standard for market sheep calls for a

Fig. 256. A Rambouillet show flock. A ram and three ewes.

form that is wide, deep, compact, low set, and straight of lines, a quality typified by smoothness in form and fleshing, and a finish and fleshing that is thick, firm, and uniform. A fleece that has ample length, density, quality, and condition and is free from objectionable materials and fibers is also required. These qualities are wanted in the breeding flock, for a farm flock lacking in these essentials will not produce lambs of high market desirability. Flocks of poor individuality may be quickly modified by use of purebred rams of good mutton type and retention of the better ewe lambs in the breeding flock, or grading-up. Greater emphasis is given the fleece in the ewe flock because if a fleece of high value is grown it will pay for the keep of the ewe.

SELECTING THE MUTTON BREEDING RAM

The farm flock can be improved most rapidly by the use of good sires. Considering the breeding potentialities of a ram, the additional cost of a ram of merit may be spread among many lambs, if a fair-sized farm flock is maintained. A ewe kept in the flock for 6 or 7 years may produce 5 to 8 lambs; a good vigorous ram may be used for from 35 to 50 ewes per year, which would mean 50 to 75 lambs per season. Too often an inferior ram is used in the flock, and it may take years to overcome the defects thus introduced. Slow growth, poor conformation, inferior fleeces, and many other faults are not uncommon in many rams in service.

The ram should conform to the mutton type and conformation. He should have all that is expected in a top market lamb. The ram should be a purebred and of the breed adapted to the area. Under most conditions, the breeding of the ram and that of the ewe should be the same. Cross-breeding is not recommended unless it is carefully planned and directed toward definite ends, and, if the crossbred ewes are used, rigid selection is necessary for success.

A ram, to be of great value in the flock, must overcome the defects or deficiencies in the ewe flock. Likewise we would specify that the ram be sound and free from defects, masculine, a good feeder, rugged, good in feet and legs, healthy, early maturing, rapid gaining, and have a good fleece.

Masculinity, or the development of the male characteristics, is due to a testicular secretion which also affects desire and power for mating. This is separate from sperm production, which comes from other cells in the testicles. One secretion may be affected without affecting the other. That is, a masculine, sexually active buck may not be fertile, and vice versa.

SELECTING THE MUTTON BREEDING EWE

Some considerations other than mutton-form quality, fleshing, and fleece are of importance in selecting mutton ewes for the farm breeding flock.

These are size, breed type, sex character, and temperament. Following is a brief statement of the requirements under each of these headings.

Size. Large size in breeding ewes is desirable, provided the size is not so great that the market lamb from such ewes is underfinished when at the desirable market weight. Big ewes of the correct mutton form and weighing 130 to 170 pounds produce larger crops of fast-gaining lambs. Such ewes have heavy fleece and large capacity for feed, and yield large quantities of milk. Rapid growth rate makes for economy of gains.

Breed type. Ewes typical and representative of the breed will make for uniformity in the flock of size, form, color markings, and fleece, which usually is a distinct asset in selling market lambs. Farm flocks are generally medium-wool sheep, and such breeds are widely adapted to conditions in farming sections. However, in some areas Rambouillets, Delaine, or American Merinos predominate in the farm flocks. A breed is chosen mainly for adaptability; consequently, the individuals should conform to the breed in essentials.

Sex character. Shepherds in general show preference for breeding ewes displaying marked secondary sexual characteristics. A refined, matronly appearance yet with sufficient size is desirable. It goes without saying that useful ewes need good-sized, sound udders. Maternal instinct and milking qualities are prerequisites for heavy spring lamb production.

Temperament. Nervous ewes may not prove useful in the breeding flock. A quiet, tractable, motherly disposition is desired.

Constitution, health, and vigor. Vigor and health are important attributes in a productive and profitable breeding flock. The ewes should have strong constitutions, ample ruggedness, good feet and legs, and be free from defects.

Age. In flock culling, age also is a consideration; old ewes or gummers are discarded, and in purchasing ewes two- and three-year-olds are preferred. Flock records are useful aids in culling the flock. Only ewes which raised good heavy lambs and are good wool producers should be kept in the flock. If the flock is culled soon after shearing and before weaning the lambs, shearing records are available.

The lamb or lambs are evidence of production, and lamb form is rapidly appraised by visual examination. It has been demonstrated that a higher level of productivity can be maintained in a flock by retaining the ewes raising twins rather than singles.

SELECTION OF WOOL-TYPE BREEDING SHEEP

The selection of wool-type breeding sheep is different from that of the mutton type, for the essentials of the two types differ. Selecting and culling is much the same, but more emphasis is placed upon the fleece with the wool type. The fundamental properties of wool-type sheep are discussed under the respective breeds. Since the difference between market and breeding requirements that exists in mutton-type sheep does not exist in wool-type, further discussion of selection in breeding fine-wool sheep on appearance is unnecessary. Wool-type sheep marketed for slaughter or feeding are appraised according to mutton standards.

Breeding for wool improvement in range sheep

For wool improvement with an ordinary band of ewes, the most effective means is to select a ram having the desired type of fleece. The extent that the ram is able to transmit the qualities of the fleece to his offspring is not known, but it can be predicted in part from his pedigree and performance.

A score card for selecting rams lists the points to be considered in fleece judging. The relative importance of each is shown: [11]

SCORE CARD FOR THE UNSHORN FLEECE OF RAMS TO BE USED FOR WOOL IMPROVEMENT

QUALITY OR FINENESS. Producing a grade of wool typical of the breed. Not a mixture of fine and coarse fibers within the staple. Not a wide difference in fineness between shoulder and lower thigh or britch 20

LENGTH. Should be clearly of combing length for the grade. If of 12 months' growth, fine wool breeds should produce on the shoulder a staple of 2¾ to 3½ inches; medium wool breeds suitable for effecting wool improvement, 3½ to 5 inches; long wool breeds, 6 to 10 inches or over. Little variation in length over the main parts of the fleece. Minimum of short wool 18

PURITY. No hair, kemp, black, or brown fibers. Cut heavily for beard hairs on wrinkles of fine wool breeds and for coarse hair on the britch of all breeds and crossbreds 16

CHARACTER. Fiber evenly crimped throughout, crimp close and distinct, fibers parallel in the staple except for sufficient cross fibers or binders to hold the fleece together. Tips free from wastiness, not frowsy. Soft, springy, and elastic 12

COLOR. Light buff color to white. Fairly even in color over main parts of fleece 6

CONDITION. Yolk moderate in quantity and evenly distributed in the staple. Not clotted, sticky, or gummy 10

DENSITY. Fine wools should be sufficiently dense to prevent dirt from penetrating far into the staple on the shoulder and sides. Avoid loose wooled individuals of all breeds, but remember that *extreme* density may be associated with short staple 18

————

100

[11] J. F. Wilson, "Wool Production and Improvement of the Clip in California," *Circ. 106,* Calif. Agr. Ext. Ser., November, 1937.

In wool improvement some selection is possible with the ewes, for only about one half of the ewe lambs are needed for replacements. The touch system of culling is suitable for use in range ewe flock selection. The manner of examination is briefly described below.

"Touch system" of culling.[12] A long narrow chute or runway is filled with a part of the ewes to be culled. The man doing the job then works rapidly through this group, grabbing a handful of wool on the back of each ewe. At the same time he notes the general appearance and the condition of the fleece. A chalk is used to mark the less desirable ones, so that they can be cut out later. An experienced culler can work over 1,000 ewes an hour by this system.

Black sheep

Several breeds of sheep are naturally black in color. After flocks of black Merinos were established in Australia, black fleeces outsold white fleeces. Occasionally this happens, but usually black and gray wool sells at a discount. Black color occurs in such breeds as the Shropshire and other down breeds and the Merinos. There are complicating factors in the inheritance of black in these breeds, but it is without doubt due to a recessive color factor.

THE PUREBRED SHEEP BREEDER

The function of the purebred breeder is to produce seed stock for commercial raisers. This is a very highly specialized field of sheep husbandry. A knowledge of selection, breeding, feeding, and management, as well as fitting and showing, are essential for success. Not all purebred flocks exhibit sheep at shows and expositions, but fitting for sale is essential for selling to best advantage. A purebred flock manager should be a good salesman. Showing a flock at livestock shows is a form of advertising; it tends to establish the flock among the breeders. Show winnings of a flock are a measure of the flock standing according to show-ring standards.

The management and handling of a purebred flock is no starting place for a novice in sheep husbandry for it is a highly competitive field which, for success, requires experience and the development of skill in all phases of sheep raising and business ability.

INFLUENCE OF VARIOUS FACTORS UPON THE GROWTH AND QUALITY OF WOOL

Many of the factors that are supposed to affect wool growth have been

[12] Fellhauer Ting, "Two to Four More Pounds of Wool Per Ewe," *Sheep Breeder,* November, 1938.

studied on fine-wool sheep in Ohio.[13] This investigation showed that stage of wool growth exerts only a slight influence, if any, on the rate of growth of wool fiber on Merino sheep under a good system of feeding and manage-

Fig. 257. Examining the fleece. A purebred Rambouillet ewe owned by U.S.D.A., Western Sheep Breeding Laboratory, Dubois, Idaho. Weight 145 pounds in range condition, length of staple 2½ inches. Note the freedom from wool about the eyes or open face. (Photo from J. E. Nordby.)

ment. This agrees with other investigations, which indicate that if disease is controlled and a natural environment is maintained, growth of wool in length is quite uniform throughout the year and up to over 5 years of age, and that growth is not influenced by shearing. The rate of growth of wool in the Ohio observations was subject to acceleration or retardation by outside influences, such as seasonal condition of feed supply and the process of weaning and starting milk flow.

[13] D. S. Bell, D. A. Spencer, and J. I. Hardy, "The Influence of Various Factors Upon the Growth and Quality of Fine Wool as Obtained from Merino Sheep," *Bull. 571*, Ohio Agr. Exp. Sta., Wooster, Ohio, July, 1936.

Sex, pregnancy, and age did not seem to influence the rate of growth of wool fiber. Breed influenced the total yearly growth, also the periodic growth, and was related to the effect of outside influences such as feed. American Merinos and Australian Merinos were used in these tests, and the former proved superior to the latter for that region.

Part IV–HORSES AND MULES

Chapter 35

HORSES—GENERAL VIEW

The horse is regarded by historians as among the first farm animals domesticated by man. There was nearly world-wide distribution of the horse in prehistoric times. Fossile remains of horses have been found in Europe, Asia, Africa, and on both continents of America. Wild horses had become extinct upon this continent before its discovery and colonization by the Europeans. It seems quite probable that our modern horse descended from the wild horses of northern Asia.

More has been written about the horse than about our other domestic animals. Rather complete investigation has been made of its origin and domestication. Public interest in horses is shown by the fact that more than 2,000 books about them have been published in English.

ORIGINS

EVOLUTION OF THE HORSE

Supposedly, the horse has evolved in 2 or 3 million years from a small four-toed animal less than a foot in height to its present form. The horse is credited with great qualities of adaptation to its environment. During Paleolithic times horses were quite numerous in Europe, but with the growth of forests in the Neolithic period they became less numerous. The changes of the horse from the small prehistoric *Eohippus,* or dawn horse, to the *Equus* species as we know it today, have been rather completely described. Geological findings form the basis for piecing together its evolution, in which the toes were reduced in number, the height and size increased, and the teeth changed materially. As height was acquired there was a corresponding increase in the length of the head, neck and legs. The increase in leg length made for a longer stride and greater speed. This was all accompanied by skeletal and muscular changes in which the horse was converted from a foxlike animal to its present form. The early horse was capable of surviving in the forest, but with evolution the conformation was better suited to grazing in grassland country. The change in the foot adapted to level rather than rough country, and to hard rather than soft ground.

TIME OF DOMESTICATION

Man's use of the horse antedates written histories. Horses were ridden by the Babylonians as early as 2000 B.C., and from there horses were taken to Egypt about 1600 B.C. by the Shepherd Kings from the north. The Chinese were no doubt using horses at a very early date.

MAN'S USE OF THE HORSE

Man's first use of the horse was as a source of food, which probably preceded domestication. Later, the horse was used for transportation. It was not until the Bronze Age that the horse ranked as a domesticated animal. Probably man first herded the horses and then trained them for riding and for beasts of burden. The principal use of the horse to modern man is his ability to do work. Other uses are minor in comparison to his physical power. For centuries horses were used in war not only to transport troops and supplies but as active units in warfare.

During the period when the "knight in armor" prevailed upon the battlefield, good horses with strength and endurance were essential for successful warfare. The knight and his armor would weigh from 350 to 425 pounds, so ample size was essential in the war horse. The Crusaders were impressed by the remarkable qualities of Oriental horses, and it is said that this caused many of the Arabian, Turk, and Barb horses to be taken to Europe to improve the native stock.

The invention of gunpowder and the use of modern means of warfare shifted the horse toward use for draft purposes. Until about 200 years ago the horse was used almost exclusively for riding. Its use in agriculture for the cultivation of the land is a comparatively recent development. In recent years the cultivation of land has shifted from draft horses to tractors.

PLACE OF DOMESTICATION

In tracing probable places of origin of the horse many historians have suggested a polyphyletic origin. It is rather commonly accepted that the modern horse descended from one or all of the following: the Oriental horse, the wild black horse of Flanders, and the ponies native to northern

Europe. One investigator would list as antecedents of the above the Lybian horse of northern Africa, the Mongolian pony of upper Asia, and the Celtic pony of Europe.

The foundation is not clear and there are many gaps in the history. Apparently, the smaller horses or ponies were farther north than the larger horses. The original English horses were described as small ponies, shaggy and hardly more than 14 hands high. Subsequent use of Oriental and Flemish stocks increased the size.

WILD HORSES IN EXISTENCE

There is only one family of original wild horses, other than those which are feral or escaped from domestication. This is the wild horse of Asia, the Tarpan or Prejvalsky horse,[1] found in the steppes in Mongolia. It is smaller than the domesticated horse and its young can be domesticated. In characteristics it is not markedly different from other family members.

The Kiang and Onager are of the wild ass species and are found in the sparsely settled areas of Asia. They have not been domesticated. The domesticated ass was derived from the Egyptian wild ass which inhabits Egypt and Abyssinia.

ZOOLOGICAL CLASSIFICATION OF THE HORSE

The family *Equidae* includes horses, asses, and zebras, which are distinctive in that only one toe (the third) is developed on each foot. They are grouped with the odd-toed, hoofed mammals which also include the tapir and the rhinoceros families. The horse is the *Equus caballus;* the ass is the *Equus asinus.*

INTRODUCTION TO THE UNITED STATES

The first domesticated horses were brought to the Western Hemisphere by early Spanish colonists. De Soto brought 237 horses to Florida in 1539, and some of these were used in his expedition into the Middle West in 1544. Coronado in 1540 started an expedition from Mexico which included horses and penetrated to a point near the boundary of Kansas and Nebraska. The American Indians domesticated the llama, the alpaca, and the dog, but they secured their first horses from the Spanish explorers. Wild horses such as are found on the western range, known as broncos and mustangs, are descended from those domesticated horses. Once introduced onto the western plains, horses increased greatly in numbers, for they are well adapted to a grassland environment. The first horses of the western plains

[1] Several spellings are prevalent.

came in from Spanish explorers or direct through Mexico; these were of Arabian descent. Saddle horses were later brought in along the south Atlantic. The introduction of draft horses was later, and it was coincidental with colonization.

When first used in this country, horses served mainly for riding and pack animals. Heavy farm work such as plowing was done by oxen. Wagons were used when moving loads by horse, but it was not until about 1840 that the buggy first made its appearance. Suitability for heavy farm work was one of the contributions of our early horse breeders. The first draft horses imported from France were small in size, like coach horses; size was increased in accordance with the United States demand for the draft type.

STATUS OF HORSE PRODUCTION

The number of horses increased in the United States up until about 1915 (see Figure 258). Horse production expanded with the growth and development of farms. The estimated number in 1867 was about 7 million head. By 1913 the horse population on farms had expanded to over 21 million head. For six years, or until 1918, the population stayed over that figure. Since then recession in numbers has been regular and marked. By 1950

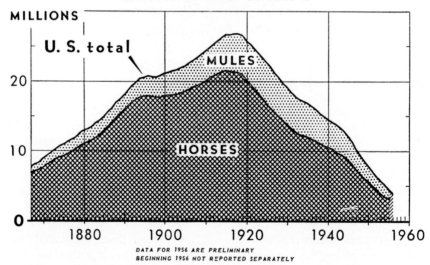

Fig. 258. Numbers of horses and mules have declined regularly for the past three decades. (U.S.D.A., Agricultural Marketing Service.)

the population was but one fourth of that of the maximum period, slightly more than 5 million head. The number for 1955 was 3.1 million head of horses on farms. The increase in use of trucks and tractors was responsible for the shrinking in numbers of work stock.

Mule numbers have likewise moved up and down. They were later than horses in reaching their peak in numbers, and their decline has been less perceptible. We had 1 million head of mules on farms in 1867. In 1925 there were 5.9 million head, by 1940 4.3 million, in 1950 2.2 million, and in 1955 there were 1.4 million.

The decrease in horses and mules has had a material effect upon American agriculture. Considering both horses and mules, the reduction in numbers from 1915 to 1955 was about 20 million head. This released for other use a considerable amount of cropland which produced feed grain and pasture. In turn, this led to accumulation of agricultural surpluses in feed supplies and to livestock production from the feeds formerly used by horses and mules.

LEADING STATES IN HORSE PRODUCTION

Horses are enumerated in the census and, in addition, the number is estimated annually. The leading states in numbers of horses are listed below.

The following are the states with large horse populations. This gives no indication of the extent of production over and above requirements. The surplus-producing states are mainly in the range area, and in marketing horses move eastward and somewhat to the south.

HORSES—NUMBERS ON FARMS IN LEADING STATES

Yearly Average—10 Years 1944–1953 [2]

STATE	THOUSAND HEAD
Texas	434
Missouri	380
Iowa	348
Minnesota	335
Wisconsin	289
Nebraska	283
Illinois	262
Oklahoma	244
Kansas	240
South Dakota	215
Kentucky	203
Ohio	192
North Dakota	190
Montana	174
New York	172
United States	6,480

[2] *Agricultural Statistics—1955,* U.S.D.A., 1956.

World horse numbers have been decreasing as well. The world total of 74.5 million head was 22 per cent less than the World War II population.

TYPES OF HORSES

The usefulness of a horse is based upon locomotion. We have a multitude of types and classes, from small ponies to large draft horses. Draft horses are essentially movers of heavy loads, capable of heavy draft. As they move heavy loads at relatively slow speed, power rather than speed is desired. Conformation which tends to denote efficiency as a drafter, is desired in this type. Ordinarily, horses are divided into draft horses and light horses. The latter group includes those in between ponies and draft horses in size. They are adapted to a wide range of uses because of their range in size. It is not uncommon to divide horses and mules into two classes, (1) work animals, and (2) pleasure horses, which includes horses used for riding, driving, and racing.

The types of horses and the breeds in the different types and their places of origin are listed below.

The following breeds are those listed separately in the last census which segregated the horses by breed. A sizable number of horses and ponies were included in the "other and unspecified breeds." In the following listing some other breeds have been added.

Of the 19 breeds given separate listing, the Percheron was the most numerous, followed by the Belgian, the Thoroughbred, the American saddle horse, and the Standardbred, in the order named. In current registrations the last three breeds named and the Quarter horse rank high. Very few draft horses are being registered.

TYPE	BREED	PLACE OF ORIGIN
Draft	Percheron	France
	Belgian	Belgium
	Clydesdale	Scotland
	Shire	England
	Suffolk	England
Carriage, or Heavy Harness	Hackney *	England
	Cleveland Bay	England
	German Coach	Germany
	French Coach	France
Roadster	Standardbred	United States
	Morgan	United States
Saddle	American saddle horse	United States
	Appaloosa **	United States
	Quarter horse **	United States

* Hackneys meeting the requirement are also classed as ponies.
** Western saddle.

TYPE	BREED	PLACE OF ORIGIN
	Tennessee walking horse	United States
	Thoroughbred	England
	Arabian	Arabia
Ponies	Shetland	Shetland Islands
	Welch	Wales

SHOW-RING CLASSIFICATION OF HORSES

The show classes for light horses are included in the discussion of the different types. In general, shows provide for light horses in the halter classes and utility classes. The halter classes are for each sex and for the various breeds. The utility classes are the saddle and harness divisions for gaited and harness horses. Then too there are classes for stock horses; also for parade horses. With draft horses we have strictly draft classes and breeding classes. The base date for age classification is January 1.

The draft gelding and mare classes are divided into the ages 4 years or over, 3 years, under 4, 2 years, under 3, and 1 year and under 2. There is usually a champion. There are also classes for draft or farm teams, in pairs, and sometimes four-horse and six-horse teams.

The breeding classes for purebreds have a general classification as follows:

STALLIONS *

(Similar age classes are offered for mares.)

Stallion, 4 years or over.
Stallion, 3 years, under 4.
Stallion, 2 years, under 3.
Stallion, 1 year, under 2.
Stallion foal.
Senior champion stallion.
Junior champion stallion.
Grand champion stallion.

GROUPS

The group classes may include the following:

Get of sire.
Produce of mare.
Mare with own foal.
Stallion and three mares, any age.

* The first-prize winners in the three younger classes show for the junior championship, while those of the older classes compete for the senior championship.

In the group class get of sire class three animals are shown, the get of one sire. Two individuals, the offspring of one mare, are commonly required in the produce of dam class. In recent years some shows have not included the class for a mare with her own foal.

DEFINITIONS OF HORSE TERMS

Stallion: the breeding male

Mare: the female

Colt: [3] a young stallion

Filly: a young mare

Foal: colt or filly under one year

Weanling: a weaned foal

Gelding: unsexed male, castrated under two years

Stag: unsexed male, castrated when maturity has advanced to the point where masculinity becomes evident in the head and neck

Geld or dry mare: a mare that has not raised a foal during the season or year

Mules: definitions included in Chapter 40

---

[3] Among horsemen the term "colt" is restricted to male foals as distinguished from female foals, which are called "fillies." In census reports "colt" refers to both male and female horses, as distinguished from mule colts.

Chapter 36

DRAFT HORSES

The draft horse is essentially a mover of heavy loads by traction. Although on farms horses are quite universally general-purpose animals, their main work is drawing or hauling heavy loads. In cities horses formerly in service for heavy hauling have been largely supplanted by trucks. The draft horses that have survived mechanization are, therefore, mainly farm horses and they are called upon to do a wide range of work. Other uses on the farm are for transportation, power, pleasure, and breeding. Horse carcasses have a value; consequently, horses are slaughtered when that return is greater than from other uses. Horse meat is generally used in dog foods and similar products.

There is a relationship between usefulness and conformation in horses; yet it is impossible to measure or estimate all the qualities that affect the drafting ability of a horse. Endurance, durability, and tractability, for example, are not reflected completely in conformation.

The conformation of the draft horse has been shaped for efficiency in drawing loads. Draft horses perform their work at a walk. Even though certain features minimized in the other classes of horses are stressed in draft-horse selection, certain characteristics are desirable in all horses and mules. Dinsmore [1] has stated that the characteristics desirable in all horses and mules, regardless of size or type, are as follows:

1. A strong, heavily muscled back, which seems short
2. A short, wide, strong, heavily muscled loin
3. A deep chest, wide through from side to side
4. A roomy middle, due to long, well-sprung ribs, and a capacious abdominal region

[1] *Book No. 219*, Horse and Mule Association of America, 1935.

643

5. Well-set legs, pasterns, and feet; that is, correct in position, viewed from front, side, or rear

6. Strong leg joints, deep from front to rear, clearly defined, with dense bone of good quality

7. Straight action and good wind

8. Good head, eyes, and temper

We lack objective measures of the performance of draft horses. Judging or selection is eye appraisal of the working capacity of the horse and includes some considerations which may not be related to ability to work. Perhaps measurements would be more useful than scores or rating, but the relation between work capacity and measurements has not yet been established.

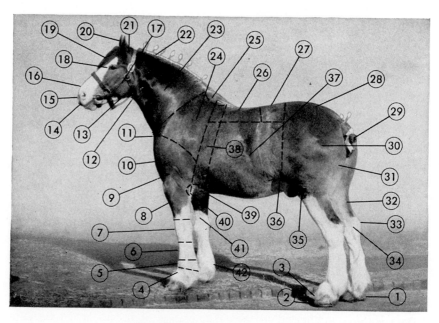

Fig. 259. Parts of a draft horse.

1—Heel	11—Point of Shoulder	21—Poll	32—Gaskin
2—Foot	12—Throttle	22—Crest	33—Point of Hock
3—Hoof Head	13—Jaw	23—Neck	34—Hock
(Coronet)	14—Muzzle, Mouth,	24—Shoulder	35—Stifle
4—Pastern	Lips	25—Withers	36—Rear Flank
5—Fetlock	15—Nostril	26—Back	37—Ribs
6—Cannon	16—Nose	27—Coupling or Loin	38—Heart Girth
7—Knee	17—Cheek	28—Croup	39—Fore Flank
8—Forearm	18—Eye	29—Tail	40—Elbow
9—Arm	19—Forehead	30—Thigh	41—Chestnut
10—Breast	20—Ear	31—Buttocks or Quarters	42—Feather

DETAILED DESCRIPTION OF THE IDEAL DRAFT HORSE

USES OF THE DRAFT-HORSE SCORE CARD

The draft gelding may serve as the ideal for draft-horse score cards, just as the beef steer was used for the ideal beef type. In horses, however, less disparity occurs between unsexed males or geldings and the individual mares and stallions used for breeding. In studying the desirable characteristics of a draft horse a score card is especially helpful because of the great number of points considered in evaluating horses as drafters. The score card is a description of the ideal and its component parts, and it also suggests the weight given to the different parts or features. The parts of the horse are shown in Figure 259. For a proper appraisal of the animal as a whole, a consideration of the major division and parts is useful.

SUGGESTED SCORE CARD FOR A DRAFT HORSE

The draft-horse score card is unique in that action is included as a major division and because in application it is suitable not only for geldings but also for mares or stallions. The latter are used for breeding as well, but little difference exists between the ideals for draft and breeding. As there is a correlation between form, conformation, and other characteristics and performance, a knowledge of useful features is of value in selecting draft horses.

1. AGE

GENERAL APPEARANCE—15 points:

2. HEIGHT—estimated hands (1 hand = 4 inches)
3. WEIGHT

1 year	950 pounds
2 years	1,300 pounds
3 years	1,500 pounds
4 years	1,700 pounds
5 years	1,800 pounds or over

4. FORM—broad, deep, massive, close coupled, symmetrical, stylish
5. QUALITY—refined; bone and joints clean, yet indicating sufficient substance; tendons sharply defined, hair fine, head refined
6. TEMPERAMENT—energetic, disposition good

HEAD AND NECK—7 points:

7. HEAD—proportionate size, well-defined features, straight face line, broad, full forehead
8. MUZZLE—broad, nostrils large, lips thin, even
9. EYES—prominent, large, bright, clear
10. EARS—medium size, fine, well set, carried alertly
11. NECK—long, muscular but not thick, well arched, throat clean

FOREQUARTERS—24 points

12. SHOULDER—long, sloping (45 degrees), muscular, well laid in
13. ARMS—short, muscular
14. FOREARMS—muscular, wide, tapering to the knee
15. KNEES—wide, deep, strong, clean cut
16. CANNONS—short, broad, flat, clean, tendons well defined
17. FETLOCKS—wide, clean, well defined
18. PASTERNS—long, sloping (45 degrees), strong and clean cut
19. FEET—large, round, even size, straight, smooth dense horn, hoof heads large, round, open; slope of wall parallel to slope of pastern; heels wide, full, one third height of toe
20. LEGS—viewed in front, a perpendicular line from the point of the shoulder should divide the leg and foot in the center; viewed from the side, a perpendicular line dropped from the center of the forearm should fall upon the center of the knee and fetlock joints and meet the ground back of the heel

BODY—12 points:

21. WITHERS—high and well defined
22. CHEST—deep, wide, full, large girth
23. RIBS—long, well sprung, close
24. BACK—short, strong, broad, heavily muscled
25. COUPLING (loin)—wide, strong, short, heavily muscled
26. UNDER LINE—long, straight, flanks low

HINDQUARTERS—32 points:

27. HIPS—wide, level, muscular
28. CROUP—long, wide, muscular
29. TAIL—attached high, well carried
30. THIGHS—deep, wide, muscular
31. GASKINS—wide, muscular
32. HOCKS—correctly set, wide, deep, clean cut, well supported
33. CANNONS—short, broad, flat, tendons well defined
34. FETLOCKS—wide, clean, well defined
35. PASTERNS—long, slopping (50 degrees), strong, clean cut
36. FEET—large, even size, straight; smooth dense horn, hoof heads large, open; heel wide, one half height of toe

37. LEGS—viewed from the rear, a perpendicular line from the point of the buttock should divide the cannon and foot; viewed from the side, this same line should touch the rear edge of the cannon from hock to fetlock, and meet the ground some little distance back of the heel

ACTION—10 points:

38. WALK—long straight stride, powerful, regular, snappy, easy, free from rolling

39. TROT—free, straight, long bold stride, regular, hocks close, free flexion of joints

Score-card points

The major divisions of the score cards are much the same as those for other livestock: general appearance, head and neck, forequarters, body, hindquarters, and in addition, action.

Age is estimated in scoring horses. Examination of the teeth will give a basis for age estimates, as indicated on page 659. Age in horses is important in two respects: first, in relation to size for age, and second, in relation to probable period of usefulness. In horse judging the first is emphasized; that is, age and weight are estimated for the purpose of considering weight for age. Probable period of usefulness is not considered in horse judging because type is stressed, or specific useful characters. Age is a factor in horse prices and in the buying of horses; see the chapter on horse marketing.

1. General appearance. The divisions of general appearance are height, weight, form, quality, and temperament.

HEIGHT. The height is the distance from the ground to the top of the withers. It is given in hands (4 inches). A horse 16 hands 2½ inches high is 66½ inches tall. The mature draft horse will range from 15 hands, 2 inches to 17 hands in height.

WEIGHT. A standard of weights for age based upon the usual weight increase of well-bred and well-fed draft type individuals is as follows:

AGE, YEARS	WEIGHT, POUNDS
1	950
2	1,300
3	1,500
4	1,700
5	1,800

These may be regarded as minimum weights for acceptable individuals. Draft horses with mature weight of 1,800 to 2,000 pounds are the most desirable on the market. Stallions are heavier than mares at comparable ages. Good representative stallions of the common draft breeds weigh 2,000 pounds or more and mares 1,800 pounds or over. Farm horses weighing

1,600 pounds are desirable in most localities. Weight is essential for ad-hesion to the ground, overcoming the tendency to slip. Weight in the drafter offsets the weight of the load. Also, heavier horses are generally more muscular than lighter horses. A correlation of 0.6 between body weight and tractive pull has been shown in dynamometer tests.[2] Weight, coupled

Fig. 260. A draft gelding of the right type, Sir James, an imported Clydesdale, grand champion gelding at the International Livestock Exposition. (Anheuser-Bush, Inc., St. Louis, Mo.)

with muscular development and adequate skeletal structure, is desired, rather than accumulation of adipose tissue. Since the outlet for heavy draft horses for heavy hauling in cities and for construction work has been nearly closed, and since on farms tractors replace horses for the heavier work, large-sized draft horses are less popular than formerly. Medium-sized light draft horses are suitable for most kinds of draft work.

FORM. The *form* of the approved drafter is wide, deep, massive, com-

[2] Ralph W. Phillips, Milton A. Madsen, and Harry H. Smith, "Dynamometer Tests of Draft Horses," *Circ. 114,* Utah State College, November, 1940.

pact or closely coupled, balanced or symmetrical, and stylish. Draftiness is synonymous with massiveness and muscularity. The drafter should have a rugged appearance. Insufficient muscling with narrow, shallow, rangy bodies is still too common in draft horses.

The good draft horse is neither low set nor rangy; moderate length of leg is desired. Low-set horses have a low center of gravity, but they are usually poor movers. Rangy, upstanding drafters are not in demand. Long-legged horses are slow maturing, and when grown out they are too large for general adaptability. Rangy horses may be awkward and cumbersome; also, their food requirement is high. Such conformation is commonly associated with "hard feeding." In none of our farm animals is balance and style so important as in horses. An active, stylish, yet manageable horse, with good carriage, is in demand as a draft horse.

QUALITY. The *quality* of a draft horse is indicated by refinement of the various parts. Bones, joints, and head indicate quality. A generally clean-cut appearance of the legs and head is desired. Ruggedness and massiveness are prerequisites, although in a measure they are antagonistic to refinement. It is apparent that we want ample bone in our ideal. A horse can be too fine or too coarse. Clean joints, such as hocks, fetlocks, pasterns, and knees, are evidence of good quality; thickness or meatiness of the joints is objectionable.

TEMPERAMENT. In temperament a draft horse should be active and energetic rather than lymphatic. However, tractability and a good disposition are essential. A draft horse needs to be steady and dependable in work. Also, it should be willing to work, with ample animation.

2. Head and neck. The head and neck of the draft horse should be in proportion to the rest of the individual. The head indicates the temperament, intelligence, activity, vigor, and breeding of the horse. A clean-cut, well-defined *head* indicating character is desired. Width and a full forehead are wanted, and the width should carry down to the *muzzle*. Width of muzzle and also width and depth of body are typical of a good feeder. Large nostrils and thin and even lips are suggested in the ideal head. The jaws should be very wide at the angle underneath and should show moderate depth. Vision is one of the essentials of a useful draft horse. Therefore, *eyes* that are normal in size and appearance are preferred. A full, bright, clear eye describes the ideal. The *ears* of a good head are of medium size, fine quality, well set, and erectly carried.

The head of the stallion indicates his masculinity; a feminine or matronly appearance is characteristic of the brood mare.

Since draft horses are commonly worked in harness with a collar, a medium length of *neck* is needed to facilitate the fitting of this important part of the work harness. Muscularity, a medium development of the crest, and good carriage are desirable qualities in the neck of a good draft horse.

The neck should be neatly joined with the head and the shoulder. An attractive appearance demands a well-carried head and neck. This is one of the most important components of style.

3. Forequarters or forehand. In weight or total score the parts included in the forequarter are exceeded only by the hindquarter. As the forelimbs are a part of the forequarter, they carry considerable weight. In fact, most of the emphasis on this division is given to the front legs.

Fig. 261. A draft mare of outstanding merit. A purebred Belgian mare, Flora, grand champion at the American Royal. Owned by Oklahoma A. & M. College, Stillwater, Okla.

Shoulders are important, for this structure affords a bearing surface for the collar. Well-laid-in shoulders that are muscular, long, and sloping are prescribed in the ideal. A straight shoulder is often associated with faulty action and improper carriage of the head and neck. It is difficult to fit a straight shoulder properly with a collar. An *arm* and *forearm* that are heavily muscled and rather wide and short are needed in the efficient draft horse. The forearm should taper gradually to the knee.

On some score cards the feet and legs are a major division; on others the legs and feet are considered with the part to which they are attached. We have discussed the forelegs with the forequarter, and the hind legs with the hindquarters. This should not minimize emphasis on feet and legs. The usefulness of a horse depends upon its underpinning. Since so much stress is placed on the feet and legs, consideration of the parts of the feet and legs becomes doubly important.

The *knees* on a draft horse should be reasonably large, wide, deep, strong, and clean cut. The set of the foreleg is dependent upon the set of the knees. They should not "buck" forward or be set too far back. Straight legs are essential for straightaway action and durability.

Desirable *cannons* are short, broad, flat in appearance, clean cut, and with tendons well defined. A cannon ample in size, strong, and rugged, yet showing quality, is a requirement for a good draft horse. Hard, smooth bone, adequate in size, is essential for endurance and durability. With tendons well back from the cannon bone, the cannon has a desirable flat appearance. Like the other limb joints, the *fetlocks* should be shapely, clean cut, well defined, and free from excess thickness. In horseman terms, a joint unduly large or not clean cut is "meaty."

Pasterns serve as a shock-absorbing mechanism. Reasonable length and a slope of 45 degrees are suggested. They should be clean and ample in size.

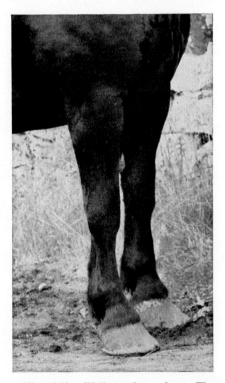

Fig. 262. Well-set front legs. The front legs are vulnerable parts of the draft horse.

A good foot is imperative for any serviceable horse. It has been found that feet that are large, round, shapely, of dense horn, and wide at the heels are durable. The forefeet should be uniform in shape and size. Size is a necessity, because upon it depends the amount of bearing surface. Depth is also a requirement. The heels should have moderate depth as well as sufficient width. The wall should slope out moderately or flare from the hoof head, which should be large, round, and open, conforming to the size of the hoof. Durability or toughness of the hoof is indicated by a dense, hard horn.

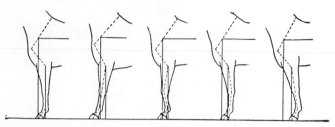

Fig. 263. Side view of forelegs. A perpendicular line dropped from the center of the forearm should fall upon the center of the knee and fetlock joints and meet the ground back of the heel. L. to r.: correct conformation; leg too far forward; knee sprung; calf kneed; foot and leg placed too far back.

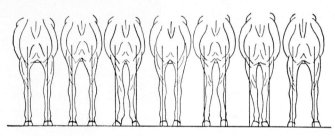

Fig. 264. Front view of forelegs. A perpendicular line from the point of the shoulder should divide the leg and foot in the center. L. to r.: correct conformation; slightly bowlegged; close at knees; toes in; knockkneed; base narrow; base wide.

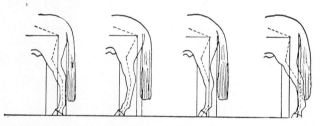

Fig. 265. Side view of hind legs. A perpendicular line should touch the rear edge of the cannon from hock to fetlock and meet the ground some little distance back of the heel. L. to r.: correct conformation; leg too far forward and hock crooked; entire leg too far under and weak below hock; entire leg placed too far back.

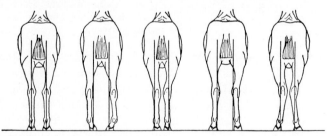

Fig. 266. Rear view of hind legs. A perpendicular line from the point of the buttock divides the cannon and foot. L. to r.: correct conformation; bowlegged; base narrow; base wide; cow-hocked and toes out—a very serious fault.

652

The legs are viewed from both side and front to observe their set. Straight, well-set legs are needed for good action and long service. The proper set of legs is shown in illustrations on opposite page, which also depict common defects.

4. Body. The *withers* of a horse should be fairly high and well defined. Depth and width of middle are desired qualities, and we stress especially a well-developed full chest with ample girth and a roomy middle with long, well-sprung *ribs.*

Along the top we look for a *back* and *coupling,* or loin, that is short, strong, broad, and well muscled. A long, fairly straight underline with low flanks completes the description of the body.

Shallow bodies or light middles are not wanted in drafters.

5. Hindquarters. Since the hindquarter includes the hind leg, this division receives more emphasis than any of the others. Heavy muscling is essential in the hindquarters of the approved draft type, but more important is a satisfactory conformation of the hind leg. The hind leg must bear the strain of the power in moving loads from the heavy muscles in the hindquarters.

The *hips* and the *croup* are required to be wide, level, smooth, and muscular. Reasonable length is demanded in the croup, and a drooping croup is objectionable. A short, sloping croup is often associated with crooked hind legs. A well-carried *tail* attached fairly high is also desired. Width, thickness, and muscularity should characterize the *thighs* and the *lower thigh* or *gaskin.*

The *hock* joint is the most important single joint in the body of the horse. The muscles flex in lever fashion and then extend the leg at the hock joint and by so doing move the horse forward. So the load is moved and the force is transmitted through the one point, the *hock.* In an ideal hock we want size, rugged, ample, bearing surface, and correct setting. The latter is most important since hocks out of line or crooked are unable to withstand the strain of hard work. The hock must be clean cut, that is,

Fig. 267. A crooked or sickled hock. Note that a perpendicular line cannot fall parallel with the rear of the cannon.

free from the enlargements which so generally indicate weakness or unsoundness.

Below the hock is the cannon which, like the cannon in the front leg, should be short, wide, flat, with well-defined tendons set well back from the cannon bone. Fetlocks, pasterns, and feet such as described for the foreleg are desired in the hind leg, except that less slope of pastern is acceptable behind. The hind feet are usually smaller and have less difference between depth of toe and heel than the front feet.

The set of the hind leg is viewed from both side and rear and lined up with other features of conformation. Proper set is essential for durability and good action. The ideal set of the hind leg and common deviations are discussed and illustrated on pages 652–653.

6. Action. The action of the draft horse is observed at both the walk and the trot. Draft horses do not work at a trot, and the only reason for checking the trot is that it may accentuate faults in action. At either the walk or the trot the feet should move straight ahead in the direction of travel. A walk that is powerful, regular, snappy, elastic, with a long stride is desired. A light springy step with animation marks a good walk. The trot should have the same characteristics plus close carriage of the hock and free flexion of all the joints.

Lameness is a serious defect of action and usually just cause for disqualification.

JUDGING HORSES

In judging classes of horses the first step is to make an observation at some distance away. Orderly examination is advisable, for there are many items to consider in appraising the value of a horse. In this initial observation, if a group is being judged, it is advisable to walk around the class to size up the lot as a whole. Individual examination to consider general appearance should follow. The horse is studied from the sides and the ends. Then a closer inspection should be made of the feet and legs. The mouth is examined to estimate age and the height at withers is noted.

After a rather detailed examination of each individual, the class is "moved" to observe its action. The walk is demonstrated and then the trot. The observed horse moves away from and then toward the judge. In other words, action is observed from the front and rear rather than from the side. In noting the action straightness, length, flexion, power, springiness, and balance are to be considered. Lameness, too, must be watched for. Finally, in placing a class a final general observation is made.

SET OF LEGS

Much attention is generally given to the set of the legs on a draft horse. (See Figures 263, 264, 265, and 266.) The score-card description is for the foreleg: viewed from the front, a perpendicular line from the point of the shoulder should divide the leg and foot in the center; viewed from the side, a perpendicular line dropped from the center of the forearm should fall upon the center of the knee and fetlock joints and meet the ground back of the heel.

For the hind leg: viewed from the rear, a perpendicular line from the point of the buttock should divide the cannon and foot; viewed from the side, the same line should touch the rear edge of the cannon from hock to fetlock, and meet the ground some little distance back of the heel.

One of the most serious defects in the set of the legs is the faulty conformation of the hocks known as "sickled" or bent hock. Horses at hard work tend to wear out at the hock joints and the front legs. Proper conformation of each will give long wearing quailities. A sickle hock is identified from a side view by noting the relationship of the parts that join at the hock. If the line dropped from the point of the buttock does not fall parallel with the rear of the cannon, the hock is sickled. The position of the hind leg may make it difficult to determine whether or not the hock is set right. It is possible to have the cannon vertical and still have a sickled hock. Then the leg is either too straight and set under the body, or else set back. Figure 267 shows a typical sickle hock.

Fig. 268. The right kind of front foot. Note the shape and symmetry. From the noted Belgian mare, Prevench. (Michigan State University.)

In the set of the leg and the foot a proper relationship between the two is highly desirable. This is indicated in part by the axis of the foot and leg. This relationship is affected by wear of the foot, for that may alter the slope of the pastern. If the toe part is grown out too long the pastern is forced back out of its natural line. When the toe is short, the pastern is thrown forward. It is apparent that an extreme in either direction causes strain and may cause unsoundness. Proper care of the feet will prevent such a condition. Trimming the feet is a part of good horse husbandry.

ACTION OF THE HORSE DESCRIBED

In movement of the horse the weight of the body is moved forward, and the legs in turn support the weight and propel the body. As the weight of the body is moved forward the front legs support more of the weight and the hind legs propel the body. At the end of a stride the foot touches the ground ahead of its natural standing position. Then, as the body is moved forward, the legs act as support and also as the member through which propelling force is exerted. When the foot is lifted from the ground in movement there is flexion of the limb, followed by forward extension and contact with the ground to regain equilibrium.

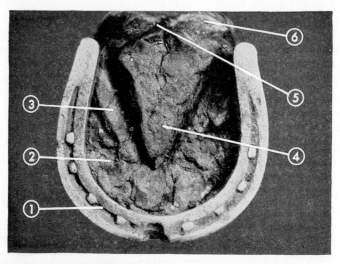

Fig. 269. A good front foot of a horse, bottom view. Note the shape, size, and width at the heel. The shoe fits the hoof and is attached by nails to the fore part of the foot so as not to interfere with the expansion at the heel. Note also the parts of the hoof. (1) Wall under the shoe. (2) Sole. (3) Bars. (4) Frog. (5) Cleft of frog. (6) Bulbs of heel. (Michigan State College.)

The manner of moving may be of several kinds. A draft horse may walk or trot. The walk is the working gait of the draft horse; it is a slow, flat-footed, four-beat gait. The trot is a rapid two-beat gait in which there is a coordinated movement of the front legs with the opposite hind legs. In other words, the right front and the left hind move forward together. The other gaits and their distinctive characteristics are described in the chapter on light horses.

DEFECTS IN ACTION

Good action is characterized by true or straight moving, long stride, and reasonable flexion. Essential for good action are feet and legs of the right conformation, combined with correct balance of the parts of the horse. It is impossible for a horse to have true action if the legs are incorrectly set or if the feet are misshapen.

Gay [3] has given the following defects or peculiarities in the movement of horses:

Forging. Striking the ends of the branches or the under surface of the forefoot shoe wth the toe of the hind foot.

Interfering. Striking the supporting leg at the fetlock with the foot of the striding leg. It is predisposed in horses with base narrow, toe wide, or splay-foot standing positon.

Paddling. An outward deviation in the direction of the stride of the foreleg, the result of a toe narrow or pigeon-toed standing position.

Winging. Exaggerated paddling, noticeable in high going horses.

Winding. A twisting of the striding leg around in front of the supporting leg similar to paddling. This is most commonly seen in wide-fronted draft horses at the walk.

Scalping. Hitting the front of the hind foot above or at the line of the hair against the toe of the breaking-over forefoot.

Speedy cutting. The spreading trotter at speed hits the hind leg above the scalping mark against the inside of the breaking-over forefoot as he passes.

Fig. 270. A draft horse in action, straight, and regular. The stride should be long, the joints freely flexed, and the hocks carried close.

Cross-firing. Essentially forging in pacers, in which they hit the inside of the near fore- and off-hind foot or the reverse in the air as the stride of the hind leg is about completed and the stride of the foreleg just begun.

Pointing. A stride in which extension is much more marked than flexion. It is especially characteristic of the Thoroughbred. The same term is also used to indicate the resting of one forefoot in an advanced position to relieve the back tendons.

Dwelling. A perceptible pause in the flight of the foot, as though the stride had been completed before the foot reached the ground. Most noticeable in actors or trick-trained horses.

[3] Carl W. Gay, *Productive Horse Husbandry*, J. B. Lippincott Company, Philadelphia, Pa., 1932.

Trappy. A quick, high, but comparatively short stride.

Pounding. A heavy contact, usually accompanying a high stride.

Rolling. Excessive lateral shoulder motion as in wide-fronted horses.

BREEDS OF DRAFT HORSES

A brief discussion of the common breeds of draft horses, their origin, improvement, characteristics and adaptabilities follows.

Comparatively few breeding establishments specializing in draft horses are currently in existence in this country. With shrinking of horse numbers, the draft and heavy harness horses suffered the most. Consequently, this discussion will be rather limited. The student should refer to the books on horses listed in the appendix for more complete information.

BELGIAN

This breed originated in Belgium from the old Flemish horses native to that general area. In that country of fertile soil, rather low land, and small farms, a large drafty type horse was a necessity for agriculture in the pre-mechanical age. The breeding of draft horses was promoted by the government through subsidies, exhibitions, and awards. In 1886 the first importation of Belgian horses was made to the United States, but it was some 20 years later before they attracted much attention.

Belgians are a wide, deep, smooth-conformation, muscular breed with medium length of legs, body, and neck. In this country much improvement was made in the set of legs, cleanness of joint, and durability of feet and legs. The color is commonly sorrel, chestnut, or red roan, but other colors such as browns, blacks and grays occur. The breed is noted for size and good disposition as well as for good feeding qualities.

PERCHERON

This breed was developed in northwestern France in the province of La Perche. The area is hilly and its valleys have excellent fertile pastures inlaid with limestone. The breed came about from the modification of a Flemish base which had some Oriental blood (Arab and Barb). Percherons were first used as coach horses but, with the development of railroads and a demand from the United States, there came a change to the draft type. Our first importations were made in the 1840's. About 1870 there developed a heavy export demand for the draft type. The Percheron Society of France was organized in 1883.

The Percheron is a draft horse with attractive conformation combined with style and action superior to most draft breeds. In size it is larger than the Clydesdale but smaller than the Shire or the Belgian. The color is mainly black or gray, but other colors occur. The breed shifted from the extreme drafty type in the 1930's to a general-purpose type, but mechanization continued to reduce the breed's numbers.

SHIRE

The East Central part of England, a low-lying, marshy land area, was the home of this breed. This is the largest of our horse breeds; it came from the Ghent war or cart horse of England, modified by Flemish breeding. Robert Bakewell bred cart horses, predecessors of the Shire. They were early brought to this country. This large, coarse breed with rather inferior feet and hairiness of the legs was never popular in the United States. The color is mainly brown, bay, or black with white markings.

CLYDESDALE

The valley of the river Clyde in Southwestern Scotland was the original home of this breed. In its formation Flemish stock was used, also some English blood, mainly Shire. In color the Clydesdale resembles the Shire; it is smaller, more upstanding, and more active than the Shire. Clydesdales are noted for their superior feet, legs and action. Like the Shires they have feather or hair on the back of their legs and around the hoof heads. Clydesdales did not have sufficient feed capacity to become numerous when draft horses were in demand.

SUFFOLK

This is another British breed, having its native home in Suffolk County, eastern England. Its origin is quite obscure; it has been bred without outside blood in Suffolk since 1700. This breed has a uniform color (chestnut) and is the smallest of the draft breeds. It has never been numerous in this country.

DETERMINATION OF THE AGE OF HORSES AND MULES [4]

The ordinary observer can readily learn to tell the age of horses or mules with considerable accuracy until the animals have passed their eighth year. Even those who are experienced may find it difficult to determine the exact age of animals older than this.

The mature male horse has 40 teeth. Of these, 24 are molars or grinders,

[4] George W. Pope, "Determining the Age of Farm Animals by Their Teeth," *Farmers' Bull. 1721,* U.S.D.A., March, 1934.

12 are incisors or front teeth, and 4 are tushes or pointed teeth. The two central incisors are known as "centrals" or "nippers"; the next two, one on each side of the nippers, are called "intermediates" or "middles," and the last, or outer pair, the "corners." The tushes are located between the incisors and the molars. As these are not usually present in the mare, she may be considered to have a total of 36 teeth; the male has 40.

The young animal, whether male or female, has 24 temporary teeth, commonly called "milk teeth," much whiter and smaller than the permanent teeth. These milk teeth consist of 12 incisors and 12 molars. The molars are the three back teeth on each side of each jaw. The milk teeth are shed and replaced by permanent teeth at fairly definite periods, which serve as an index of the age of young colts.

The temporary central incisors or nippers may be present at the time of birth; otherwise they appear before the colt is 10 days old.

At the age of from 4 to 6 weeks the two temporary intermediates, upper and lower, appear. These teeth immediately adjoin the nippers.

When the colt is from 6 to 10 months old, the corner incisors, two above and two below, are cut. This gives the young animal a full set of temporary front teeth.

By the time the colt has reached the age of 1 year the crowns of the central incisors show wear. In another 6 months the intermediates or middles become worn, and at 2 years all the teeth are worn. During the following 6 months there are no changes that will distinguish the exact age. At about 2½ years, however, the shedding of the milk teeth begins, and at 3 years the temporary central nippers, two above and two below, are replaced by the permanent central incisors.

At 4 years the four permanent intermediates have taken the place of the four temporary middles.

When the animal is about 4½ years old the shedding of the four corners begins, and at 5 years a permanent set of corners are well up but not in contact.

In a 6-year-old horse the corner incisors are on a level with the adjoining teeth, with a well-marked dental cavity or "cup" showing practically no wear. The nippers show wear over the entire surface; the "cup," though visible, shows indications of gradual disappearance and at this stage is without a hollow.

When the animal is 7 years old, not only the nippers but also the middles show wear. With each upper corner tooth there is an indentation caused by wear from the corresponding tooth below it, resulting in a downward triangular projection of the posterior edge. This projection is commonly termed "dovetail," or "swallowtail."

In the 8-year-old horse all the incisors are worn. The cup has entirely disappeared from the nippers, but shows to a slight extent in the middles and is still well marked in the corners. At this stage what is termed the "dental star" makes its appearance as a yellow transverse line just back of the front edge of the table, or flat surface, of the nippers and middles.

Between the ages of 9 and 13 years there is a gradual change in the contour of the tables of the incisors. In a 9-year-old animal the nippers take on a more or less rounded contour; the dental cavity or cup has disappeared from all but the corners; the dental star is found in both the nippers and middles and in the nippers near the center of the table. At 10 years the middles become rounded, and the dental star, now seen on all the incisors, is near the center of both the nippers and middles. At 11 or 12 years the corners have a somewhat rounded form, and the dental star approaches the center of the table. As the horse reaches 13 years of age all the lower incisors are unmistakably rounded, the dental star is found in the center of all the tables, and the enamel rings which formerly surrounded the cups have entirely disappeared.

In a horse about 14 years of age the tables of the incisor begin to change from a rounded to a triangular contour. This change occurs in the nippers at 14 years, in the middles at 15 years, and in the corners at 16 or 17 years.

During the 4 years after the appearance of the triangle, there is a gradual approach of the tables to the form of a rectangle. The teeth during this period are usually elongated and directed obliquely. The dental arch also becomes contracted and pointed, and the under edges of the lower jaw are thin and sharp as compared with their appearance in a young horse. Should the animal live more than 20 years, these conditions become more marked and are accompanied by excessive wear and loosening or loss of molars.

Chapter 37

LIGHT HORSES

A horse not sufficiently large to be called a draft horse or a chunk, and too large to class as a pony, is termed a "light horse." Since there is considerable range in size and usefulness there are several groups of light horses. Light horses include, for example, saddle horses suitable for hunters and Hackneys, which perform as carriage or heavy harness horses. As previously pointed out, we have several breeds of light horses, more than draft type. In aggregate numbers light horses are much less important than draft horses. In the last census enumeration which listed registered purebreds, there were more than seven times as many draft type as light horses.

The automobile and truck have replaced a great proportion of the light horses which formerly found service as buggy or delivery horses. However, the automobile has not detracted from several of the kinds of light horses, particularly those which might be classed as pleasure horses. In fact, if anything, the motor car has extended the use of pleasure horses since it has made their use available to a greater number. The automobile in many respects represents an addition to American life rather than a replacement of other forms of transportation. In regions where good roads are unavailable horse transportation is still in use. On trails and rough land, horses are indispensable.

The light horse has three principal uses: (1) riding, (2) driving, and (3) racing. It is obvious that some horses may serve in more than one capacity. Light horses are mainly used for pleasure, yet they have many economic uses, as will be pointed out later.

A discussion of the various groups of light horses follows. This separation into groups is based on use, and in some cases on breed also, since some breeds represent fields of service. There is some confusion about groups of light horses, as to whether each group constitutes a definite breed

662

or merely a group suited for a definite use. In order to be classed as a breed, a group must have a common origin, distinguishing characters, and ability to transmit these characters.

The riding or saddle horses are (1) running horses, (2) western saddle horses, (3) three- and five-gaited horses, (4) hunters and polo ponies, (5) other saddle horses and (6) other light horses.

THE RUNNING HORSE OR THOROUGHBRED [1]

Running horses might be classed as racing, for they are used for that purpose.

Fig. 271. A noted Thoroughbred in action, Native Dancer winning the Oneonta Handicap at Saratoga. (Wide World Photo.)

The running horse or Thoroughbred was developed in Great Britain for the primary purpose of racing under the saddle. The Thoroughbred came from improved light horses of England which owed much of their stamina, endurance, speed, and symmetry to imported stock of Arabian, Barb, and Turkish blood. Native light horses were judged on the basis of their turf or track performance, for racing under the saddle was reported as early as the latter half of the twelfth century. Later, imported horses contributed to the improvement. From Great Britain the Thoroughbred has been taken to all parts of the world.

---

[1] The term "Thoroughbred" is used for a breed of horses. It is also used as an adjective to designate breeding. However, horsemen regard such usage as incorrect, and among them thoroughbred is not synonymous with purebred.

In addition to running horses, the Thoroughbred provides us with many saddle horses, hunters, and polo ponies. Either straightbred or crossed, Thoroughbreds produce good army horses for officers and cavalry mounts. They are useful in crossing with other breeds for the quality and temperament transmitted to the crosses. The Thoroughbred leads all of the horse breeds in number of registered purebreds in this country.

DESCRIPTION OF THE THOROUGHBRED

The common colors of the Thoroughbred are bay, brown, and chestnut, with white in varying degrees on the legs and face. Blacks, duns, and roans also occur.

The standard horse colors from the color guide specified for Thoroughbred horses follow.

STANDARD HORSE COLORS FROM THE COLOR GUIDE SPECIFIED FOR THOROUGHBRED HORSES BY THE AMERICAN JOCKEY CLUB

BAY.   This varies from a light yellowish tan (light bay) to a dark rich shade, almost brown, and between these a bright mahogany (blood bay).

BROWN.   This is sometimes difficult to tell from black or dark bay but can be distinguished by noting the fine tan or brown hairs on the muzzle or flanks.

BLACK.   If distinguishing between dark brown and black, the black can be determined by noting the fine black hair on the muzzle.

CHESTNUT.   This varies from a dark color to a light washy yellow (light or golden chestnut is sometimes said to be sorrel), between which come the brilliant red-gold and copper shades. Never have black mane, tail, or points.

DUN.   This varies from mouse color to a golden dun, and very generally is accompanied with black points and stripe.

GRAY.   This is a mixture of white hairs and black, sometimes scarcely distinguished from black at birth, getting lighter with age.

ROANS.   There are two classes of these—red or strawberry, produced by the intermingling of red, white, and yellow hairs, and blue, produced by intermingling of black, white, and yellow hairs.

The weight of the mature Thoroughbred is about 1,000 pounds and the height is about 16 hands. There is considerable range in weight and height.

The form of the Thoroughbred exemplifies development for speed to a very high degree, since they have been bred mainly for racing. In general appearance they are upstanding and rather angular. A small, well-proportioned head with clean-cut features and a straight face line is typical. The shoulders are sloping and muscular. The withers are quite high and distinct. The thighs and the quarter are very muscular and rather angular. In general, the legs are quite fine in bone, clean, and well set, while the feet are rather small. Compared with horses that race at the trot or the pace, running horses have greater development of the forequarter and a shorter back, and are usually more level at the croup. They also have straighter hind legs and are relatively long from the back to the ground. The walk or trot is rather low and pointed; that is, extension is much more pronounced than flexion. At the run or gallop the action of the Thoroughbred is at its best. The gallop is a fast three-beat gait in which two diagonal legs act together, their one beat falling between the successive beats of the other two legs. Thoroughbreds are quick on the getaway and have a long stride, with very little waste motion. As a group they are active and energetic in temperament. Some individuals are highly nervous and erratic.

RECORDS OF THOROUGHBREDS

The distances at which thoroughbred or running horses are raced vary. Also by the handicapping system used the weights carried by running horses are variable and based upon previous performance. The distances are often expressed in furlongs which are ⅛ mile or 220 yards.

There follows a list of records for commonly used distances.

WORLD RECORDS FOR THOROUGHBREDS FOR VARIOUS DISTANCES
UP TO AND INCLUDING 1956

DISTANCE, MILES	TIME	HORSE, AGE, WEIGHT, TRACK AND LOCATION	DATE
¼	:20⅘	Big Racket, 4, 111, Hipodromo de las Americas, Mexico City, Mexico	Feb. 5, 1945
½	:45⅕	Manzanero, 6, 121, Hipodromo de las Americas, Mexico City, Mexico	Feb. 5, 1954
¾	1:06⅕	Gelding by Blink-Broken Tendril, 3, 123, Brighton, England *	Aug. 6, 1929
1	1:33⅕	Swaps, 4, 128, Hollywood Park, Inglewood, Calif.	June 9, 1956
1⅛	1:46⅘	Noor, 5, 123, Golden Gate Fields, Albany, Calif.	June 17, 1950
1¼	1:58⅕	Noor, 5, 127, Golden Gate Fields, Albany, Calif.	June 24, 1950
1½	2:23	The Bastard, 3, 124, Newmarket, England	Oct. 18, 1929

* The ¾-mile course at Brighton is started from a hill and is down grade to within one third of a mile of the finish.

THREE- AND FIVE-GAITED SADDLE HORSES [2]

Saddle horses were a necessity in frontier days and, consequently, to meet the need, there was developed a breed called the American saddle

[2] A combination horse is one that is shown in harness appropriately hitched and in the three-gaited saddle class.

horse. The states of Kentucky, Tennessee, Virginia, and West Virginia were the first to develop this type of horse, which was unique to this country. This breed was developed in colonial days to meet the need for an easy riding horse suitable for travel over poor roads and trails. Later, Missouri came to the front as a saddle horse producing state, and many noted saddle horses were raised there.

With the availability of other modes of transportation there was less need for the saddle horse in his original field. Although saddle horses have been replaced for making long journeys, their usefulness for transportation over rough, semimountainous ground still remains unchallenged. Saddle horses are serviceable for riding over plantations. Stockmen, ranchers, rangers, farmers, livestock buyers and sellers at large markets, and mounted police all continue to use saddle horses. The demand for them as pleasure horses still continues; there is growing interest in saddle horses in the large cities where riding for recreation has been made available to large numbers.

THE FIVE-GAITED SADDLE HORSE

Five-gaited saddle horses are derived principally from the American Saddle Horse breed. In fact, the chief distinguishing characteristics of this breed are the so-called "easy" gaits—the rack and the slow gait in addition to the walk, trot and canter. The slow gait may be either the running walk, the fox trot, or the slow pace. Horses of this type have been bred extensively in Kentucky and Missouri. They are widely distributed in the United States and are popular in and around the large cities where a horse is used for pleasure and recreation. The gaits, or various ways of going, are described by Gay [3] as follows.

Walk. A slow, flat-footed, four-beat gait; one of the most useful, whether in harness or under saddle, if executed with snap and animation, as it should be.

Trot. A rapid, two-beat gait, in which the diagonal fore and hind legs act together. The fast-stepping trot is distinguished by the length and rapidity with which the individual strides are accomplished and is executed with extreme extension. The high-stepping trot is characterized by height and spring of stride, the horse placing himself, going collectedly, and executing each step with extreme flexion and precision.

Canter. A restrained gallop in which the weight is sustained chiefly by the hind quarters, the lightened forehand rising and falling in high, bounding fashion, the gait executed in a slow, collected, rhythmical way, on either lead at command. Since the canter, like the gallop, imposes a special wear

[3] Carl W. Gay, *Productive Horse Husbandry,* J. B. Lippincott Company, Philadelphia, Pa., 1932.

on the leading fore foot and its diagonal hind, the lead should be changed frequently. When the simultaneous beat is of a lateral instead of a diagonal pair of feet and falls between successive beats of the other lateral pair, the leading fore and hind on the same side, it constitutes a cross or *lateral canter,* and conveys a twisting motion to the rider. The gallop or run of the racing horse, the Thoroughbred, is described on page 665.

Fig. 272. A five-gaited saddle horse of the approved type. Note the full mane and tail. The gaits required are: the walk, the trot, the canter, the rack, and one of the slow gaits.

Rack. A fast, flashy, four-beat gait, more clearly defined by the discarded name "single foot." It is rarely executed voluntarily but only under compulsion of hand and heel. It is characterized by a display of knee action, and many horses can rack very fast. Although agreeable to the rider, it is most distressing to the horse, and should therefore be called for with discretion.

Pace. A rapid, two-beat gait, in which the lateral fore and hind legs act together. It is characterized by quick get away, a minimum of concussion, some side motion, the absence of much knee fold (although some pacers are trappy), and the necessity for smooth, hard footing and easy draft for its execution. It is difficult for most pacers to travel in heavy footing, such as fresh snow, sand, or mud, and they have a jerky, unsteady way of pulling a wagon, if any pull is necessary. The increased draft of an additional person up behind or of a rough bit of road will swing most pacers into a trot if they can trot at all. Jogging downhill will force some trotters to pace; an upgrade will set pacers to trotting. The pace is more essentially a speed than a road gait.

Running walk. A slow single-foot or four-beat gait, intermediate between the walk and rack suggestive of a continued breaking out of a walk. This is the natural gait of the walking horse. It is the business gait in the South and West, where gaited horses are ridden extensively, since it can be maintained all day. It is good for 6 to 8 miles an hour, with the greatest possible ease to both horse and rider.

The fox trot. A short, broken, nodding trot, in which the hind legs go in a more or less lateral step. It is used as a substitute for the running walk.

The stepping pace. Distinct from the ordinary pace of the harness horse and characterized by very little if any side motion and a somewhat broken cadence in the action of the lateral pairs of legs. This is the usual slow gait.

Description of the five-gaited horse

The five-gaited horse is distinguished from the three-gaited by knowledge of gaits and by its trimming. The five-gaited horse is untrimmed and carries a full, flowing mane and full-length tail. Usually the fore top and the first lock are braided and the mane is trained to the right. Three-gaited horses are partially trimmed, having their manes "hogged" or clipped short and their tails "plucked" or shaved for a short distance from the base.

In horses of this class, dark colors are preferred: chestnut, dark bay, brown, and black. Other colors, especially grays, are not uncommon, but conspicuous colors or large white flashy markings are relatively uncommon. Since some of the gaits are not natural and must be acquired, individuals without the qualities desired are not trained in the gaits.

Size. The desired size is usually within 1,000 to 1,150 pounds in weight and 15 to 16 hands high. However, more range than this in size is prevalent.

Conformation. Much stress is placed upon eye appeal. Beauty of conformation is paramount in determining the value of a five-gaited saddle horse. A good saddle horse should have symmetry and style, spirit and animation, combined with tractability and ease in riding.

The *head* of the saddle horse should indicate intelligence, a tractable disposition, and refinement. The head is carried high on a rather long, shapely, refined, nicely arched *neck;* this gives the effect of "much horse in front of the rider" desired because it adds to the rider's sensitivity and ease in handling the horse. A short, thick, straight neck makes a saddle horse more difficult to control.

Fig. 273. A five-gaited saddle gelding, Oakhill Chief, a noted show-ring winner. Owned by Miss Jean McLean, Portsmouth, Va. (Photo by McClasky.)

The *shoulders* should be long, sloping, and smoothly muscled. They should extend smoothly upward with rather high, well-defined withers. The saddle will then be placed well back, and, with a deep but rather narrow forequarter, will give the rider a comfortable seat. Well-set legs with ample slope of pasterns are essential for an easy ride; they will give the elasticity of step needed. The back of the saddle horse is relatively short, the croup comparatively level, and the under line rather long.

Five-gaited saddle horses usually have their tails set. A well-carried flowing *tail* adds much to their attractiveness.

Temperament. Although spirit and dash are desired in saddle horses, it is required that they respond promptly to the signals of the rider and that they be well-mannered. By temperament and disposition the saddle horse should be well suited for his work. Riders prefer horses that have good dispositions and good manners and that are attractive and ride well.

Action. The action of the saddle horse should be free, energetic, medium in height, and true. The step should be light and springy and, above all, surefooted.

Fig. 274. A noted five-gaited saddle horse, Hurricane, winner of the five-gaited stake for geldings, International Livestock Exposition. Owned by Red Top Farm, Libertyville, Ill. Chester Caldwell up.

The *gaits* have been previously described. A five-gaited horse must know and perform the prescribed gaits.

THE THREE-GAITED SADDLE HORSE

These are the walk-trot-canter horses, and they meet the requirements for five-gaited saddle horse except that they perform only at three gaits. Three-gaited horses are often referred to as "hacks." They may be of the American Saddle Horse breed, but many are Thoroughbred or Standardbred. The three-gaited horse is the accepted saddle horse of England and this country; it is preferred by the average rider.

Since the difference between five- and three-gaited horses is mainly in performance, further description is unnecessary.

Fig. 275. A three-gaited saddle mare, Edith Fable, a noted show-ring winner. Owned by Miss Jean McLean, Portsmouth, Va. (Photo by McClasky.)

SADDLE HORSE EVALUATION

E. A. Trowbridge [4] has stated that there are four main considerations in evaluating saddle horses:

1. Conformation, including quality and soundness
2. Action, including required gaits
3. Manners, including form, training, and obedience
4. Personality, including expression, attitude, and physical make-up

Saddle horse halter score card

There follows a score card for saddle horse evaluation or judging. This should help the student to understand the parts of the saddle horse and

[4] *Proceedings,* American Society of Animal Production, 1938, p. 92.

the emphasis placed on various considerations. It is to be used in connection with the applicable section on draft horses such as set of legs for example.

SADDLE HORSE

Scale of Points

SIZE—10 points:
WEIGHT—900 to 1200 pounds
HEIGHT—14-3 to 16-1
Extremes undesirable

FORM—25 points:
Saddle horses should possess beauty, refinement, symmetry and style
BODY—round, full smoothly muscled with well sprung ribs
BACK AND LOIN—short, wide and well muscled
CROUP—long, level and muscular
QUARTERS—deep muscular
GASKINS—heavily muscled
WITHERS—prominent, showing good saddle base
SHOULDERS—deep, well laid in, sloping (45 degrees)
CHEST—fairly wide, deep, and full
ARM AND FOREARM—strongly muscled

FEET AND LEGS—20 points:
FEET—proportionate to size of horse, with good shape, open deep well, dense texture of hoof
LEGS—correct position, front, side or rear view
PASTERNS—long, sloping (45 degrees)
CANNONS—clean, flat with tendons well defined
KNEES—broad, tapering gradually in to cannon
HOCKS—deep, clean-cut and well supported

HEAD AND NECK—15 points:
Head and neck alertly carried, showing style, character and good breeding
NECK—long, nicely arched, clean-cut, gracefully carried; throat-latch clean
HEAD—proportionate in size to body, with clean-cut, lean features, straight face line and large prominent eyes
EARS—medium in size, pointed, well and alertly carried

QUALITY—10 points:
BONE—flat with tendons well defined
JOINTS—clean and sharply defined

ACTION (Front or rear view)—20 points:
WALK—straight, long, springy, with a free easy stride
TROT—prompt, free, straight, true, and balanced, with hocks carried closely; high flexion of knees and hocks

THE HUNTER AND THE POLO PONY

Much has been written about both of these specialized saddle horses. In breeding they are largely Thoroughbred.

The *hunter* is the type of horse used to follow the hounds in fox hunting. Therefore size, ruggedness, and endurance are essential in this type.

The *polo pony* is used in playing the game of polo. In this game men on horseback equipped with long-handled mallets compete in four-man teams on a playing field 300 yards long and 120 to 150 yards wide. The game is very much like hockey.

Fast, rugged, intelligent horses that can follow the ball are wanted in this game. Formerly ponies were used in polo, but now greater leeway in height is permitted; the range is from 14:2 to 15 hands, and the weight range is from 850 to 1,000 pounds.

OTHER HORSES OF THE SADDLE TYPE

As there are other horses used mainly as saddlers, they will be discussed briefly here.

Fig. 276. A typical Arabian stallion, Jadaan. Owned by W. K. Kellogg, Arabian Horse Ranch, Panora, Calif. (Courtesy of C. E. Howell, University of California.)

Arabian

This is the oldest breed of horses. It is recognized as the fountainhead of all our other light breeds, and its influence has been felt in many other horse breeds. The Arabian is probably a descendant of the wild Libyan horse of northern Africa. As a breed the Arabian is noted for its beauty, style, quality, endurance, docility, and activity. It is used mainly under saddle, where it performs well at the walk, trot, and canter.

In size the Arabian is from 14:1 to 15:1 hands high and from 850 to 1,000 pounds in weight. The common colors are gray, bay, chestnut, and brown. Occasionally blacks and whites occur. White markings on the face and legs are common, but the spotting usually attributed to this breed is mainly in its crosses.

One rather common objection is to its small size. However, Arabians have shown up exceedingly well in endurance rides. They are sound, durable, and enduring. They are less speedy than Thoroughbreds. This breed is quite popular in California and the southwestern states.

Fig. 277. A Tennessee Walking Horse, Melody Maid. Owned by Oakwood Acres Stables, Fayetteville, Tenn. Urban Small up.

The Tennessee walking horse

This breed was developed in middle Tennessee; the association of breeders was formed in 1935. Typical individuals stand about 15:2 and weigh from 1,000 to 1,250 pounds. Horses of this breed are noted for good disposition, gentleness, and intelligence. They are different from other saddle horses in that the running-walk gait is emphasized. The head is somewhat low in carriage and, at the running walk, there is a distinct nodding of the head and swinging of the ears. The gait is very easy on the horse and the rider. It is a natural gait somewhat faster than a walk. The front foot strikes the ground just before the opposite hind foot, and the hind foot oversteps the front foot from 6 to 15 inches with a sliding motion. A running walk, a flat-foot walk, and a good canter are required in classes for plantation horses.

The Palomino [5]

These are the golden-colored stock and pleasure horses that have become very popular in the western states. The origin is probably from several

Fig. 278. An American saddlebred Palomino, winner in parade classes.

[5] Numerous articles by Robert Denhardt have appeared in *The Cattleman,* especially in the January, 1939, September, 1939, and March, 1941, issues.

sources in California, other western states, and Mexico. A register association has been formed and the first yearbook was issued in 1937. There is good demand for such horses; they are light horses of riding type. Palomino breeders are not wholly in agreement about conformation and utility of the breed. The Palomino Exhibitors Association requires that horses, in all Palomino breeding classes, be shown at hand and be registered in the Palomino Horse Association and Stud Book Registry.[6] Color is to count 50 per cent and, for a full score, body color must be of pure gold. Mane and tail shall be white, ivory, or silver. The conformation of Palomino shall be judged on standards for western saddle horses or stock horses, and this conformation shall count 40 per cent. Manners shall score 10 per cent, and emphasis is placed on docility combined with animation and alertness. The Palomino color is also found in other breeds.

The quarter horse

The quarter horse is so called because of its ability to run a fast quarter-mile under saddle. A typical individual is primarily a stock horse or western

Fig. 279. A quarter horse in action, in a cutting-horse contest. Saddle horses are popular in many sections. They are useful on farms and ranches, as well as for pleasure. Owned by Three D's Stock Farm, Fort Worth, Tex.

saddle horse; for ranch service intelligence and performance are essential. Quarter horses have become very popular on the ranches and farms of this

[6] From *Western Livestock Journal*, Vol. 18, No. 42, July 15, 1940.

country. They are also used for racing. They are useful in cattle raising, being unexcelled in handling cattle. (See Figure 279.) A good quarter horse stands 15 hands high, weighs 1,200 pounds, and can do a quarter-mile from a standing start in 23.4 seconds or better. Speed and agility are essential traits in a top quarter horse.

The Appaloosa

This attractively colored horse, with white over the loin and hips, bearing round dark spots, is also a western saddle or stock horse. It is also used for pleasure and for parade.

ROADSTER OR LIGHT-HARNESS HORSES

Before the general use of automobiles the road horse performed an important role—that of furnishing rapid transportation. Horse-and-buggy travel has passed into oblivion except in remote areas, but road horses still serve as delivery horses and general-purpose farm horses. Also horses of this type have survived for racing because of their speed at the trot and the pace. Since the racing harness is made light to permit maximum speed on the road, these are called light-harness horses. Horses of this type have many uses other than racing, for they are very versatile. The harness used for delivery is heavier than the racing harness.

The light-harness horse is distinctly an American creation, and the prevailing breed is the Standardbred or American Trotter. As implied by the name, these horses meet a certain standard which is speed, performance.[7] Within the breed the Hambletonian family is the most eminent, and this name is applied by some to the entire breed. Within the breed are some families that are mainly trotters and others that are mainly pacers. It is not uncommon for individuals to do both gaits well.

THE STANDARDBRED OR AMERICAN TROTTER

The Standard is less uniform than some light-horse breeds, because size has to be secondary to speed. In weight, light-harness horses range from 800 to 1,250 pounds, and in height from 14:2 to 16:2. The best specimens in racing condition weigh about 1,100 pounds and stand about 15:2 hands.

The colors of bay, chestnut, brown, and black are common. There are a few grays and very few roans and duns.

Since speed is the major purpose for which this breed is raised, this is placed first in the requisites. Speed is imperative to win in races and also in roadster classes at horse shows. However, there are other important

[7] On January 1, 1933, registration on performance alone was no longer granted and registration of both the sire and dam was required.

considerations in light-harness-horse selection. They are endurance, durability, temperament, and attractive conformation. The latter is subordinate to the other qualities. It is obvious that an obstinate temperament may influence value. Also, to make a satisfactory performance in successive heats of a race, or in races during a season, endurance and durability are essential.

General appearance.   Standardbred is rather rangy, leggy, deep-chested, narrow, and angular. The physical form has been secondary to speed in selection. Maximum speed with a minimum draft is the requisite for the Standardbred.

The feet and legs in most instances are well set and clean. One rather common fault is the set of the legs, particularly in the hocks. Sickled hocks and cow hocks are not uncommon. The action should be straight, true, elastic, regular, uniform, and with a long stride. High action is undesirable since it reduces speed and may cause undue exertion.

Gaits.   Of the two speed gaits the pace is the faster. In performance the former standard for recording called for a record of 1 mile paced at

Fig. 280.   A trotting horse in action, Good Time, twice elected "Harness Racing Horse of the Year" by the turf writers.

2.25 or better and a trot at 2.30 or better. In present-day recording an individual is accepted for register only if it is the progeny of a registered sire and dam.

Although the pace is usually faster than the trot, the trot is preferred, because of its smoothness and because it is superior in mud. The lateral coordination of the pace and consequent rolling of the body is accompanied by jerking of the vehicle.

Records made by Standardbreds. Billy Direct, a stallion, holds the world's record for any driving horse on a mile racing track. On September 28, 1938, as a four-year-old, he paced a mile in 1 minute 55 seconds (1.55) at Lexington, Ky. Adios Harry, paced a mile in the same time at Vernon, New York, July 16, 1955. Dan Patch, a stallion, as a nine-year-old paced a mile in 1.55¼ at Hamline, Minn. This latter record was made under somewhat unusual circumstances, since one horse going at a gallop or run but hitched to a sulky served as a windbreak.

Fig. 281. A trotter and a pacer in action. Greyhound, on the right, is a trotter. The right front and the left hind feet move forward at the same time, and vice versa. Cardinal Prince, on the left, is a pacer, with lateral coordination. Fore and hind legs of each side move forward together. (Acme Photo.)

Greyhound, a gelding, holds the mile record for trotting, made at Lexington, Ky., on September 29, 1938. The time was 1.55¼. At the time of the record, Greyhound was 6 years old. He was hitched to a regulation sulky.

The fastest records made by mares are: at the pace, Her Ladyship, with a record of 1.57½ made at Indianapolis, Ind., and at the trot, Rosaline, with a time of 1.56¾ made at Lexington, Ky. Both records were made in 1938.

MORGAN

The descendants of Justin Morgan [8] are known as "Morgans." This breed has played an important part in the formation of the Standardbred and the American saddle horse. It is considered by some as a family of the Standardbred, by others as American saddle horses. An association of breeders, "The Morgan Horse Club," organized in 1909, maintains a registry. As a breed Morgans are noted more for utility than for speed. In the area of their origin, New England, this breed has been widely used as a general-purpose horse. From it have come individuals that have made creditable performance as saddlers, hunters, polo ponies, army horses, ranch horses, and carriage horses. This breed has made an excellent showing in quarter-mile cow-pony races and in endurance rides.

In size, the average Morgan weighs about 1,000 pounds and stands 16 hands high. The common colors are chestnut, brown, bay, and black, and white markings are not common.

THE CARRIAGE OR HEAVY-HARNESS HORSE

This type of horse has been nearly replaced in the utility field and now is confined mostly to the show ring. Horses of this type are mainly an English development, where they were used as carriage or coach horses. They are called heavy-harness horses to distinguish them from roadsters or light-harness horses. Although the harness used is heavy it is in no sense a draft harness.

At one time there were several breeds of this type, but at present the heavy-harness breeds other than the Hackney have gone out of existence.

The Hackney rarely stands higher than 15:3. In fact, some are in the pony class, that is, under 14:2. In weight they range from 800 to 1,300 pounds. Chestnut, bay, brown, and black are common colors, and white markings are quite common.

Compared with the other types of light horses, the heavy-harness horse is rather heavily made, heavy fronted, and short legged. Fullness and smoothness of form are desired rather than angularity of conformation. Quality and refinement are essential for beauty of conformation. The natural

---

[8] Justin Morgan was foaled in 1789 and lived for 32 years in Vermont. He was 14.2 hands high and weighed 950 pounds. He was noted for his speed, endurance, intelligence, and draft ability.

Fig. 282. A harness-horse winner, Mountain Raven, winner of the fine harness horse stake, International Livestock Exposition. Owned by Red Top Farm, Liberty-ville, Ill.

Fig. 283. A champion Hackney pony, Superlative, imported from England. Owned by Nan-Su Farm, Northbrook, Ill. (James Gilchrist, Manager.)

action at the trot is characterized by extreme height. Shoeing and training are directed toward development of a high, trappy action.

Since the Hackney is primarily a show horse, qualities which enhance the attractiveness are given preference over those which denote service. In other words, endurance and durability are required in the heavy-harness horse, but they are subordinate to style, beauty, flashy action, and striking performance.

PONIES

There are three breeds of ponies in the United States: the Shetland, the Welch, and the Hackney. The upper limit in the pony class is a height of 14:2 hands. Hackney and Welch are the larger of the ponies, and from these come most of the show ponies in the driving and riding classes. Hackney ponies with beauty of conformation and high flashy action are shown in the heavy-harness classes.

The Shetland is limited to a maximum of 42 inches or 10:2 hands in height. Small in size and docile in disposition, this pony is popular as a children's pony.

Chapter 38

HORSE FEEDING
AND MANAGEMENT

Most of the experimental feeding work has been done with horses rather than mules. The general principles of feeding are practically the same for both. Under the chapter on mules the differences in feeding and management are discussed.

Economical feeding of the horse is the first step in the reduction of cost. Feed cost is the largest single item in the cost of keeping horses. Under usual conditions it amounts to 70 to 75 per cent of the total. In order to keep down feed costs we must feed adequately but not excessively on feeds which furnish the needed nutrients at a relatively low cost. It is also important in keeping costs low to keep down the other overhead costs and to use work animals to their maximum capacity. The matter of economical rations for horses and mules is often neglected. It is rather common opinion that less attention is given to feeding horses than to feeding other livestock. Horses are in service for a long period. Therefore, rations that will adequately nourish for a long time are needed. As horses are comparatively long-lived, temporary deficiencies in feed intake are slowly reflected in the animals. Such inadequacies cause long-term harm and are to be avoided.

NUTRITIONAL REQUIREMENTS OF HORSES

The horse has a relatively small, simple stomach, but it can use roughages quite well, for it has an intestine of large capacity. Roughage feeds are used for the major part of the ration because they supply nutrients at a lower cost than do the concentrates. Excessive feeding of roughage, on the other hand, may lower the efficiency of a horse. Ruminants may be fed all the roughage they want without ill effects, but this is not true of the horse, which has a smaller stomach capacity and a different type of digestive tract. The roughage intake in horses can be too high, considering both the health of the horse and economy of feeding.

Horses are different from cattle in their maintenance requirements. Because of their more nervous dispositions horses require more feed for maintenance for an equal amount of weight. Actually, we have little experimental evidence upon which to base rational feeding of horses, as compared with other livestock. Horse feeding tests have been few, and the estimates of digestible nutrients available are made for ruminants, not horses.

A 1,200-pound horse that is doing no work requires the following nutrient materials daily, according to the Morrison Feeding Standard.[1]

1,200-POUND IDLE HORSE

Dry matter, pounds	11.7–14.3
Digestible protein, pounds	0.7–0.8
Total digestible nutrients, pounds	8.1–9.9
Phosphorus, pounds	0.035
Calcium, pounds	0.039
Carotene, milligrams	60
Net energy, therms	6.5–7.9

The horse at work requires more nutrients than does the idle horse and, as the work is increased, the suggested feeding standards are greater accordingly. This increase for increased activity is mainly an increase in the amount of the nutrients, principally energy, rather than a change in the ratio of digestible protein to total digestible nutrients. Growing colts and brood mares nursing foals have a higher requirement of nutrients than do idle horses. The actual need of a horse or mule is related to size, age, fatness, activity or work, and individuality.

The needs for a horse at light work are met when ⅓ to ¾ pound of grain and 1¼ to 1½ pounds of roughage are fed daily for each 100 pounds of live weight. When idle, horses should be fed mainly roughage or on pasture. When work is increased, concentrates are increased and roughage is decreased. The average horse needs from 2 to 2½ pounds of total feed for each 100 pounds of live weight daily. In practice, the maintenance of weight, the thrift, and the spirit of a horse indicate state of nutrition. Horses fed unbalanced rations or insufficient amounts for the work they are doing lose weight and become unthrifty and spiritless.

[1] F. B. Morrison, *Feeds and Feeding,* 22nd edition, The Morrison Publishing Co., Ithaca, N.Y., 1956.

FEEDS USED FOR HORSES AND MULES

Farm-grown grains form the basis for the concentrates used for horses and mules. Of these grains, oats, corn, and barley are the more commonly used. Of the hays, alfalfa, clover, timothy, soybean, prairie, Johnson grass, and grain hay are generally used. There is more regional difference in roughage fed than in grains or concentrates.

The coarser roughages such as straw, corn fodder, and sorghum fodder supply considerable feed in some areas. Such feeds are carbonaceous and consequently low in protein, and they are quite high in crude fiber. Feeds that contain large amounts of crude fiber are quite low in net energy value, that is, in energy which can be used to perform physical labor. Some supplements such as bran and linseed meal and, in the south, cottonseed meal, are used to balance the locally available feeds. When the ration is mainly of low-protein feed a high-protein feed supplement is advisable.

Home-grown or locally produced feeds are the most economical to use in rations. No single feed combination is the best, and several have been found to give satisfactory results. What to use in the ration, then, depends upon what is available and economical.

Bone unsoundness is more prevalent in horses than in other farm animals. It is believed that faulty nutrition is in many cases responsible for such unsoundness. Horses seem very sensitive to variations in the ratio of calcium to phosphorus; so there should be a good supply of Vitamin D, which increases the absorption and retention of calcium and phosphorus and compensates for an unfavorable ratio between the two. The period of least solar irradiation and perhaps Vitamin-D-depleted feeds (late winter) is followed by the period of greatest activity.

PROBLEMS IN FEEDING

It is convenient to divide the problems met in feeding horses into the following: (1) feeding for work; (2) feeding idle stock; (3) feeding the brood mare; (4) colt feeding; (5) feeding light horses. Each will be discussed separately in the paragraphs which follow.

FEEDING FOR WORK

It has been previously pointed out that the needs of a horse are proportional to the work done. It is apparent that the greatest increase as physical work is increased should be in energy-yielding nutrients. Since very few feeds contain only energy-yielding nutrients, the ration is stepped up in total amount of feed, and feed grains are substituted for roughage as activity increases.

That an increase in nutritive material is needed with activity and draft has been demonstrated experimentally. It was found that horses moving at a rate of 2.2 miles per hour used 77 to 144 per cent more energy than when they were not moving. Also, it was found that 1.87 therms of energy were expended for each horsepower of draft performed.

Draft horses are more efficient in the performance of work when they travel at a speed of from 2 to 2.5 miles per hour. When they move at a faster rate than a walk, energy expenditure is stepped up because of greater muscular activity. The walk is done with a minimum of movement and near normal heartbeat, respiration, and body temperature.

Level of feeding is often not varied with the amount of work being done. This is not only uneconomical but distinctly harmful. Regularity is an essential in feeding, but the amounts of feeds, especially concentrates, should be reduced by at least one half when the horses are idle. Use of pasture, especially in connection with irregularity of work, is advantageous, since it supplies many of the essentials often scarce in usual feeds. Pasturing provides exercise and healthful surroundings, and reduces the labor for care.

FEEDING IDLE WORK STOCK AND PREPARING
FOR SPRING WORK

Horse labor on the farm is a maximum in the spring of the year while the crop is being put in. Feeding and management of the work stock on the farm is therefore directed toward having the horses in the peak of physical condition for spring work. Nutritive needs during the wintering period are comparatively low, but high efficiency in work performance and long-time usefulness cannot be expected if the winter ration is inadequate. The winter ration must be sufficient in amount and quality for best results, yet it should not be excessive or expensive. Cornstock fields and stubble fields with pasture can supply a large part of the nutrients needed, but these should be supplemented with leguminous roughage or other feeds.

The practice of permitting the work stock to exercise and graze on the pastures and fields has been very successful. Access to a strawstack in addition will help in keeping feed cost down.

Housing can be supplied by open sheds affording protection and dry quarters.

Two to 4 weeks before the beginning of spring work, conditioning for that work is to be started. The amount of this fitting for work depends upon how each animal has wintered. In prework feeding the ration is improved in quality, coarse roughages are decreased, quality roughages are increased, and concentrate feeding is commenced. Changes in the ration are to be made slowly, but the farm work stock should be on a medium work level of feeding when the farm work starts. Medium work requires about 1 pound of good roughage to an equal amount of concentrates for each 100 pounds of live weight.

The conditioning plan and rations designed to prepare for spring work may be used for horses to be marketed, but it should be started some time in advance of the usual time. The active period of the horse market precedes spring work. Heavy feeding is needed for fattening, and exercise is not to be neglected, for it is essential in fitting.

Fig. 284. Feeding capacity is essential for a good draft horse. This 2-year-old Belgian stallion has large capacity for feed and has made rapid growth.

FEEDING THE BROOD MARE

Some special attention is advisable in feeding brood mares for colt raising. The growth of the fetus and the suckling of the foal demand extra nutrients over and above the needs for work or an idle winter season. This may be taken care of by feeding more grain and good-quality roughage. It is a matter of providing more feed and also feeds adequate to supply sufficient protein, minerals, and vitamins to mares during pregnancy and suckling.

The method of handling during the idle season need not be different from that for other work stock, but more liberal feeding is essential for best results.

COLT FEEDING

The young colt at an early age picks at grain, grass, or roughage to supplement the dam's milk. Supplementary feeding may begin when the foal is 1 to 2 months old, and such feeding is advisable for maximum growth and development. Limited supplemental feeding, rather than heavy feeding, has been found most desirable, for a heavy ration may result in damage to the feet and legs.

Farm feeds are sufficient for colts, and oats top the list. Preparation by rolling appears to be economical.

Colt raising is a profitable adjunct to maintenance of horse labor on the farm, since it involves little cash expenditure and causes only about 2 weeks' loss of time from work for the mare at foaling time. Colts represent mainly feed, much of which is unmarketable. It has been found that colts are raised to a workable age (about 2⅔ years) on 2¼ tons of grain and 2½ tons of mixed hay in addition to some pasture and field grazing.

FEEDING LIGHT HORSES

In general, the principles of feeding draft and farm horses can be applied to the feeding of light horses. However, smaller quantities of roughage are commonly used for light horses, for a heavy middle interferes with performance. Economy of feeding is a secondary consideration in feeding light horses; consequently, the best-quality feeds are used.

FEED COST FOR A HORSE

The amount of feed needed for a farm horse depends upon its size and its work. The pasture and field feed available affects the amount of other feed needed. With working periods of 6 months a farm horse needs about 1½ tons of feed grain and 2½ tons of roughage in addition to pasture and field feed. Coarse roughage such as straw or stover can be used as one half of the roughage, but the remainder should be good-quality hay. Four tons of feed, then, is sufficient for farm work stock which work up to about 120 10-hour days.[2]

[2] For a 10-year period Iowa farmers received $1.16 per bushel for corn, 64 cents for oats, and $12.70 per ton for loose hay, which would make a feed cost of $92.82 per horse, exclusive of pasture and field feed.

FEED REQUIRED PER WORK ANIMAL PER YEAR AND THE LAND REQUIRED TO PRODUCE IT

The estimated amount of feed required per animal per year,[3] on a standard ration, would be 145.5 bushels of oats or 71.7 bushels of corn or 83.6 bushels of barley and 2.2 tons of hay. The standard ration is a ration suitable for light work and is about twice an economic maintenance ration. Consideration of average yields for a 10-year period shows that an average horse would require 1.7 acres of hay and 4.2 acres of oats or 2.5 acres of corn or 3.7 acres of barley.

MANAGEMENT OF HORSES

The management as well as the feeding is important for efficiency. Management includes all the essentials in effective utilization of horses and mules for the purpose or purposes desired. A manager must provide ample feed supply, equipment, and man labor and he must keep records as well as attend to many other details. Care and management are somewhat specialized for such phases of horse husbandry as the brood mare, raising the colts, working horses and mules, and light horses of different kinds. For example, when under hard work, shoeing may be needed. A shod horse has better footing and is a more efficient worker under certain conditions. Even under conditions other than hard work, foot trimming is needed. Trimming of the feet of colts, young horses, and idle horses is needed for serviceability. Proper training is another essential for efficient horse and mule use. A well-trained, dependable horse is the object of breaking and training. Proper harness fitting and hitching are also needed for satisfactory service.

[3] *The Farm Horse,* U.S. Dept. of Commerce, Bureau of the Census, 1933.

Chapter 39

HORSE BREEDING

Horse breeding is quite different from breeding of other farm animals, since a longer time is required both for gestation and for rearing to sexual maturity. Since reproduction is slow and the age of first breeding late as compared with other livestock, errors in breeding or breeding stock management may be very costly. Smaller herds are general, and horse raising is usually a side line to other farming enterprises. Most farms raise but a few colts, and stallions are quite generally made available to others than their owners for service.[1] Specialized horse breeding farms are known as breeding studs.

THE REPRODUCTIVE PROCESS

Mares of draft breeding may mature at a younger age than light-horse mares and can be bred when they are 2 years old. There is wide variation in the age at which fillies come in heat. Nutrition as well as individuality is related to age of first heat. If mares are heavily worked it is advisable to withhold breeding until they are 3 or 4 years old.

The average heat period is about 7 days in length. The estrus cycle is quite variable in length; however, the period of heat usually starts 16 days after the end of the last heat, completing the cycle in 21 to 23 days. Mares come in heat from 9 to 11 days after foaling. Since the heat period is long and the life of the spermatozoa is comparatively short in the female reproductive tract, time of mating is a factor in fertility. Mating 2 to 5 days before the end of the heat period is apparently accompanied with a rather

---

[1] Horse breeding is practiced most widely in the mountain and west north central areas, where colts are reported on about one-fifth of the farms which have horses and mules.

high proportion of fertilization. Mares commonly ovulate 1 to 2 days before the end of heat.

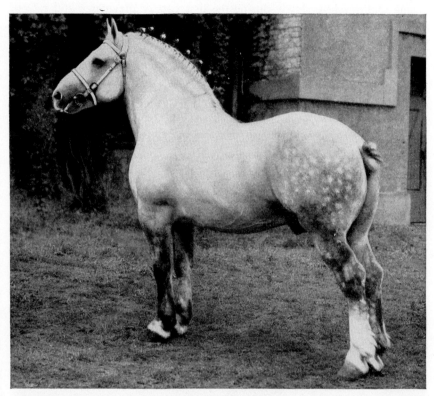

Fig. 285. Percheron stallion, Marceau, grand champion at the National Percheron Show and International Livestock Exposition. Owned by R. L. Smith, Stanley, Kan.

The natural breeding season of the horse is in the spring and summer, as the hours of daylight increase. The breeding season appears often to be shorter nearer the poles and, in the tropics, mares show a tendency to have two seasons of breeding, coinciding with the two periods of increased daylight.

The gestation period is about 335.9 days, with a standard deviation of about 10 days. Because of the relatively long gestation period, it is difficult to produce a colt from each brood mare every year. Some time between the fourth and the thirteenth days after foaling a mare will come in heat and can be bred. Multiple births in horses are not common; about 1.5 per cent of twins are produced. Studies on the relation of exercise to conception have indicated that for high percentage of pregnancies the mare should rest quietly for a while after breeding. Slow travel in returning the mares home after breeding was associated with a relatively high percentage of pregnancies.

The foal develops slowly during the first part of pregnancy and rate of growth is increased as pregnancy advances. The size of the foal is probably controlled by internal secretions of the dam. For example, a Shetland pony mare artificially inseminated with sperm from a draft-breed stallion will have a foal to which she can give birth. A reciprocal cross may be three times larger at birth and one and one half times heavier at 4 years of age.

Fig. 286. A grand champion Percheron mare, Nerva, an imported mare. Owned by Fairholme Farms, Lewisville, Ind.

Well-grown stallions can be used to serve mares when they are 2 years old. The capacity of a vigorous two-year-old is 10 to 15 mares a season. Three-year-old stallions are usually limited to 35 to 50 mares, and four-year-olds to 50 to 75. A mature stallion will serve from 75 to 100 mares in a season if handled properly. Mares are commonly bred when they are 3 years old.

Much irregularity in the breeding of horses can be attributed to improper feeding and management. Good rations and proper care are needed to maintain the vigorous healthy condition essential for a sure-breeding stallion and mare.

ARTIFICIAL INSEMINATION WITH HORSES

Artificial insemination has been quite successful with horses. It is possible to inseminate from 8 to 12 mares from a single service, and the sperm can be kept fertile for a fair length of time. Because of the number of mares that can be inseminated from a single service and the storing properties of the semen, artificial insemination should be more useful in horses than in swine, but less useful than with cattle and sheep. Its use in horses, especially when an artificial vagina is employed, permits the insemination of several mares from a single service, conserving the energy of the stallion or jack. A valuable sire can sire more colts with this practice, and some mares, infertile to ordinary breeding conceive when artificially inseminated. Also, nervous or irritable mares may be inseminated without danger to the sire.

BREEDING SYSTEMS

Very little information is available on breeding systems, such as grading up, crossbreeding, and inbreeding for horses as compared with other farm animals. Most investigations with horses have been confined to measurement of growth in young and to the physiology of reproduction. Strictly genetic studies are comparatively rare. Research has been useful in providing tests for diagnosis of pregnancy and for vitality of semen, etc.

Grading up, that is, use of purebred stallions on mares of common or nondescript breeding to produce *grades,* has been widely practiced.

Crossbreeding has been used in producing horses for specific purposes, such as polo ponies and hunters.

Inbreeding or its milder form, line breeding, has served some horse breeders in building higher-than-random relationships with certain highly approved individuals.

Hybridization has also been practiced; horses have been crossed with the ass and with the zebra. So important is the hybrid, the mule, that it is discussed separately in Chapter 40.

BREEDING STOCK SELECTION

The ideal form of various types of horses has been described. In the individual for the breeding herd we want the same ideal conformation plus sex characteristics, primary and secondary. As with other livestock, selection may be based upon physical characteristics of an individual, pedigree, or performance. The pedigree may be expanded to include the performance of the individual's ancestors. In practice, the choice of a stallion hinges upon a composite of form, performance, and pedigree. Progeny testing, when available, is a great aid in selection.

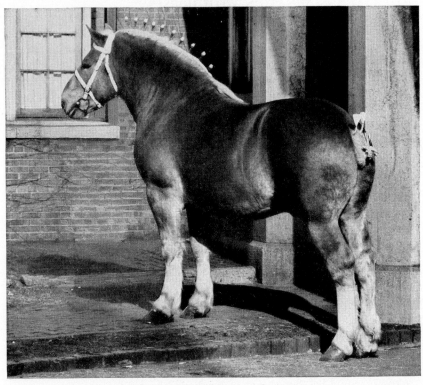

Fig. 287. Belgian stallion, Kenfluer Jay Faceru, a recent International Livestock Exposition grand champion. Owned by H. C. Horneman, Danville, Ill.

In horse breeding we have lacked measures of performance, although we have had pulling contests for draft horses, endurance trials for saddle horses, and track records for race horses.

In purchasing a stallion much care must be exercised, since a good stallion represents a relatively large investment. Soundness should be passed upon by a competent veterinarian. Unsound horses are not permitted to stand for public service in some states; that is, certain unsoundnesses bar them from public service.

A sire should be free from unsoundness of the feet, legs, wind, and eyes. Large size has been demanded in draft stallions since many of the mares to which they are mated are undersized. Extreme size is not wanted; a draft stallion weighing 2,000 pounds is sufficiently large. Since the demand for city draft horses and horses for logging is now comparatively small and most draft horses are farm horses, great size is no longer essential. J. H. Edmonds states that medium-sized horses are better workers and breeders, do more work, live longer, and require much less care and attention than the big, overgrown kind.[2]

Stallions should closely comply with and be close to the ideal type. Ideal form, feet and legs, action, quality, and other features are similar to those of the draft gelding. Sexual characteristics should show proper development and potency, if not guaranteed, should be tested. A masculine, well-developed, sound draft stallion, properly reared and handled, should be the goal of the stallion buyer.

Breeding mares to be acceptable should meet the requirements of their type as previously described. Type, form, size, good feet and legs, and soundness are wanted in brood mares. Quality, femininity, and reproductive capacity are important.

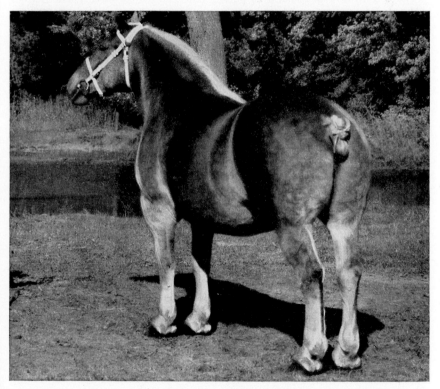

Fig. 288. Belgian mare, Matilda, a recent International Livestock Exposition and National Belgian Show grand champion. Owned by Porath Sons, Northville, Mich.

[2] *Proceedings,* American Society of Animal Production, 1940, p. 87.

PEDIGREE

The record ancestry is also useful in selecting a breeding stud, especially if it informs about the merit of the individuals in the pedigree. Names and numbers in a pedigree are of value only as they convey merit or demerit of individuals. A pedigree indicates that the individual is purebred, but that in itself may not be helpful, for the range in merit of purebreds is considerable. A purebred, however, is generally superior to a grade because its nondescript breeding is remote. Grade stallions are licensed to stand for public service in some states; in 1934, of the 13,753 stallions licensed, 9,666 were classified as purebreds.

PERFORMANCE TESTS WITH HORSES

There follows a discussion of performance tests that have been used in evaluating horses. Endurance trials have been used for saddle horses and speed tests or track records for race horses. Neither endurance nor speed can be predicted accurately from appearance. Even such measurements as chest length, width, depth, and girth do not indicate speed or endurance.

Endurance trials

Endurance trials or rides were performance tests for cavalry horses in which 300 miles are covered under saddle in 5 days. In evaluation 60 per cent of the score was allotted to condition of the horse at the finish and 40 per cent for speed. Vulnerability of the legs showed up in these trials; 57 per cent of the entrants experienced leg trouble.

Standardbred records

Speed records are used to a large extent by breeders of race horses. The history of the Standardbred in record making is most interesting. Their standard of performance was established in 1879. This placed great emphasis upon performance and upon performance of progeny. Although grades and crosses were admitted to registration if they complied with performance requirements up until 1933, most of those registered carried a preponderance of Standardbred breeding in their immediate ancestry. Speed has been increased; which is due only in part to breeding. Faster tracks, better management, better vehicles and harness have also been factors. These improvements, with breeding, have been responsible for the making of records in recent years. These records and their use constitute an extensive subject quite beyond the province of this text.

Fig. 289. A Clydesdale stallion, Strathmore Guard, a recent International Live-stock Exposition grand champion. Owned by Nelson Wagg, Claremont, Ontario, Canada.

Testing draft horses

It is common for draft horses to develop a tractive pull of one tenth to one eighth of their weight and travel at 2.5 miles per hour for 20 miles a day. Thus a 1,500-pound horse would develop 1 horsepower of tractive pull, since the tractive pull at one tenth of the weight would be 150 pounds and the speed would be 220 feet per minute. Speed (220) times tractive pull (150) equals 33,000 foot-pounds per minute, or 1 horsepower.

A tractive dynamometer is used to test the draft ability of horses. By testing we have gained information about features of form, training, harnessing, and shoeing, in relation to pulling ability.

In pulling contests a Collins dynamometer is used to measure tractive pull. Briefly, the mechanism of the dynamometer permits movement of the vehicle only when the tractive pull equals the weight set on the machine. A distance of 27½ feet is used in pulling contests to facilitate the calculations.

A draft team is given ample time to complete the pull, for the contest aim is maximum pull. This would not necessarily mean maximum horsepower unless the pull was completed in minimum time. For example, one team taking 8 minutes to complete the 27½-foot pull, say at 3,000 pounds tractive pull, would develop less horsepower than a team completing the pull in 7 minutes.

Fig. 290. A Clydesdale mare, Porrs Lona, an International grand champion. Owned by Nils C. Schantz, Plattsville, Ontario, Canada.

Pulling contests for draft pairs were begun in 1923, and the growth of such competition has been quite remarkable. It is common to divide teams on the basis of weight in such contests. (See Figure 252.)

The results of pulling contests were formerly summarized each year by the Horse and Mule Association of America. Wayne Dinsmore, secretary of that organization, stated [3] that the results thus far have shown that:

1. Very few pairs can exert a tractive pull in excess of their own weight: out of many thousands of pairs tested, only about 30 have accomplished this. Weight is therefore a limiting factor, almost absolute.

[3] *Leaflet 241,* Horse and Mule Association of America.

2. Crooked hind legs, commonly termed sickle hocks, are seldom found in good pulling horses. Well-set hind legs are usual in good pulling animals.

3. Great heart girth usually is found in great pulling horses. It probably is true that where horses are equal in weight but one is greater in heart girth

Fig. 291. Shire stallion, Blooms Conqueror, International grand champion. Owned by Schaffenacher Bros., Mt. Pulaski, Ill.

than the other, the animal with the greater heart girth carries more weight in the fore quarters and has greater room for heart and lungs; but the precise reasons why greater heart girth usually goes with greater pulling power are still unsettled.

4. Careful training is essential. A good horseman trains his animals by gradual increase in load and avoids getting them stuck. He develops them as carefully and patiently as a skilled trainer of race horses. Physical fitness does not come suddenly. It is the result of good care, feed, and regular work, with wise training.

5. Courage that will not admit defeat is possessed in greater degree by some horses than others. This cannot be determined except by test; but all

men who have trained horses by pulling contests know that there is a vast difference in the courage possessed by young horses that have not been spoiled in training. Some will try, again and again, on loads they can hardly move; others quit after one or two attempts, throw their heads over the other

Fig. 292. Shire mare, Josephine, an Iowa State Fair grand champion. Owned by Geo. J. Stoll & Sons, Chestnut, Ill.

horse in the pair, and try to go in any direction that will avoid the pull. Such animals must be handled carefully and brought along very gradually; even then, they are likely to quit in a contest when the load becomes very heavy. Courageous horses and mules never quit; they will try again and again when asked to do so.

It is probably the courage that is inherited: hence sires whose progeny show excellent courage should be sought out and used by men who want especially good pulling teams.

The relationship between success in pulling contests and ability to do work has not been demonstrated. If a definite relationship exists between a short pull and farm work, as appears probable, pulling tests may be used to evaluate breeding stock. Draft tests of mares and perhaps stallions and their offspring may be helpful in selecting breeding stock for work stock production. A measure of performance comparable to the speed tests used for Standardbreds should be useful in constructive draft horse breeding.

Chapter 40

MULES

Crosses between the two species of the family *Equidae*—the *caballus* or horse and the *asinus* or ass—produce a hybrid. The term "mule" is reserved for the cross of the male ass or jack on a mare. The reciprocal cross, that is, the stallion upon the female ass or *jennet,* is known as a "hinny." Since jennets can be used to produce jacks and jennets, which are generally worth more than mules, few hinnies are produced. Many species, crosses, or hybrids are infertile or partially infertile. The mare mule is seldom fertile, and there are few authentic cases of actual reproduction by female mules. There have been no reported cases of fertility in male mules. Castrating of the horse mule colts is practiced when they are 12 to 18 months of age. Therefore, the males have practically no opportunity to demonstrate fertility.

Sterility of mules is explained by the difference in the genes of the horse and the ass. The hybrid receives a set of genes from each parent, and these work together properly in the mule; but, supposedly, they will not pair so that the reduction division in maturation prior to fertilization can take place.

DISTRIBUTION OF MULES IN THE UNITED STATES

Mules are used extensively in the performance of farm work; they predominate in the cotton belt and adjoining states. Cotton growing is credited with giving impetus and stability to mule raising. The states having large numbers of mules are listed below.

During the period used there was a reduction in numbers. It should also be pointed out that the list is based on total population of the states and does not indicate numbers raised. The chief mule-producing states are Texas, Kansas, Oklahoma, Missouri, Indiana, Iowa, Illinois, and Nebraska. The movement of mules in marketing is toward the south, and many of those southern states' mule populations were produced in the corn belt. Jack stock, on the other hand, is produced more heavily in Missouri, Kansas, Texas, Oklahoma, Kentucky, and Tennessee. It seems, therefore, that the breeding of jacks is north of the areas of greatest mule use and that mule raising has extended farther north than jacks raising. Raisers of horses turned to the raising of mules when more profit could be made from mules. Mares that raised a mule colt rather than a horse colt returned more profit to farmers, for the cost of raising was no greater, except for the service fee, usually higher with jacks.

NUMBER OF MULES ON FARMS IN LEADING STATES

January 1, 1944–53 [1]

STATE	YEARLY AVERAGE, THOUSAND HEAD
Mississippi	292
North Carolina	265
Tennessee	241
Georgia	238
Alabama	233
Texas	200
Kentucky	172
Arkansas	166
South Carolina	152
Louisiana	130
Missouri	98
Virginia	71
Oklahoma	50
Florida	29
Illinois	28
United States	2,542

MULES ON FARMS

In Figure 258 the horses and mules on farms from 1867 to 1949 are shown graphically. The peak year in horse numbers was in 1915; the peak in mule numbers was 10 years later, in 1925. Mule numbers have not declined so rapidly as horse numbers. Apparently, mules have not suffered so much from competition of trucks and tractors as horses. In the cotton belt the replacement of work stock by motor power has been less complete than in many of the other agricultural areas.

JACKS

The domestic ass or jack stock descended from the African and Asiatic races of the wild ass or the wild form of the *Equidae asinus*. Domestication

[1] *Agricultural Statistics,* U.S.D.A., 1955.

of the ass is reported prior to domestication of the horse. References are made in the Bible to both asses and mules; in fact, the presence of mules six centuries before the Christian era is recorded in history.

Columbus is credited with bringing asses to this continent on his second voyage in 1493. A number of the breeds of jacks have been brought to this country. Breeds imported include the Catalonian, Maltese, Poitou, Majorca, Andalusian, and Italian. Most of the stocks came from countries adjoining the Mediterranean Sea. Ashton [2] gives greatest credit to the Catalonian breed in formation of the Mammouth or American Jack. He states that this breed generally represents the type now most in demand by American breeders.

A breed of jacks, evolved in Kentucky, Tennessee, and Missouri from these imported stocks, was valuable because it produced good mules. The imported stocks were generally not so suitable for mule production; as they were too small and not drafty enough. In France the Poitou breed is used in producing mules that are quite large and comparable to our American mules.

Some breeds of asses are quite small and unsuited for raising mules. The stock which came to us from Spain through Mexico is an example. These small "burros" are, with similar breeds of asses, serviceable in warm, mountainous countries for pack, saddle, and draft purposes.

DESCRIPTION OF A MULE JACK [3]

A good mule jack should be not less than 15 hands high and should possess plenty of weight and large bone, with quality, style, and action. The most essential points of conformation in a good jack are: a straight, strong back, closely coupled and well muscled over the loin; a long, level rump; and a deep body with well-sprung ribs to allow for lung development. Vigor and strength of constitution are indicated by a broad chest and large heart girth.

The legs should be set straight, be well muscled, and have plenty of bone. The length of legs should be in proportion to the depth of the body; height obtained principally by length of leg is undesirable. The size of the bone is very important. It is usually determined by measuring the circumference of the cannon bone about half way between the knee and the fetlock joint. This should be about 8½ inches in a jack of 15 hands' height. It is also desirable to have large, well-shaped feet and good, sound hocks. The head should be well proportioned, with the profile of the nose straight or slightly Roman. The ears should be long, well set, and alert, and should

---

[2] John Ashton, "History of Jack Stock and Mules in Missouri," *Monthly Bull.,* Missouri State Board of Agr., Vol. 22, No. 8, August, 1924.

[3] J. O. Williams, "Mule Production," *Farmers' Bull. 1341,* U.S.D.A., August, 1923.

measure, horizontally, on a mature animal, 33 inches or more from tip to tip.

Fig. 293. An outstanding Jack, Bourbon McCord, a grand champion at the Kansas State Fair. Owned by Golden Rule Stock Farm, Fort Scott, Kan.

MEASUREMENTS OF A GOOD JACK

Weight, 1,300 pounds; height (standard measure), 15 hands, 3 inches

	INCHES		INCHES
Ears from tip to tip	34	Around body at girth	70
Around face and jaw	39	Around body at loin	67
Around neck at throatlatch	36	Around hoof, below coronet	
Around arm	21	(next to hair)	16½
Around cannon	8½	Above hock	17½
Length from poll to tail	84	Below hock	9½

Some common defects in jacks are: flat, narrow chest, which indicates a weak constitution and lack of vigor; light-muscled loin and long coupling; short, drooping rump; excessive length of leg; light bone; poor hocks, with a tendency toward curbiness; small feet with contracted heels; and short or droopy ears.

Most breeders of American jacks prefer a block color with white points, that is, white around the muzzle, eyes, and along the under line. Gray jacks sire gray mules which turn white when aging; that is objectionable.

An association of breeders of jacks and jennets was organized in 1888. For a time certain minimum measurements were required for registration, but now only progeny of recorded parents are eligible for registration.

Jacks used for jack stock perpetuation are known as "jennet jacks"; those used on mares are called "mule jacks."

BROOD MARES FOR MULE RAISING [4]

Only sound brood mares of good quality should be selected for producing high-grade mules. Breeders of work horses usually take particular care in choosing good mares for breeding purposes, but ordinarily mule breeders make no consistent effort in selecting mares for production of mules. The idea seems to prevail that a mare not suitable for breeding to a stallion is good enough to produce a mule. This is a mistake; no matter how good the jack may be, it is unreasonable to expect uniformly good mule foals from inferior mares. The same care should be applied in selecting mule mares as in selecting breed mares to raise horse colts.

Mares used in mule production are of no fixed type or breed, and vary from large, heavy draft mares to smaller mares of the light-horse type. As the mule is a work animal which cannot directly reproduce its kind, it is not essential that mares used for producing them be of any fixed breeding. It is necessary, however, that the mares be of the correct size and type. Mules foaled from mares of the draft type are large, heavy and excellent for draft purposes, but they are relatively sluggish in temperament and they cannot stand the heat as well as mules produced from mares of light-horse breeding. Mules from mares of light-horse type, on the other hand, are usually too small because their dams were not large enough. Experienced breeders state that a very desirable mule mare has about one fourth draft blood and three fourths light-horse blood. A mare of this breeding weighs between 1,100 and 1,500 pounds and produces good-sized mules, with style, action, and stamina.

In conformation, the mule mare should possess all the qualities desired in the brood mare used for producing work horses. Some of the most important points in the good mule mare are: a broad chest and large heart girth, indicating a vigorous constitution; a roomy barrel to allow for full development of the fetus; a straight back, strongly muscled over the loins; well-set legs with broad, flat, sound bone of good quality; large, well-shaped feet; and feminine character, indicating "breediness." To sum up, the mare should combine size with quality, type, soundness, and breediness. The

[4] *Farmers' Bull. 1341,* U.S.D.A., August, 1923.

last term covers a variety of characteristics which make the mare a good mother.

It has been observed by Mississippi farmers that mares should outweigh the mules they are to produce by 100 to 150 pounds.[5]

AMERICAN MULES

Mules raised in the United States from American jacks excel mules raised anywhere in the world. George Washington in 1785 and 1786 imported both Spanish and Maltese jacks and jennets. Washington extolled the qualities of mules for farm work, and his success with them created much interest in importing jack stock and raising mules.

The mule has proved very useful for draft, especially on farms and plantations in the south. It is much larger and stronger than its sire the jack and also more tractable. It is more surefooted, more patient, and more durable than its mother the mare.

Mule colts are most numerous in the west south central region, next in the east south central and the east north central, in proportion to total horse and mule numbers in those sections.

SELECTION OF MULES [6]

The general form and appearance of a mule should closely resemble that of a horse, and in judging mules the same general points are to be looked for. The nearer a mule approaches the ideal desired in a draft horse the more valuable it is from a market standpoint. There are certain characteristics derived from the paternal side, mainly the bray, disposition, ears, tail, and feet. Aside from these, the mule does not differ materially from the dam.

Mules vary in height from the little 12-hand pit mule to the large draft mules standing 17½ hands. The range in height of various classes of mules is given under market classes of mules.

Weight ranges from 600 to 1,600 pounds. Weight of the larger type of mules ranges between 1,150 and 1,400 pounds. In this range are classified the majority of marketable mules.

The form of the mule should be compact, with deep body, broad chest, full flanks, short back, and well-sprung ribs. Light, waspy flanks, long, narrow bodies, and long backs are not desirable.

Quality is rather difficult to define, but is recognized by every capable judge. It is indicated in the mule by a fine, trim ear, clean-cut head and

[5] Paul F. Newell and C. J. Goodell, "Work Stock Feeding Management and Production," *Extension Bull. 95,* Mississippi, June, 1938.

[6] *Farmers' Bull. 1341,* U.S.D.A., August, 1923.

joints, flinty, flat bone, well-defined tendons, and soft hair. Quality often marks the difference between a "market topper" and an ordinary mule. A short, thick ear, a coarse head, round, spongy bone, and a hard coat of hair are indications of poor quality against which the judge should discriminate.

The natural tendency of the mule is to be lazy and obstinate. An active, energetic mule is much desired.

It is in the hindquarters of the mule that the greatest faults of conformation are usually found. The croup is often very short and steep, the hips too sloping, the thighs too narrow, the bone too light, and the hind legs sickle shaped. These are faults of conformation that judges should discriminate against sharply. It is in the hindquarters and loins that the draft animal obtains propelling power. These portions of the animal, therefore, should be correctly built and properly developed. The loins should be broad, short, and thickly muscled; the croup long and level; the hips long, level, and muscular; the thighs thick, long, and well muscled; and the hind legs well

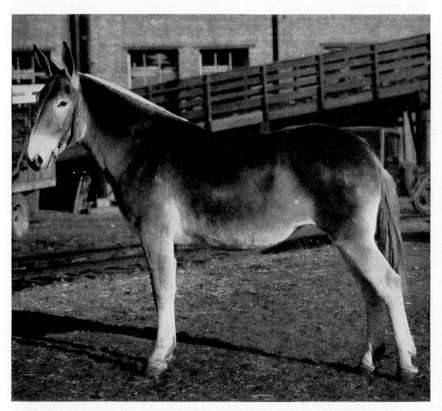

Fig. 294. A draft mule of the correct type. Tillie, grand champion mule of the American Royal. Owned by Hineman Jack Farms, Dighton, Kan.

set, with broad, clean-cut hocks and flat, dense bone. The mule should stand on sound, well-shaped feet.

Although the mule is essentially a draft animal, it is often used for general utility, especially in the south. Style and action may not be as important in a mule as in the light breeds of horses, but they can add materially to its value. A small, alert mule, with a long, free stride at the walk and a snappy, balanced trot, is highly desired.

ADVANTAGES OF MULES

Mules are more resistant to hot weather than horses and they are easier to feed, since they are less often foundered and have fewer digestive disturbances. Self-feeding with corn, other grains like oats, and hay works quite well with mules, for they are sensible about eating. In the hands of an inexperienced driver a mule may work better than a horse. Under most conditions it is far better able to care for itself. Mules are less nervous and fretful than horses, and they accept more willingly hard work, abuse, and poor handling. They perform more satisfactorily under adverse conditions and they are less subject to lameness. The hoof of a mule, which has a tough outer wall, is very resistant to wear and stands up well over a period of years with hard work and shoeing. Mules retain good condition even when worked hard and abused; consequently they depreciate less in value than horses. Their stabling needs are less. Mules are more uniform in color and form than horses; consequently, they can be matched for teams more easily. Heavy work, poor drivers, poor feed, and poor shelter favor the use of mules. The toughness of mules as work stock accounts for their demand.

As mules consume feeds which horses refuse, work can be done at less cost with mules than with horses. One investigation indicated that the hourly cost for work done was least with mules, somewhat higher with geldings, and highest with mares.

As draft animals mules are not so good as horses. Their records in pulling contests are decidedly poorer than those made by horses on an equal weight basis. This is due in part to the fact that mules crouch less in the pull against the collar and tend to lean forward when in draft. This causes mules to slip easily on pavement when pulling heavy loads. The smaller feet of the mule are a disadvantage under some conditions, for they have less surface for adhesion. Mules, on the other hand, are more sure footed than horses and better suited to uncertain footing. The small feet make a mule unsuited to soft ground, and they avoid wet and muddy spots.

Mules are tough mouthed, tricky, and lack the spirit usually shown by horses. Since they are eccentric, slow in response, and not so dependable in emergencies there is less pleasure in driving them.

MARKET CLASSES OF MULES

On the large livestock markets mules are classified according to their use and graded in accordance with their general value. As is the case with other livestock, market classes are variable and there is a disparity in the use of grades. Following is a tabulation of the common market classes of mules, with range in height and weight.

MARKET CLASSES OF MULES AND RANGE IN HEIGHT AND WEIGHT

CLASS	RANGE IN HEIGHT, HANDS	RANGE IN WEIGHT, POUNDS
Draft	16 to 17½	1,200 to 1,600
Farm	15½ to 16	900 to 1,250
Sugar	16 to 17	1,150 to 1,300
Cotton	13½ to 15½	750 to 1,100
Mining or pack	12 to 16	600 to 1,350

Within the classes market price depends upon weight, conformation, quality, temperament, condition, action, and age. Each of the market classes listed above is divided, based upon value or market price, into the grades choice, good, medium, common, and inferior.

The following description of the market classes is adapted from U.S. Department of Agriculture, *Farmers' Bulletin 1341.*

DRAFT MULES

The draft-mule class includes the largest mules standing from 16 to 17½ hands high and weighing from 1,200 to 1,600 pounds. Some exceptional draft mules exceed the maximum weight given for this class. Draft mules are used principally for heavy teaming in large cities, especially in the warmer climates; for contract jobs, such as road grading and railroad work; and for lumber work. Mules used for contract work are generally designated by an appropriate descriptive name, such as "railroaders." The heaviest draft mules usually find their way to lumber camps. Contract mules must have more quality than lumber mules, but extreme weight is not so essential. The greatest demand for draft mules is for those between 5 and 8 years old.

There is no special preference in regard to sex, but mare mules are usually higher priced than horse mules. The highest prices paid are for mules having weight combined with heavy bone, large, well-shaped feet, strong, short backs, closely coupled, with abundant muscling over the loin and hindquarters.

FARM MULES

Mules purchased on the market for farm work in the middle western states are known as "farm mules." There is more variation in quality and type in this than in any other class, for the demand is not so specific. Mules in this class may be plain draft mules or cotton mules that lack finish and condition, for the farmer often likes to buy mules with the prospect of developing them into more valuable animals. Many of them are worked for a season and then fitted for the market, where they are placed in one of the other specific classes, such as "drafters," "sugar mules," or "cotton mules."

A survey of farmers by the Horse and Mule Association of America in midwestern states indicated that they preferred mules with a fast walk, alertness, and ability to endure hard work in the heat.

SUGAR MULES

Sugar mules are purchased for shipment to the sugar plantations of the south. This class of mules is somewhat rangy in type and should have good quality, style, and finish. They are heavier and more compact than cotton mules but not so heavy as draft mules. The range in weight should is from 1,150 to 1,300 pounds. In selecting sugar mules special attention be given to quality and adaptability to the work. The feet should be large and well shaped. Mare mules are preferred for the sugar trade.

COTTON MULES

As the name implies, cotton mules are purchased for work on cotton plantations. The typical cotton mule is somewhat lighter and more angular than the sugar or surface-mining mule, but heavier and weightier than the pit mule. Although there is considerable gradation of quality and age in this market class, the planters of the south are more and more inclined to favor increased weight and quality. A choice cotton mule weighs about 1,150 pounds and is alert and active, but most mules in this class range from 750 to 1,100 pounds. The age limits vary. Mules from 5 to 7 years old are preferred, however, and bring the best prices.

MINING AND PACK MULES

There is a wide range in weight among mining mules, varying from 600-pound pit mules to 1,350-pound surface mules. Good feet and freedom from blemishes are required to qualify for top prices for the mining trade.

Pack mules are similar in requirements to mining mules. In rough terrain pack mules are used to carry heavy loads upon their backs.

PACK MULES

Pack mules are much like mining mules in conformation. To carry heavy loads on their backs they must be thick and blocky, with strong back and loin, and they must be sure-footed.

LIVESTOCK RECORD
ASSOCIATIONS

BEEF CATTLE

Aberdeen-Angus
    American Aberdeen Angus Breeders' Association
    3201 Frederick Blvd., St. Joseph, Missouri
Brahman
    American Brahman Breeders' Association
    1208 Louisiana St., Houston 2, Texas
Brangus
    American Brangus Breeders' Association
    P.O. Box 232, Vinita, Oklahoma
Charbray
    American Charbray Breeders' Association
    841 1st Natl. Bank Bldg., Houston, Texas
Charolaise
    American Charolaise Breeders' Association
    841 1st Natl. Bank Bldg., Houston, Texas
Galloway
    American Galloway Breeders' Association
    East Lansing, Michigan
Hereford
    American Hereford Association
    Hereford Drive, Kansas City 5, Missouri
Polled Hereford
    American Polled Hereford Association
    1110 Grand Ave., Kansas City 6, Missouri
Santa Gertrudis
    Santa Gertrudis Breeders' International
    Kingsville, Texas
Scotch Highland
    American Scotch Highland Breeders' Association
    Belvidere, South Dakota

Shorthorn
>American Shorthorn Breeders' Association
>7 Dexter Park Ave., Chicago 9, Illinois

Polled Shorthorn
>Polled Shorthorn Society of the American Shorthorn Breeders' Association
>7 Dexter Park Ave., Chicago 9, Illinois

Zebu
>Pan-American Zebu Association
>818 Gunter Bldg., San Antonio, Texas

DAIRY CATTLE

Ayrshire
>Ayrshire Breeders' Association
>Brandon, Vermont

Brown Swiss
>Brown Swiss Cattle Breeders' Association
>Beloit, Wisconsin

Dutch Belted
>Dutch Belted Cattle Association of America
>N.W. 32nd Ave., Miami, Florida

Guernsey
>American Guernsey Cattle Club
>Peterborough, New Hampshire

Holstein
>Holstein-Friesian Association of America
>Brattleboro, Vermont

Jersey
>American Jersey Cattle Club
>1521 E. Broad St., Columbus 5, Ohio

Red Dane
>American Red Danish Cattle Association
>Marlette, Michigan

>American Dairy Cattle Club
>Interlaken, New York

DUAL-PURPOSE CATTLE

Devon
>American Devon Cattle Club
>Agawam, Massachusetts

Kerry
>American Kerry and Dexter Club
>707 W. Water St., Decorah, Iowa

Milking Shorthorn
>American Milking Shorthorn Society
>313 South Glenstone, Springfield 4, Missouri

Red Poll
> Red Poll Cattle Club of America
> 3275 Haldrege St., Lincoln 3, Nebraska

SWINE

Berkshire
> American Berkshire Association
> 601 W. Monroe St., Springfield, Illinois

Chester White
> Chester White Record Association
> Rochester, Indiana

Duroc
> United Duroc Record Association
> Peoria, Illinois

Hampshire
> American Hampshire Swine Record Association
> 1111 Main St., Peoria, Illinois

Hereford
> National Hereford Hog Record Association
> Chariton, Iowa

Inbreds
> Inbred Livestock Registry Association
> University Farm, St. Paul 1, Minnesota

Landrace
> The American Landrace Association, Inc.
> Noblesville, Indiana

Mule Foot
> National Mule Foot Hog Record Association
> DeGraff, Ohio

OIC
> OIC Swine Breeders' Association
> Goshen, Indiana

Poland-China
> Poland China Record Association
> 501 E. Losey St., Galesburg, Illinois

Red Berkshires
> Kentucky Red Berkshire Association
> Lancaster, Kentucky

Spotted Poland-China
> National Spotted Poland China Record Asssociation
> 8180 Rosemeade Lane, Indianapolis, Indiana

Tamworth
> Tamworth Swine Record Association
> Hagerstown, Indiana

Yorkshire
> American Yorkshire Club
> Lafayette, Indiana

SHEEP

Cheviot
American Cheviot Sheep Society
Lafayette Hill, Pennsylvania
Columbia
Columbia Sheep Breeders' Association of America
P.O. Box 315, Logan, Utah
Corriedale
American Corriedale Association
108 Parkhill Ave., Columbia, Missouri
Cotswold
American Cotswold Record Association
Sigel, Illinois
Delaine
American Delaine-Merino Record Association
4000 Water St., Wheeling, West Virginia
Black-Top Delaine
Black-Top Delaine-Merino Sheep Breeders' Association
Route 4, Howell, Michigan
Black-Top Delaine
Black-Top and National Delaine-Merino Sheep Association
Cannonsburg, Pennsylvania
Texas Delaine
Texas Delaine-Merino Record Association
Burnet, Texas
Dorset
Continental Dorset Club, Inc.
Hickory, Pennsylvania
Hampshire
American Hampshire Sheep Association
72 Woodland Ave., Detroit 2, Michigan
Karakul
Karakul Fur Sheep Registry
Friendship, Wisconsin

United Karakul Registry
P.O. Box 649, Twin Falls, Idaho
Lincoln
National Lincoln Sheep Breeders' Association
West Milton, Ohio
Montadale
Montadale Sheep Breeders' Association, Inc.
61 Angelica St., St. Louis 7, Missouri
Oxford
American Oxford Down Record Association
Eaton Rapids, Michigan

Panama
American Panama Registry Association
Rupert, Idaho
Rambouillet
American Rambouillet Sheep Breeders' Association
2709 Sherwood Way, San Angelo, Texas
Romney
American Romney Breeders' Association
Withycombe Hall, Corvallis, Oregon
Shropshire
American Shropshire Registry Association
P.O. Box 678, Lafayette, Indiana
Southdown
American Southdown Breeders' Association
212 S. Allen St., State College, Pennsylvania
Suffolk
American Suffolk Sheep Society
P.O. Box 226, Moscow, Idaho

National Suffolk Sheep Association
P.O. Box 324, Columbia, Missouri
Targhee
United States Targhee Sheep Association
Big Timber, Montana
Tunis
National Tunis Sheep Registry
Route 5, Fulton, New York

GOATS

Angora
American Angora Goat Breeders' Association
Rocksprings, Texas
Milk Goats
American Milk Goat Record Association
P.O. Box 30, Elyria, Ohio

American Goats Society
Mena, Arkansas

HORSES AND JACKS

Albino
American Albino Horse Club
Butte, Nebraska
Appaloosa
Appaloosa Horse Club
Route 3, Moscow, Idaho

Arabian
> Arabian Horse Club Registry of America
> 111 W. Monroe St., Chicago 3, Illinois

Belgian
> Belgian Draft Horse Corporation of America
> P.O. Box 335, Wabash, Indiana

Clydesdale
> Clydesdale Breeders' Association of the U. S.
> 910 Goff Bldg., Clarksburg, West Virginia

Cream (American)
> American Cream Draft Horse Association
> Hubbard, Iowa

Hackney
> American Hackney Horse Society
> 11 Park Pl., New York, New York

Jack and Jennet
> Standard Jack and Jennet Registry of America
> R.F.D. 2, Lexington, Kentucky

Morgan
> Morgan Horse Club
> 90 Broad St., New York 4, New York

Morocco
> Morocco Spotted Horse Co-operative Association of America
> Greenfield, Iowa

Palomino
> Palomino Horse Association
> P.O. Box 446, Reseda, California
>
> Palomino Horse Breeders of America
> P.O. Box 82, Mineral Wells, Texas

Percheron
> Percheron Horse Association of America
> R.R. 1, Box 101, Fair Oaks, Indiana

Quarter Horse
> American Quarter Horse Association
> P.O. Box 2290, Amarillo, Texas

Saddle Horse (American)
> American Saddle Horse Breeders' Association
> 929 S. 4th St., Louisville 3, Kentucky

Shetland
> American Shetland Pony Club
> Lafayette, Indiana

Shire
> American Shire Horse Association
> 504½ Grand Ave., Des Moines, Iowa

Standardbred
> The United States Trotting Association
> 1349 E. Broad St., Columbus 5, Ohio

Suffolk
    American Suffolk Horse Association, Inc.
    Clinton, New Jersey
Tennessee Walking Horse
    Tennessee Walking Horse Breeders' Association
    P.O. Box 87, Lewisburg, Tennessee
Thoroughbred
    The Jockey Club
    300 Park Ave., New York 22, New York
Welsh
    Welsh Pony Society of America
    White Post, Virginia

REFERENCES

GENERAL ANIMAL HUSBANDRY

Briggs, Hilton M., *Modern Breeds of Livestock*. The Macmillan Company, New York, N. Y., 1949.

Bundy, Clarence E., and Ronald V. Diggins, *Livestock and Poultry Production*. Prentice-Hall, Inc., Englewood Cliffs, N. J., 1954.

Clawson, M., *The Western Range Livestock Industry*. McGraw-Hill Book Company, Inc., New York, N. Y., 1950.

Crampton, E. W., *Applied Animal Nutrition*, W. H. Freeman and Co., San Francisco, Calif., 1956.

Coffey, Joel S., and Lyman E. Jackson, *Livestock Management*. J. B. Lippincott Company, Philadelphia, Pa., 1940.

Deyoe, George P., W. A. Ross, and Walter H. Peters, *Raising Livestock*, 2nd ed. McGraw-Hill Book Company, Inc., New York, N. Y., 1954.

Ensminger, M. E., *Animal Science*. The Interstate Printers & Publishers, Danville, Ill., 1950.

Ensminger, M. E., *The Stockman's Handbook*. The Interstate Printers & Publishers, Danville, Ill., 1955.

Garrigus, Wesley P., *Introductory Animal Science*, J. B. Lippincott Company, Philadelphia, Pa., 1954.

Maynard, L. A. and J. K. Loosli, *Animal Nutrition*, 4th ed. McGraw-Hill Book Company, Inc., New York, N. Y., 1956.

Morrison, F. B., *Feeds and Feeding*, 22nd ed. The Morrison Publishing Company, Ithaca, N. Y., 1956.

Nordby, Julius E., W. Malcolm Beeson, and David L. Fourt, *Livestock Judging Handbook*. The Interstate Printers & Publishers, Danville, Ill., 1947.

Peters, Walter H., and Robert H. Grummer, *Livestock Production*, 2nd ed. McGraw-Hill Book Company, Inc., New York, N. Y., 1954.

Reference Book of the Meat Packing Industry. American Meat Institute, Chicago, Ill., 1941.

Sampson, Arthur W., *Range Management*. John Wiley & Sons, Inc., New York, N. Y., 1952.

Smith, W. W., *The Elements of Livestock Judging*. J. B. Lippincott Company, Philadelphia, Pa., 1941.

Widmer, Jack, *Practical Beef Production.* Charles Scribner's Sons, New York, N. Y., 1945.

BEEF CATTLE

Ensminger, M. E., *Beef Cattle Husbandry.* The Interstate Printers & Publishers, Danville, Ill., 1951.

Nordby, Julius E., and Herbert E. Lattig, *Beef Cattle.* The Interstate Printers & Publishers, Danville, Ill., 1936.

Nordyke, Lewis, *Cattle Empire.* William Morrow & Company, New York, N. Y., 1949.

Osgood, Ernest Staples, *The Day of the Cattleman.* University of Minnesota Press, Minneapolis, Minn., 1929.

Peake, Ora Brooks, *The Colorado Range Cattle Industry.* Arthur H. Clark Company, Glendale, Calif., 1937.

Raine, William M., and Will C. Barnes, *Cattle.* Doubleday, Doran & Company, Inc., New York, N. Y., 1930.

Snapp, Roscoe R., *Beef Cattle,* 4th ed. John Wiley & Sons, Inc., New York, N. Y., 1952.

Towne, Charles W. and Edward N. Wentworth, *Cattle and Men.* University of Oklahoma Press, Norman, Okla., 1955.

Williams, D. W., *Beef Cattle Production in the South.* The Interstate Printers & Publishers, Danville, Ill., 1950.

BREEDING

Asdell, S. A., *Cattle Fertility and Sterility.* Little, Brown & Co., Boston, Mass., 1955.

Lush, Jay L., *Animal Breeding Plans,* 3rd ed. Iowa State College Press, Ames, Iowa, 1945.

Perry, Enos J., *The Artificial Insemination of Farm Animals.* Rutgers University Press, New Brunswick, N. J., 1949.

Rice, Victor A., Frederick N. Andrews and Everett J. Warwick, *Breeding and Improvement of Farm Animals,* 5th ed. McGraw-Hill Book Company, Inc., New York, N. Y., 1957.

Rice, Victor A., Frederick N. Andrews, and Everett J. Warwick, *Breeding Better Livestock.* McGraw-Hill Book Company, Inc., New York, N. Y., 1953.

Winter, L. M., *Animal Breeding,* 5th ed. John Wiley & Sons, Inc., New York, N. Y., 1954.

DAIRYING AND DAIRY AND DUAL PURPOSE CATTLE

Eckles, Clarence H., and Ernest L. Anthony, *Dairy Cattle and Milk Production.* 5th ed. The Macmillan Company, New York, N. Y., 1956.

Eckles, Clarence H., Willes B. Combs, and Harold Macy, *Milk and Milk Products.* McGraw-Hill Book Company, Inc., New York, N. Y., 1943.

Espe, Dwight, *Secretion of Milk,* 3rd ed. Collegiate Press, Inc., of Iowa State College, Ames, Iowa, 1946.

Gilmore, Lester O., *Dairy Cattle Breeding.* J. B. Lippincott Company, Philadelphia, Pa., 1952.

Hammer, Bernard W., *Dairy Bacteriology.* John Wiley & Sons, Inc., New York, N. Y., 1948.

Harrison, Edwin S., *Judging Dairy Cattle.* John Wiley & Sons, Inc., New York, N. Y., 1940.

Henderson, Harry O., and Paul M. Reaves, *Dairy Cattle, Feeding and Management.* John Wiley & Sons, Inc., New York, N. Y., 1954.

Herman, H. A., and F. W. Madden, *The Artificial Insemination of Dairy Cattle.* Lucas Brothers, Columbia, Mo., 1947.

Hinman, Claude H., *Dual Purpose Cattle.* Roberts Brothers, Springfield, Mo., 1953.

Judkins, Henry F., R. W. Smith, and Merrill J. Mack, *Principles of Dairying.* John Wiley & Sons, Inc., New York, N. Y., 1941.

Petersen, W. E., *Dairy Science,* 2nd ed. J. B. Lippincott Company, Philadelphia, Pa., 1950.

Yapp, William W., and William B. Nevens, *Dairy Cattle, Selection, Feeding and Management,* 4th ed. John Wiley & Sons, Inc., New York, N. Y., 1955.

HORSES

Denhardt, Robert M., *The Horse of the Americas.* University of Oklahoma Press, Norman, Okla., 1947.

Ensminger, M. E., *Horse Husbandry.* The Interstate Printers & Publishers, Danville, Ill., 1951.

Gay, Carl W., *Productive Horse Husbandry.* J. B. Lippincott Company, Philadelphia, Pa., 1932.

Gorman, John A., *The Western Horse.* The Interstate Printers & Publishers, Danville, Ill., 1944.

Kays, D. J., *The Horse.* Rinehart & Company, Inc., New York, N. Y., 1953.

MEATS

Bull, Sleeter, *Meat for the Table.* McGraw-Hill Book Company, Inc., New York, N. Y., 1951.

Ziegler, P. Thos., *The Meat We Eat,* 4th ed. The Interstate Printers & Publishers, Danville, Ill., 1949.

MARKETING

Conway, H. M., *Cattle Handbook.* National Livestock Marketing Association, Chicago, Ill., 1935.

Dowell, Austin A., and Knute Bjorka, *Livestock Marketing.* McGraw-Hill Book Company, Inc., New York, N. Y., 1941.

Norton, Lawrence J., and L. L. Scranton, *The Marketing of Farm Products.* The Interstate Printers & Publishers, Danville, Ill., 1949.

Pearson, James H., *Livestock Education Procedures in Marketing.* National Livestock Producer, Chicago, Ill., 1937.

Shepherd, Geoffrey, *Marketing Farm Products.* Iowa State College Press, Ames, Iowa, 1946.

SHEEP

Baker, E. T., *Feeding and Management of Sheep.* Orange Judd Publishing Company, Inc., New York, N. Y., 1947.

Collins, Spelman B., *Profitable Sheep.* The Macmillan Company, New York, N. Y., 1956.

Ensminger, M. E., *Sheep Husbandry.* The Interstate Printers & Publishers, Danville, Ill., 1952.

Horlacher, L. J., and Carsie Hammand, *Sheep.* The Interstate Printers & Publishers, Danville, Ill., 1942.

Kammlade, William G., Sr., and William G. Kammlade, Jr., *Sheep Science,* Revised ed. J. B. Lippincott Company, Philadelphia, Pa., 1955.

Towne, Charles W., and Edward N. Wentworth, *Shepherds Empire.* University of Oklahoma Press, Norman, Okla., 1945.

Wentworth, Edward N., *American Sheep Trails.* Iowa State College Press, Ames, Iowa, 1948.

SWINE

Anderson, Arthur L., *Swine Management,* 2nd ed. J. B. Lippincott Company, Philadelphia, Pa., 1957.

Carroll, W. E., and J. L. Krider, *Swine Production,* 2nd ed. McGraw-Hill Book Company, Inc., New York, N. Y., 1956.

Smith, W. W., *Pork Production,* 3rd ed. The Macmillan Company, New York, N. Y., 1952.

Southwell, Byron L., John T. Wheeler, and A. O. Duncan, *Swine Production in the South.* The Interstate Printers & Publishers, Danville, Ill., 1940.

Towne, Charles W., and Edward N. Wentworth, *Pigs from Cave to Corn Belt.* University of Oklahoma Press, Norman, Okla., 1950.

Ensminger, M. E., *Swine Husbandry.* The Interstate Printers & Publishers, Danville, Ill., 1952.

WOOL

Wool—The Raw Material. Boston Wool Trade Association, Boston, Mass., 1946.

Matthews, Joseph M., *The Textile Fibers.* John Wiley & Sons, Inc., New York, N. Y., 1947.

Von Bergen, Werner, and Herbert E. Mauersberger, *American Wool Handbook,* 2nd ed. Textile Book Publishers, New York, N. Y., 1948.

Hopkinds, Giles E., *Wool as an Apparel Fiber.* Rinehart and Company, New York, N. Y., 1953.

INDEX

3/26/60